the drama of
Luigi Pirandello

the drama of

Luigi Pirandello

Domenico Vittorini
author of the (the modern italian novel)

with a foreword by
Luigi Pirandello

dover publications inc new york · new york

Sponsored by the
CURTIS INSTITUTE OF MUSIC

Library of Congress Catalog Card Number: 57-13243

Manufactured in the United States of America.

To
MARY CURTIS ZIMBALIST

Founder of the
Curtis Institute of Music
in Philadelphia.

Foreword

New York 30 VII 1935 XIII

Mio caro Vittorini,

tra I tanti Pirandello che vanno in giro da un pezzo nel mondo
della critica letteraria internazionale, zoppi, deformi, tutti testa e
niente cuore, strampalati sgarbati lunatici e tenebroni, nei quali io,
per quanto mi sforzi, non riesco a riconoscermi neppure per un
minimo tratto (il piu imbecille di tutti credo che sia quello di
Benedetto Croce), ha voluto anche lei metterne su uno, tutto suo,
non per il gusto di storpiarmi e poi mostrarmi zoppicante; non per
il gusto di presentarmi mascherato da una testa d'elefante e col
cuore atrofizzato mediante quella pompa a filtro che è la macchinetta
infernale della logica; io annaspante tra le nuvole o intenebrato
nelle grotte; ma anzi tutt'al contrario; e di questo, come è naturale
e come può bene immaginarsi, io le sono molto grato, caro Vittorini.
Molto grato perchè, tra tanti che credono di saper molto bene ciò
che sono, io che non lo so affatto e ho sempre rifuggito dal saperlo
come da una soperchieria a tutta la vita che mi si muove dentro di
continuo, trovo in lei uno che mi fa andar dritto sulle gambe e mi dà
tanto cuore quanto me n'abbisogna per amare e compatire questa
povera umanità, sia quando ragiona e sia quando sragiona; uno che
cerca di spiegare che se tanti mi credono strampalato è perchè mi
muovo a mio modo e non come gli altri vorrebbero; sgarbato,
perchè ho sdegno delle loro garbatezze; incomprensibile, perchè non
sanno ancora vedere e pensare e sentire come me.

Comunque, caro Vittorini, zoppo, deforme, tutto testa e niente
cuore, strampalato sgarbato lunatico e tenebrone, io esisto e
seguiterò ad esistere, e loro no. È vero che questa non è una cosa che
abbia per me molta importanza. Uomo, ho voluto dire agli uomini
qualche cosa, senz'alcuna ambizione, tranne forse quella di vendi-
carmi d'esser nato. Ma pure la vita, anche per tutto quello che m'ha
fatto soffrire, è così bella! (Ed ecco un'altra affermazione senza
nemmeno un'ombra di logica, ma tuttavia così vera e sentita.) Basta,
io la ringrazio cordialmente, caro Vittorini, dello specchio che con
questo suo libro lei mi presenta, in cui con tanto gradimento
io posso rimirarmi.

LUIGI PIRANDELLO

Foreword

(*Translation*)

New York 30 VII 1935 XIII

Dear Vittorini,

The world of international literary criticism has been crowded for a long time with numerous Pirandellos—lame, deformed, all head and no heart, erratic, gruff, insane, and obscure—in whom, no matter how hard I try, I cannot recognize myself, not even in the slightest degree. (The most senseless of these phantoms I believe to be the one fashioned by Benedetto Croce.) You too have now decided to present your own Pirandello, not for the pleasure of maiming me and then exposing me as I limp along; not for the pleasure of showing me masked with the head of an elephant and my heart atrophied by that infernal pump which is the machine of logic, lost in the clouds or wandering in the murky bowels of the earth. Indeed, you have done just the opposite of this, and as is natural and as you can well imagine, I am very grateful to you, dear Vittorini. I am very grateful because, among so many who think they know so well what I am, I, who have no conception of what I am and have always refrained from trying to find out for fear of offending all the life which continually seethes within me, find in you one who makes me walk upright on my own legs and grants me as much heart as I need to love and pity this poor humanity of ours, both when it is rational and when it is irrational; one who tries to explain that if so many believe me erratic, it is because I move in my own way and not as others would like me to; gruff because I grow indignant with their affectations; incomprehensible because they do not yet know how to see, to think, to feel as I do.

At any rate, dear Vittorini, lame, deformed, all head and no heart, erratic, gruff, insane and obscure, I exist and I shall continue to exist, while they will not. It is true this is not a matter of great importance for me. A man, I have tried to tell something to other men, without any ambition, except perhaps that of avenging myself for having been born. And yet life, in spite of all that it has made me suffer, is so beautiful! (And here is another positive statement without even a shadow of logic, and yet so true and deeply felt.) Well, I thank you cordially, dear Vittorini, for the mirror of this book which you place before me, in which I can behold myself with so much gratification.

LUIGI PIRANDELLO

Preface

THE present book was grown out of a course on the works of Luigi Pirandello, and was made possible by a grant from the University of Pennsylvania which enabled me to go to Italy to collect material and to obtain a fresh perspective on the contemporary theatre.

Italian criticism is on the road to Damascus as far as Pirandello is concerned. After years of silence and incomprehension, critics are beginning to feel that Pirandello is the only truly gigantic figure in the world of Italian letters of today.

I have looked at Pirandello first in the light of contrasts and similarities that can be gathered around him from the background of the Italian literary tradition. There are writers to whom his tormented humanity bears marked resemblance. There are others to whom he is hostile to the point of being antithetical.

I have studied only those events of his life which have a direct relation to his work. Other happenings belong only to him. It may be of interest to the historically minded scholar to collect every detail of a writer's life. I have been more interested in Pirandello as a man and an artist, and I have looked upon his art as a result of his sensitiveness and of the experiences to which life subjected him. Such appears to us to be the genesis of the art of Luigi Pirandello, a modern tragedian.

I am deeply grateful to Dr. William J. Phillips of the English Department of the University of Pennsylvania for his patient and competent assistance in putting my manuscript in its present form.

The fact that Luigi Pirandello has written the Foreword to this book indicates how much I owe to him. He arrived in New York on July 20 as I was correcting the page proofs. He was most kind in granting me long interviews and in discussing with me the basic elements of his art as well as my interpretations of his plays. I can truthfully say that I have lived a few hours in the light of true greatness.

August 1935, Philadelphia   D. V.

New Preface

MANY important events have taken place since the original publication of this book in 1935. Pirandello's literary and dramatic contributions have become more widely read, dramatized and critically analyzed with keen interest.

Luigi Pirandello has been honored by having the translations of five of his major works included in Everyman's Library under the title of *Naked Masks;* a most *signficant* recognition. These works have been competently edited by Eric Bentley, who provided a new and improved English translation of *Così è (se vi pare)*, entitled *Right You Are.* Mr. Bentley has also listed five other volumes in which Pirandello's works are available in English as well as all the works that have been dedicated to him in contemporary Italian criticism.

Pirandello felt that in his art he was addressing himself to the world rather than to the inhabitants of his native and beloved Italy. We know that he did not cherish his universal thinking in vain. *Henry IV* and *Six Characters in Search of an Author* belong to the repertoire of the well-known Hedgerow Theatre Group in Rose Valley, Pennsylvania. *Six Characters in Search of an Author* also had a flattering production in the 1955-56 season in New York City.

In Italy, meanwhile, his work has received wide and enthusiastic recognition. His plays have been published in four volumes by Mondadori of Milan under the title *Maschere Nude,* the meaningful symbol that Pirandello saw as an expression of what he was attempting to say to other men.

Many books and essays have been dedicated to Pirandello as an artist after his death in 1936. Clear realization of the wide scope and depth of his ideas as well as his originality has replaced the lack of comprehension which he experienced during his three months' visit to New York.

Since Pirandello's death, the world of letters has developed greater insight into the philosophical implications of his art. We know that Pirandello considered himself a

New Preface

philosophical author as evidenced by his own comments. In the preface of *Six Characters in Search of an Author*, he wrote: "I have never been satisfied with representing the figure of a man or woman for the sheer pleasure of representing it; nor with narrating a specific event, gay or sad, for the sheer pleasure of narrating it; nor with describing a landscape for the sheer pleasure of describing it." He attributed to such objective authors the quality of being "historical" or "descriptive." He pointed out that there were other writers for whom "a human figure, an event, a landscape become enriched with a peculiar life-sense that lends to them a universal value. These are writers of a nature strongly philosophical." He added, "I have the misfortune of belonging to the latter type." It was only natural that a writer who took his art so seriously and who had studied himself so perceptively should seek a more congenial medium of expression than the naturalistic fiction of his youth. For Pirandello this medium was drama, a form of expression in which he enclosed the thought content of his life experience and in which he was to acquire full stature as an artist. He was about fifty years old when he turned to the stage.

Pirandello was a man who keenly experienced the poignant loneliness of life. In his imaginary characters, one can detect the sad vicissitudes of his life and the tormented thoughts of his searching mind. He delighted in relating the fact that he had been born near Girgenti in a place called Chaos during a raging cholera epidemic. He attributed to these circumstances the motifs of chaos and pain that are ever present in his art.

I hope that I will not be considered vain if I communicate to readers of this new edition that the copy of the first edition which I gave to the Maestro with deep gratitude and filial devotion remains on his desk; left when death claimed him on December 19, 1936.

Domenico Vittorini

January 21, 1957.

Contents

INTRODUCTION

PART ONE: IN THE WAKE OF NATURALISM

PART TWO: THE DRAMA OF BEING AND SEEMING

CONTENTS

CONTENTS

xiii

INTRODUCTION

I
Pirandello in the Tradition of
Italian Letters

Pirandello appeared in the literary world of Italy when the movement that critics usually designate under the name of "naturalism" was in full blossom.

Naturalism was an event of paramount importance in Italian life. It focused the human mind clearly and deliberately towards the consideration and acceptance of the material and controllable aspects of reality, and it enjoined artists to seek inspiration from the objective study of life close at hand. While other currents were found side by side with naturalism, it is indisputable that this movement occupied the center of the artistic and intellectual life in the eighties.

The concern for the concrete and objective goes beyond the field of art, and it encompasses the political and social aspects of Italian life as well. In 1870 the country achieved its national unity, and this important political event was accompanied by a noticeable stir in the economic field. Italy was reëntering the currents of European thought and life from which it had been excluded after three centuries of political slavery to France and Spain.

In the drama, veering away from historical themes that had been predominant in the days of romanticism, naturalism proclaimed the value of instinctive life as the raw material of art. It would be erroneous to believe that naturalistic elements had never appeared in the theatre, but it would be equally anti-historical to ignore the significance of the naturalistic school in its attitude towards the outside world in its relation to art. The term "school" shows the nature of the process that led to the crystallization of tendencies that beforehand had represented scattered efforts, unrecognized by the official hierarchy of the arts. Naturalism gave an official sanction to realism that before had been looked at askance

3

as an inferior art mode. In fact, realism was found primarily in dialectal and popular literatures. Comedy that assigned to itself the observation of the everyday reality was looked upon as inferior to tragedy that had inherited stateliness and grandeur from the classical drama.

To understand the interplay of the various forces that are at work in Italian literature, it is necessary to view Italian life as the expression of two antithetical points of view that act not only in the literary field, but in the political, religious, and social fields as well. For the sake of simplicity, we may call these two attitudes the rhetorical and the realistic. Behind them there is the clash between conservativism and modernity which goes on unceasingly: conservativism that clings to old forms and upholds them with the tenacity with which life defends itself to the very end; modernity that seeks and presents new values which necessarily mean the death of the old ones. This clash is a tragic struggle between the old and the new, and leaves one perplexed before the alternative of ruthlessly discarding what represented the life of yesterday or accepting the new life which victoriously advances, crushing and conquering the old one.

Italy was born at the root of the gigantic plant of Rome. Classical traditions never died out, and they were a positive asset at a time when Europe, after the turmoil of the barbaric invasions, was trying to fashion a new civilization. At the same time, however, it was inevitable that the presence of the old plant should rob the young and tender shoot of air, sunlight, and of the nourishment that the new historical soil afforded to it. The magnificent growth that one notices in the twelfth and thirteenth centuries centered around the life of the merchants who conquered European and Eastern markets and accumulated the wealth that made possible the raising of stately cathedrals and universities. It was also accompanied by the appearance of a new means of expression: the vernacular. Those centuries bear all the earmarks of greatness, and they realize a truly new political outlook through the guilds that attracted the active participation of a large part of the social body.

The central fact of which we must not lose sight, however, is that Italy was no longer classical and imperial Rome; that the typical individual of that time was no longer the togated Roman; that the vernacular was a distinct language that bore only a resemblance to classical Latin; that the economic life was no longer the same as in the days of Rome, now that the masses had been made a part of the process of production and of consumption. Yet schools and churches tried to recast Italian history in the old mold of that of Rome; they tried to stifle the vernacular by forcing on it the stately composure of Latin prose; they proclaimed the glory of the past and the misery of the present; and they pointed at the literary men of the classical period as models who had to be imitated if literature was to rise again to the heights of old. Tradition molded a new universe different from the one in which people lived, with stars and planets, trees and flowers, not as people observed them, but as the literary tradition had handed down. It was a universe filled with men who likewise bore literary stigmas. They moved, acted, felt, and spoke— at least they tried to—as Homer or Virgil or the Provençal poets dreamed that men did or should speak. Pirandello instructs us at this point as follows: "Rhetoric and imitation are ultimately one and the same thing. They have wrought immeasurable harm in every epoch, not only of Italian literature, but of Latin, and therefore in a varying degree, of all Romance literatures." [1]

It would be absurd to imagine that in ordinary life people, the rhetoricians themselves, felt and spoke differently from people of today. The togated form was superimposed; it bred artificiality and restrained the personal and individualistic elements in art. It is strange to pass from the rhetorical prose of Dante's *Convito*, that only here and there breaks forth into a sincere outburst of passionate feelings, to the limpid and eternally modern poetry of the *Commedia*. Poetry, since it was still outside the boundary of rhetoric in Dante's day, kept the natural, spontaneous form that it possessed in the great heart and mind of the poet. The *Convito*, modeled after

[1] "L'opera di Alberto Cantoni," *Nuova Antologia*, 1906, pp. viii, ix.

Latin prose, is opaque and often dull in its medium of expression.

More striking contradictions are found in writers of a later period when rhetoric held an indisputable sway in literature. If Politian and Tasso succeeded in letting their poetic genius reveal itself, they did so by breaking the rules of rhetoric that had forced them to sing of epic battles for which their temperament was totally unfit. As epic poems, Politian's *Stanzas* and Tasso's *Jerusalem Delivered* are failures. The greatness of the two works is revealed through the exquisite treatment of the love theme and through their poetry of nature where dewy mornings and delicately green vistas pass before us with a resonance that speaks of great poetry. It must not be forgotten, however, that these elements had nothing to do with wars and battles, and that they were condemned by the custodians of the Temple of Rhetoric as in the case of Tasso. The failure of Politian and Tasso as epic poets was quite natural, because in the fifteenth and sixteenth centuries the greatest exploit of man was not that of waging a war as in the days of primitive Greece and Rome.

In the theatre, the struggle between rhetoric and realism was intense and bitter. Rhetoric carefully codified by Giraldi and Speroni in the sixteenth century made it easy to write many tragedies, but it interfered with the creation of real drama. The classical drama of that century was stillborn since the erudite efforts of Trissino, Giraldi, and Speroni were utterly barren of results. If we wish to find a significant dramatic work, we must turn to Machiavelli's *Mandragola* and to Bruno's *Candelaio*, two comedies that with a steady hand dissect the moral lowness of their times and indulge in a laughter that is tragically painful.

The fundamental blunder in the attitude of learned humanists like Trissino, Giraldi, and Speroni consisted in their confusing culture and art. If we depart from the usual criterion of literary evaluation by relegating the rhetoricians to the background and placing the realists in the foreground, we see that the harvest of realism in the drama of the sixteenth century is very abundant. We can admire it in the

Commedia dell'arte with its genial and grotesque elements, and in the comedies of the quixotic Aretino, and those of Lasca and Cecchi. We should find even more and important material if we were to go to the rustic farce and the popular comedy that flourished in Tuscany, a dramatic production to which criticism has given scant attention.

The two currents, that of rhetoric and that of realism, continued distinct and hostile until we find them in the eighteenth century represented by the tuneful and courtly Metastasio and the charmingly realistic Goldoni. These two dramatists stand near each other in an almost antithetical light: Metastasio providing his sentimental, historical dramas for the court of Vienna; Goldoni moving in his dear old Venice among his contemporaries and studying them with his good-natured humor and with a smile that is deeper than it seems.

Pirandello, at least in the beginning of his career, links himself to the naturalism of the eighties. The crystallization of the naturalistic movement into a definite set of æsthetic principles meant the defeat of the rhetorical attitude within the walls of the citadel of official criticism and art. Naturalism became a conscious effort to recognize the æsthetic value of life in its entirety by bringing it into the precincts of art without the veils of rhetoric. It meant the rising to the height of dignified art of subjects pertaining to life in the province. Romanticism in Italy had fought the first battle in behalf of popular literature, although it had failed to realize its goal since on the whole it took to an evanescent art lost in the distances of history. This was particularly true in the theatre where the historical theme assigned to drama did not blossom into significant works. Naturalism resumed the battle for a modern art, and succeeded in defining its nature and having its importance recognized by all men who called themselves modern.

The naturalism whence Pirandello derives is that of the south, that of Sicily, to be more exact. The naturalism of the north was different in that it was more intellectual. The poet Carducci, for instance, disguised his realism under the renewed garb of a genial and personal classicism, although he expressed a sanguine love for the earth. On the other hand, for Giovanni Verga and Luigi Capuana, Sicilians like Pirandello, naturalism meant Sicily—Sicilian life with all its color and richness of human pathos. Verga showed the way to Pirandello in his *Cavalleria Rusticana* (*Rustic Knighthood*) and in the *La Lupa* (*The She-Wolf*), where the most absolute objectivity is applied to the theme of instinct, only relieved by the element of the picturesque.

The drama of Luigi Pirandello has developed from that realistic nucleus, as have other aspects of the contemporary theatre, in that modern playwrights have never forgotten that their works have to reach a public that lives in contact with the daily life. This realistic nucleus is found even in the lyrical drama of Dario Niccodemi and Massimo Bontempelli, and in the fantastic drama of Alberto Casella as well as in the historical drama of Sem Benelli. The practical concern which naturalism stressed has been very beneficial to the contemporary drama, since it has prevented it from being unduly evanescent.

This is particularly true of the theatre that goes by the name of "grotesque," with which Pirandello is usually identified, and in which fantasy predominates to a spasmodic degree. The theatre of the grotesque expresses a frenzied state of mind that forces man to burst into laughter before the harrowing contradictions of life. It flourished especially during the War, and it assumed the form of contrast between essence and appearance, between the face and the mask, the pathetic and the ludicrous. The formula and the æsthetic background of this dramatic form were afforded both by Pirandello's fiction and by his ideas of the grotesque elucidated in his volume *Umorismo* (*Humor*). The content was given by the sentiment of each individual writer.

The best of the immediately modern Italian drama was produced by working around the æsthetic nucleus of the grotesque. Around it can be gathered *La maschera e il volto* (*The Mask and the Face*) by Chiarelli, *Marionette, che passione!* (*Marionettes of Passion*) by Rosso di San Secondo, *L'uomo che incontrò sè stesso* (*The Man Who Met Himself*) by Antonelli, Ridi, pagliaccio (Laugh, Clown, Laugh) by Martini and the section of the drama of Luigi Pirandello that corresponds to the genial intuition of the grotesque, which we have chosen to call the drama of "being and seeming."

The art of Luigi Pirandello is a challenge to many categorical assertions as to the meaning and character of Italian literature. Some critics have stated that Italian literature has always sought the grandiose and that it is both turgid and hollow, with no interest in introspection and ideas. Others, following a diametrically opposed point of view, have stressed the so-called realistic traits of the Italian people and have pointed out the sensuous character and the absence of idealism in the annals of Italian letters. Before the vast mass of the literary production of a people that reflects its life thought over a period of seven centuries, both statements could be amply documented, a fact that would destroy the validity of both claims, proving the uselessness and unscientific character of many a demonstration.

Pirandello is a realist. In his long and great career as a writer he has sought to portray individuals as such rather than to present them through the concept of man, stately but abstract. He has always molded his art after the individuals that he has met, known, and studied, who have touched both his sense of humor and his heart. His powerful imagination and his genius have done the rest in transporting them from the tumult of life into the serenity of his art.

We are not using the term "realist" in the usual sense of the word. Pirandello is a realist in the sense that he tries to encompass within the scope of his art the basic, instinctive needs of man together with the secret torment of his soul and the mobile life of his intellect. Man is one in his various attributes, and Pirandello has pictured to us the drama of humanity as he sees it and feels it. In so doing he has joined the ranks of the great who have from time to time appeared under all skies.

II

Pirandello, Man and Artist

In Luigi Pirandello, the artist and the man are so closely interwoven as to make it imperative to know him intimately in order to understand his art.

Judging from his outward appearance, he is a continental gentleman accustomed to the life of European capitals, notably Rome, Berlin, and Paris. He is distinguished, well-dressed, affable, but not cordial. I should not say that Pirandello is a kindly person. He has been too embittered by experience to be such. His intellect is too sharp, and it goes too directly into the darkest sides of all questions for him to possess the happy gift of kindness. Kindness, like the kingdom of heaven, is of the poor in spirit. If in the end he proves to be friendly to his characters, the latter have been perplexed for a long time, gazing hesitatingly at the quizzical face of their author.

Following is a presentation of one of his characters that might be viewed as a self-portrait: "A good-looking, well-preserved man, although in his fifties. Penetrating eyes, full of life, and on his still fresh lips an almost youthful smile. Cold, reflective, entirely deprived of those natural qualities that easily win over our sympathy and trust. Not succeeding in simulating any warmth of affection, he tries to appear at least affable, but his graciousness, in trying to be spontaneous rather than reassuring, embarrasses and sometimes disconcerts one." (*Naked*, p. 4.)

Pirandello is a thinker and a man of unusual honesty. For this reason he knows the difficulties that life offers to those who possess these two rare attributes. Men who are not given to thought and are not honest solve the difficulties of life in a very swift manner: either they do not see them or they suppress them. Pirandello has always compelled himself to stand face to face with the many contradictions that human existence offers. He has seen them, analyzed them, and grieved over them even if he has outwardly appeared to laugh. He is not a kindly person, but he is extremely compassionate and sympathetic towards human weaknesses.

We are interested in the vicissitudes of his life which have a direct bearing on his art. We shall not tarry too long on his birth and childhood. That he was born at Girgenti in 1867 during an epidemic of cholera has the vividness of the picturesque, yet it is an event wholly independent of him, and one which he shared with so many other children who were born at that time.

It is necessary to have known the monotonous, sluggish, unchanging conditions of life in southern Italy during the eighties in order to understand many events pertaining to Pirandello's childhood. We should study this period of Italian and European civilization without indulging in meaningless recriminations. History, like nature, has its instincts and milestones, and is often cruel in all its awesome grandeur. The present is the child of the past, and we should feel reverence before the conditions that existed then, and the noble efforts that were made to hasten the turning and the advancing of the wheels of progress.

I think of a town where I lived when a child, and I see men and things caught alike in the tentacles of immobility: division of classes, poverty, shabby houses sleeping under the blazing sun with pots of red flowers at the small and dark windows, which made one think of hearts that bled in silence without ever losing their taste for beauty. At times the silence of the town merged with that of the fields till it was suddenly broken by the passing of a group of tattered children filling the air with shouts; then silence again, only interrupted by the beating of the hoofs of a donkey led by a peasant woman. In the mass of poor hovels stood two or three big houses, immutable in their bulky strength, always dark, dingy. I remember old servants as devoted as slaves and as sweet as mothers. At dusk they would tell us stories of ghosts and of brigands who had kidnapped our grandfathers long before we were born and had held them for ransom of flour, pork, oil, and wine. Our little hearts beat fast, and our fancy with eagerness and fright followed the brigands who lived in the woods and had long, dark beards and rifles, and rode lean, swift horses.

Pirandello knew one of these humble, tender, and unforgettable servants in Maria Stella, who was a part of the household. She used to tell little Luigi ghost stories, and she kindled his already ardent fancy. He has related to his Italian biographer, Federico Vittore Nardelli, that he often heard shouts from a dark street behind his house where rivals met and decided by the flourish of a knife who was right. He remembered that his mother had gone to the window, had hastily glanced into the street and had closed the shutters.

Imagination works most feverishly when we are in a situation and environment that know no change. The primitive and sluggish atmosphere of Sicily was bound to inspire a sensitive boy like Pirandello with the sense of the inevitable in life—there is no greater philosopher than the Italian peasant or the Sicilian donkey—and later the artist portrayed the stoic passiveness that the child had noticed in the men and women whom he saw caught in that changeless existence. Everything lasted in those distant days. People wore plain heavy clothing that was meant to do for their lifetime. The lastingness of everything meant no change, no production, but a massive solidity of life that would be a torment to us men of today and that meant a quiet, although monotonous, existence for our ancestors.

There hung over Sicily, still in a somewhat medieval economic condition, a pall of inertia broken by sudden outbursts of jealousy and of crime. A few old people still recollect this life which has for them, as it should have for us, the delicate and melancholy charm of what is no longer, but was once alive with hopes and fears, sorrows and joys, tears and smiles.

Such an environment could not but be conducive to an introspective attitude—that is typical of many Sicilians. They are smoldering fires under dark, solemn faces that often look hieratic, behind eyes composed in a fixity that bespeaks conscious restraint. It also developed a great power of observation in the future artist, an observation not of the external, decorative kind, but one that pierced through the shell of men and things, blossoming into a subtle and penetrating psychological art.

All people look, and most of them see, but only a few observe. Pirandello is among the few. Of a character very dear to his heart he has written: "All his pleasure is in observing. He seems to be absent minded and never to see anything. Mother gets provoked: What! Didn't you see this? Didn't you see that? No. He hasn't seen anything, but he has noticed, on the other hand, only he among all other persons, certain things that when he says them amaze us." (*When One Is Somebody*, p. 101.)

Federico Vittore Nardelli in Pirandello's biography, called *L'uomo segreto* (*The Unknown Man*), has recorded many facts that must have left a deep impression on Pirandello as a child, since he can recollect them even today. The chief actors in the drama of Pirandello's life were his parents, his wife, Donna Antonietta, and his father-in-law. His father, Stefano, was a wealthy owner of sulphur mines in Sicily. He was bearded, extremely tall and powerful. He was very violent, and was fired upon four times. Once he had a dangerous experience with Cola Camizzi, a member of the Mafia who wanted to collect money from him. Stefano paid him not with money, but with a slap that knocked him down. The thug ambushed him and shot him in the shoulder.

Cola Camizzi appears in retrospect in one of Pirandello's dramatic sketches, *The Other Son,* as the head of a group of brigands who harass and terrorize the island. Such an experience as the one encountered by Stefano was not out of the ordinary at that time. People, especially if well-to-do, often took the law in their own hands and never went out without a rifle, even if brigands were beginning to be a romantic and hazy memory. During the political turmoil of preceding years, security was rather scarce and individuals learned how to rely on themselves for protection. Hence, the habit of carrying weapons and the feeling of physical prowess that was characteristic of the generation of Pirandello's father.

Pirandello lived his childhood in the twilight hour of heroism and grandeur that set in after the epic battles for Italian independence. Italy had been slumbering for centuries in a medieval economy that Cavour had but slightly changed. The country had attempted to solve two great problems at the same time—the political and the economic. It wanted to follow in the footsteps of industrialized countries like England and Germany, while it aspired to reach national unity. Through great sacrifices and heroism, the country had achieved its political independence, and it was asking its still rural soul to hurl itself into the turmoil of industrial life.

Pirandello's mother, Donna Caterina, was such a modest and long-suffering woman as only women of that time knew how to be. Living with a man as despotic and violent as Stefano required frequent appeal to those virtues. Her life was entirely absorbed by family duties, since women of the *bourgeoisie,* even if they belonged to well-to-do families, had to work very hard at a time when home comforts were extremely limited. Husbands in those days were not particularly given to faithfulness, and economic limitations led to the slavery of women. Today women rebel and go to court. In the past they shed tears silently, and one day Pirandello learned that the eyes of a mother are made not only to look at us with tenderness and fondness, but also to cry. That day was a great test for his character. He was only in his teens. He discovered that his father had fallen in love again with a cousin to whom he had once before been engaged. In their renewed interest, he and she met in the parlor of a convent on the excuse of visiting their common aunt, the abbess. Pirandello dashed into the parlor one day and told the woman of the grief of his mother. His father had hidden behind a green curtain, but the son could see the tips of his black shoes.

Among the events worthy of notice in his childhood is the one pertaining to the commandment that he had just learned in church: Clothe the naked. He had received from his father a new sailor suit and had proudly put it on. On his way to church he met a poor boy who was all in rags. Luigi took off his suit and gave it to him because the Bible said that that was the thing to do. The mother of the poor boy, very much disturbed, blushing and gesticulating, returned the sailor suit to Luigi's mother, and Luigi, the future humorist, learned that day that it is not easy to practise the commandments.

Pirandello has immortalized in a short story, *The Little Wax Madonna,* an event that filled his childhood with wonder and indignation. During the month of May which is dedicated to the Virgin, there was a lottery every Sunday evening after the rosary. The winner received a little wax statue of the Madonna under a glass cover. Tickets cost two *sous.* The day of the last lottery Luigi met a pale little boy, Luzzu, who had never been able to take part in the lottery because he had been sick. Luigi gave him his own ticket, crossed out his name, and inserted Luzzu's. When the ticket bearing the name of the winner was drawn, the priest, ignoring the poor boy's name, called out that of Luigi Pirandello in order to ingratiate himself with the lad's wealthy father. Luigi was surprised and indignant. He protested, he shouted, he burst into tears. It was of no use. The people took him, forced him into a procession, and they marched to the Pirandello home singing hymns. Donna Caterina, so Nardelli informs us, returned the statuette to the curate, and Luigi never went back to the church again. That fact must have impressed his mind with the irony of the situation in which the winner was refusing the prize while the people stifled his sobs and cries with the rolling of drums and with songs.

Pirandello began to write poetry at the age of sixteen, and even at that early age he had conceived a hatred for rhetoric, the refuge of young people who usually began to try their wings in poetry by following the pattern of Petrarch. Pirandello in his first poems attacked the "old words worn out with usage" that surround and hide our thought "like flies a spittle."

Fiery, impetuous, like all repressed people when they suddenly flare into bursts of passion, Pirandello at eighteen became engaged to a girl four years older than he. He was ready to give up studying and help his father in his business in order to get married. After three months' trial, Don Stefano sent him to the University of Rome. He saw that Luigi was not meant to be a business man.

As Pirandello grew up, other facts struck him and left deep imprints on his literary works as well as on his character. Among these were of paramount importance the scandal of the Roman Bank in 1894 and the repression of the uprising of the peasants at Palermo in 1898. Pirandello later wrote a novel that deals with the Roman scandal: *I vecchi e i giovani* (*The Old and the Young*). He has described as follows his impressions of those days that formed the warp and the woof of his novel: "Every evening, every morning, newsboys shouted in the streets of Rome the name of this or of that deputy in the national parliament, connecting it with a swindle or fraud against this or that bank. Yes, just so. From the Italian sky there rained mud in those days and people indulged in mud-slinging as a pastime. Mud clung everywhere on the pale and convulsed faces of assailed and assailants, on the medals once received on the battlefield, on war crosses and citations, on frock coats and on the insignia of public buildings as well as of newspaper offices." Pirandello felt powerless before such a national shame, and used his art as an outlet for his indignation.

He was equally powerless before the events that led to the declaration of martial law in Sicily in 1898 that cost so many victims among the poor peasants. He gives his own version of the situation: "Those Sicilian peasants, finding in their rage against injustice the courage to affirm with violence a right of their own, had gone to till the crown lands. Frightened by the intervention of the troops, they had hastened to ask the city government to divide the land among them. In the absence of the mayor, an official had appeared at the window, and, to ward off any possible hostile demonstration, had told them to go back and till the land; but the crowd had found the militia in their way." (Nardelli, *L'uomo se-*

greto, p. 97.) In the encounter, many met death at the hands of the soldiers.

The mood that colors the novel *The Old and the Young*, is the reflection of Pirandello's state of mind when he went to the University of Rome. His recollection of his student days here, as confided to Nardelli, is far from being happy or even pleasant. The historical school prevailed in the lugubrious halls of the Sapienza. Pirandello felt pity and disgust for the manner in which old Professor Nannarelli taught Italian literature and Professor Occioni, Latin literature. Fearless, and at times violent like his father, Pirandello clashed with the latter professor while in his second year at the University. The matter was referred to the faculty council with the possibility of serious consequences. The great Ernesto Monaci, one of the founders of Romance philology, whom Pirandello revered and appreciated as we all did who had the privilege of being his pupils, suggested that Pirandello go to study for his doctor's degree at Bonn in Germany.

Pirandello worked very hard at Bonn because he wanted to be able to graduate, find a position, and get married. He has always had the good or bad fortune, one hardly knows which, of taking life seriously. Three years of absence had weakened his love for his *fiancée*, but he was ready to keep his promise. Having returned from Bonn he hastened to Sicily to his *fiancée*, but the two soon realized that an abyss had opened between them. The engagement was broken by mutual consent. Pirandello then went to Rome and lived in an old abandoned convent at the top of Monte Cave, near Rocca di l'apa, where a small inn had been opened. Six other literary men and artists had found refuge there: Fleres, Ojetti, Mantica, Cesareo, Vianini, and Giusti, personalities of the republic of Italian letters during Pirandello's youth. Writing absorbed his life entirely, and he wrote there *L'esclusa* (*Excluded*), one of his best novels.

Pirandello's literary career developed in a parallel line with the æsthetic school which predominated in Italy around the nineties and condemned his great art to obscurity. Those were the days in which the *Convito*, *Capitan Fracassa*, and *Cronaca Bizantina* made their appearance; journals that were the expression of perfect technicians of art, of men who reacted against the new democratic strain that was appearing in the Italian social body and that the reactionaries, both literary and political, were forcing into the arms of the extreme left. Pirandello, a liberal in politics, was an anti-rhetorician in art, a combination that by way of contrast corresponded to the position of the followers of the æsthetic school who backed political reactionary methods.

He fought stubbornly and passionately against the cult of the superman that D'Annunzio had popularized. An individual like Pirandello could not accept that superhumanity that on the wings of rhetoric and under the bewitching veils of imagery said little or nothing about man, his inner anguish and torment. The public, always ready to brush aside an individualistic and honest writer, paid him with indifference. No editor accepted Pirandello's writings for many years. His works, a great many short stories and novels, were not known until 1915, when the literary world of Europe heard through James Joyce and Benjamin Crémieux, an Irishman and a Frenchman, that there was something new and vital in the literary production of this unknown writer. Even then the Italian public was indifferent. Pirandello was not daunted, however. Like an old paladin, but without the splendor of shining armor, living in the cold flame of his own thoughts, he continued his struggle until the public was forced to take notice of him. The War compelled people to draw within themselves, and the art of Pirandello was duly appreciated after the War in the stormy years of 1918 to 1925, when Italy was on the very brink of national disintegration.

Pirandello's literary production began with poetry, developed into the novel through a form of ironical realism all his own, and finally flowed into the theatre where he produced the best that his genius had to offer to art and to mankind. There is the literature of man and of mankind—literature useful for a quarter of an hour, for an hour, for a month, for a year; and there is the literature that defies time, rising towards immortality. There are works, characters, vicissitudes, and pages that assign to Pirandello's drama a place in the latter class.

At Bonn he wrote poetry which was collected into a volume bearing the title of *Pasqua di Gea* (*Springtime of Gœa*), dedicated to Jenny, a girl he met in that city. In spite of the classical name, Pirandello strictly adhered to the inspiration that he always derived from life as humans live it.

Luigi Capuana, one of the leaders of the naturalistic school, to whom Pirandello was introduced by the gay and genial humorist Ugo Fleres, advised him to write prose. The great Verga recognized in the novels and short stories that Pirandello submitted to him not only another Sicilian islander, but also a kindred soul in his tormented way of feeling life. He must also have seen other traits that were dear to him: unadulterated art, honesty, clear thinking. He felt that with Pirandello "a new light was appearing."

Pirandello's literary dream was broken by his father, who reminded him that it was time for him to get married, and he finally agreed to marry Antonietta Portulano, a girl he had never seen. Their marriage was arranged by their parents. Portulano was a business partner of Stefano Pirandello. They had made money speculating on sulphur, and they agreed to seal another bargain with the lives of their children just as they had played on the falling and rising prices of the market.

Antonietta had received the rudimentary education that girls of the *bourgeoisie* used to receive in a convent. Her mother had died in childbirth because she had refused to have a doctor attend her, on account of her husband's jealousy. Signor Portulano was as jealous as only a Sicilian can be, if we accept Pirandello's verdict on the score.

The two were married in January 1894, after a very brief and superficial acquaintance, and they settled in Rome, where they lived on the generous allowance given to Pirandello by his father, and on Antonietta's dowry. The first years of their marriage were the most pleasant. I do not use the banal word happy because it is hard to conceive of Pirandello being in a happy mood. There were three children from the union: Stefano in 1895, Lietta in 1897, Fausto in 1899. Stefano now writes poetry under the pen name of Stefano Landi, since he does not wish to exploit his father's celebrity. Fausto is an artist.

The first ten years of Pirandello's married life were absorbed by his family and by his literary activity. He was asked to contribute to the *Marzocco,* a famous publication with decidedly æsthetic tendencies, edited by Angiolo Orvieto. At first he refused, saying that his ideals were too different from those of the *Marzocco.* He finally accepted with the understanding that he would have complete freedom to do as he chose. His first article was one on Giovanni Verga, exalting the art of the great Sicilian writer. His closed, concentrated, and passionate nature made him continue his violent attacks against the predominating literary fashion represented by D'Annunzio.

Pirandello's anti-D'Annunzian attitude goes beyond the field of pure literature. It also encompasses the temperament and the moral temper of the two men. D'Annunzio was always ready to pass from one love affair to another, and even to imagine *affaires d'amour.* Like an eternal adolescent, he boasted of them, and did not hesitate to reveal even the most intimate actions and sentiments of those women whom he tied to the chariot of his lust. Pirandello, bound by pity and self-respect to his tragic family, always remained true to his wife.

A terrible blow awaited him, however, in the ruin by flood of his father's sulphur mines in which all the family fortune was invested, and in the loss, in a certain sense, of his wife. His family life became the oppressing weight, the stifling and torturing prison, that he has portrayed in the lives of so many of his characters. Donna Antonietta had suffered a great deal when Fausto was born. The serious financial reverses in which her dowry was lost found her in that weak condition, and the shock was so great that it affected her mind.

Without any other source of income except that of his pen, Pirandello was compelled to seek a position as a teacher. Thanks to an influential friend who held his literary merits in high esteem, he was appointed Professor of Italian Literature at the Istituto Superiore Femminile di Magistero, a sort of Teacher's College in Rome.

From 1904 on, Pirandello lived a life of torment that gave him the sensation of being closed in an unbreakable cage, caught there forever. Never has the feeling of the weight of daily existence, of its unbearable character, and of the need of liberation been expressed with more humanity and pathos than in the work of Luigi Pirandello, as he presents the sense of oppression experienced by his characters who are caught in a plight from which they have no hope of extricating themselves.

His characters are the reflection of his very self, and they are, therefore, shy, introspective and self-effacing, much in the manner of their creator. Pirandello has never looked complacently at himself. If he had done so, he would never have put on his characters' lips words like these: "I could spit at my image when I see myself in the mirror." For this reason he does not glorify his characters. He tells one of them consolingly: "I am sorry to tell you that you do not cut a very nice figure in this comedy."

As his wife accused him of duplicity and of unfaithfulness, he saw near himself the shadow of another man, of the one that his wife had created, hateful and low, the one who made her shout and go into hysterics. Pirandello must have often wondered which of the two was the real one. The imaginary man had as much reality and consistency for her, as well as for him in his bruising effect, as the consciousness of his own actual self had for him. Indeed, he was gradually forced to acknowledge that the fictitious self was so strong as to crowd out the real one. This sad realization gave life to the experience of one of his heroines, who goes home under an assumed name and sees the fictitious being cloud and almost kill in her the feelings of the real mother for her own child who looked upon her as an intruder.

Pirandello did all that a human being could to allay his wife's suspicions. He stayed at home constantly, and gave up his friends, drawn into the whirl of his wife's insanity, patient and resigned, but letting his fantasy work in the immobility to which he condemned himself. He went so far as to give his wife every penny he made, keeping for himself sixty centimes a day for carfare to school. But it was of no avail.

Donna Antonietta's derangement of the mind grew worse, and it took more and more the form of jealousy. She even left her husband and went back to Sicily for three months with her children. Gradually she became violent and passed from moods of tenderness to outbursts of fury. An old, honest, and compassionate physician advised Pirandello to keep her with him rather than send her to a sanitarium, believing that it would be better for her. Pirandello agreed and took that cross as he had taken so many others, stoically and compassionately. It was in this closed torment that was born, at least in germ, the drama of Luigi Pirandello.

He suffered everything in silence, and through his mind flashed irrational thoughts while in his heart surged a feeling of powerless revolt. When he wrote he gave vent to that tormented inner life by envying madmen who could shout whatever they wanted, who could reveal their strangest thoughts and queerest emotions with impunity. He must have written his agonizing pages while his wife frantically pounded at the door of his studio, accusing him and threatening him.

In the tortures of his daily life, near his children whose childhood and adolescence were overshadowed and saddened by the madness of their mother and by the stoical resignation of their father, he learned what it is to aspire to a life different from the one to which we are condemned. He also learned the comforting power of illusion; an illusion, however, which tantalizes us with a prospect of what life might have been and was not. His characters are the embodiment of himself pounding at the portals of the mystery of destiny as desperately as his wife pounded outside his door. Why? Why? What can a man do after asking in vain without receiving any answer? Laughter, if he can laugh, is his salvation. His heart is too bitter and his nerves too tense to respond to the soothing effect of tears.

The World War contributed, together with the circumstances of his private existence, to make life appear more irrational, absurd, and cruel. Stefano, his oldest son, mindful of his ancestors who had fought with Garibaldi, joined the army as a volunteer. Every minute marked the agony of the father who pictured what might happen. Concern over Stefano made Donna Antonietta more upset and violent. She began to persecute Lietta too, accusing her of wishing to take the reins of the household away from her. The girl tried to commit suicide with an old revolver, but the bullet lodged in the barrel and she was saved.

We can easily imagine Pirandello's life. Stefano was a prisoner in Bohemia amid suffering and privation. Fausto was in the army, dangerously ill as the result of being drafted while still recovering from an operation. Pirandello felt himself to be but a poor, crushed man who could not even have the consolation of feeling his sorrow and anguish like an ordinary mortal. His fame had spread and he could not go out in the streets of Rome without attracting an attention that offended the feeling of his own humility. One day, while dining alone at a little inn in Rome, two young men looked at him so insistently that he in a fit of rage threatened to throw a bottle at them. He has lent this experience to the hero of one of his plays, *When One Is Somebody*. It was at this time that Pirandello thought of the most agonizing cases of mental torture and enclosed them in his comedies: *As Well as Before, Better than Before; All for the Best; Man, Beast, and Virtue; Each in His Own Way; Right You Are if You Think You Are; Cap and Bells; Think It Over, Giacomino; Liolà; Mrs. Morli, One and Two;* and *The Pleasure of Honesty.* Tragedy and laughter, and the greater the tragedy the more spasmodic the laughter! Donna Antonietta's death in 1918 ended a pitiful and tragic situation.

Pirandello had turned to the theatre during the War. He was urged to do so by Angelo Musco, a great actor who was determined to make a success of his comic ability at any cost. Musco wanted a comedy and begged Pirandello to write one for him, the amusing Musco who during the War made people laugh and forget their sorrows at least for a brief time. Once

Pirandello began to write plays, he wrote passionately and relentlessly. He has confessed to Nardelli that in one year he wrote nine plays. *Think It Over, Giacomino* was written in three days; *Right You Are if You Think You Are* in six. Two great actresses, Emma Gramatica and Marta Abba, played the leading feminine rôles, while Pirandello watched most carefully how they as well as the other actors interpreted their respective parts.

Pirandello has never begged for honors nor for recognition, either from the government or from the public. He has stubbornly kept on writing, unmindful of the fact that some praised and exalted him while others jeered at him. Only late in his career as a dramatist has he received any honors. It was not until the French Government proposed to bestow the Legion of Honor on the now famous writer, that the Italian Government realized it had not taken any notice of him. In order not to be second to a foreign government, Italy hastened to give Pirandello the *commenda* of the Crown of Italy. Mussolini has given him the high *commenda* of the Order of Saint Maurice, and has made him a member of the Italian Academy. He received world recognition with the award of the Nobel prize in 1934 which has been not only the acknowledgment of his literary merit but also a vindication of his unadulterated art.

Fame and wealth have not changed him. He has remained the same modest man, determined and strong willed. In the year 1925 he set out to found a national theatre. With a small group of interested persons he took over the Odescalchi Theatre in Rome, where Guido Podrecca showed his marionettes before he paraded them all over the world. The building was remodeled and designated to become the cradle of a new Italian renaissance in the drama. Mussolini attended the opening night when, in a gorgeous setting, Pirandello's short play, *In a Sanctuary*, was given. The Premier declared this movement sponsored by his régime. Marta Abba was engaged, and from Milan she came to Rome, where she appeared in the rôle of Ersilia Drei in *Naked* and later distinguished herself in other famous rôles. Another great actor, Ruggero Ruggeri, joined the troupe. Pirandello with his company went to England, France, and Germany. Artistically the enterprise was successful. Financially it was a fiasco; it cost Pirandello six hundred thousand *lire*.

Among all the irksome experiences of his dramatic venture, he found joy in the love of his children, who always stood by him, understanding his good and long-suffering heart, and in his tender friendship for beautiful Marta Abba. Pirandello's drama seems to be made for her with its desperate and agonizing truth. She interprets his tragic figures with a passion and an adherence to their anguish that reveals in them new beauty and depth. The author is grateful to his interpreter for giving life to his characters by living them in her flesh and soul. She is like a daughter to him.

In these last years Pirandello has lived a wandering life in France, South America, and the United States, even in Hollywood, where he will soon supervise the filming of *Six Characters*. He has no attachments, no home, no possessions. He has divided his royalties among his three children with the sense of equity and justice that has always characterized his actions. From his pen will undoubtedly flow other works before he faces the last tragedy of man—death

III

Pirandello's Philosophy of Life

Pirandello has subjected to a pitiless but passionate *critique* man and life, exploring every fold and nook, and presenting to us convincingly the sad and pitiful spectacle of the tragedy of being human. In this he has the justification of sincerity and, above all, that of having lived the sadness with which he has enveloped life.

Standing before the panorama that the universe offers to every thinking man, Pirandello is struck by the fact that one is born plant, beast, or man by mere chance, and that one is fatefully and irrevocably closed in that form for the span of one's earthly existence. Man, however, is different from plants and animals in that he cannot entrust himself to instinct with the same subconscious and happy abandonment as can lower beings. For, as soon as man yields to instinct, he sets in motion the so-called intellect which is nothing more, in the majority of cases, than a mechanism of deception through which he attempts to give idealistic motives and terms to his instinctive actions. One can follow Pirandello step by step as he analyzes life and envelops it in the web of his pessimism, pointing out its harrowing contradictions. On the whole, Pirandello's philosophy is not very comforting. Standing pensively and grievingly before the spectacle of daily existence, he has concluded "that there is nothing to conclude, because it is so," which is a conclusion in itself.

This philosophy was fashioned after the experience and observation of many years, upon realizing that life constantly loses its bloom; that the faces of those he had once known as children had begun to look old; that the strength of these people had ebbed away; that their skin, once soft and velvety, was rough and full of wrinkles; that their eyes, once sparkling with youth, were dimmed by age. Deeply touched and perturbed, with the conviction of one who is stating an opinion that sums up his life, he concludes that "everything is indefinite, fleeting, and evanescent." (*Each in His Own Way*, p. 3.)

The author starts from the premise that our knowledge about our very self is painfully limited. Mattia Pascal, one of the best-drawn characters in Pirandello's fiction, states, in looking back at his former life: "One of the few things, indeed, perhaps the only one that I knew as a positive fact was this: that my name was Mattia Pascal." (*Mattia Pascal*, p. 1.) Man does not know much about himself beyond an intimate knowledge of his physical being and worldly possessions: his clothes, his money, his home, his estate.

This belief, instead of making Pirandello cling to the tangible sides of his life and self, leads him to a complete detachment from them. He does not understand why we give so much importance to the gross and solid aspects of tangible reality. He is unwilling to grant that the human body is our most personal possession, since it decays so steadily, though imperceptibly. Life is a short-lived dream, and shadows are the most important element in it, since we live on memories of what has been or in longings of what is yet to be. In the changes that unceasingly go on in us, we cannot cling to our tangible and actual reality, since this reality is in a constant state of flux, and therefore it offers nothing solid and permanent.

This attitude of detachment from the tangible aspects of life is brought about by the author's unsatisfied desire to find something solid on which to rest, since there is in Pirandello, as in all human beings, a great longing for life, warm and fluid, happy and joyous. If he proclaims the glory of abstraction, it is only after he has been violently and bitterly offended and disappointed by actual experience. There is therefore in him and, by way of reflection, in his characters, a constant clash between his longing for the gifts of sensuous life and the sad disappointment experienced when his lips touch a cup that is empty, or a fruit that is withered and bitter. This is one of the deepest *motifs* in Pirandello's drama, and it has been beautifully realized in *Henry IV*, although it circulates in many of his plays.

As Pirandello looks at his fellow-men and at himself, he discovers that we are all "immobilized" in the concept that each of our friends and acquaintances forms of us. Moreover, we are also crystallized in the concept that each of us forms of himself. As we grow old and youth recedes from us, we poignantly cling to that fading image. The author has no other explanation to offer upon noticing that we cover most religiously the bald spots on our heads, we dye our hair, we straighten up when we walk in the streets, and slouch into sad figures when we are unobserved. To him a portrait is a touching attempt to stem the advancing destruction of death by holding close to us the image of what we used to be.

Man not only encloses himself in a concept, but he also immobilizes in it every one of his emotions and feelings. This is a natural though tragic necessity, and it dwarfs human sentiments. The Philosopher, a character in one of Pirandello's early plays, points out that churches are nothing but the tangible form of man's religious instinct, that "not satisfied to abide in the heart of man, it has built a house for itself—and what a house: domes, naves, columns, gold, marble, precious canvases! As a house of God, the universe is unquestionably larger and richer than a church; the spirit of man in adoration before divine mystery is incomparably more noble and precious than any altar. But this is the fate of all sentiments that wish to build a house for themselves: they are, of necessity, dwarfed and become a little childish because of their vanity." According to Pirandello, this is how the infinite which abides in man fares when it takes a tangible form, without which, however, it could not reveal itself. In the clash between the beauty of what is not and the misery of what is, we are saddened by their irreconcilable contrast.

Pirandello has gone deeply into the secret chamber of man's heart and has discovered tragic wants. He has seen that there are things that we dare not confess even to ourselves, moral deeds that lie like heavy stones in the depth of our conscience. Who can go before his fellow-men with an unveiled soul? In this realization there is an echo of the great but terrifying words: "He that is without sin among you, let him first cast a stone."

The author has also been tempted to look at his existence in retrospect, and has discovered that the ideas of his youth are no longer his, and that the beliefs of yesterday have become the illusions of today. It was inevitable that at this realization a sense of emptiness should envelop him. Every basis for his thought crumbled under him, and he felt himself wandering in a universe where extinguished stars moved in a meaningless whirl as if ready to plunge into the abyss of nothingness. One of Pirandello's characters has expressed this belief in unforgettable words: "If we think over the illusions which we no longer entertain, the things which now do not *seem* as they *used to seem*, we feel suspended in a void, since we must also argue that what we feel today, that is, the reality of today, is destined to appear as the illusion of tomorrow." (*Six Characters in Search of an Author*, p. 130.) This is all the more true since history proves that in the forward advance of progress new ideas dislodge and kill old ones, just as in life children are fated to take the place of their parents, and one generation passes over the tombstones of another.

Pirandello is not abstract in his approach to the theme of his pessimism of life. He calls our attention to such aspects of the existence of his characters as may be easily compared with those of the existence of each one of us. He recalls to our mind the day when we, like the Son in *Six Characters in Search of an Author*, discovered that our parents lived as man and woman, for themselves, outside the image of father and mother which we had conceived of them and in which they lived for us. We are also compelled to mourn with another of Pirandello's characters the fact that not even the deepest affections, not even love for our mother, can resist the fatal onslaught of life. Life is a ruinous torrent and carries along in its fury men and things, irrevocably.

No happy outlook is brought to us by observing the relations between man and his fellow-creatures. Our acts appear to others as if they were enveloped in a haze and smoke which veil the flame that glows in them when we act spontaneously. With eager earnestness and passionate conviction he points out that we grow up in the belief that we are one, a definite individual, with a clear-cut contour, with definite qualities, and with a personality. Life proves that we are not, that in reality this subjectiveness of man's perceptions create in us as many-faceted persons as are individuals who look at and know us. Closed in his subjectivism, man interprets the acts of others according to his own ideas of human behavior. The result is an incommunicability that offers one of the most recurrent and fertile *motifs* in Pirandello's theatre.

Brought face to face with the grimacing countenance of the daily tragedy, Pirandello seeks the cause of man's isolation, and he finds that words are a most inadequate means of expression. "The core of the evil is exactly here!" says the Father in *Six Characters in Search of an Author*, "In the words we use! We all have a world of things within us, each his own world. And how can we understand each other if, to the words that I say, I give the sense of things that are within me, while he who listens to them, inevitably, receives them with the sense that they have for him, from the world that he has within him?" (*Six Characters in Search of an Author*, p. 30.)

To understand the impenetrability of human beings, we must keep in mind the accusations that poor deranged Donna Antonietta hurled at her husband in her frantic state of mind. In his own flesh and soul, Pirandello lived the isolation of his characters, an isolation that leads to hostility and hatred.

All that poets have said to exalt life has appeared cold and empty to him as it echoed in his tragic soul. Man fosters the illusion of the glory of his will power, yet he has to acknowledge that his will is limited in two paramount facts: birth and death. They are both independent of his will and "between the two events many things happen that we all wish would not happen, and to which we unwillingly must submit." (*Each in His Own Way*, p. 64.) Men will say very proudly: This day which is just dawning will be ours; we

30

shall mold it as we wish. In reality we repeat what others have done before us. Traditions and customs are there, tyrannically imposing on us what others have decreed and obeyed. We speak and must repeat the words that have always been said. "Do you believe that you live?" queries one of Pirandello's characters. "You are re-chewing the life of the dead." (*Each in His Own Way*, p. 107.)

We might argue with the author, in an imaginary conversation, that man can boast of a definite asset in human conscience. Pirandello would look at us with his wistful and whimsical eyes and say that he is aware that conscience exists in the poor of spirit who do not need it, but he is unable to find it in the over-intellectualized beings that he meets in his imaginary wanderings.

A man like Pirandello cannot think of nature in positive terms, any more than can the mariner and the aviator who know the fury of the tempest on the high sea and the slashing of the storms in midair. Both the mariner and the aviator see in nature an enemy to conquer, just as Pirandello sees in it the cause of the plight in which his characters are struggling in a vain attempt to free themselves. He calls our attention to the fact that life is monotonously, if not serenely, unfolding when, suddenly, an earthquake sows destruction and sorrow and leaves us uncertain whether human lives have more purpose than the Japanese beetles that the dark, callous, rough hand of a farmer snatches from the sweet-tasting ear of corn in order to throw them into a jar full of gasoline. Pirandello has allowed Leone Gala in *Each in His Own Rôle* to voice his deep-seated feeling that life is something that allures and hurts. Leone Gala proclaims his defense against the evil that life does to all, inevitably. Life is cruel: "You eat meat at the table. Who provides it for you? A pullet or a calf. You never think of it. We all hurt one another reciprocally; and each hurts himself. It is inevitable. It is life." (*Each in His Own Rôle*, p. 36.)

We are brought into the presence of evil and death while a ghastly spectacle unfolds before us. There are parents whose children are born imbeciles, unable to use their limbs,

31

unable to speak. There are hospitals filled with pain, wars that kill millions, maim more millions, torture body and soul. At the fringe of this life lurks death, and it chills every joy and destroys every affection.

If the thought of nature is not comforting to Pirandello, that of modern civilization is not less barren of solace to him. He sees in it only the frantic efforts to escape the sadness of life. Man moves, builds cities, crosses the ocean, conquers the air, only because he tries to escape his inner torment, the torment of his intellect. He is engaged in a mad race for speed which is followed by disappointment because our thought moves faster than mechanical contrivances. The sad plight of Pirandello is that he cannot suggest contemplation in the oriental fashion. The peaceful life of a distant mythical past is beyond our reach, gone forever, the penalty that we pay for progress. Intimately and ultimately civilization is to Pirandello a synonym for tragic artificiality. Yet we must submit to it because there is no escape.

The element that contributes most in building the gloomy structure of Pirandello's pessimism is instinct. Man is compelled to yield to it even when he is perfectly aware of the dire consequences that it will entail. Pirandello considers instinct an acid which corrodes the best that life possesses. His drama begins where instinct ends. His characters are people who give themselves to passion and cannot live in it. They readily pass from passion to hatred, and they cling to it with a cruel and spasmodic tenacity. Their brain and their heart stand vigil on the flesh that yields; they rebel and the result is the lucid madness of the individuals that we see suffering in Pirandello's drama.

If we exclude the early plays conceived in the light of naturalistic principles, Pirandello's art presents a sensuality that is neither self-satisfied, beastly, nor wholesome. His drama opens at the moment when instinct has lost all its impetuousness, and the warmth of passion has been chilled by the cold dissecting power of the intellect. As a consequence, only reason predominates in the psychological life of the characters, and it leads them in their aimless wanderings over the bleak desert of their existence.

The background of most of Pirandello's plays is a wrong relation, the experience of which leaves his characters desperately disappointed. Instinct and lust appear paltry and despised, especially as the characters rebel at having their whole lives and beings identified with a moment of weakness. The rebellion of the characters is accompanied by a perplexed state of mind in the author, who seems unable to understand the power of something which is so devastating and yet seems so negligible and hateful when looked at with a certain objectivity. Pirandello is disconsolately silent before this perplexity, and often takes refuge in laughter. This thoughtful and grieving silence, mingled with a burst of laughter at human weakness, is reflected on Pirandello's countenance, and it forms the most appealing trait of his tragic personality.

There arises at this point the problem of morality as a substratum of Pirandello's art. Many people, especially if vowed to ethical orthodoxy at any cost, would call Pirandello immoral. Yet there is no other modern writer for whom morality is as intimately imbedded in the very texture of life and art as for Luigi Pirandello. This is evidenced by the fact that his drama is almost always brought about by the breaking of a moral law; by the fact that Pirandello never treats instinct as an aphrodisiac; by the unraveling of the plot that reaffirms the validity of the moral law. Pirandello does not need the glamour of immorality to make his art attractive, just as he never allows it to become laden down by the weight of didacticism. He is often provincial in the familiar tone of most of his plays, although he reaches the universal in the implications that he lends to the everyday occurrences on which he builds his drama.

Many may resent the drastic pessimism that is found at the basis of Pirandello's thought. Pirandello does not wish to give a universal value and meaning to his pessimistic sense of life. His exasperated subjectivism rejects any categorical and universal interpretation of it. If truth has as many aspects as there are thinking individuals, a life concept is the projection of each single experience. Pirandello refuses to be dogmatic.

Pessimism forms the background of Pirandello's drama, but the author has skilfully veiled his pessimism behind humor and laughter, relieving the extreme tension that oppresses his pitiful characters. In the foreground one sees ludicrous figures, victims of instinct and of Pirandello's sense of humor that expresses itself in laughter at human weakness, a laughter that hurts him although it relieves his tension.

In spite of the fact that the central part of Pirandello's picture of life is painted in dark hues, there shines in the distant horizon a feeble, iridescent light which is derived from the author's idealism. Like the idealists of all times, Pirandello contrasts the drab and sorrowful condition of man on earth with the vision of a perfect life lost in the distance of imagination whence all life originates. His idealism takes the form either of a cosmic and religious sense of universal life or of a lofty ideal existence to which man aspires when actual life offends him. This evanescent Platonism, which in its vagueness will not stand very close analysis, often echoes in Pirandello's drama, and it assumes greater importance in his latest plays. Idealism and pessimism are closer than we may at first surmise, since pessimism is often nothing but disappointed idealism.

Pirandello is fully aware of the existence and validity of man's ideal aspirations. He confesses: "We all have seen, in certain moments, appear and kindle within us a light that seems to emanate from other skies—which permits us to gaze into the most profound depths of our souls and gives us the infinite joy of feeling ourselves lost in a moment of eternity—eternal with it." (*Each in His Own Way*, p. 53.) That light shines for but a moment; it affords to Pirandello a fleeting instant of inner illumination and then disappears, leaving him in a night of terrifying darkness. This moment of inner illumination is the only eternity granted to man, but man makes the mistake of considering it a natural state and of attempting to enclose it into a system. It is natural that he should soon realize the futility of his efforts, since that moment cannot repeat itself. The result is a feeling of ennui, boredom, and nausea that stifles him, while he longs in vain for the region whence his dreams emanated.

Pirandello joins the Book of Ecclesiastes and the ascetics of long ago in proclaiming his indifference towards the gifts of the earth. Since this indifference rises through a life experience, it is beyond racial lines and outside the narrow boundaries of time limitations. It is universal, and as such it is to be found in the art of all those whose sensitiveness has been hurt by the rough hand of the daily life.

The sharp contrast that Pirandello feels between his aspiration and the result of his fearless and cold analysis of reality is determined by the objective character of his temperament that strips evil of any alluring quality, thus preventing him from abandoning himself to his belief in a good and primitive life. His drama often springs out of the conflict between the aspiration of his soul and the cold objectivity of his temperament.

It is not correct to stress unduly the term "idealism" in relation with Pirandello's thought. Idealism, outside the realm of true philosophy, has a literary patina of dubious alloy, and it points at the academic attitude of a dilettante who deals with imaginary problems and with fantastic solutions. Pirandello's idealism does not go beyond seeing grains of gold, our dreams, scattered among the ruins of the human heart—remains and echoes, but distant echoes, of the goodness that God has given to man. The ruins and the desolation of human life have attracted Pirandello's attention more than the glittering bits of the precious metal. If we chance to use the term "idealism," we should qualify it with the adjunct of "tragic."

Pirandello is inherently a primitive, with a complicated and over-active mind. His heart longs for peace and tranquillity, while his eyes long to see and his intellect to analyze what the lack of positive moral elements has produced in life. These elements have no connection whatsoever with idealism, while they testify to Pirandello's moral approach to a life concept. His ascribing to lack of simplicity and sincerity the ludicrous and painful situations in which his characters are caught points at a deep ethical attitude, and it draws a sharp line of differentiation between Pirandello and his characters, between the point of departure of the play and the final conclusion to which he is led by his deep soul. Between the beginning that portrays Pirandello outside the precincts of the Temple of Thought, where life is mockery, and the end that shows him within the temple, in the presence of sacred life and human sorrow, there is an abyss. On one side there is Pirandello who, having reached the breaking point, bursts into broad though painful laughter; on the other there is Pirandello, the thinker and man, on whose heart experience has left deep marks and scars. Pirandello, having begun with laughter, ends by revealing to us his belief that only humility can save man from the crushing weight of his human destiny. In this fashion the element of the grotesque that permeated the plays conceived and written in the chaotic years that followed the War gives place to his attitude of passive silence with a strong religious undercurrent. Silence had been the only weapon at his disposal for many long years, and it becomes now a great force in the life of his characters.

More than an idealist, Pirandello is a modern stoic, who has found the traditional cold and stiff posture too uncomfortable and commonplace, and who has renewed stoicism, either through laughter, or through his tragic idealism. In both cases, Pirandello's art acquires a cosmic resonance which is the distinctive quality of all true and great art in which men can mirror themselves.

His art is not made out of peaceful, rhythmic life, nor is it conducive to quiet, idyllic thoughts. It bruises, it wounds, it smarts; but it presents a wide horizon of life, and it never fails to awaken in our hearts pathos and sympathy for the vicissitudes of his poor characters. His art is not made out of the plain and of the obvious, just as his characters are not

pleasant people. They are not individuals that life has caught
in the peaceful mold or prison of the everyday life: a nice
home, a plump wife, two charming children, getting up in
the morning, shaving, bathing, going to the office, lunching,
going back to the office, dinner, quietly reading the newspaper
while smoking a pipe, and finally going to bed. His characters have actually experienced what even our fancies dread.
They have lived beyond the laws of society and humanity.
They have existed in a vacuum with only their tragedy, the
horror of vice in their flesh; they are, none the less, free
of all fetters, primeval beings in the whirlwind of the irrational.

In spite of the statement of many critics to the contrary,
the outstanding characteristic of Pirandello's thought is that
of being constantly close to life. Life has always been envisaged by him in terms of man's existence on this planet.
In fact, his drama centers around the consideration of what
happens to a human being endowed with instinct and reason,
sentiment and intellect.

In the course of literary history we find ourselves before
writers who aim at transcending the actual and historical
reality by losing themselves in dreams and idyls. We also
meet others who do not flinch at accepting their human lot
with its share of pleasure and sorrow, of ugliness and beauty.
These writers followed two antithetical processes, since they
either concealed what was to them the hideous countenance
of daily life behind the bewitching network of their dreams,
or they shunned dreams and compelled their art to portray
only the massive and seamy aspects of everyday life.

In Pirandello these two processes, welded together, in-
tegrate each other, and the two planes of reality, that of the
actual and that of imaginary life, are tragically fused into
one. The result of this new process is, from an æsthetic point
of view, that Pirandello's art can adhere more closely to life
where the dispassionate observer finds a dream side by side
with the most instinctive and elementary needs of man. From
the point of view of sentiment, the obliteration of the boundary between the actual and the imaginary realities leads

Pirandello's characters to the high plane of pure tragedy, since they are denied an escape from the talons of the grief that tortures them.

Pirandello takes into account that it is instinctive with human beings to protect themselves by allowing their fancy to picture beautiful vistas and idyllic lands, but his tragic sense of life is so impelling and overpowering that he cannot allow his characters to abide in the fantastic realm of their imagination. If the exaltation of the characters is so great that they identify themselves with their assumed reality, the illusion is only momentary, because the author shows them the fictitious quality of their attitude and how ludicrous they look. This prevents the obliteration of the original ego, and differentiates very sharply Pirandello's art from that of the traditional idealists. In the traditional process the original personality disappeared completely to give place to a new ego, primitive in the Arcadian fashion or garbed in the long robes of Platonism. In Pirandello the two personalities remain, tragically merged into one, writhing in a grief in which the truth of art defies the truth of life.

We do not speak of obliteration of reality and personality in the same sense as does Adriano Tilgher, a brilliant critic of Pirandello and of modern art.[1] Tilgher reduces Pirandello's attitude to the old transcendentalism. He also speaks of the negation of human personality in Pirandello's characters. No true dramatic art is possible without personality, and the conscious madman is in art a well-defined dramatic character. Illusion in Pirandello is forced on his characters by external circumstances, and, therefore, is no longer illusion. It is lucid madness, grief that writhes in the heart of man tied to his daily existence like a modern Prometheus.

Pirandello had ample opportunity to study this clear and conscious madness in himself as he contrasted it with that of poor Donna Antonietta. He looked at the painful circumstances of his life, at his acts and feelings, as if they were the life and acts of another being. He saw himself just as if he were a character in a strange drama, the creation of a

[1] *Voci del tempo*, 1921; *Studi sul teatro contemporaneo*, 1923.

cruel and fantastic artist. This harrowing contemplation induced the madness that he gives to his characters. His was a terrifying madness, and he felt it beating in his own veins, tormenting his brain, searing his soul, withering his body. Yet he continued to live and to work, finding in his art a solace for the tragedy that life had assigned to him.

Part One

IN THE WAKE OF NATURALISM

IV

Introduction

In considering Pirandello's plays it has seemed convenient
to us to classify them under five headings: In the Wake
of Naturalism; the Drama of Being and Seeming; Social
Plays; the Drama of Womanhood; and Art and Life. This
classification has a twofold justification: a pragmatic, though
arbitrary and subjective one, which, for the sake of clearness,
groups the various plays around a central and predominating
theme; and another, deeper and more significant, that corresponds to the general direction of Pirandello's development.

The line of development followed by Luigi Pirandello in
his art goes from a somewhat external and even picturesque
naturalism to an introspective and tormented individualism.
The two stages, however, are not separated by a clear-cut line
of division. On the contrary, if one looks below the surface,
he discovers that the early naturalism shows traces of the
later individualism, just as the introspective stage has never
lost at least the memory of the time when Pirandello's art
was devoted to a direct analysis of life studied at close range.
Whether in the elementary humanity of the earlier plays
or in the complex individuals of the later ones, we find the
reflection of his tormented spirit and sad existence. This is
the essential part of Pirandello's drama, and it should be
constantly seen behind the division to which we have subjected his large and imposing dramatic production.

Cap and Bells should be included among the plays of
"being and seeming" because of the implications that it
contains, although the hero, Ciampa, bears all the outer
marks of Sicilian naturalism. The same can be said of characters that are found in plays studied in other groups. The
utmost has been done not to allow the formal element of
divisions to interfere with seeing Pirandello's plays as an
indivisible though varied whole.

43

Naturalism has left clearly distinguishable traces on Pirandello's art. It can be seen in his concept of life which has never failed to recognize the power of instinct, in the Sicilian setting of most of his early plays, in the presentation of elementary characters, as well as in the objective attitude that he assumes in portraying both events and characters. These traits, consciously or subconsciously, stated in theory and often denied in practice, are found in the works of the masters of Sicilian naturalism—Giovanni Verga and Luigi Capuana. They are also noticed in Pirandello's dramatic works, although the younger man has gone beyond naturalism, compelled by the bitterness of his experience to rely on his imagination and to feel detached from the instinctive side of life.

Pirandello has taken from naturalism—and not only from that of his time but from that of all time—the concept of a suffering and pitiful humanity. In his conscientious and objective method of observation he has deprived life of any lyrical and lofty attributes. He has obeyed the dictates of the naturalistic school in rendering the background of his plays with great precision, as we can readily see in *Liolà*, in *Limes of Sicily*, and in the sketches that we have grouped together considering them in the light of the school that Pirandello admired and followed in his youth. *Liolà* might have been written by Verga, if Pirandello had not broken the pledge of objectivity and if he had not allowed his humor to take hold of the situation, which ends with a cold and diabolic burst of laughter, of which the good Verga was not capable.

Many of the dramatic sketches that have been included in this section are dramatizations of short stories that had been written at an earlier date. *The Imbecile, At a Sanctuary, The Jar, The Patent, Limes of Sicily, The Duty of a Physician* had appeared under the garb of the short story until Pirandello's repressed dramatic genius urged him to recast them into plays. Other dramatic works that will be considered later have also been taken from short stories. Such are, for example, *Either of One or of No One, Think It Over, Giacomino; It Is Only in Jest, All for the Best.* In a sense the naturalistic trend in Pirandello's drama is only a reflection of an earlier stage of his art.

Pirandello in the beginning of his literary career sought strong and vivid passions. It was but natural that he should place the setting of his early works of fiction in his beloved island. In one of his plays he speaks of Sicily in these terms: "The action takes place in a city in the interior of Sicily, where, as you know, passions are strong and smolder under cover till they break forth with a fearful violence. Among all most fierce is jealousy." (*Tonight We Improvise*, p. 26.)

Pirandello owes a great deal to naturalism. The clear, detailed descriptions of his scenes afford a solid basis for his drama, while the penetrating observation and rendering of the outward appearance and gestures of his characters give a complete characterization of the latter that leaves little to the actors in interpreting them. It is also due to Pirandello's contact with naturalism that the soul is made to reflect on the physical being of the characters, with the result that the psychological study of them never degenerates into abstraction. It can be truly said that Pirandello's characters are complete personalities, and that they stand out unforgettably in one's memory, projected against the everyday life that the author has given them as a background.

Pirandello shares with Verga his tendency to describe primitive people and passions. The characters that we shall soon meet: Micuccio Bonavino, Cecè, Liolà, Chiarchiaro, are characters caught through the observation of reality close at hand and rendered with directness and objectivity. In his early plays Pirandello placed himself before odd figures that he noticed in old Sicily, described their outward characteristics, and wove a slight dramatic action on them. Only indirectly is the drama of his characters that of Pirandello, the playwright. One does not feel the presence of the author in the elementary and healthy sensuality of Liolà nor in the sketches in which he reveals a charming but external naturalism.

The author, however, felt ill at ease in these humble and limited characters, and he soon passed to an art which presents characters that show traces of an intense and passionate subjectivism. There are suggestions of this new mood in Tommaso Corsi in *The Duty of a Physician,* in Andrea Fabbri in *The Vise,* as well as in the hero of *The Man with a Flower in His Mouth.* These characters are clear examples of the author's departure from his external naturalism, and they point at a more psychological and introspective art.

Someone may be led to doubt or even to reject the relation between naturalism and the drama of Pirandello by noticing the emotional people that he takes from provincial life in Sicily. Though humble people of the lower classes, they gesticulate like persons possessed of the evil spirit, they roll their eyes excitedly, and they have a great deal of temperament and sentiment. These characters may appear as pure fantastic creations to anyone who has not known the Italian people whom Pirandello had the opportunity to observe and study in his childhood and youth. We still remember these odd figures whose gestures were exalted, whose lives were miserable, and whose thoughts were extraordinary. They were heroes of an imaginary greatness, grotesque mixtures of gentleness and violence, with strange eyes now widened in a frenzy, now soft with delicate feelings. The leveling factor of modern life has destroyed these picturesque figures, and with them a great deal of suffering and a vast amount of unwritten poetry has gone, perhaps forever.

The consideration of naturalistic elements in the drama of Luigi Pirandello is of paramount importance. The most daring situations where instinct irresistibly has led human beings into the snares that nature has set for them are found in Pirandello, as in all great artists. Instinct, however, is presented as a life force, and it affords the pattern on which the artist can weave his own introspective and speculative thoughts. The fact that the love theme predominates in Pirandello's drama must not lead us to confuse him with writers affected by eroticism. Love has constantly and justly occupied a central place in art because it has a large part in life. The greatness of the artist, however, is proportionate to the degree in which he has succeeded in making us feel the presence of the whole life of the character through his love experience. Reduced purely to love, a work is gross eroticism or ethereal Platonism.

Pirandello's early contacts with naturalism has prevented his drama from degenerating into empty lyricism. Since he often deals with characters who are forced to walk in the clouds, he has used a naturalistic setting to enhance the solidity and charm of the actual life from which his typical characters have been excluded. A lyric dramatist would give a diffused and hazy rendering of the scenery, and he would allow the concreteness of the landscape to degenerate into the diaphanous mist of idyl and symbolism. Pirandello is so concerned in rendering accurately the observable reality as even to give geographical names of the places where the action develops.

Italo Siciliano, one of Pirandello's most bitter and superficial critics,[1] has stated that the latter has failed as a dramatist because he did not continue to derive his inspiration from the modest, though solid world of naturalism, and has lost himself in the midst of cerebral and abstract themes. The fact is that Pirandello's naturalistic plays cannot compare with those in which he has gone beyond the limited boundaries of this movement. If any criticism should be made, it is that Pirandello often encloses big problems in little people, with the result that they are too small for the task that he assigns to them.

In the plays that we are about to study there is nothing that bespeaks the complexity of later plays, of the cerebral process which he attributes to some of his characters in later works. We are using these plays, therefore, by way of introduction to the significant works of Pirandello. As time has gone on he has identified himself more and more with his characters until, in his latest plays, as, for instance, *When One Is Somebody*, he is so close to his main character as to merge completely with him. The drama of Pirandello the artist has gradually coincided with that of Pirandello the man. This explains why the analysis of life that appears in his

[1] *Il teatro di Luigi Pirandello ovvero dei fasti dell'artificio*, 1929.

latest works is infinitely deeper and more penetrating than that of the earlier plays.

Most of these are simple sketches in which the author tried his hand in passing from the short story to the drama. They are useful, however, to show the distance that separates these simple attempts at drama from the full blossom of Pirandello's art. They also serve the purpose of showing how Pirandello links himself with Sicilian naturalism while rising towards an art of his own that has made him a gigantic figure in the history of contemporary drama.

V

Humble Themes of Sicilian Life

LIMES OF SICILY

and Other Dramatic Sketches

Sicily and southern Italy naturally attracted the attention of a man who had remained so intimately a Sicilian in the intensity of his emotions which smoldered in his heart like a fire ready to burst into vivid flames. One of the jewels of this production of a minor tone is *Limes of Sicily*. It would seem opportune, however, to discuss briefly a few other dramatic sketches with a Sicilian background in order to create the proper setting for the touching story of Micuccio Bonavino, the modest and humble hero of *Limes of Sicily*.

We shall consider first four very short plays in which Pirandello appears to have assumed the objective attitude that the masters of Sicilian naturalism had advocated. He sketches from life, much in the manner of an artist who goes from place to place in search of characteristic bits that he may notice in the primitive atmosphere of Sicilian villages.

*

*   *

IN A SANCTUARY

(*La sagra del Signore della nave*)

In his *In a Sanctuary* Pirandello relies especially on a pictorial technique for effect. The play brings to one's memory the celebrated painting, The Vow, by Francesco Paolo Michetti, where in a riot of colors are represented those who go to a sanctuary to make vows to the statue of a saint in the midst of clouds of incense, imploring to be healed by divine power. Pirandello has caught the vivid lights, the picturesqueness, the tumult of a festival day in a maritime city of southern Italy where people who have been miraculously saved from the wrath of the sea go to render their thanks to a renowned effigy of Christ.

There echo in the play the voices of numerous vendors, the noises of a sanguine life full of strength and violence. The sound of distant drums covers this confusion. Pirandello has transported into his play in all its truth the vividness of the old Italian fairs. We see "old men with faces baked by the sun, and short, curly beards, wearing huge, conical hats with hanging ribbons, velvet clothes worn out and discolored, a green one here, a brown one there, short trousers, heavy blue cotton stockings, rough and heavily hobnailed shoes." Here is one of the sailors: "The old sailor, tall but bent, with a wooden and almost black face, stiff and smooth gray hair, hard, angry eyes, his beard cut in an oval shape all around his face."

The author stresses the naturalistic aspects of life as he watches the flood of humanity that surges around the sanctuary: prostitutes in garish colors, profligate youths whose blood courses more rapidly under the scorching sun, pigs killed and prepared and cooked, there in the public square. There are long tables covered with white tablecloths where roast pork is served, together with abundant red wine. Wine and blood, good and bad odors are rendered with great directness and objectivity.

A slight episode is grafted on this primitive and colorful background where the religious and the beastly are not contrasted but actually merged. Among some people seated at the table to eat a fresh-killed pig, there arises a discussion about the intelligence of the pig that allows itself to be fattened in order to be killed. The intelligence of the pig is attacked by a young pedagogue, an exponent of thought and culture who is "thin, pale, and blond; he dresses in black and is sickly. A born poet, he defends his incorruptible faith in the ideal values of life and, above all, in human dignity against the irony of prolonged fasting and against the ob-

scene brutality of daily experience." Pirandello with benevolent irony contrasts him with the violent and sanguine life
that surrounds him. The idealist does not understand what
relation there is between the religious festival and the heavy
eating and drinking. What is more entertaining is that he
tries to find out from those who kill and prepare the pigs.
He grows pale and trembles when the men take hold of a
huge pig and slaughter it with a long knife that cuts the
throat of the animal while the poor beast squeals in pain
and the blood gushes out of the large wound.

The wan pedagogue teaches the humanities to the son of
Signor Lavaccara who, on that very day, has sold his fat
pig that he loved very dearly, and is still grieving over the
fate of the poor animal. He had cried when they had taken
it away from his stable. One could chat with that animal.
He had even given him a name—Nicholas. His son called
him "and he came to eat the bread from his hand; he came
like a little dog." Signor Lavaccara, "well provided with an
enormous wealth of pink flesh that shakes around him," arrives just as they are killing his hog. He frantically shouts:
"No, no! Tell him not to slaughter it. I shall give him back
his money! I shall give him back his money!" His wife closes
her ears so as not to hear the pitiful cries of the animal and
moans: "Poor Nicholas! Poor Nicholas!" So also does the
son entrusted to the care of the pedagogue, who is horrified
at the idea that the boy should have been allowed to come
there in that confusion and before that display of bestiality.
He teaches the humanities according to the old method that
consists in elevating oneself above the grossness of life. What
is a pig and its intelligence compared to the divine intelligence of man? How can Signor Lavaccara say that his
Nicholas was more intelligent than a man?

Upon hearing the romantic and platonic pedagogue offend
the memory of his dear and, to him, noble pig, Signor Lavaccara becomes furious. His idea of a pig, patterned on his
wonderful animal, is so high, its humanity so pronounced,
that he proves to the pedagogue that the actions of man if

51

we look closely are not superior to those of a pig. The people who surge around them—brutalized by wine, heavy eating, and harlots—the noise, the heat prove beyond any doubt that Signor Lavaccara is right.

*

* *

THE OTHER SON

(*L'altro figlio*)

Here too we find picturesque Sicily with its young women wearing bright kerchiefs and its poor old women looking like bundles of dirty, black rags. Here are some of the women as Pirandello has sketched them: "Gialluzza, a small, thin woman in her thirties with hair once blond, now lifeless like tow, that she wears in a big knot at the back of her head; Marassunta, an old woman in her sixties, in mourning, wearing a discolored cotton dress, her black kerchief tied under her chin; Tuzza, in her forties, with her eyes always fixed on the ground and with a mournful voice; Marinese, red-headed and gaudy." The picture, significant in its dusky colors and one in which life seems to be caught and made immobile, is completed by "Jaco Spina, an old peasant with a black knitted cap and in shirt sleeves, who lies on his back, his head resting on a donkey's saddle, while he is listening [to the women], smoking his pipe. Some children, burned almost black by the sun, run here and there."

We are taken back to the early years of our century when emigration took away from Sicily all the young men, while old mothers were left behind, poor and broken-hearted. Maragrazia is one of them. Pirandello has caught her in all her miserable and almost revolting ugliness and poverty, insisting on the thick net of wrinkles that covers her face, on her eyes with turned-back eyelids, bloody with continuous weeping, on her sparse and disheveled hair. "She seems a heap of rags; rags greasy and heavy, always the same, winter and summer, torn and tattered, without any color, and smelling of all the filth of the streets." She is wretchedly poor and unhappy. Her two sons have gone to the Argentine, and they do not even write to her. On that day twenty-four men are leaving the village to seek their fortunes in America. One of these young men, Tino, passes by and takes leave of the women who, Italian-wise, were seated on their doorsteps. Maragrazia begs Ninfarosa, an intelligent young woman who knows how to write, to compose a letter to her children. Tino will take it to them.

The poor woman is considered a nuisance by everyone in the neighborhood. Ninfarosa deceives her and does not write down the heart-breaking message that the mother is sending to her sons. She just scribbles a few signs, folds the sheet, and gives it to her. The village physician happens to go by and Maragrazia asks him to read the letter to her. Ninfarosa's deceit is discovered. The physician is perplexed and indignant. In excusing her act, Ninfarosa tells him that this old woman has another son with whom she refuses to live, saying that he is not her son.

The explanation that the doctor hears from the old mother takes us back to the days when Sicily was overrun by bandits. In a night of terror her husband was killed by them, and one of them attacked her—and this child was born. With stubbornness and almost hatefulness she asks the doctor whether it can be said that he is her son. The doctor, more sympathetic than the women of the neighborhood, writes a long letter to her sons in the Argentine, a real letter.

In reading this short dramatic sketch entitled *The Other Son* our interest is attracted by the picturesque, narrow street in the little village of Farnia in Sicily. Pirandello gives us the name of the village, out of his respect for the scientific accuracy on which naturalism insisted. He objectively shows the cruel indifference of the women for the heartaches of the poor old mother. All the stage directions are given with meticulous care, rendering most accurately the clothes of the women, their postures, their names, and feelings that do not go beyond the realm of sensations. Life is presented in its unchanging monotony and in its quaint picturesqueness with a sudden plunge into a gruesome past very much stressed by way of contrast.

*

*   *

THE PATENT

(*La patente*)

The Patent is a dramatization of a short story that has a distinctly provincial and Sicilian flavor. It deals with a poor man, Chiarchiaro, whom human malice has goaded into a sort of frenzy that makes him hate all mankind. People have spread the rumor that he is a sorcerer. Everyone has refused work to him, as well as to his three daughters. Everyone shuns them. Now Chiarchiaro is suing two influential townspeople whom he surprised making conjuring signs as they passed by him.

A strange, truly Pirandellian judge who, in spite of his queer ways, has a lot of compassion for his fellow-men, sends for Chiarchiaro in order to make him withdraw his charges, because, as the matter stands now, he knows that he will have to convict Chiarchiaro. Judge D'Andrea enters the room carrying a small cage in which he has a goldfinch. It is his constant companion. It had belonged to his mother who had died the year before, the only person he held in affection in this world. He takes the goldfinch from the small cage and puts it into a larger one. "Hush now," he tells it, "and let me administer justice to these poor, fierce, little men."

His colleagues are constantly poking fun at him on account of his goldfinch. "What about you dressed up like that?" he retorts, referring to the funereal, judicial robes, and sending forth a vitriolic attack against those who take life too seriously. We are all funny, one way or the other. He and his colleagues are not so serious now as they were when, as children, they played the game of judge. "All the greatness was in the robe, and within we were children. Now it is the reverse. We have grown up, and the robe, having lost its

54

sacredness for us, has become the game of our childhood."
The implication is that, at best, life is august in its appearance, but once we lose respect for the stately appearance with
which man clothes himself, everything crumbles with it. His
colleagues chide him about the fact that he passes his leisure
time in talking to his little bird. The Judge admits it: "I talk
to him imitating his voice with my whistling as well as I can,
and he answers me. If he answers me it means that he finds
some sense in the sounds that I make. Just as we, my dear
friends, believe that nature talks to us with the poetry of
her flowers and with the stars of her heavens while perhaps
nature does not even know that we exist."

When Chiarchiaro arrives, the Judge is surprised at the
eloquence and logical arguments of the poor sorcerer. No,
Chiarchiaro will not withdraw his charges against the son of
the mayor and against the city alderman. He, Chiarchiaro,
is a sorcerer and hopes that the court will convict him, thereby
giving him a patent as sorcerer. Men with impunity have
called him a sorcerer until they have reduced him to the
point that he feels that with the hatred that he has accumulated
within him he can destroy a whole city. Now he must be
convicted, and thereby recognized by the law as a sorcerer.
That conviction will be his diploma, just as the Judge had
to take his diploma before he could practise law. Chiarchiaro
will have a profession!

The Judge asks, almost overcome with astonishment, what
he will do with it. With ill-controlled vehemence Chiarchiaro
answers: "What shall I do with it? Can't you really see
that much? I shall put it on my visiting cards as a title. Ah!
does that seem little to you? It is my patent! It will be my
profession! I have been stabbed, your Honor! I am an honest
man and a father. I used to work honestly. I have been
dismissed and thrown into the street because I was a sorcerer.
The only thing left to me is to begin to practise the profession
of sorcery."

He will put on a strange suit that he has made himself.
He will frighten people. He will let his beard grow; he will
put on awesome glasses. He will go in front of gambling

houses. The proprietor, the gamblers will pay him, not to have him there in front of the place. He will go near various shops, jewelry stores, factories, and they will all pay him in order to send him in front of a rival shop. He will make money as a sorcerer. "It will be a kind of tax that I shall exact from now on," concludes Chiarchiaro. The Judge seriously says, "The tax of ignorance." Chiarchiaro does not agree with him. It is the tax on everybody's health because he could actually destroy everyone and everything through the hatred that has filled him, because of men's malice.

As Chiarchiaro is insisting on the need of his being convicted, the window suddenly opens and strikes the cage, knocking it down and killing the poor bird. At that noise the other judges and the court employes rush in, asking what has happened. In a broken voice Judge D'Andrea explains: "The wind . . . the window . . . the goldfinch." Chiarchiaro with a shout of triumph rejects that explanation: "The wind? The window? It was I. He did not wish to believe and I have given him proof." Turning to the astonished and frightened spectators, he adds: "And you will die, one by one, just as that goldfinch died." They all are awed, but his reputation is made. They all beg him not to use his evil power on them. Chiarchiaro imperiously shouts: "Then you pay here, immediately—pay the tax!— All of you!" They all pay and Chiarchiaro, turning towards Judge D'Andrea in exultation, cries: "Did you see? And I haven't got the patent yet! Start the lawsuit! I am rich! I am rich!"

Chiarchiaro is the first character that gives evidences of traits that, enriched and deepened, will blossom into more complex personalities in later plays. He possesses that fixity of thought and intensity of passion that become exaltation and lead to conscious artificiality. Pirandello has fashioned him by endowing him with a simple psychology such as only a poor peasant can possess. In all his humble personality he is a real character because he possesses an intensity in his passion that colors every act of his life and every feeling of his heart.

The play, a little jewel of its kind, is made by the philosophical judge, D'Andrea, and by the wretched and pitiful Chiarchiaro. The tragic element has stealthily penetrated into the humble theme, and it has permeated the structure of the play.

*
*   *

THE JAR

(*La giara*)

The Jar is also taken from a short story. More than anything else it shows an attempt on the part of the dramatist to present an exasperated logic in primitive characters.

Zi Dima is a gruff mender of oil jars, those huge jars, taller than a man, in which in Sicily they keep their precious golden liquid, olive oil. Every day he takes his implements, and goes from town to town mending jars. There are two methods of doing it. One is by using a powerful glue that he has invented, another by sewing the broken pieces with a steel thread.

One day Zi Dima is called to fix a jar for Don Lolò, a wealthy farmer, known all over the countryside for his stubbornness and for his *penchant* for lawsuits. Zi Dima suggests his own method: to glue it with his marvelous glue. Don Lolò wants his jar sewed. Two stubborn, relentless wills are pitted against each other. Zi Dima must yield. It is Don Lolò's jar, after all. He enters the jar and sews it by first drilling holes and then passing fine wire through them. When he tries to come out of the jar, he can't. The neck is too narrow.

A legal question arises: Who will pay for the jar that will have to be broken? Zi Dima from the inside of the jar tells Don Lolò that it is his fault and asks Don Lolò to break it and let him out. Don Lolo naturally does not wish to break his precious jar. He argues very acutely against old Zi Dima and finds an indescribable pleasure in indulging in the legalistic subtleties which are his hobby. Zi Dima is very philosophical about his plight. He lights his pipe and peacefully waits in his new shelter. Don Lolò, one of those gigantic men that one often saw in the fields, people always ready to use violence, gets madder and madder, and finally kicks the jar and sends it rolling down the hill. The jar breaks against a tree. "I win!" shouts Zi Dima, rising from the débris of the jar.

This is the elementary subject matter that Pirandello has dramatized without being able to wipe out the original flavor of a delightful short story. Pirandello is more interested in the delineation of characters and in their picturesque individualism than in the dramatic development of the slight event that he relates. One need only look at Don Lolò to be convinced of this: "He is a huge man in his forties, with the suspicious eyes of a wolf. He is extremely irascible. He wears an old white hat with a huge brim, and has golden rings in his ears." His language is not different from that which one hears in the country among laborers and farmers: "May St. Aloe help you to break your neck, you and your mules." So he greets a muleteer who wishes to know where he is to unload the manure that he has carried to Don Lolò's farm. In his love for lawsuits, Don Lolò carries a copy of the civil code in his pocket, and studies it so that no one may dare dispute what he says and does. His lawyer has given him that copy of the code because he has tired of seeing him in his office every day. Now he can study his own cases by himself.

The descriptive and therefore external character of the early plays is evidenced by the long and minute scene descriptions. The characters stand before us in a clear-cut contour, but they do not possess the depth of character that Pirandello has created in later plays. They are more picturesque than dramatic. Pirandello has kept the names of his characters in the original Sicilian form, another proof that in the beginning of his dramatic career he was a direct derivation of Sicilian naturalism.

Don Lolò and Zi Dima are perfectly executed little etchings such as Pirandello has lavished upon his literary work, be it the short story or the drama. The author has skilfully presented also the temperaments of the contained and gruff Zi Dima and the quarrelsome and violent Don Lolò, both studied in the natural setting of old Sicily.

*

*   *

LIMES OF SICILY

(*Lumie di Sicilia*)

More complex, although woven on a very humble personage, is *Limes of Sicily*. Limes are fragrant fruit that grow in that island and which in the play are taken as the symbol of the purity and simplicity of Sicilian life as contrasted with the sensual and vulgar life of the continent.

Micuccio Bonavino, the hero, is a simple Sicilian peasant who has traveled from his little home town to a tumultuous city of northern Italy in order to see again his sweetheart, Teresina, who is now a celebrated singer. We meet Micuccio in her house as he arrives after the long journey, a jarring note in the luxury of the singer's home and in contrast to the sophisticated servants, with the "collar of his rough coat turned up to his ears, a dirty bag in one hand, and a little valise and a musical instrument case in the other." Micuccio had brought with him a bag of sweet limes to offer to Teresina, that they might bring to her the memories of the past when they loved each other through their common passion for music. Micuccio played the piccolo and Teresina sang. He was determined to make a great singer out of her. He sent her to a conservatory at Naples for four years with the money collected from the sale of a piece of land that his uncle, a priest, had bequeathed him. Teresina had had a marvelous career. She had sung in Milan, Rome, Spain, Russia.

Micuccio does not find Teresina at home. She is at the theatre. There will be a reception in her home that evening for her friends who by chance are all of the masculine sex. Micuccio can see only Zia Marta, Teresina's mother, who in spite of the worldly life of her daughter and in spite of

59

her velvet dresses and hats has kept intact her simple soul and the sincerity of a good peasant woman. She stays with Micuccio while Teresina entertains her smart friends in the big and beautifully illuminated parlor. Marta reveals to Micuccio all the misery of that life: "Appearance, luxury, debts, money, then want, masked by tricks and subterfuges." They sit by themselves in a little room and dine together, served with foods that Micuccio has never before tasted. Micuccio has seen another world. He never knew that such beauty and luxury could exist. He is so overwhelmed that he can hardly eat.

Zia Marta and he go over the beautiful, even if not always happy days, spent in their village. In that house, dedicated to corruption under the name of art, there passes on the wings of memory the peaceful beauty of the field and there echoes the chirping of the swallows that made their nests in the ceiling of the garret where Zia Marta and Teresina lived, and where Micuccio cherished his modest dream of love for the girl with the beautiful voice. Zia Marta has not forgotten the little women with their modest virtues whom want had taught how to beg without seeming to do so: "Do you remember Annuzza with her little clove of garlic? She came with this excuse, a clove of garlic, just as we were about to eat something." Annuzza is dead now. Zia Marta envies those dead; at least they rest in the cemetery of their little village. Who knows where she will be buried? Her life is far from being happy, as she confides to Micuccio whom she loves as a son. Here she cannot even make the sign of the cross when she begins to eat.

As Micuccio talks, his words uncover patches of blue in the sky of far-away Sicily: marriages, children of people they know, the quiet, happy life, even if monotonous, of their town. A wave of laughter and high voices that bespeak the beast comes to them. Zia Marta is perturbed. Micuccio's face registers his emotions, from astonishment at the luxury of Teresina's house to joy in seeing Zia Marta again. There is longing in him, too—that of seeing Teresina. Teresina, in fact, comes. "She is dressed in silk, covered with magnificent jewels, her bosom bare in very low-cut gown, her back and arms bare. She enters hastily, and it seems that suddenly the little room is illuminated by a violent light." Micuccio is "dazzled and stupefied as if before a fantastic apparition." He can only utter the name "Teresina." She says a few words, indifferent and artificial, like many greetings that people exchange, and returns to her friends.

Micuccio sees the abyss that time has opened between them. Slowly the truth begins to penetrate his simple mind while anguish oppresses his poor heart. Now he understands fully the nature of that laughter and of the noise that comes from the room where the party is going on. He learns from Zia Marta that Teresina is no longer worthy of him. There is nothing to do but to leave the house and return disconsolately to Sicily. Before going out he remembers that he has his beautiful and fragrant limes with him. He pours them out of his bag on to a table. "Limes," cries Zia Marta, with tears in her eyes, "our beautiful limes!" They both look at them in silence. Micuccio has an idea. It seems to have slowly emerged from the nebulous distance of his mind: "What if I should begin to throw them on the heads of all those fine gentlemen?" As Zia Marta looks at him imploringly, he changes his mind and leaves with his valise and his piccolo.

Teresina enters the room and sees the limes. She is not moved by them. She gathers up as many as she can and invites her admirers to see and enjoy them, unmindful that their touch will contaminate them. The play ends with the wanton laughter and the loud and gay voices of Teresina and her friends; Micuccio is forgotten. Pirandello has left the two lovers to their destiny.

Micuccio is perfectly drawn, and he is as close to a dreamy peasant as the artistic rendering allows him to be. In his humility and simplicity he carries a deep, philosophical *motif* which is derived from the author's sad realization that change is an inevitable element of life and that it is useless to struggle against it. Micuccio, by remaining immobilized in his little village, had not changed. Teresina had. How could the two understand each other? The final separation was a logical consequence of the change that Micuccio had helped to bring about.

Pirandello does not bring Teresina back to the old and perfumed world of limes and orange groves. He is too sophisticated to do that, but he brings out in the conversation between Zia Marta and Micuccio all his attachment for his island which he relinquished, but which he could not forget, when he wanted to try his wings on the open spaces of the continent.

A bitter philosophy permeates the play and moves like a shifting and ominous light over its vicissitudes, seeming to say: If we do not change we are denied the stir of modern life, civilization; if we change we join lots with Teresina. The author is perplexed in choosing between the primitive but necessarily limited conditions of life in Sicilian villages and the life of capitals full of movement and splendor. It is hard to choose between being like Micuccio and being like Teresina, although Pirandello's sympathies are with the quaint peasant and with his beloved Sicily.

VI

Painful Mirth and Tragedy Make
Their Entrance

LIOLÀ

and Other Minor Dramatic Sketches

Theꞓ naturalistic theme in the particular and well-defined characters that naturalism assumed especially with Verga, Pirandello's great master, appears also in *Liolà*. The setting and the characters of this play share in a distinct manner the most salient traits of Verga's art. Liolà is a happy-go-lucky young peasant, not different from Verga's primitive fishermen, with the difference that Verga reveals through his elementary and humble characters his thoughtful and tender temperament, while Pirandello lets his humorous mind bring into the play a deep note of painful mirth before the contradictions of life.

Before analyzing *Liolà* we shall briefly discuss three short plays in which the author has enclosed very dramatic, highly passionate, and tense moments.

*

*   *

AT THE EXIT

(All'uscita)

At the Exit is, according to the author, a profane mystery play, having as a setting the exit, or entrance as we would call it, of a cemetery. Characters and events are suspended midway between life and death. The characters are the "vain appearances" of the Fat Man, of the Philosopher, of a Woman who was killed by her lover, of the Child with the pomegranate, while the solid aspects of tangible life are represented by a Peasant, his Wife, an old donkey, and a Child.

The drama is taken from a newspaper account of a crime committed by a lover who kills his mistress and then tries to commit suicide. Pirandello has given a fantastic treatment to the play, imagining that the husband of the woman, impersonated by the Fat Man, is already dead. He sits sadly at the exit of the cemetery thinking of his past life, regretting that he did not enjoy the fresh and pure beauty of flowers, the melody of a nightingale to which he could have listened in his garden. His life was harassed by his wife who possessed a "harrowing, torturing laughter that used to burst forth from that cruel red mouth of hers, between the cut of her lucid teeth." He confesses: "Every time I heard her laugh, it seemed that the earth trembled, the sky became cloudy, my little garden withered, bristling with thorny thistles. Laughter springs from her bowels like a frantic rage of destruction."

This woman had a lover, and she treated him just as she had treated her husband, while she had for the latter the "voluble affection, a little playful, a little biting, of the first days of their engagement." The lover could not stand that distressing and maddening laughter, and killed her. As the Fat Man sits there at the cemetery exit, his dead wife comes to him and relates how she was killed. She says: "A shot; I felt a sensation of cold here; I fell; he lifted me from the ground, put me on the bed, kissed me repeatedly, then wounded himself. I felt him slide to the ground, moaning at my feet. There endured to the very end on my lips the warmth of his kisses. But perhaps it was only blood." In fact, it was blood that she wiped away, her face twisted in spasmodic laughter. She comments: "It was blood. No kiss ever burned me. While the ceiling of my room seemed to lower itself closer to me and everything was becoming dark, I hoped that that last kiss would at last give me the warmth for which I had always longed from the very depth of my being. It was my blood, instead, the useless burning of my blood."

She confides the inner secret of her intimate life to the vain appearance of the Philosopher while her husband shakes his head bitterly. He fails to understand now the actions and feelings of this woman just as he had in life. At this moment a child is seen advancing on his rosy feet over the grass of the cemetery. A new being is awakened in the tragic woman. She becomes gentle and soft and walks towards the Child, who has died with a last unrealized desire in his little heart: the longing for a pomegranate. He has a pomegranate now in his tiny, chubby hands. The Woman breaks it and the Child eats the red, juicy grains, from the palms of her hands; then he disappears. She weeps bitterly over her unrealized desire for a child.

Pirandello has enclosed here, behind the passion of the Woman and the resigned patience of the husband, a drama of denied motherhood. The warmth of her blood (Pirandello treats this element very naturalistically) led her to profligacy and death because her motherhood was thwarted.

The husband points out to her a little peasant family that advances in the dusk behind a donkey that is carrying home a bundle of grass and a child. A sense of quiet peace, of rustic tranquillity, rises from the group and tantalizes those two beings for whom life had held tragedy and sorrow. Would it not have been better to live that quiet life, to have had a child from whom to learn the joy of laughter and the purity of life rather than to roam in the tragic desert of passion and hatred?

The vain appearances that evanescently move in the play seem to be the result of the detachment with which Pirandello views at times the outside world. Looked at from an impenetrable subjectivism, our fellow-men appear to the author like the impalpable appearances that we meet in this play. For years Pirandello moved among men like a shadow among shadows. However, he is opposed to those who complicate life and by so doing fail to live it with simplicity and candor. If the husband had lingered over the serene aspect of nature which he let pass unnoticed under his eyes; if the woman had had the joy of a child, their life would not have ended in tragedy and death. The longing for a child has taken here a physical, carnal, although deeply poignant form.

It is interesting to note this solid part of Pirandello's thought which he uses as a basis for his art, because, although it disappears in some of his plays, especially those written in the turmoil and chaos of post-war days, it finally reaffirms itself in his latest plays. Indeed, if we look beyond appearances, it is ever present in his dramatic production, even if hidden by his humor and at times by his gloomy pessimism. The happy peasant family, standing for the massive aspects of life, is presented with an idea of contrast with the unhappy and tormented couple whose tragedy endures even beyond the boundaries of this life.

*

*   *

THE VISE

(*La morsa*)

The Vise is another short play portraying an intensely dramatic moment as an expression of the author's tragic state of mind. There is a uniform, closed sky, as in an impending storm, which weighs heavily on the tense situation that has caught three human beings in a snare; then there comes a sudden flash that spells death.

Giulia in a moment of folly had run away with Andrea Fabbri, who had become her husband. He himself did not understand how he had done it. He was not made for frivolity. He was a man of steel, a hard worker. To atone for his irresponsible action he has begun to work like a madman, and in so doing has neglected the sentimental woman who has become the mistress of her husband's best friend, Antonio Serra. This is the situation that holds them as if in a deadly vise. Antonio fears that the husband suspects them; that he has seen them kissing each other goodbye the day that he and Andrea left on a business trip. The silence of the husband, prolonged for several days, hangs over them like a crushing weight. He tortures them, until, denying his wife the right to see her children again, he forces her to commit suicide.

She dies, redeeming herself by asking her husband to promise her never to reveal to her children the shame that led to her death.

This short play, similar to the small but strong sketches that a great master may have drawn in an interval between two great paintings, is interesting especially for the vividness with which Pirandello has rendered the tense and closed character of Andrea and the tormenting suspense of the guilty ones. Pirandello obeyed the dictates of naturalism in looking upon instinct as an overpowering force, but he reached the height of artistic greatness by lending to his characters his own intensity of feelings. Andrea is a figure sculptured as only Pirandello knows how to do it. A few touches of his strong fingers, and Andrea, crushing in his honesty, genius, and strength of character, destroys the ephemeral whim of another poor Madame Bovary.

*

* *

THE DUTY OF A PHYSICIAN

(*Il dovere del medico*)

Tommaso Corsi, the main character in *The Duty of a Physician*, like many of the individuals portrayed in plays of this period, has that hidden weakness that leads him to sin, not for love, not even for passion, but just by chance. Endowed with an impetuous character, he lives furiously, without reflecting. Anna, his wife, analyzes as follows his temperament and behavior: "He did not give time to his judgment as he did not give weight to his acts. It was useless to make him stop to consider his wrongdoing. A shrugging of his shoulders, a smile, and that was all." She has to confess, however, that no vice had ever clung to him. He had remained spontaneous, always joyous, the same friendly person to all.

One day he was discovered with the wife of a friend, the most fatuous woman one could imagine. The husband shot at him. Corsi, in self-defense, killed the husband. Realizing what he had done, he tried to commit suicide, but a physician, an intimate of the family, bandaged his wound and saved him. Anna, a long-suffering and superior woman who, knowing her husband's temperament, has been big enough to forgive him, passed sleepless nights and anxious days at his bedside as he wavered between life and death.

Pirandello has wished to stress the uncontrollable factor of passion in life by making Corsi an almost ideal man, so he says of him: "He is very tall and most handsome. His face is as pale as wax, and a little drawn, but his eyes shine almost in a childish way." The woman who led him to his downfall is portrayed as a worthless person, and her husband as a fit companion for her. Corsi is meant to have all our sympathy, although the author unflinchingly leads him towards his punishment.

As he is convalescing he is sincerely penitent and touched by his wife's goodness. He says to Anna, taking her face between his hands and drawing it near his with infinite tenderness: "You understand, you feel that it is true if I tell you that never, never in my heart, in my thought, have I betrayed you." It was infamous to be caught in that shameful moment of stupid idleness. His life was wrapped up in her and in his children as he saw and understood, more clearly than ever, the very moment that his rival fired at him. If Corsi fired back it was not only in self-defense, but also because he could not allow himself to be killed for that woman.

Now he is better, almost well, but a grave decision is impending on his wife and on his friends, a lawyer and the physician. He must be told that he is to be prosecuted and very likely will be sentenced to life imprisonment: "It will be terrible," says Anna to the doctor. "He is like a child. He is moved, weeps, laughs at anything at all. Just a moment ago he was saying as soon as he is fully recovered he wishes to go to the country for a month."

When Corsi hears of the possibility of his having to go to prison for life, he is distraught. The very fact that he tried to commit suicide is against him, since this action can be construed as a recognition of guilt. He sees now how cruel his friend has been in saving him. He asks the doctor by what right he has done so. He should never have done that, since he did not have any right to dispose of the life which he had given back to him. He vehemently tells his friend, the physician: "I had placed myself outside the law by inflicting on myself a punishment graver than that which the law can give."

It is too cruel for Corsi to have to face the possibility of going to prison for life, now that he knows how great and beautiful his wife's love is, how sweet his children are, what a pleasure it is to work for them. Corsi reopens his wounds. His friend the physician, realizing that he has no right to save him, murmurs: "No, no, I cannot. I must not." Corsi dies.

The approach of the humanity of the characters is still governed by the consideration of those sides of human life which naturalism claimed as its own, but the author has allowed his art, be it within the narrow boundary of a short dramatic sketch, to enrich itself with psychological depth and complexity.

There is nothing here of what is usually referred to as a Pirandellian complex. Tommaso Corsi is not at all tortuous or intellectual. The author views him, as well as the other characters, with great objectivity, and beyond them he feels the tragedy of human life. The play encloses a short, tense, and striking action centering on the despair of a man who wishes to touch his lips to a pure and cool water that suddenly recedes and intensifies his thirst, much in the manner of the mythical Tantalus.

*
* *

LIOLÀ

(Liolà)

The setting of *Liolà* is in the "country around Agrigento, today." We find ourselves in a farmhouse with olive and almond trees in the background. There is no idyllic peace, however, in the little nook to which Pirandello leads us that we may witness the awakening of a dramatic action.

A few young peasant girls are singing while shelling almonds, and their joyousness is contrasted with the surly nature and grumbling of Zio Simone, an unpleasant old man who complains of everything: the scant harvest, the slowness of the girls at work, his childless marriage to Mita. He had married her only in the hope that, being young and strong, she might give him an heir. And she, poor Mita, had accepted her cross because she was poor and Zio Simone enormously rich.

There is in this comedy the open and objectively drawn sensuous atmosphere that one finds in the fields, where civilization does not cover the instinctive side of life with frills and conventions. The fact that Zio Simone wanted a child, and Mita, beautiful and healthy, had not given him one, is discussed quite openly. There are not any morbid innuendoes on the part of the women, although their conversation ripples with openly sensual amusement. Zio Simone vents his rage on poor Mita and rudely sends her home, calling her a good-for-nothing who serves only to make him the butt of everybody's ridicule.

There pass at that moment the three children of Liolà, a happy, handsome young peasant who knows only how to sing and enjoy life. Those three children are the fruit of his love affairs with young girls of the village who have not known how to resist the ardent lover. When the girls had presented him with the children, Liolà had been neither embarrassed nor disconcerted. He had taken them home to his old mother and he had worked for them very happily, because it did not cost much to feed and clothe children in agricultural sections, where children are a real asset in tilling the fields. The author contrasts the free and joyous life of Liolà with the torpid, narrow-minded, and hateful one of old Zio Simone. Liolà, who chances to pass, tells him: "Stop being like that, with your feathers all ruffled like a sick capon."

There is in the play an echo of the life that Verga depicted in *Cavalleria Rusticana*. We find in both the same country setting, the same primitive people and passions. As in *Cavalleria Rusticana* Lola and Santuzza are rivals, so are here Mita and Tuzza, a cousin of Zio Simone. Mita had been the sweetheart of Liolà, and since Liolà still seemed to think of her, even now that she was married to Zio Simone, Tuzza had wanted to take him away from her and she had fallen as others had fallen.

It was truly hard to resist a young man like Liolà. Here is his self-portrait: "I am no bird for a cage. I love to fly with unclipped wings. Today here, tomorrow there: in the sunshine, rain, or wind. I sing and I am intoxicated and I do not know whether more by my songs or by the sunlight." Wherever he appears he brings joy and life. Girls hasten to go to work where they know they will find Liolà. He takes his three children with him in his cart and they are growing like their father to love to sing and to dance. He is an extemporaneous poet of no mean ability, and on festival days one can hear him reciting his verse to an enthralled audience.

Tuzza and Zio Simone both find themselves in an unpleasant situation: Tuzza because of her impending motherhood and Zio Simone because of his offended masculine pride. Tuzza gives him the opportunity to save his face and to have an heir by her. She confesses to him that she is going to have a baby by Liolà. Her plan is that he should claim the child as his. Zio Simone accepts.

A man who is willing to do this deserves a lesson. His lot is not to be envied when his fate is in the hands of such a humorist as Pirandello. Zio Simone boasts before the world that he has a son by a woman other than his wife. He will have to pay dearly for the sorrow that he brings to Mita. The revolting satyr has gone home and has announced the fact to Mita that Tuzza is the other woman, and that if no child has come to their home it is Mita's fault. The poor girl has cried bitter tears in silence and humiliation. He has beaten her, has dragged her by the hair through the house.

Although accustomed to suffering, Mita cannot endure her life with Zio Simone, and she returns to her aunt's home. Zia

Gesa had brought her up and had been a mother to her. It had been she who had forced her to marry the old satyr. Poor Mita had accepted with grief and resignation Zio Simone's proposal of marriage, and life had been a blistering load on her poor shoulders.

Zia Gesa's house is next door to Liolà's. Is it to be wondered at if nature and dramatic logic take their course? Liolà goes to Mita's house, and the old love blossoms again. Now Zio Simone will have two children, one by Tuzza and another by his wife, two children that he will have to claim as his own while in reality they are Liolà's.

Mita yields because Liolà brings back to her the memory of their happy childhood when love had come with the same simplicity and beauty that clothe the flowers that grow by the wayside. Moreover, Liolà appears ready to vindicate her against Zio Simone, Tuzza, and Tuzza's mother. He relates to her the scheme that the three had conceived on the day that Liolà, obeying the pangs of conscience, had gone to Tuzza's home to ask for her hand in marriage. No longer jovial, but with strength and sentiment, he tells Mita: "Goodness only knows what I had to swallow, when I went there to do my duty, and under my very eyes that nasty mother made your husband go into the room where Tuzza was. I saw you, Mita, I understood the harm that would come to you, and I swore to myself that they would not go scot-free."

Pirandello sees to it that they do not go unpunished. Tuzza's offer to Zio Simone loses its weight and value after Mita tells her husband that she is going to have a baby. Placed by this change in the situation between Tuzza and Mita, Zio Simone, just as Liolà had thought, defends Mita, who is his real wife, against Tuzza who used him to cover her wrongdoing and shame. Tuzza and her mother, Zia Croce, cannot expect to have Zio Simone's money now that he is going to have a baby by his wife.

There is the morality of life and the morality of books. The two do not always dovetail. Pirandello claims justification by the morality of life in giving to his comedy the solution that he does. He lets Liolà and Mita triumph over the greed of Zia Croce and the deceitful scheme of Zio Simone and Tuzza. He vindicates, too, gentle and suffering Mita in that he allows her to belong to the man whom she had loved in her youth, the only glimmer of light in a sad and drab existence.

The solution that Pirandello gives to his play reminds one of Machiavelli's *Mandragola*. Here the cowardly, old, and repulsive Messer Nicia, the husband, is punished by being made the butt of ridicule, with love triumphant over the schemes and machinations of greed and ignorance. Pirandello, too, places a sentimental nucleus at the very heart of this somewhat salacious comedy: Love—even if it is free love—struggling against greed and deceit, with love triumphing at the expense of its two sordid enemies.

VII

A Humorist Looks at Virtue

MAN, BEAST, AND VIRTUE

and Other Minor Plays

We have repeatedly explained the relation of the dramatic sketches that we are studying to the naturalism of Verga and Capuana. No great artist has ever been a slave to a literary movement, and Pirandello is no exception. He naturally felt the influence of the artistic current that predominated in his youth, but his genius was never cramped by it. If Liolà is a child of Sicilian naturalism in his elementary simplicity and rustic grace, other characters appear in whom Pirandello is trying to enclose a more subtle and complex sense of human personality. His contacts with naturalism do not prevent him from leaving the imprints of his personality and the at times quixotic traits of his mind on the instinctive themes that he chooses. In fact, naturalism assumes an extremely humorous and even grotesque tone in *Man, Beast, and Virtue.* Before analyzing this play we shall briefly study three short sketches in which the study of the individual stands out in sharp contrast to the objective tendency that we have noticed in the dramatic works we have already reviewed.

*
*   *

CECÈ

(Cecè)

Cecè is more interesting to the critic than to the lover of dramatic art. Pirandello has lent to a superficial individual utterances that are in sharp contrast to the levity of his temperament and the worldly character of his actions. The dramatic vicissitude presented in the play is very slight. Cecè, the protagonist, true to his character, only thinks of having a good time. He is one of a class of people living with perfect leisure and luxury in the hustle and bustle of our civilization, people the old civilization transmitted to us, who seem to thrive also in the midst of the feverish activity of the new one.

One day, as he is trying to kill time in a café with other men of his type, he sees pass by a beautiful woman whose bad reputation they all know: Nada. His friends scoffingly say: "She is too high for you." He wagers that she will be his. After a short time he announces to his friends that he has won the bet. It goes without saying that he soon tires of Nada, all the more that she is, like women of her sort, very extravagant and a drain on Cecè's pocketbook.

As Cecè is meditating on the best way of getting rid of her, Squadriglia, a one-eyed road builder and contractor, calls on him to thank him for using his good offices with the Minister of Public Works in Squadriglia's behalf. He wishes to show his gratitude to Cecè by offering him money. Cecè is surprised at the clumsy way the boorish contractor has chosen. He proposes a different way, as eccentric as can be any suggestion coming from Cecè: to tell all the possible and conceivable evil about him to a person that he would designate.

Squadriglia is half surprised and half indignant. Cecè explains that Nada has three three-thousand *lire* notes signed by him which he must have back at any cost. She is expected at his apartment at any moment. Squadriglia must receive her and tell her that Cecè is a scoundrel, a son who is taking his old parents to their grave. He must make his picture so exaggerated as to make the woman realize that the notes in her hands are worthless.

When Nada arrives, after the first surprise is over, she hears such ignominious charges and accusations against Cecè that she is easily persuaded to accept a small amount of money in return for the three notes. Since Squadriglia has to catch a train, he makes a hasty exit and leaves Nada in Cecè's apartment. The latter is not long in returning. He feigns surprise upon hearing that she has given the notes to that man. With his histrionic ability he pictures vividly to the surprised Nada his plight now that that man, the worst usurer in the city, has the notes in his possession. For punishment, Nada must give Cecè enough kisses to make up to him the evil that will engulf him.

Pirandello has lent to Cecè both physical and mental characteristics that can be recognized in more complex and truly tragic characters. He is presented as follows: "Although showing in his face the signs of a life of debauchery, he is still full of vivacity and restlessness. He has the air, if not exactly of a lunatic, of an absent-minded person. He changes his expression rapidly at the darting of different images in his most mobile imagination. He is smoothly shaven, most attractive, and has shining eyes and red lips. He dresses with exquisite elegance." Cecè is made to express typically Pirandellian ideas about human personality, but this *motif* is only an external element in the play, since it is not developed and does not have any connection with the unfolding of the action. It is strange to hear on Cecè's lips such words as these: "Is it not tormenting to think that you live diffused into a hundred thousand individuals who know you and whom you do not know?" This *motif* is the central theme of one of Pirandello's greatest novels, *One, No One, a Hundred Thousand*, in which the plurality of the human personality has assumed an almost religious meaning merging with the annihilation that the mystics of all times sought through their being lost in the Deity. We also hear Cecè utter these deep and tormenting words: "I am sure that you agree with me that we are not always the same. According to our humor, moments, relations, we are now one way and then another; happy with one, sad with another, serious with this man, funny with that one." This is the theme that permeates the tragedy of the Father in *Six Characters in Search of an Author*, and it is accorded in various plays a deeper and always new treatment.

Cecè is as worthy of expressing these ideas as a rough contractor like Squadriglia is capable of understanding them. In fact, they jar on his lips to the same extent that the practical and uncouth Squadriglia finds them incomprehensible. Pirandello places them in the play as if gathering them from some distant obscure part of his mind. Their presence here, however, shows that the author needed the medium of a more subjective art to express feelings that the worldly and superficial Cecè could not logically utter.

Looking at the play in its minor details, one notices the evident concern of the author with describing characteristic traits of his characters. Squadriglia, for instance, is "a huge, rough man, a little ill at ease in his city clothes, used as he is to wear his working togs. He has only one eye and no trace of the other on his face because he had skin grafted over it when a mine burst and took it out."

The play is a short dramatic sketch that shows Pirandello's humorous side while hiding the tragic element that is placed on Cecè only as an external ornament.

*

* *

THE IMBECILE

(*Imbecille*)

The Imbecile is projected against the party spirit which divided Italy at the beginning of the century into two hostile camps: the Republicans, or Leftists, and the Conservatives.

We are introduced into the office of a Republican newspaper which from all external appearances shows that Republicanism not only meant war on the king, the church, and capitalism, but that it stood for a heroic life deprived of capitalistic comfort. In fact, the office of the *Republican Sentinel* shows "disorder and filth on the old and worn-out furniture and even on the floor." Men with leonine heads and Mephistophelean beards, and wearing vivid red neckties, emblem of revolution, move excitedly in the newspaper office.

A man, Luca Fazio, is seated in the vestibule waiting to see Leopoldo Paroni, editor of the newspaper. Fazio is desperately ill with consumption, as is evidenced by a violent cough that he tries to stifle by pressing his handkerchief against his mouth. To a man who is face to face with death the disputes of men of different parties, their hatreds and their clashes such as the one he hears is in progress in the streets of Costanova, seem unspeakably small and meaningless.

The clash, the clamor of which reaches him, is one into which personal animosities have been injected and in which personal gain is trying in vain to hide behind patriotism and humanity. Feelings run so high that the two factions are embroiled in the public square and come to blows in the midst of a wild confusion. Far from a struggle between contrasting ideals is the struggle between the Honorable Mazzarini who is in power and Paroni who would like to take his place.

While the last newspaper reporters are about to be sent into the fray by the courageous Paroni, who prefers to watch the battle from the window of his office, a woman arrives and announces that Pulino, a destitute and sickly man, has committed suicide. "What an imbecile!" shouts Paroni. "He should have first shot my enemy, Deputy Mazzarini, and then killed himself. I should have paid his fare to Rome." (Seat of the Deputies.)

Luca Fazio rebels at hearing the term "imbecile" applied to the poor, dead Pulino. He rises like a ghost from his corner and takes Paroni into a room. After ordering him to lock the door, he points a pistol at him and informs him that Deputy Mazzarini has paid his fare from Rome to Costanova with the understanding that he, Fazio, should shoot Paroni and then commit suicide. Paroni must admit that his political enemy has beaten him in the battle of wits. At the sight of the revolver, he falls on his knees, his Republican ardor and courage dampened.

Fazio looks at him with supreme disdain and scorn and does not carry out his threat to kill him. Instead, he compels Paroni to write under dictation the following words: "Luca Fazio, before committing suicide, came to my office, armed with a revolver and informed me that in order not to be called an imbecile by Mazzarini or anybody else he had to kill me like a rat. He could have done it, but he preferred not to because he felt loathing and pity for my cowardice. It has been enough for Luca Fazio that I have declared to him that I am the true imbecile." "Now sign," Luca orders him. After Paroni with a trembling hand has affixed his signature to the paper, Fazio takes it and walks out of Paroni's office. On the following day that document will be found on his dead body. He will stand immune from the charge of stupidity. Paroni will be indicted for his cowardice in offending the memory of poor Pulino. He has signed his own political death warrant and forfeited his human dignity by calling himself an imbecile.

The character that creates the play is Luca Fazio. There is in him true dramatic force, concentrated and powerful. He looks at the world from his observation tower where death is ready to hoist its victorious banner while he, unmindful, with cynical coldness looks at human cowardice. He is a giant near the boastful and verbose politician Paroni.

The play is grimly ironical. There rings through it Fazio's cold and desolate laughter that dwarfs into nothingness the political passions of man.

Pulino and the peasant woman who announces his death bring into the play the voices of the average daily existence. Luca Fazio stalks into it as a symbol of the tragic individualism that the author is trying to express.

*

* *

THE MAN WITH A FLOWER IN HIS MOUTH
(*L'uomo dal fiore in bocca*)

Who has not seen a man with a flower in his mouth? We may even have noticed one on cheap illustrated cards or in a photograph that a sailor has had taken of himself for his sweetheart—at least an Italian sailor—or a sergeant in the army of his Majesty the King. But imagine that instead of a flower, be it a rose or a pink, that man has in his mouth a red spot that proves to be a cancerous growth. What then? Then we shall have the genesis of this short play that bears the long and intriguing title of *The Man with a Flower in His Mouth*. We find in it a typical attitude of Pirandello: tragic laughter before a ghastly aspect of life.

The author calls this short play a dialogue. It is a dialogue between two men, one of whom looks at human life as a tragedy while the other accepts it, submitting in silence to its torturing monotony and to its cruel whims. They meet by chance after midnight at a café in a railroad station.

The peaceful man has just missed the train because of the innumerable purchases he has made for his wife and daughters who are summering away from the city. The poor man had been carrying so many packages that by the time he had arranged them, two on each finger of both hands, the train had left. While he is waiting for the next train, a strange individual sitting at the table next to his begins to talk to him and discusses his tragic philosophy.

He is a man who is forced to cling with his imagination to other people's lives like a climbing rose to the bar of an iron fence, that he may stand the tragic weight of his life. His great solace is in observing other people: "Not of the people I know. No, no. I could not! I experience a loathing, a distress. But I must adhere to the life of strangers; around them my imagination can work freely, not at random, however, but rather taking into account the slightest details discovered in this and that man." This is the only way by which the speaker can divert his thoughts from his own misfortune. Life, or death, has branded him by putting a flower in his mouth in the form of an epithelioma or cancer: "Death, do you understand, has passed; it has thrust this flower in my mouth, and has told me: Keep it, my friend. I shall be around in eight or ten months."

Can that man be other than he is? He is restless; he cannot stay one minute at home as his poor wife would like him to do. So he goes out and stands in front of show-windows admiring the cleverness with which shopgirls tie packages. He is afraid to stay in his own company, to penetrate into his own heart, to ponder over his life. Woe unto him if he did. He might even become murderous, as he confesses to his alarmed and trembling companion. The tragic man reassures him that he is not going to destroy him and asks a favor of him: "Tomorrow you will arrive at dawn at your home town that I imagine lies at some distance from the station. You can walk that distance. Count every blade of the first tuft of grass that you meet on the way. I shall live as many days as there are blades of grass. Good night, sir." He disappears, leaving his chance companion there frightened to death.

The play, short as it is, is a document of Pirandello's power of observation. He, too, has gone through the wide and narrow streets of towns, cities, and capitals, and has sought relief from the distressing thoughts that crushed him by letting his eyes wander from one aspect to the other of the life that stirred around him. The play affords an insight into the nature of the imagination that Pirandello lends to his characters. He does not allow human fancy to go in search of idyllic situations and dreamy landscapes, but he does allow his characters a detached feeling from the earthly reality when the weight of their lives becomes so crushing.

Here, too, there is grim humor, together with pity for the man whose days are numbered, whom death or life has treated with such an ironical cruelty. Pirandello has altogether left the objective element in his art and has become tragically subjective, portraying an individual whom a bitter misfortune has compelled to detach himself from life, from himself, to live in the contemplation of a life from which he is excluded.

*
* *

MAN, BEAST, AND VIRTUE

(*L'uomo, la bestia e la virtù*)

The most naturalistic of Pirandello's plays is *Man, Beast, and Virtue,* in which the treatment of the theme of instinct has assumed an extremely ironical form. Rarely has the author indulged in such broad laughter and poked such malicious fun at man as in this play. The thoughtful look habitual to his eyes has disappeared, and a twinkle of malice darts from them.

The play involves Signor Paolino, a teacher who lives by giving private lessons, Signor Perrella, captain of a ship, who comes home only at long intervals, and the virtuous Signora Perrella. Pirandello, in a humorous vein, has presented in these characters three very odd individuals. Signor Paolino voices the opinions of the author in the same tense and excited manner as that in which Pirandello's typical characters do in most of his plays. Paolino shouts what he thinks and is vehement, blunt, and sanguine. He breaks forth into violent tirades against insincere people like one of his neighbors, Signor Totò, a druggist, the personification of a miser, who goes every morning to Signor Paolino's home to be offered a cup of coffee. He has a habit of "rubbing his hands together under his chin as if to wash them at the fountain of his saccharine, stupid graciousness." Paolino quite bluntly tells him: "Get a housekeeper." He is equally declamatory and violent with two pupils who go to him for a Latin lesson. "They have an indescribably beastly aspect. Giglio resembles a black billy-goat. Belli a big monkey with eyeglasses."

The only lesson taught that day is an outburst against human hypocrisy. He calls the pupils' attention to the fact that the Greeks called comedians *Upocrites*. Signor Paolino thinks that that is grossly unjust, since he doesn't see any harm if a poor man plays the rôle of king. It is just his profession, his duty. But when does evil appear? "When one is not a hypocrite by profession, for duty, on the stage, but out of pleasure, gain, wickedness, habit, as it is in life, because to be civilized means exactly this—within, as black as a crow, without as white as a dove; within as bitter as gall, on your lips honey."

At this point, Signora Perrella comes to see the high-strung, eloquent professor, accompanied by her son, Nonò. She is, judging from appearances, "virtue, modesty, reserve personified," but the unpleasant truth is that she is going to have a baby and that Signor Paolino, the private teacher of Nonò, is the father of that baby. On that very day Captain Perrella will arrive and everything will come to light. The poor woman has difficulty in controlling her nausea. She opens her mouth like a fish, and looks so ridiculous as to excite the laughter of her son Nonò. Only by using a beautiful book as a bait can Signor Paolino extract from the child the promise not to laugh, especially in the presence of his father.

Captain Perrella is a terrible husband, and in another city has a mistress with five children. He never even looks at his wife. He comes home, eats his dinner, locks himself in his room and sleeps until the next day when he leaves again for a long voyage.

Now the only thing that will save Signora Perrella will be virtue, virtue that will make of the terrible captain a good husband, thus avoiding shame and scandal.

Signor Totò, the druggist, with his brother Nino Pulejo, a physician, will have to combine their efforts and knowledge and prepare a love potion that will make the husband amorous. The strange concoction prepared by Totò is disguised in a cream cake that is placed by Paolino in the middle of the dinner table. If Captain Perrella will partake of that particular piece of cake in which the potion is concealed, virtue will be saved.

Paolino is the stage director of the whole affair. He orders Signora Perrella to get rid of her awkward and modest attire and to display all the beauty and charm that she possesses. His plans are somewhat in danger when Captain Perrella, upon seeing his wife all painted and in a very low-necked gown, breaks into laughter that forbodes no good. He refuses to have her sit in front of him for fear of having a sudden fit of laughter and choking. She meekly exchanges places with Paolino. After a long, anxious dinner, interrupted by the captain's fit of temper at Nonò's lack of manners, the medicated part of the cake disappears into the voracious mouth of the captain. On the following morning, Paolino discovers that the virtue of Signora Perrella has been saved.

As in other plays, morality is looked upon here by Signora Perrella and Paolino as a means of hiding a wrong situation and, therefore, is accorded a humorous treatment. Pirandello is moved to laughter when he sees that these people have recourse to morality only when they are in danger of being discovered. The play is a projection of that laughter, and it is the way that a humorist has chosen to proclaim the importance of morality.

The play is in the literary tradition of Machiavelli's *Mandragola*. As in Machiavelli's celebrated work, the husband is duped and held in ridicule because he is responsible for the illicit love affairs of his wife. It was due to Captain Perrella's immoral living that poor Signora Perrella was led to sin.

The comedy has the appearance of being highly immoral, yet these light, ludicrous, and obscene events assume a deeper note as they pass through Pirandello's personality, and what seemed a scoffing mockery ends in serious implications. As a result of this undertone of seriousness, the author is lenient with Paolino and especially with the neglected Signora Perrella, while he is very severe with the captain. Pirandello puts on Paolino's lips a lengthy discourse to show that the responsibility is the husband's.

Paolino is the character who is closest to Pirandello's heart in this play. Not that he is a hero, an exceptional individual, or a great personality, however. He is as close to the average person as any of Pirandello's characters, but he shares with other characters that repressed, livid resentment against man and even against life. He, too, has been exasperated by experience, and he is always ready to pour his hatred on everything and on all. "You are all lined with deceit," he shouts. "The patent side of passions, even the most agonizing, has the power, I know, of moving all to laughter. Of course, you have never experienced them or you are used to covering them."

Man, Beast, and Virtue is a strange fable with a startling morality. The morality is that the beast, inherent in all men, saved honesty and virtue that man was about to offend.

In spite of his somewhat philosophical utterances and his excited gestures, Paolino is not yet endowed with a tragic soul. He still is, to a certain degree, external, which shows that Pirandello was forcing himself into the elementary psychology of an individual like the irascible teacher who is still too enveloped in the net of sensuous life to possess the fixity that a tormenting idea, arising from a sad experience, gives to individuals that Pirandello portrays in his best plays.

From characters that we have here and there met in these rudimentary attempts at drama, we can see that the author was tending towards more complex personalities. Our attention has already been attracted by solitary individuals crouched in a dark nook and revealing through their suffering and sneering posture their tragic sense of life. Such is the hero of *The Man with a Flower in His Mouth,* and such is Luca Fazio, whom death is pitilessly stalking.

When such characters appear we are nearing the portals of the majestic and tragic structure that Pirandello has created with the agonizing dramas he has revealed in his art, and we can truly say: Here begins the true and significant drama of Luigi Pirandello.

Part Two

THE DRAMA OF BEING AND SEEMING

VIII

Introduction

After the objective attitude towards reality shown in varying degree in the plays that give evidence of inspiration from Sicilian naturalism, Pirandello appears in a mood that he qualifies as humorous or grotesque. He distinguishes very sharply between humor and irony. To him irony is a rhetorical figure of speech that means the opposite of what it says with the purpose of hurting. It does not possess the deep and tragic implications of humor. Humor is a peculiarly philosophical attitude that obliterates the dividing line between laughter and grief, and it presents man as harboring in his heart a strange feeling of exaltation and of scorn, of pity and of derision for himself. Humor is understanding and compassionate, and, if the humorist laughs, there is a vein of grief in his laughter.

Pirandello's æsthetic ideas are discussed in a book that he published in 1908 under the title of *Umorismo* (*Humor*) which shows the vastness and depth of his intellectual background and also the seriousness with which he prepared himself for his art. It is fortunate that his reflective attitude has not marred the spontaneity of his inspiration. In this book the author studies the nature of humor in European literatures, insisting especially on English, Spanish, and Italian humorists. He considers a typical expression of humor to be Giordano Bruno's attitude towards art and life inclosed in his saying, "Sad in mirth, mirthful in sadness." Pirandello also ponders admiringly over Machiavelli's profession of literary faith: "If at times I laugh or sing, I do it because this is the only way I have to provide an outlet for my painful tears."

Pirandello's ideas on the grotesque, which he believes to be the artistic expression of humor, have led many critics astray in that the latter have tried to interpret the whole of Pirandello's production through the æsthetic canons expressed in his book on humor. To apply these æsthetic beliefs to the whole of Pirandello's drama would be the same as to study Dante's *Divine Comedy* in the light of the æsthetic ideas of the *Convito*, or Tasso's *Jerusalem Delivered* in that of his discourse on the heroic poem. The critic and the poet do not necessarily harmonize in every writer, and often the poet sees distances and heights and depths that the vision of the critic can neither encompass nor fathom.

The ideas expressed in his *Humor*, however, dovetail with a section of his drama, the foreground of which is occupied by the ludicrous appearance of reality which hides or veils a ghastly anguish that torments the characters. Indeed, these ideas are the genesis of the drama of "being and seeming."

In this new field of artistic search and creation Pirandello's master is no longer, as in the days of his naturalism, Giovanni Verga. His place has been taken by the humorists of European literatures, and especially by Alessandro Manzoni [1] and a younger writer, Alfredo Cantoni, who had coined the phrase "Smiling in appearance, grieving in reality," and about whom Pirandello wrote a masterful critical essay.[2]

Humor detects contrasts and shadows, and reaches especially the fundamental clash in man—that of sentiment and of reason. It considers reason as an infernal mechanism that reduces life into concepts. When a situation is looked upon and lived as an abstract concept, we can move in it with the utmost ease because we can mold concepts to suit our taste and pleasure, since concepts do not possess the unwieldy and unbending solidity of actual facts. Concepts, however, being the result of intellect and reason, are the negation of life, which in its essence is fluid and spontaneous. We seek a refuge in them only when we have become so cerebral as to be deprived of spontaneity of feeling and of living.

For Pirandello good and simple people possess spontaneity of life (a characteristic also shared by plants and animals), but their life is necessarily limited, uneventful, and prosaic.

[1] See D. Vittorini, *The Modern Italian Novel*, Philadelphia, 1930.
[2] "L'opera di Alfredo Cantoni." In *L'illustrissimo—Nuova Antologia*. Rome 1906.

90

Over-intellectual people enlarge the boundary and scope of their life, but they fall prey to intellectual complications and to artificiality. Their inner life is a place that fears light, since terrible shames are hidden there. Since they are compelled to go among men and they want to appear decent and even heroic, they hide themselves behind a fictitious personality that expresses itself with exalted gestures and idealistic words.

Pirandello calls this process *"costruirsi"* or "to build up oneself." In its simplest forms this process refers to the social mask we wear when we go among our fellow-men and lavish smiles that hide grimaces, honeyed words that are spoken in order to conceal real feelings. In its essential character, however, this process portrays a conscious self-deception which we force on ourselves, because without it we could not stand the weight of a painful situation in which we are caught. There are moments in life—the author had experienced them —when it is not possible to appear to others as we actually are; to show our poor souls stripped of the many veils that we throw around them.

Pirandello has shown in his plays that there are cases when loathing for life and for ourselves is so great that it transforms us into madmen. The typical Pirandellian character of this stage of his drama is a man distressed, with mobile eyes, tense, and unable to relieve that tension, for fear that his whole being, moral and physical, may disintegrate. When all alone, he grits his teeth and clenches his fists, while within him disgust rises like a polluted tide. Who could then show himself as he is, not only to others but to himself? It is then that reason begins to function, and it covers with idealistic hues a situation which is inwardly putrid. Reason lends to Pirandello's characters beautiful masks which they press against their faces while they walk among their fellow-men, composed and stately. However, there is the face and there is the mask which never become one, and Pirandello's characters know it. They feel from time to time that the face wants to appear or that circumstances in life threaten to remove the mask. They desperately cling to it, and press it with agonizing strength over their faces, feeling the hurt, the bruise, the burn, yet ready to endure that suffering because it is more bearable than the one inflicted on them by what they know about themselves.

This process, which has given life to immortal characters in Pirandello's drama, presupposes a ghastly moral shame and an acute and tormented sensitiveness. It is also predicated on the assumption that all men are, to a varying degree, theatrical, especially if highly intellectual. An intellectual man acquires in reflection what he loses in spontaneity. It is a law of life, and the mask that man dons is a logical means of self-defense. Since Pirandello's drama begins when the voice of instinct has been silenced and his characters are stranded on the bleak shore of disillusionment, all their life centers in their intellectual raving. Pirandello listens to them, smiles at them, sometimes cruelly, sometimes pitifully, and he shows them that in reality there is no use gesticulating like energumens, shouting and protesting. They are face to face with life, and they must accept it as it is.

Pirandello is compassionate with his characters, but he is also aware that their exaltation is artificial. He knows that as soon as we become exalted, since exaltation appears in people who are not endowed with simplicity, it becomes artificial and conscious of itself. Sentiment is then absent from us, and we must make up for it with the cold power of reason. Then we exaggerate, we shout, and we try to persuade others and ourselves to something of which we are not convinced. As long as we endure in the tension of exaltation, we are not conscious of the extreme lack of sincerity in us, but, if we should happen to look into a mirror and see ourselves in it, we immediately realize the unbearable ugliness of our deception. Seeing ourselves live suspended in the revolting image of our falseness destroys our exaltation, and we appear in all the pity of our betrayed humanity.

The result of this intuition is that the plays of the "grotesque," which largely make up the section of the drama of "being and seeming," move from ridicule to pathos. This prevents Pirandello's drama from being either low farce or an evanescent dream.

It is well to point out that the process of self-deception does not destroy the initial ego in Pirandello's characters. The natural and normal self becomes temporarily obliterated by hard and cruel necessity, and through the juxtaposition of these two selves, the original and the artificial, there arises the drama of "being and seeming," with the inevitable clash between them. More than from his brain the drama derives from the heart of Pirandello, and his work is a delicate and passionate analysis of a humanity that suffers and tries to appear at least calm; that inwardly bleeds through shame and outwardly puts on the veneer of decency. It is not at all necessary to think of the subconscious or of Freud, unless we wish to appear erudite to make an impression on the unsophisticated. Let us see how pitiful are the characters of the plays that we are going to study in this section: Ciampa, Ersilia Drei, Elma, Henry IV. Under the masks there suffers in them the human heart with an agonizing sorrow. It is unjust, therefore, to state that between "being and seeming" there is no difference, and that in Pirandello there is not a point at which the actual reality ends and the fantastic one begins, a statement very dear to Pirandello's critics. Pirandello's characters wilfully and consciously try to destroy the actual reality because it is unbearable for them, but they cannot free themselves of it.

It is evident that Pirandello's characters have at least temporarily the postures and mannerisms of supermen. It must not be forgotten, however, that their author does not take them seriously, and that the drama consists in dissecting their artificiality. In this fashion the drama is urged towards its climax, and after a moment of exaltation the characters reënter their ordinary life, either like Ciampa with a loud and jarring laughter, or tragically like Henry IV plunging into a lucid madness that is the only solution life has left for him.

From an æsthetic point of view the intuition of the grotesque transforms man into his own enemy, and the center of the play is transported into his very heart, affording to the author the opportunity of a searching and tormenting analysis.

The real genesis of these plays is in Pirandello's experience. With the secret of his painful and tragic domestic life hidden in his heart, he moved among men for years. Could he have revealed to them the truth of that condition? He learned then what it is to "build up oneself," and he discovered that most human beings had to seek in that process a screen for the cruel pranks that life had played on them. These plays reflect the most distressed period of Pirandello's inner life. This period begins with Ciampa's laughter in *Cap and Bells;* it develops through the cynical, but pain-giving utterances of Leone Gala in *Each in His Own Rôle;* it scoffs and jeers at everything human with Diego in *Each in His Own Way;* it softens before the calamities that befell Martino Lori and Ersilia Drei in *All for the Best* and *Naked;* it rises to a tragic height before the mental tortures of the emperor Henry IV; and finally it opens the haven of a peaceful and pure life before Elma in *As You Desire Me*, although the author does not allow her to find a shelter there for her harassed and tortured flesh and soul.

The immense surge of humanity that suffered in these plays cannot be the result of an abstract process. In the silence of long years of work Pirandello has created a galaxy of true and great characters, a crowd of poor, grieving creatures whose mouths are twisted in a grimace that tries to be a smile, whose eyes are staring and dull, and whose hearts are pierced by a long pin that they try to remove from their hearts to let it transfix their brains, for, though that may be more painful, at least it allows them to live.

IX

The Blinding Effects of Truth

CAP AND BELLS

(*Il berretto a sonagli*)

In *Cap and Bells* we are led back to the atmosphere of old Sicily in the days when, here as elsewhere, men were tyrants over women. As one character puts it: "They make of us soles for their shoes." That a wife should close one eye and perhaps both on her husband's escapades was a necessary corollary of the men's tyranny and the women's lack of economic freedom.

The household of Cavalier Fiorica is in a turmoil because Donna Beatrice knows what everybody in town suspects: that Cavalier Fiorica, her husband, has had for a long time an affair with a young woman who is married to Ciampa, an old man employed in a general store owned and run by the debonair Cavalier Fiorica. Fana, the old servant, who has seen Donna Beatrice come into this world, views the difficulty in the traditional attitude, "the Lord's will be done." Noble women of old had their lips sealed even if their hearts bled. Had not Donna Assunta, Donna Beatrice's mother, done so in her younger days? Even Fifì La Bella, her brother, thinks that Donna Beatrice is destined to end badly if she keeps harping on the theme of "Shameful men, infamous husbands." Fana never heard of "using violence with those who are stronger than we. Men are led back home quietly, with grace, and with gentle ways." Poor Fana's advice is wasted, for Donna Beatrice, in despair, has confided her trouble to La Saracena, a fearful and reckless woman of the lower classes, "an enormous, powerful woman in her forties, a veritable terror, boastful, with a large yellow silk handkerchief draped over her shoulders, and a blue shawl, also of silk, tied tightly around her waist." La Saracena is bodily detached from the setting of old provincial Italy; one of those women always ready to run errands of any kind, to take a hand on election days, to defend virtue and vice alike with a tongue that feared no word. Her ideas are entirely opposite from those of the quiet Fana. "There is no need of a tragedy," she tells Donna Beatrice. "You will just give him a good lesson. I kicked my husband out of the house four years ago. Now he follows me like a poodle. He shakes in his boots." But Donna Beatrice's husband was not one with whom such methods could be used. Physical strength played a large part in marital relations in those days, and sociologists might well remember that it has had and has a place even today, outside of the boundaries of the law.

The characters, as we can see, are ordinary individuals, and the atmosphere created by their thought and feelings closely follows that of everyday life. We are even more definitely convinced of this when quaint old Ciampa appears on the scene, sent for by Donna Beatrice, who wishes to send him to Palermo just before her husband returns. Ciampa is still the child of Sicilian naturalism: "In his fifties, with long, thick hair, unkempt, pushed back, without a mustache, his cheeks covered by two large whiskers that extend even under his hard, penetrating, and most mobile eyes like those of a madman, behind his heavy spectacles. He has a pen over his right ear and wears an old coat of a custom officer's uniform." He is odd in his appearance and still stranger in his elementary psychology, if we believe what Pirandello tells us. Ciampa appears before Donna Beatrice, using at first the mellifluous words that used to be customary in addressing the wife of the master who gave employment and almost had the right of life and death over his employes: "I kiss the hands of my lady. Always exposed to the orders of my mistress." His mobile eyes are riveted on Donna Beatrice, who speaks with insinuations that hurt. Her jealousy of Ciampa's wife makes it impossible for her to hide her feelings, that is, it makes her truthful. Often, however, the truth cannot be gazed upon. It blinds; it burns into one's eyes. Ciampa notices her strange way of speaking and tells her, "It seems that you have your mouth . . . well . . . as if you had eaten crab

apples this morning." At this, as she attempts to hide behind
the untruthful statement that everything is as it always has
been, he informs her that "the instrument is out of tune." He
explains to her and to us, too, that "we all have three switches
in our heads: the serious, the civil, the mad one. We need
the civil one above all others, since we have to live in society,
and that's why it is in the middle of our foreheads. . . . We
should devour each other like so many hungry dogs. . . .
But that will not do. For example, I should devour Mr. Fifì.
That would not do. What do I do then? I give a little turn to
the civil switch and I go towards him with a smiling countenance, my hand stretched out: 'How glad I am to see you, my
dear Mr. Fifì.' "

We here find ourselves before Pirandello's biting analysis
of man as a social being. If we forget to turn on the civil
switch, we utter strange words that are followed by stranger
deeds. Donna Beatrice speaks as she does because she is
oscillating between telling the truth and continuing to deceive
her fellow-men. At this point Ciampa, a mixture of bookkeeper and journalist (he is very proud of his literary leanings, so proud that he always carries a pen over his ear),
waxes philosophical. He turns on for a moment the serious
switch. "We are all puppets, Mr. Fifì," he exclaims. "The
divine spirit enters into us and becomes dwarfed into a puppet. . . . It should be enough to be born puppets through
divine will. No, we all add another puppet to that one: the
puppet that each of us can be or believes himself to be. And
then quarrels begin. Every puppet wishes to be respected,
not so much on account of what he believes he is as for the
rôle that he has to represent outside. Face to face with himself, no one is satisfied with his rôle; each if placed in front
of his own puppet would spit in his face. But not others;
others must respect that puppet." The inference is that we all
try to save appearances. Donna Beatrice hates her husband,
but when she goes out with him she takes his arm, and so they
advance through the main street of the town, answering with
smiles the greetings of those who take off their hats to them.
Ciampa is no different. "How can you know, my lady, why

one often steals; why one often kills; why one often—imagine him ugly, old, poor—for the love of a woman who keeps his heart as tightly as in a vise, but does not allow him to say 'ouch' without immediately stifling that complaint on his lips with a kiss, so that this poor old man is destroyed and intoxicated—how can you know, my lady, with what physical pain, with what torture, this old man can submit even to the point of sharing the love of that woman with another man—rich, young, handsome—especially if the woman gives him the satisfaction of saying that the other man is master and that things are so arranged that no one will become aware of it?" What can poor Ciampa do more than try to save his respectability? It is easy to say "Rebel, give up your job." It is easy to talk of rebellion. Rebellion is often lined with banknotes. Another idea has often crossed the threshold of Ciampa's brain: kill. But he who kills goes to prison. Blocked in his natural reaction, Ciampa has recourse to that life-saving process that Pirandello calls *"costruirsi"* (to build up oneself), forcing on himself the illusion that his dignity and name are safe as long as he saves appearances. So he locks his wife in his room when he goes out and shows everybody that he has the key. He offers to take his wife to Donna Beatrice's house, now that he has to go to Palermo, that no one may point the finger of suspicion at him.

Donna Beatrice refuses to keep Ciampa's wife as a prisoner during his absence. She has decided to burn her bridges behind her and to rebel. She will have her husband caught in the company of his ladylove. In fact, she swears out a warrant for him. Spanò, the head of police and a friend of Donna Beatrice's family and of the not less powerful one of Cavalier Fiorica, feels that he would be in a very serious plight if he should have to arrest Fiorica. He sends a colleague, Logatto, a stubborn, hot-headed Calabrian, to perform the unpleasant task. When Logatto finds Fiorica in Ciampa's quarters, he places him under arrest. One can imagine what happens. Spanò describes the scene: "As Fiorica felt the officer's hands on him, he became a fury of hell. If I had been there I should have endured everything; even if he had slapped me, I should have put up with it for the sake of our friendship. That mulish Calabrian, on the contrary, insisted on citing him for contempt and assault and arrested him."

Now it would seem that Fiorica and Nina Ciampa will be convicted, since they have been found together in Ciampa's apartment. But what of it? Does not the house belong to Fiorica and do not Ciampa and his wife work there in the store? Why so much ado about nothing? Their appearance did not afford any reason for a charge of immorality. Donna Beatrice is, nevertheless, jubilant. She has found a courage that she never suspected in herself. "I am free!" she shouts to the members of her family who have gone to her house after the scandal spread like wildfire all through the town. Her brother rejoins, "Free? You are crazy. Free to come to my house, now, without being able to put your nose out of the door! She calls herself free, forgetting that she is without a social status . . ." So declares Fifì, who does not particularly relish the idea of having at home a sister who is neither married nor single. "The shame is his," proclaims the elated Donna Beatrice. "It is yours, too," replies practical Fifì. The salient point of the situation is that Donna Beatrice has to return to her husband, and that was not easily done in the good Sicily of the nineties. That husband of hers had a devil in every hair, as they put it very graphically, and heaven help her if he ever laid hands on her. Spanò warns, "It would be prudent for the lady not to be found at home if I succeed in having him freed." This is all the more true since circumstantial evidence is in favor of the husband. In his suitcase they have found a prayer book and a box of sweet almonds for his wife. Fana always said that Donna Beatrice lived like a queen at home.

The one who is really crushed is Ciampa. He has gone to Donna Beatrice's house to hand her the jewels that she had pawned at Palermo to pay the latest of Fifì's gambling debts. Ciampa is as pale as a ghost; his face and clothes are covered with mud. He has broken his spectacles and, unable to see, has fallen and cut his forehead. His appearance is a pitiful symbol of the condition of his mind and heart. He is blind now. His painfully fabricated structure of respectability has been torn down by the alleged discovery. Now that the mask is removed there is only one thing to do: kill both Cavalier Fiorica and his wife.

Here we see the power of that fictitious belief that Ciampa accepted when he felt that to lock the front door of his home relieved him of responsibility. As soon as Donna Beatrice makes it impossible for him to believe that his respectability is saved, he becomes a potential murderer. He has been compelled to turn on the serious switch, and the serious switch leads to violence and death. Would it not have been better if he had been permitted to continue to use the civil switch, the one that forces us to utter sweet words when anger and hatred make our eyes look like those of a beast, when we are ready to cast aside all laws and conventions, stripping life of its cloak of decency? Truly that would have been better for Donna Beatrice, too. What will she do when her husband's rage is vented on her? Fifì and Spanò try in vain to console Ciampa and convince him that nothing incriminating has been found. Furthermore there is a legal document now that testifies to the innocence of his wife. Old Ciampa is not convinced. He feels that since the police, the town, the whole world know of his shame, there is no possibility for him to reënter the groove of his daily existence. His life has been destroyed, even if his life was his hidden shame. The carefully made puppet of himself has been broken by Donna Beatrice. He will kill and destroy. Everyone tries his best to convince him that to kill will be folly.

In the course of the conversation, Fifì happens to use the word "crazy," referring to Donna Beatrice. It is as if a sudden ray of light has penetrated into the dark night of Ciampa's life. That word affords him the possibility of restoring the poor and pitiful puppet of but yesterday by proclaiming Donna Beatrice mad, thereby destroying the validity of her testimony and actions. He seizes that word and repeats it with joy and exaltation. They all repeat it—Donna Assunta, Spanò, the people who gradually slip into the room. Crazy! Crazy! Donna Beatrice is crazy!

Ciampa suggests that she go for three months to a sanitarium so that everyone will believe that what has happened has been the result of her madness. Life will resume its course as before. They will all be wiser for the experience, but none the less tragically grieving and pretending. Crazy! If so her testimony is not valid. So much ado about nothing. Crazy! What is most astounding is that that word—a magic word—offers a way out for all of them. Donna Beatrice will be pardoned by her husband. He himself will be able to take his wife back. Donna Beatrice will have to pay. Is that too serious a punishment for her? Has she not branded three persons with shame before the whole town? And then, is it a punishment? For three months she can shout what howls in her heart. She can be herself by turning on the mad switch. To Ciampa, only madmen tell the whole truth. He instructs Donna Beatrice: "It does not take much to play the part of a mad woman. I shall teach you how to do it. All you have to do is shout the truth before everybody. No one believes you and everybody takes you to be crazy." Donna Beatrice, furious and convulsed with rage, asks: "Ah, so you know I am right and that I was right in doing this?" Ciampa does not agree with her. "Ah, no, no, turn the page, my dear lady. If you turn the page, you will read that there is no greater madman in the world than the one who thinks he is right!— Please, go! go! Have the pleasure of being mad for three months. Does that seem trifling to you?" He envies her: "I wish I could do it, as I would like to! To snatch completely upon the mad switch, to put on, down to my ears, the cap and bells of madness and dart into the public square and spit the truth in people's faces. Begin! Begin to shout, Donna Beatrice." Donna Beatrice realizes that Ciampa's solution is the only solution. She sees that she must accept, but having the prerogative of being truthful, she begins to vent her resentment on Ciampa by imitating the voice of the he-goat, the animal that in old Europe is the symbol of a betrayed husband: "Bèèè! bèèè!" Ciampa is overjoyed. She is harmless now, so he laughs, "while the curious neighbors leave the scene, urged now by the chief of police, now by Fifì, com-

menting on Donna Beatrice's misfortune. Ciampa throws
himself on a chair, in the middle of the stage, breaking forth
into a horrible laughter of rage, of cruel pleasure, of desperation."

The underlying belief in the form of a bitter morality is
that only the mad can be truthful, that the fate of the sane is
infinitely sadder and more tragic than that of people who
are demented. Think, in fact, what an unbearable pressure
his curbed hatred exercised on poor Ciampa's breast. What
a relief it is to be able to shout one's hatred. There is a living
hell within him. There is no coolness that refreshes the burning of the flames, no hand that touches the hurt and soothes
it; only that inner rage, that burning sensation, that sometimes breaks forth into violence, murder, revolution.

The fundamental tenet of Pirandello's artistic creed, "to
build up oneself," has blossomed here into one of its
strangest forms—the self-deception of Ciampa. Pirandello
has enclosed a big problem in a small man, and out of him a
giant has grown. Ciampa is a Prometheus of his own kind,
less stately than the classic one, but closer to our humanity.
His life is all in that mask that by constant pressure has
become one with his face. There is no differentiation in him
between face and mask, so that when his mask is removed,
it uncovers tendons and nerves which hurt and bleed.

Here, too, we find traces, deep scars, of social satire, over
the elementary environment that serves as a setting. There
are men who have no scruples in calling a person like La
Saracena a witch and then using her to run errands for them.
One of these is Fifì La Bella, a good-for-nothing, given to
gambling and women, who is always ready to ask favors of
his sister, Donna Beatrice, but who sides with her husband
instead of defending her against his profligacy. Deepening
the satirical tone, Pirandello shows us that La Saracena and
the chief of police, who are given the task of uncovering
the guilty lovers, are themselves the negation of morality.
Pirandello laughs and grieves as if saying: "See in whose
hands lies the fate of honesty!" Both the central theme and
the characters are light, even ludicrous, and close to life,

but they are made to carry the weighty burden of a tragic sense, acquiring thereby a deep significance.

The play, under its apparent humor, has an undercurrent of unspeakable sadness revealed not only by the ulcerated wounds in poor old Ciampa's heart, but in the plight of Donna Beatrice as well. Pirandello tries his best to persuade her not to rebel against her life, and suggests that she resign herself to her fate. He wants her to share the stoic resignation of which he knew the bitterness but also the poignant comfort.

This play has often been interpreted and staged as a play of jealousy, Donna Beatrice's unfounded jealousy of poor Ciampa's wife. As such it is a maimed work, with all its deep, tragic sense cut off. Even a cursory reading should persuade us that we are before Pirandello's typical drama with light characters who acquire a deep and tragic meaning when they become the receptacle of the humanity of their creator. The old rhetoricians claimed that only the kings and princes were worthy of tragedy. Pirandello has shown that the tragedy of the everyday life and that of an ordinary mortal like Ciampa can be deep and true.

X

Illusion and Heroism

ALL FOR THE BEST

(*Tutto per bene*)

Pirandello, in his musing and searching attitude, has always stood inquiringly before life. He has looked upon reality as on a prism for him to observe, turn in his hands, and study in its many facets. In *All for the Best*, he shows how in the light of a sudden revelation even a sublime existence may appear ludicrous. We are confronted by a husband whose whole life has been absorbed by his cult of the memory of his dead wife and his love for his only daughter. One day he suddenly discovers that she is the daughter of another man. It is natural enough for us to look at other people's lives. The whole universe is a panorama at which we may look from our observation point. There are situations, however, in which we become the object of our own observation, and we are led to see ourselves suspended in the past in a posture which is ridiculous and shameful.

The central figure of the play is Martino Lori. After Silvia's death, he has lived like an automaton for sixteen years, mechanically performing certain duties all hinging on her memory. An intimate member of the household describes him thus: "He has eyes that cannot be described. You ought to see how he looks! How he listens! As if things, voices, the very voices best known to him, that of his daughter, of his friends, had an aspect, a sound, that he fails to recognize, as if life all around had—I don't know—lost its consistency." Every day he goes to the cemetery, no matter what the weather, to put flowers on his wife's grave. He is not interested at all in the world around him. In his passive attitude he has allowed his daughter Palma to look upon a friend of the family, Senator Manfroni, with the affection and trust that are due only to a father. The very home where they live, although it bears the name of Lori, is actually dominated by the scientific and political personality of the illustrious Senator.

Lori is typically Pirandellian in that he is an outsider in life. He does not belong in the company of Ciampa, Henry IV, Delia Morello, Michele Rocca, the Father in *Six Characters in Search of an Author,* and of other characters in whom exaltation becomes conscious and leads them to "build up themselves." Lori, unlike these characters, has been relegated to a position outside of warm, fluid, joyous life, not by his sophisticated and over-developed intellect, but by a great misfortune. Pirandello places him near the realists, the practical, and contrasts him with them.

There is a galaxy of ultra-realists in the play. At the very beginning we make the acquaintance of La Barbetti, Silvia's mother, a woman who managed to have three husbands, one of them a great scientist, Silvia's father. She is almost illiterate, makes ridiculous blunders every time she speaks, but undaunted, she refuses to be confused or mortified. She has known how to be gay without losing her respectability, at least in society. Pirandello uses his placid but searing irony on this lady who comes to Lori's house on the day of Palma's wedding with the evident intent of a reconciliation. Silvia, in her love for her great father whom La Barbetti had abandoned, had always refused to have anything to do with her. She now brings a wedding gift to Palma and makes her understand that she will be heiress to her fortune if the Lori family will be cordial and decent. Indignation at La Barbetti's impudence almost overcomes Lori. Palma, however, does not see why she should refuse a nice gift from her grandmother on account of a past that does not exist at all for her. She lightly announces to the bridegroom: "I have discovered a brand new grandmother right here, in the vestibule."

Senator Manfroni, the chief realist in the play, is equally emphatic in condemning Lori's exaggerations. To his way of thinking, Lori is always exaggerating. The Senator is the

perfect gentleman, who, for Pirandello, is a man of great
distinction, accustomed to live in exquisite luxury, the master
of others, but especially of himself. He is master of himself,
however, not in the lofty meaning usually attributed to this
expression, but in that he assumes a steel-like, cold attitude
towards everything and everybody, a man capable of controlling every noble emotion, of checking every lofty feeling,
replacing emotions and feeling with the lucid and shrewd
workings of his mind. He is internationally known as a great
physicist, but in reality he has stolen his discoveries from
Bernardo Agliani, Silvia's father. He has taken notes that
the master left unfinished at his sudden death and has published a book under his own name that made him famous.
Near the Senator, other realists move and act, steeped in their
normal life that affords them a goodly share of pleasure and
joy. Palma, her bridegroom, Marquis Flavio Gualdi, their
friends, are all individuals who live in a pleasant present
while Martino Lori is lost in an evanescent, shadow-like past,
the only reality life has left for him.

A clash is inevitable. To the practical minded, idealists
are absurd and foolish. To the idealists, the practical are
equally absurd and offensive. This contrast may even turn
children against their parents. In fact, Palma treats her
father with condescending patience, with coldness, almost
with haughtiness. When she is about to start on her wedding
trip with her aristocratic marquis, she does not want her
father to accompany her to the station, insisting on taking
leave of him there at the house. Lori is unspeakably hurt and
goes to the cemetery to tell his pain to his dead wife, while
Palma joyously goes towards life. All is just as it is in the
world of reality where the majority of people cling to its
tangible aspects while a few, when rejected by the living,
turn towards the dead for comfort. After the marriage, in
the whirlwind of new social duties and conquests, the distance
between father and daughter becomes more accentuated. It
compels Lori to ponder over his position in his home. He has
to admit that it is truly strange, and moreover that it always

has been so. He begins to brood over it. Vividly and harrowingly, there comes back to his memory what happened the very day that Silvia died. Manfroni had sent him out of the death-chamber, telling him that his little daughter wanted him. When he had returned, he had found Manfroni sobbing on the bed where Silvia lay in the glimmer of four candles. Manfroni had gradually taken his place as a father to Palma because he was Lori's intellectual superior, a wealthy man with consequential friends who might be useful to Palma in the future. That is how Palma had happened to marry a rich marquis. Flavio would never have married her if she had not been given to him by the Senator.

Lori cannot even go to the palace of the new Marchioness. What would be the use of his going there with that long, gloomy face of his, his unseeing eyes, his evanescent personality? One evening he masters his courage and goes to Palma's house to discuss with her that situation which has become unbearable to him. Palma does not even invite him to dine with the family. Lori remains alone in the parlor, heart-broken, while the others laugh and dine. They are the practical ones. He is the idealist! Later that very evening, Palma unwittingly calls Manfroni by the name of father in Lori's presence. Lori is astonished and crushed when he realizes that the name is not addressed to him, but to the Senator. Palma, exasperated by both her mistake and the fact that she believes that Lori has always pretended not to know the truth, tells him that she called Manfroni father because he is her father, as Lori well knows. There are two crushing blows in that statement: one the offense to Silvia's memory; the other a cutting accusation directed against him by Palma who believes that he knows. His whole life is disturbed. The past is desecrated, made grotesque and hurting. He sees himself going to the cemetery while people laugh, thinking that that was a farce on his part. People have thought that of him for sixteen long years. He sees men and women nudging each other at his passing, telling each other that he had accepted that situation because it meant advancement in his career, money, comfort. Had not Manfroni succeeded in making Lori knight-commander and minister of state from a mere clerk?

What will happen now to the picture of perfection that he has embodied in his wife? Lori goes over the past, trying to mend it, trying to save whatever he can of it. Silvia must have sinned with the Senator before she married, while she was looking for a position after her father's death. It must have been a short-lived folly. Lori cannot lose hold of that picture of a perfect wife. Nothing will be left to him if that is destroyed, especially now that he knows that Palma is not his daughter. "When you were born," he cries to Palma, "she had already repented. She was mine, mine! She was mine from that moment, was mine, only mine, from your birth to her death, for years, mine as no other woman ever belonged to a man. For this reason, I have remained thus. . . . She wiped out with her great love every vestige of her betrayal." He remembers now and understands why Silvia, during these three years, had insisted that he keep Manfroni away, gradually but firmly. She had repented. She was only his, Lori's. What torments him most is that Palma thought that he knew: "How could you believe that I knew?" he says. "Ever since you were a child you have seen me go every day to her grave." Palma confesses that her coldness, her disdain were due to the very fact that she thought he knew. Lori feels lost and cries: "She dies for me in this moment, killed by her betrayal. Do you understand that now I have nothing at all that offers me any support? Where am I now? What am I here for? You are not my daughter . . . I am as if emptied. I have nothing left in me." In fact, the discovery of the truth has destroyed the memory of his wife that he has kept alive in his bleeding heart, renouncing life, and it has robbed him of his daughter. Feelingly he tells her: "You are nothing to me and I am nothing to you— nothing. If you only knew how fully I realize now that the years of this nothingness have been so many!" Here again Pirandello shows the power of an illusion. Everything crumbles when that illusion disappears.

Lori, however, cannot permit absolutely everything to vanish. Pirandello presents him as desperately trying to salvage something from the wreck of his life. Lori goes to visit Manfroni that very night. He waits three hours for him to come home. With directness, almost with violence, he requests the Senator to reveal to him when it was that Silvia had become his. Manfroni is disconcerted at first, but it does not take long for a man who has "complete mastery" over himself to regain his composure. Men like him are, to Pirandello, like those toys that always stand up no matter how you throw them. Manfroni has to confess that it was immediately after her marriage, when Silvia, accustomed to the intellectual and refined atmosphere of her father's home, grew tired of the narrow life that a little clerk afforded her. She wanted to go back to teaching and she went for help to Manfroni, her father's pupil. She wanted to run away with him but found that to Manfroni his career meant more than her love. She returned to her husband; her love for Manfroni turned to hatred. After three years she died. Their sin had given Manfroni a place in the household. "All for the best!" It was a consolation for a man like Lori, a humble heart, satisfied with the crumbs that fall from the table of those who are seated at the banquet of life, to know that his wife had returned to him, repentant.

This, however, does not destroy the ridicule and shame which surrounds Lori's past. He cannot live now; but before he destroys himself he will seek vengeance: he will unmask Manfroni before the whole world; he will tell that Manfroni stole his discovery from Agliani. He has the proof. He shouts: He can compare the original draft of the discovery and Manfroni's book. He wants Palma to know, in his desire to destroy the affection she has had for Manfroni, to make him appear before her what he is—a cold mechanism of perfidy.

Only Palma can calm him. She is touched by the pitiful condition of this man who, after all, had given her his name and protected her from shame. She tells him that she believes him, that he has all her esteem and affection. Her affection will give him the feeling that she is his daughter. He will

live in the warmth of that affection. Lori picks up the broken
pieces of his life, puts them together, makes for himself a
little nook still warmed by the memory of his wife, by the
remembrance of those three years of perfect and tender love.
He cannot complain. He can also count on Palma's affection
that is greater now than before, when she called him "father."
Lori needs that little affection and he accepts it gratefully,
murmuring, "All for the best."

The play is very compact, held together by the passion
of Lori, around whom it is built. Had Pirandello lived at the
time when playwrights were concerned with the dramatic
unities of time, place, and action, he could easily have afforded to respect them, since the impetuosity of his characters naturally crowds the action into a very short time and
a narrow place.

As usual Pirandello does not judge. He puts it up to us to
decide whether the conduct of Lori, the idealist, after poor
Silvia's death, is to be preferred to that of Manfroni and
Palma; whether it is logical and normal to grieve and remember to the point of being crushed, or whether it is better
to forget. Pirandello, thoughtfully and grievingly, places
before us the spectacle of what happens in the alternate succession of life and death, although it is evident that his
sympathy is with poor Lori.

There is nothing in Lori of the tortuous reasoning that
Pirandello gives to others of his characters. The tortuous
thinking belongs to the average person, who is Lori's antagonist.

The comedy has a strong undercurrent of social satire in
that it shows the false renown of an unworthy scientist. Pirandello directs the darts of his ridicule toward Senator
Manfroni. He flays him as a lover, as a father, as a friend,
and as a scholar. "You never had any real passion," says
Lori to Manfroni, and he makes him appear the slave of his
own career. It is of no use to have published books, to have
become a member of a foreign academy, to have had honors
heaped on him from all sides, to be a rich and illustrious
senator. His weakness is within. His greatness stands on a

very weak basis. Lori can destroy it, if he wants to. In the end the man of sentiment, unhappy in the eyes of the world, fares better than the one who for a career has silenced every voice of sentiment. Lori acquires the affection of his daughter, while the Senator sees his own share in it diminished and almost destroyed. Perhaps Pirandello, the humorist, has stealthily intervened so as not to make the solution too lofty and bordering on sentimentality. Perhaps that mind of his that is always bent on seeing the humorous side in the most idealistic situations has suggested that Lori was very practical after all, that dreamy-eyed idealists always get something out of life in spite of appearing so desolate and lonely. They are, at least, sure to get our sympathy. Pirandello's humor is a mobile light that flickers here and there, but in the end it is obscured by his sympathy for the passionate resignation of Lori. It is this sympathy that has made of Martino Lori a figure that stands high above the proud marionettes of Pirandello's practical and worldly antagonists.

XI

The Tumult of Life and the Aloofness of Concepts

EACH IN HIS OWN RÔLE

(*Il gioco delle parti*)

Each in *His Own Rôle* is a play in which the treatment accorded to the theme of "being and seeming" is humorous, at least on the surface. Pirandello has remained true to the æsthetic principles set forth in his *Umorismo*: ludicrous exterior, a tragic soul. The action centers around a very serious point of social etiquette: If the wife is offended the husband must defend her by challenging the offender to a duel. The husband, in fact, challenges the offender, makes arrangements for a deadly duel, and then compels his wife's lover to fight it, for had the lover not taken his place the night the wife was offended?

Leone Gala, the protagonist, lives in perfect accord with his wife by being separated from her. In appearance he is a well-dressed, distinguished-looking man who unobtrusively walks through the streets of a modern city, letting his eyes rest indifferently on the various aspects of life. He occupies an apartment by himself, and is waited on by one servant, Filippo, who has to listen to his master's deep, philosophical discussions. This exemplary husband and not less extraordinary man has reduced life to two functions: to eat and to think; cooking utensils and books; kitchen and library. He allows his wife perfect freedom. Once a day, he goes to her apartment, inquires after her health, stays half an hour, and on the dot he leaves to return to his philosophical musing. Then Filippo is the victim of long and abstruse discussions. Bergson is the chief target of his attacks. To Gala, the spokesman for Pirandello's ideas, it is useless to attempt to discuss the relation between reality and reason. Reality is a blind, overpowering current that carries everyone in its fury. The only way to cope with it is to put ourselves outside of it. Bergson tries to rationalize reality by stating that reason "can only consider the sides and character of reality which are identical and constant," while "what is fluid, living, mobile, obscure in reality, escapes to reason." Gala with amusement criticizes: "I do not know how it escapes to it, for the very fact that Mr. Bergson can say it. How has he managed to reach this conclusion except through reason? Then, it seems to me, it does not escape to it." This and numerous other discussions take place while Gala goes to the kitchen, dons a spotless white cap and apron and, aided by Filippo, prepares his daily food, while his mind tries to ward off the onslaught of reality upon his peaceful existence.

Outwardly, Leone Gala is ludicrous, but when we become acquainted with his intimate thoughts we find ourselves before a tragic individual. The cold indifference which characterizes every act, every word, even every motion of his body, is consciously assumed and tragically lived. Caught in the clash between reason and sentiment (sentiment is here instinct, the turmoil of being alive, life), he has, in order to survive, emptied his every act of the mysterious and disturbing fluid of sentiment. Now he lives according to "reason." Gala's reason is not that of the classical drama of Racine and Corneille, but a detached attitude that prevents whatever happens around him from reaching him. By means of this attitude he can live in a vacuum. He is a body without sensitivity, a pitiful phantom that goes through life without living it. Married to a woman who was totally irrational, he thought that his only solution was to live apart from her. Having found life as irrational as his wife, he experiments to discover to what extent he can detach himself from life also. He can truly say of himself: "I live in such a climate, my dear, that I can afford not to pay attention to anything at all; to be indifferent to death as well as to life." He has understood that life is a game, "a sad event, my dear, when one understands the game of life." The only remedy is to find a desperate defense against it: "the firmest, the most stable, because no hope urges you to yield in the slightest degree either to others or to yourself." It is a defense against all men, against ourselves, against life, "against the evil that life does to all inevitably."

For a man who has reached such a sublime and categorical pessimism, the only solution is to live in one's intellect, "not to live for ourselves, but to see others live from the outside, for that short time that we are compelled to live." The essential thing in Gala's mind "is to find a concept in which to fix ourselves so that we may revolve around it and live in it." He means by concept an act of his life, deprived of the impetuousness of instinct and of sentiment. He finds in this abstraction a method of conduct that makes him impervious to the tangible aspects of life, by making them exist only in his own mind. Not a flower and its exquisite perfume, but just the cold picture of a flower, such as a scientist would have; not man with his intricate mental processes, his contradictions, his changes, but just figures and statistics that do not set at play the disturbing element of our sentiment; not Silia, his wife, with her caprices and her feminine irrationality, but only the form of a wife, just as he, to her, is the form of a husband without any content: such as these are his concepts.

Silia, a pretty young woman, full of whims, is characterized by an extreme uncertainty of her acts and emotions, swiftly passing from love to hatred, from enthusiasm to indifference. She is fantastic, restless, and speaks of feeling the limitations of her body. She confesses that the only pleasure that she has derived from it has been that of tormenting men. She has taken Guido Venanzi as a lover, just for a diversion, perhaps just to be perverse. Now she is terribly bored with that superficial man. "Everything you say is a yawn," she tells him in an uncomplimentary way. Her torment is Leone Gala. He is the puppet master who makes her move by invisible threads. She feels his presence as an incubus. "I free?" she says to Guido as the latter is in her apartment late one evening. "I see him constantly. He gave me this liberty as something worthless, while he went to live by himself after having taught me for three years that liberty does not exist." Through his tortuous reasoning, Gala has taught her introspection; he has destroyed her instinctive spontaneity, and with it the joy that a gay, pretty woman can derive from life. She sees his eyes constantly ("Oh, so hateful, piercing like two needles, under the appearance of a blank expression"). She hears his voice in the prison of her liberty that he has built for her. She frantically cries, "I am crushed for hours by the thought that such a man can exist, almost outside of life and as a nightmare in the life of others!" She is so desperate that she decides to get rid of her husband at any cost. She is exasperated to the point of saying, "I would pay with my life if someone would kill him."

The opportunity arose one night when Gala made his daily visit. Her lover, Guido Venanzi, was entertaining Silia by boring her. Gala insisted as usual on his concept of reason and instinct, expressing delight at the degree of the rational isolation which he had attained. To be more convincing he brought forth an example derived from his experience as a cook. He taught no other than Guido Venanzi, who must have laughed up his sleeve while listening, that a concept of life is like an eggshell without the content. The content is instinct, turbulent instinct, and we must empty it if we wish to live according to the method of perfect life that he has found. "You pass a pin through the empty shell as a pivot and you amuse yourself in making the shell turn around it. It is very light now, and you play with it as you would with a celluloid ball, tossing it from one hand to the other, here, there, here, there; then, paf! you crush it between your hands and you throw it away." In its practical application this example referred to Silia, who was meant to represent the egg without its content of instinct and sentiment. He had taken it, perforated it, removed the content. Now Silia was only the concept of the wife. She was harmless. Silia was so angered that when Leone left the house she threw the empty shell of an egg at him from the window. Instead of hitting him, she hit a group of four tipsy gentlemen who happened to be passing.

They went upstairs, mistaking her for a young Spanish dancer who lived in that neighborhood and who was quite immoral. That was a serious insult, and among well-bred people an insult is paid for with a duel. Silia had a most brilliant idea: to have her husband (had he not remained her legal husband, at any rate?) avenge her honor in the hope that Miglioriti, one of the debonair gentlemen who had invaded the apartment and one of the best swordsmen in the city, might free her of him.

On the following morning, Silia herself brought the news to Leone. She thought that at least that news would shake him out of his indifference. Leone, who did not even know what a sword looked like, agreed to challenge Miglioriti. Upon doing so, he demanded terrible terms, a duel to the finish, with pistol and sword. The seconds were duly chosen, the place was decided on, the exact hour indicated. The calm of Leone was extraordinary. Silia, who at first had rejoiced, was greatly perplexed. The reason for Gala's calm appeared very vaguely in a conversation between him and the two lovers. Gala accepted his rôle as a challenger on the grounds that Guido Venanzi, who was in the apartment with Silia, had not come forward to defend her when the four intoxicated young men entered. Gala had done this because he was revolving around the pivot of the concept of a husband as he explained: "Be sure that I shall not move from my pivot no matter what happens. I see both myself and you playing —and I am amused. That's all."

It was a game of rôles. Strangely enough, there was a general feeling in social circles that it was the part of Guido rather than of Leone to defend Silia. Leone dominated all with his enigmatic calm. He prepared everything, ordered everything. He arranged that the duel be fought on the following morning in the garden adjoining his apartment. The fatal morning came. His apartment was filled with friends, his seconds, and the doctor. Leone still slept. Guido Venanzi, upon going to call him, was surprised to find that he was not ready. Ready? He had done his part when he had challenged Miglioriti; now it was Guido's part, as a lover, to defend the woman in whose house he had been when she was insulted. Guido could not resist his arguments, fought the duel, and was killed. These are the jests of life and death.

Although Pirandello has treated with ill-concealed amusement Gala's cerebral way of dealing with life, he sympathetically realizes what that detachment means to poor Gala. For this reason he has allowed him to outwit his wife and to make a victim of her lover. Gala has foiled death because he has been able to keep away from the swift river of passion and instinct by reducing life to a series of cold concepts.

Leone Gala, although focused at a closer range, is as tragic as Henry IV, the Father in *Six Characters in Search of an Author*, or as any tragic character that Pirandello has given us. When he laughs one can detect under the froth of exasperation a longing in his heart for the freshness and richness of the life that he has renounced. He has an intellect as sharp and cutting as a Toledo sword. When he finds Guido in his wife's apartment he accepts the situation with the utmost calm, but looks in such a penetrating way at him that the latter is compelled to explain that he has gone there to drink a glass of chartreuse. "It it green or yellow?" queries the subtle Gala. "Green, I believe," answers the confused Guido. Whereupon Gala prophesies, "You will dream of crushing a lizard with your teeth." One can see Pirandello laughing gleefully at his diabolic humor. Gala, in whom Pirandello has disguised himself, is not an attractive character. The fact that he has been endowed with disconcerting and even unpleasant traits is a mark of the objectivity of the author's method. When we see Gala, an intellectual gentleman, incongruously attired as a cook, we realize the effect that the misfortunes of life can have on us. This is humor for Pirandello who never took his sorrows too tragically, but always bore them with a quizzical smile that wandered like a subdued light over his countenance. Had he not done so he might have been one of those individuals who bother their fellow-men with their laments. Pirandello always has a stoical soul, and when the breaking point comes he relaxes into a smile or even laughter. Then out of that state of mind, a character like Leone Gala comes to life.

The author himself gives us the key to this play in *Six Characters in Search of an Author*, confiding to us that Leone Gala was reason and his wife was instinct. It is unjust to call Gala abstract or cerebral. He is conscious that he is unnatural. What counts more is that he knows that he cannot be natural. "Woe to me if I were," he says. If he had been, he would have gone back to Silia whenever her physical appeal overcame his studied indifference. He would have "degraded" himself for having yielded to instinct, and afterwards he would have felt all the lowness of his acts. He expresses this feeling to Silia, who acknowledges his superiority together with her defeat. He tells her: "Don't you think that sudden flares of emotion rise also in me? I don't allow them to cut loose: I seize them; I tame them. I nail them." Emotions are to him wild beasts, and he is the tamer: "I swear to you that sometimes I feel inclined to be devoured by one of these beasts . . . even by you—now that you look at me so tranquilly and repentantly. But no! because believe me: it is all a game. And this would be the last and would destroy the pleasure of all others. No, no, . . . Go, go." He is another character whose destiny is to live in desolate isolation and exasperated loneliness.

As is his custom, Pirandello is more occupied with the complications that instinct can create than with the power of instinct itself. The undercurrent of the play is forced renunciation of instinct and of life. One should not be misled by the salacious events that are here portrayed. A violent asserter of the freedom of instinct is on the same footing as one who denies the right of instinct. They are both equally preoccupied with it. In the development of Gala's character and under the ludicrous events which he creates, we detect the incertitude of one who is perplexed by the strange powers of instinctive life.

In spite of Gala's tortuous and elusive "concepts," there is a very practical side in the method of life which he evolves

and which he imposes on himself. Pirandello has afforded
him in that method a way of finding life livable. It gives
him a superiority over all. He is inaccessible, since no one
can hurt him. He has disposed of his rival in a clever manner
and he can still continue to pass from one hand to the other
the lucent, empty eggshell, playing with it as with a celluloid
ball, light, so light.

XII

The Many Faceted Prism of Truth

RIGHT YOU ARE IF YOU THINK YOU ARE

(*Così 'è* [*se vi pare*])

Pirandellian humor also runs through *Right You Are if You Think You Are*. Humor, however, colors only the external side of the play, because the pathetic element affirms itself, and becomes larger and deeper as the play develops, till finally it culminates in the last scene, one of the most dramatic that Pirandello has created.

The play is constructed on clear-cut lines dividing a group of the *élite* of a provincial town, who are curious to the point of being cruel, from three individuals who are the victims of their morbid curiosity. There is a typical Pirandellian character between the two groups: Lamberto Laudisi.

In his looks, in his intellectual traits, he bears the marks of one of those characters in whom the author has embodied his wisdom of life. Laudisi stands on the boundary line of instinctive life and reflective intellect. He has reached the conclusion that the only solution for the tragic snares in which humans are caught is a complete categorical subjectivism. What Laudisi claims is that truth is not a bare, brutal, and clumsy fact, but the feeling which animates that fact. He concludes that feelings are so personal, subjective, and elusive as to defy our cold apprehension. He is a pitiless observer of "human stupidity" and he characterizes with this uncomplimentary epithet the cult of the absolute certitude that his sister's family and her friends want to reach concerning a situation which cannot be expressed in rational terms. Laudisi is described to us by his author as follows: "Slender, elegant, without foppishness, in his forties, he wears a bluish purple smoking-jacket with cuffs and black embroidery. Endowed with a subtle, witty intellect, he becomes quickly irritated, but then he laughs and lets people do and say whatever they please, finding delight in the spectacle of human stupidity." Laudisi claims that each human being is an unbreakable unit and that each one of us is unable to penetrate into the mystery of another: "What can we *really* know of other people? Who they are . . . how they are . . . what they do . . . why they do it . . ." Each of us can only feel the outside world, men and things, in a subjective way—which is real to each one of us, but stands in sharp contrast to the results of other people's contacts with the same reality. This actually means that reality, in certain cases, does not have an identity of its own, but that it acquires as many aspects as there are individuals in whom it mirrors itself. Laudisi is very practical in his categorical subjectivism. He does not mean that we "must no longer believe even what we see and touch." What he wants is that we shall believe what we feel and see but also "respect what others see and touch, even if it is the opposite." This belief is a particle of Christian charity seen by a philosophical and somewhat paradoxical mind.

As is evident from the aforesaid, Pirandello does not generalize. He is directing our attention to a specific situation in which a logical approach, based on actual data, does not help at all. Three persons—Signora Frola, Signor Ponza, and Signora Ponza—are involved in one of those situations that make the appeal to the irrational acceptable to human beings, and give to the observer a feeling that life stands on the brink of the abyss of nothingness. Signor Ponza claims that his present wife is his second wife, whom he married after the death of his first wife Lina, the daughter of Signora Frola. Signora Frola claims that Lina is not dead, and that the Signor is demented in believing her his second wife. Signor Ponza has just arrived in town as a secretary in the prefect's office, and lives with his wife on the top floor of a tall, lonely building in the outskirts of the town, while Signora Frola lives alone in an apartment. Every day she goes to see her daughter, but is not allowed to go upstairs to her apartment. She stays down in the courtyard, her mother-love satisfied with a glimpse of her child and with receiving loving messages from her by means of a basket she lowers with a string as is the custom in Italy. The strange thing is that Signor Ponza is deeply devoted to his mother-in-law. He is as tender with her as if he were her own child. He looks after her, goes to visit her every day and passes with her as much of his time as possible.

The whole town is agog over this irrational behavior. Who ever heard of a mother, especially in Italy, who was not allowed to see her daughter? Whoever heard of a son-in-law who spent all his leisure time with his mother-in-law? A flame of curiosity rises and sweeps over the town. Everyone wants to know definitely what the mystery is. The most curious gather at the Agazzi home to map out a campaign. Signor Agazzi is a counselor to the prefect and, therefore, a superior of Signor Ponza.

When the play opens Signora Agazzi is discussing with her brother, Lamberto Laudisi, the unheard-of rudeness of Signor Ponza, who refused to receive her and her daughter Dina when they went to call on Signora Ponza. They had called there before and, after waiting for fifteen minutes at the door, had to leave somewhat embarrassed. Under Laudisi's questioning they have to confess that they went there out of curiosity, but that, at any rate, it is customary to pay a visit to a newcomer, especially when she lives next door. They emphatically state that it was certainly due to Signor Ponza's influence that the dear old lady, Signora Frola, had not come to let them in.

They went to call again and Ponza himself came to the door. "It is his countenance that disconcerts the whole town," says the horrified Signora Agazzi. Ponza had made a little bow and had stood silently before them, his terrible eyes riveted on the two confused ladies. He had finally spoken, saying that his mother-in-law was ill, and that she thanked them for their kindness. With these words he had stood there waiting for them to go. Signora Agazzi and her daughter, mortified, had hastened to leave.

Now Signor Agazzi, as Ponza's superior, is protesting to the prefect and asking for an apology. There is a conclave

122

in the Agazzi home concerning this deplorable episode. A group of other scandalmongers arrive: Signora Sirelli, red-headed, plump, complacent, bedecked with rings, and burning with curiosity; her husband, the object of her biting sarcasm, a man about forty, "bald, fat, with pretenses to being elegant," and Signora Cini, a friend of theirs, "an awkward old lady, full of eager malice, covered by an air of naïveté." All that these people know is that Signor Ponza, his wife, and his mother-in-law are in deep mourning because they come from a town in Marsica which has been destroyed by an earthquake; that they have lost all their relatives in that disaster. Signor Ponza has a tragic face with the eyes "of a wild beast and not of a man," as young Dina informs her friends, who are eager to receive any information to assuage the burning curiosity that devours them.

They are all determined to know the truth. Signor Agazzi has brought pressure to bear on the prefect, and Signora Frola will have to apologize for the rudeness of her son-in-law in not allowing two ladies, the wife and daughter of his superior, to call on her. In fact, Signora Frola comes to call in the midst of all this hubbub. She is "a neat, modest, most affable little old lady, with a great sadness in her eyes, but constantly softened by a gentle smile on her lips." Signora Frola tells them that she and Signor Ponza live in a sort of isolated world which they themselves have closed with their own hands with the result that their harmony is perfect and they live quietly in it. Her explanation has the effect of only whetting more the desire to uncover what is behind the strange conduct of Signor Ponza. They cannot believe that it is due to "a sort of malady, a fullness of love—but closed —that's all! . . . An overpowering fullness of love, in which his wife must live, without ever coming out of it, and which no one must enter." They all qualify Ponza's behavior as pure "egotism." Gently Signora Frola, in her compassionate understanding, agrees that perhaps it is, but "an egotism which gives itself entirely, as a complete world of its own, to his wife." When she leaves, the words "mystery," "violence," "barbarism," echo in the room.

Signora Frola has hardly left the house when Signor Ponza arrives. He is "thickset, dark—with an almost fierce look, with bushy black hair, low forehead, heavy black mustache like a policeman. He clenches his fists continuously and speaks with difficulty, with ill-contained violence. While he is speaking, his eyes remain hard, fixed, gloomy." He announces that Signora Frola is crazy and that her madness consists exactly in believing that he does not want her to see her daughter. "What daughter, in God's name, if her daughter has been dead four years?" exclaims, almost shouts Signor Ponza. He informs his listeners that two years before, he had remarried, but Signora Frola still believes that his second wife is her daughter. Tenderly he refers to the beneficial effect of this belief: "It has been lucky for her because she had fallen into a sort of gloomy desperation at her daughter's death, while her lucid madness makes her happy in the belief that her daughter is alive." As soon as Signor Ponza leaves, the gentle Signora Frola quietly returns.

As readily as they had accepted Signor Ponza's version of the mother-in-law's madness, they accepted Signora Frola's explanation that he, Ponza, is in an unbalanced state of mind. He has come to believe that this is his second wife after his first wife, Lina, was sent to a sanitarium for a year. Upon her return, he had claimed that she was no longer Lina. He called her Giulia, and he was so assertive in his belief that they were forced to perform a second wedding, a mock ceremony. Would a mother speak so calmly of the situation if her daughter were dead?

The two speak with so much plausibility that it is hard not to believe them both. One oscillated between the two explanations, unable to take sides, and almost excusing the cruel curiosity of the Agazzi family and of their friends. The fatuous, bald-headed, and round-bellied Signor Sirelli, much to the surprise of his red-headed wife, has a practical idea: let us put Signor Ponza and Signora Frola together; let us put them face to face, then we can be sure that the truth will be discovered.

Sirelli's suggestion is followed: the two confront each other.

Signora Frola, who beforehand has expressed her belief in Ponza's madness, when the latter appears and furiously inveighs against her for having left her apartment, sweetly agrees with him as to the identity of his wife. Everyone gloats over the fact that now the truth has been discovered. If Signora Frola treats Ponza like a spoiled child and pretends to agree with him, it is evident that Ponza is crazy. But Ponza, after acting so violently, as soon as his mother-in-law leaves the room, reacquires his composure and says: "I beg your pardon, ladies and gentlemen, for being compelled to offer such a spectacle to you in order to remedy the harm that you unwittingly do to this poor woman." Then he has been feigning; not he, but Signora Frola is crazy! How swiftly our opinion changes before a reality which is inconstant and variable because it is colored by the sentiment of those who participate in it! In order to help Signora Frola endure the sorrow of her daughter's death, a sorrow that normally would have killed her, Signor Ponza, according to what he says, shouts the truth to her as if it were his own madness. It is the only way to keep her illusion alive. What a madman believes cannot be the truth—then, Lina, her Lina, is alive. The disappointed spectators of the strange scene between Signor Ponza and Signora Frola ask of him: "What? Did you pretend?" Ponza, in the fixity of his pitiful exaltation, answers: "I was compelled to. Don't you understand that this was the only means by which I could let her live in her illusion, that of shouting to her the truth in this fashion as if it were my madness?" Of course they do not understand. How could they, normal and happy people, understand this pitiful contrivance, indispensable to two persons who are helping each other bear the burden of their sorrow by not accepting, each for the sake of the other, the naked and crushing truth that would make life unendurable for at least one of them? Laudisi ironically laughs: "There you are, ladies and gentlemen, the truth is discovered."

The only solution is to hear the person herself about whose identity there is doubt—Signora Ponza. If they ask her who she is; whether she is the first or second wife of Signor Ponza, they will certainly get the correct answer. The truth will undoubtedly be disclosed.

They do so. The prefect compels Ponza to bring his wife to Agazzi's house. Signora Ponza advances rigidly, in deep mourning, her face hidden by a dark, thick veil, impenetrable. She has lost the distinctness of human features that make human individuality. Her tragedy has blurred all that constitutes her personal identity. As soon as Signora Frola sees her, she calls her: "Lina, Lina!" rushing towards her and clinging to the veiled woman with the thirst for love of a mother who has not for years held her daughter in her arms. But at the same time is heard the voice of Ponza who dashes on the stage shouting: "Giulia, Giulia!"

At his shouts the veiled woman stiffens in the arms of Signora Frola. She begs both of them to leave. Signor Ponza and Signora Frola go out clasped in each other's arms, caressing each other, in tears. The veiled woman speaks: "What else can you wish from me? As you see, there is here a misfortune that must be respected, because only in this way can the remedy prevail that compassion has lent it. The truth is only this: I am both Signora Frola's daughter and Signor Ponza's second wife; yes, and for me, no one, no one!" The prefect insists: "Oh, no, for you, my dear lady, you must be one or the other." "No," she replies, "for myself I am the one that people believe me to be."

There follows a stony silence in which are merged the disappointment of the curious, the quickened wound of the three victims, and the tragic laughter of Laudisi. There is also our reverence before the tragedy of three human beings who had to clothe truth with illusion to bear its terrifying countenance. Beauty of symbol is blended perfectly in harmony with depth of sentiment!

The central idea of the play is the belief that we are absolutely subjective and that the only way to live and to let other people live is to accept this point of view. Lamberto Laudisi does so, and he respects the odd situation existing in the Ponza household. The others, totalitarian logicians, apply to this specific case a generic idea, and by so doing they create their own discomfort and destroy the peace which, even if based on illusion, allows three persons to live peacefully. The gentle, merciful, and human power of illusion has taken life in a situation of unspeakable sorrow and tragedy and has given Signor Ponza and Signora Frola the calm that they have reached by forcing on themselves a belief that did not correspond to the truth, but was more endurable than the truth. Truth was their own grief and tragedy.

Let us not laugh at Pirandello's claim of the power of illusion! Illusion is empty when it is sought by idle dreamers and by seekers of idyls. Then it is sentimentality. But when illusion is a bitter necessity, it is sublime and pitiful, and such is the one that unfolds before us in this play.

The true heroine of the play is Signora Ponza. Pirandello has embodied in her the symbol of reality, which is veiled, nonexistent, until we give a meaning to it by letting our sentiment infuse life into it. Pirandello predicates the subjective value of truth, and the play pivots on this query: Is truth, objective and categorical truth, always possible? Laudisi reveals to us Pirandello's point of view when he states that he is not interested in the actual data about the Ponza family: "Reality for me does not consist in the facts, but in the sentiment of those two, where I cannot penetrate except through what they reveal to me." The facts concerning them "have been annulled, not by an external accident—a fire, an earthquake; but by themselves in their hearts . . . creating, he to her, or she to him, a phantasm which has the same consistency of reality, in which they live perfectly, in full accord." They "breathe in that reality, they see it, feel it, touch it." Why shouldn't we respect it?

Sirelli and the others wish to "explain," assuming an attitude coldly scientific and selfish: The truth is one, either Signor Ponza is right or Signora Frola. They lack the gift of sympathy and understanding. At this point, Pirandello's thought merges with the teachings of great religious leaders who in their exalted individualism glorified "holy madness" which was nothing but their sentiment in contrast with the objective and instinctive reaction of the average man. Piran-

127

dello has put in challenging form and somewhat intellectualized what we usually find in the form of a religious precept. The admonition "be charitable" is very close to the subjectivism of Lamberto Laudisi. When we are charitable we give up our own point of view, which is our interpretation of the outside reality, and accept the other man's point of view which contains his interpretation of the same reality.

If we allow our minds to ponder over the author's doubt of the benefit of a categorical but unbending, even heartless concept of truth, we see that a gentle though sad vein of human sympathy runs through his attitude. What can absolute knowledge do when we find ourselves face to face with the death of a person dear to us? It does not help us to bear our grief to think that to die is the common lot of humanity; nor to know the nature of the disease, and to follow its progress step by step on the doctor's chart. What good did it do Pirandello himself to know that his wife was demented? Did that knowledge destroy the reality he had to face for so many years?

It would be futile to speculate upon whether Signora Frola or Ponza is right. The play hinges on the fact that the identity of the wife remains a mystery. The author has been able to lead us through three long acts, balancing with perfect ease between humor and pathos, without satisfying the curiosity not only of the Agazzi family, their friends, and the town, but also our own. We should act against the desire of the author if we attempted to tear aside the veil from Signora Ponza's face. If we did, we should imitate the critics of Dante who attempt to identify a sinner among those that Dante condemned to the loss of their physical and personal identity. It is immaterial to know who Signora Ponza, veiled and grieving, actually is. We must accept her heart-rending confession, and grieve with her.

XIII

Changing Character of Human Opinions

EACH IN HIS OWN WAY

(*Ciascuno a suo modo*)

Pirandello has projected in *Each in His Own Way* one of his most tormented and pessimistic moods, although his pessimism is the direct reaction of the belief that only humility and stoic silence can help man in the tragedy of being human.

The setting is laid in a more aristocratic atmosphere than in his earlier plays. His characters here are also more intellectual and, therefore, more tormented and complicated, since life for Pirandello becomes more tormented and complicated as it departs from a presupposed idyllic beginning where goodness and happiness reign. "I, too, have learned to do my acrobatic stunts, by myself, coming from the country to the city—here—in all this falsity and unreality, which becomes more false and unreal from day to day," says the tragic heroine, adding that there is no way to revert to the original simplicity, and that "to try to recreate this simplicity in us and around us appears—is, indeed, false."

At the outset we find ourselves in the aristocratic home of Donna Livia Paleguri. The Subtle Youth and the Old Gentleman, guests at a formal tea—one eager, the other cautious to the point of hypocrisy—discuss the question of forming and reaching opinions, and whether or not we have opinions. Diego, another guest and Pirandello's spokesman, denies that we have real opinions since we change them according to circumstances and persons involved. He denies also the validity of what we call conscience, which is nothing but "others" in us, that is, what others think reflected in us: public opinion that determines our acts.

"Everything is mobile, fleeting, without weight. I turn here, there. I laugh. I hide myself in a nook and weep. What

129

torment! What anguish! Continually I hide my face from myself, so ashamed am I at seeing myself change." So, disconsolately speaks another guest, and these words reveal the state of mind of the author which in turn colors the thoughts and actions of the characters. Everything is spasmodic, tortuous, torturing, because there is no basis for the thinking and the acting of these beings who are deprived of opinions, of beliefs, of conscience.

Pirandello is not making here a generic case. The generic and average man is for him, as we have repeatedly stated, an abstraction. He is concerned with individuals only, his characters. Granted their inability to form a definite opinion, their irrational behavior is a logical consequence. It is also the negative reflection of a positive side: If an individual were capable of a clear and deeply and sincerely felt opinion, rational behavior would follow. Pirandello, however, goaded by his life-experience, has seen around him and in himself largely the negative side. It is easier to see the positive one in the quiet chamber of our imagination.

The inspiration of the play came to the author supposedly from a newspaper clipping, telling of an actress from Turin for whom a promising young sculptor, Giacomo La Vela, committed suicide. Almost on the eve of their wedding she had given herself to the *fiancé* of La Vela's sister, Baron Nuti. Pirandello realizes very well why that has happened: instinct, a tragedy of instinct. But what will those characters say if he asks them? Will they confess humbly and contritely what they have done? He knows that they will not. Thereupon he places them in his comedy with a slight change in the name of the actress, but replacing the sculptor, La Vela, with a painter, Giorgio Salvi, and Baron Nuti with Michele Rocca.

Delia Morello is one of those celebrated and glorified harlots who were very popular in Italy in the beginning of the century, women of singular beauty, moving in the best of masculine society. Artists and writers sought their company because these women were interested in the arts, too, since a little smattering of culture was good bait for intellectual people. They had inherited the place of prominence that Imperia occupied in the sixteenth century, in the very city and in the very court of the Popes. Delia was not intellectual. Pirandello does not like intellectual women. She was full of the sensitiveness that tragedy develops in human beings.

The value of men's opinions was quickly tested that afternoon in the palatial home of Donna Livia Palegari, who was very much concerned over the report that her young son Doro had, the previous evening, taken the part of the actress Delia Morello. Referring to the suicide of Giorgio Salvi, Francesco Savio, an intimate friend of Doro, had accused the actress of having perfidiously contributed to the death of the promising painter. Doro had risen furiously to defend her, defying the ridicule and indignation of all. He had given an idealistic explanation of what had happened. He had maintained that it could not be said, that Delia Morello had "wilfully planned Salvi's ruin by giving herself to the other man, almost on the eve of the wedding; because the true ruin of Salvi would have been, after all, his marriage to her." When his mother, both scandalized and fearful of a duel, reproaches him, he tells her that he is sincerely ready to acknowledge that he has been wrong in taking Delia Morello's part against his friend Francesco Savio. The mother is overjoyed.

At that very moment there arrives Francesco Savio who confesses that he too has seen the foolishness of his own position, and has come to tell his old friend how sorry he is. The strange thing is that a new dispute arises when Francesco repeats the arguments that Doro has advanced in Delia's defense. To Pirandello that is quite natural. In the first place, they have merely changed positions; so that they are as far apart now as they were the previous evening. Besides, when we hear another person repeating something that we have said and know to be false, we naturally resent it. That falseness becomes galling, irritating beyond endurance. Translated into terms of everyday life, Doro's reaction is parallel to our resentment when we hear another person saying to us, "You fool," an epithet that we have numberless times applied to ourselves. Through Francesco's words Doro had seen himself in a mirror that distorted his features and made grimaces at him. His arguments were hollow, annoyingly hollow, as he well knew. Why should that idiotic Francesco have come there to repeat them to him? That is why he called Francesco "buffoon" five times in a fit of rage, and the latter, offended, left the house.

As soon as the two friends separate with the certainty of a duel, Delia Morello comes to thank Doro for believing her innocent. She has "recognized" herself in the arguments advanced by him. He has expressed what she has never been able to understand about herself. Doro, who has just acknowledged the weakness of his own reasoning, under the sway of Delia's beauty, believes again that she is innocent. He is ready again to defy public opinion and ridicule, and even to go against his mother. "See," grievingly laughs Pirandello, "that is the value of man's opinions and actions!"

These rapid changes and most unforeseen reactions are not easily understood unless we picture Doro and his friends as persons yielding one moment to the sincere impulse of instinct (instinct is always sincere), and at another moment to the complicating force of reason or "conscience," as Pirandello calls it here. Conscience is identified in the play with the process that we well know by now, and that Pirandello calls *costruirsi* or "to build up oneself." These characters are not telling the truth (how could they tell the truth?) and therefore they transform the hideous reality into a network of clever explanations, which make the original situation both ludicrous and sad. For this reason Pirandello has projected on the screen of his art a crowd of grotesque figures, puppets, as he calls them, shouting, gesticulating figures with staring eyes, tense, as if possessed by evil spirits like young trees furiously tossed by the wind. The most tormented of all is Delia Morello.

Pirandello has not made of Delia a monster of iniquity as did Donna Livia Palegari and her aristocratic friends. She is sincere in all her complicated falseness. She is "one of those women born by chance—always outside of themselves—wanderers who will never know where they are going to end. And yet, so many times, she seems to be a little frightened child imploring help." Pirandello is not cruel to his characters. He is too sophisticated not to see the truth, but he is sorry to see what he sees. Tears and mourning are not the only means of showing sadness. There is also laughter, the tolerant laughter peculiar to him that shows his sympathetic sorrow. Diego, who laughs with that tolerance, tells us, "That's my way of laughing and my laughter hurts me more than anyone else." Delia lived tragically under the weight of her shame when she heard the explanation that Doro first gave to her actions. She is in a state of exaltation now. Doro by his defense has created an artificial atmosphere in which she can see her past in a light which is not maddening and unbearable. She has been able "to build up herself" through the idealized image created by Doro. That image is her salvation, and she clings to it with the same desperate passion with which one clings to life.

Delia is not concerned with what people will think of her. She tells Doro, "My gratitude is for what you have thought, felt—and not because you have shouted it to everybody else." He has revealed a new being in her, a being that before she had tried in vain to find. "I struggle, I suffer—I don't know—as if beyond myself, as if I must always pursue the person that I really am, in order to stop her and ask her what she wants, what she suffers, what she would like me to do to calm her, to give her peace." Now that a new self has been revealed to her, she hates all the artificiality with which she has covered her face and destroyed her soul. She has discovered— or did she know it before this?— that she hated the adoration that men had for her body, neglecting "her." She is sincere as she speaks of the neglect of her soul by men, but she adds: "And I punish them exactly where their longings converge. I excite those desires that nauseate me, in order to avenge myself better—and I avenge myself by offering this body to one whom they least suspect!" There are in her, sincerity and fraud, innocence and malice, as she at times catches, as if on the wing, a fluttering dream; again, at times, she shows the tricks of a prostitute. The subconscious merges with the fantastic as she tries to excuse her wrong to Giorgio

133

Salvi, whose beautiful intellect and soul perished because
of her.

They had met at Capri. He had asked her to sit for a portrait, then to be his model. She had consented. He looked at
her with the eyes of an artist, though, like all others, only at
her body. Sentiments were colors to him. The ideal pleasure
that he took in her beauty made her frantic, because she
could not avenge herself as she did with other men. What
Doro had said was so true: "To a woman an angel is more
irritating than a beast." Hatred for Giorgio, handsome and
intellectual, grew in her in a slow, veiled, tortuous manner.
The moment to avenge herself had come. She let her body
shine before him in all its sensuous splendor. He, too, became intoxicated with it. She denied herself to him. She gave
herself to Michele Rocca, his sister's *fiancé*. But when she
did (it was so, just as Doro had imagined) it was that they
might be surprised together, making her marriage with Salvi
impossible, for his own sake and in his interest.

Doro happens to mention Francesco's arguments which
interpret Delia's conduct in quite a different manner. He does
it to contrast the brilliancy of his defense with the drabness of
Francesco's attack. Delia, in the version of Doro, appears to
have dissuaded Salvi from marrying her. For this reason she
had denied herself to him and, believing he would refuse, had
imposed upon him terrible conditions; such as introducing
her to his lovely mother and to his exquisite sister, of whose
loftiness and purity he was both proud and jealous.

In Francesco's version, her refusal to marry Salvi, and her
declining to give herself to him, were perfidious means of
obtaining more and more concessions, so that she might become the absolute mistress of his life. Only in this fashion had
she succeeded in having Giorgio introduce her to his family,
and she had gone there, victorious, before society, near the
purity of his little sister—she, "the spurned, the contaminated
one." In Francesco's opinion, Delia had given herself to
Rocca because she knew that Rocca had been opposed to her
being taken into the family. To avenge herself, Delia had
decided to allure, to attract him into the whirl of her sen-

suality "only for the pleasure of showing to that sister the timbre of the pride and honesty of such spotless paladins of morality." What depths of stupidity Francesco had reached in his senseless explanations! Much to Doro's amazement, Delia says, "Who knows that I have not done it for that reason?" The actions of these human beings are not to be considered in the light of rationality. There is in them obscure thinking and, therefore, obscure behavior. Doro is not different from Delia. He is going to fight a duel with Francesco, and admits that he does not know why.

The one who pricks the iridescent soap bubbles of all these people is Diego. He is not different from the others in excitement and tension, but he knows the game and acknowledges it, while the others seem unable to see their own artificiality. He knows how to read himself clearly, fearlessly; and Pirandello has assigned to him the rôle of representing him. Therefore Diego performs the unpleasant task of taking these characters apart, piece by piece, and showing them that there is no other alternative for them and for himself: either they must be tragic with reality or ludicrous with fiction. Pirandello has lent him his own tormented soul and intellect, while Diego describes the tragic grief that torments him by saying, "I have reduced my soul, by constantly burrowing into it, to a mole-hole." Two years before, he had lost his mother after a long illness that had made her unrecognizable He had spent nine sleepless nights near her as she moaned, almost unconscious, disfigured, on her deathbed. He had known the agony of counting by the striking of the clock the last hours of a dying person. He had discovered that no affection is strong enough to stand the neglect of the most elementary needs of life. Sleep and hunger conquer even our deepest love, love for our mother. In a fit of futile revolt, he had caught himself wishing his mother dead. Once he had seen himself in the mirror of his wardrobe, bending over his moaning mother, and he had seen on his own face "the expression with which he was stealthily anticipating his own freedom with an almost joyous fright."

Diego has fathomed the human heart down to those mysterious and terrifying depths. He has reached a tragic nihilism about life. Life wavers between a ghastly nothingness for those who think, and the stupid monotonous certitude of the everyday existence with its solid but limited and cramping reality, for those who cling to the tangible and concrete side of life. Life is to him "a continuous destruction which not even the strongest affections escape." One can easily imagine how fluid and fleeting are "the opinions, the fictions that we create for ourselves, and all the ideas that in the ruinous flight of life we succeed in perceiving. We learn something contrary to what we knew, we experience a sudden change in our impressions, we hear a word uttered in a different tone, and Mr. So-and-So who was white becomes black. Images of numberless things flash continuously through our mind and change our mood without our realizing it." How can he believe in conscience and opinions? How can he take seriously the words of these characters, puppets of passion and illusion? He tells Doro that it is his love for Delia that makes him take her part and declare her innocent. Doro denies it and Diego reveals his crushing pessimism. Woe unto us if we look into our own hearts!—"Conscience is an elastic network whence—if it should loosen a little—escapes madness, which nestles and hides within each of us. Then there wander before you, disconnectedly, images accumulated in so many years, ambiguous acts, shameful lies, ferocious hatreds, crimes meditated in the shadow of your thoughts, even in their slightest details, unrevealed desires."

There is another man whom Diego has to dissect, whom he has to bring before the pitiless light of his inquiry— Michele Rocca. Rocca has come from Naples upon hearing of the incident between Doro and Francesco in which he was involved. He has come to challenge Doro to a duel for insulting him while defending Delia. He, too, has his idealistic interpretation of his actions. The mere fact that he can talk relieves him of the tension that has oppressed him since the day of the tragedy. Excitedly, but also theatrically, he states that he did not wish to steal Giorgio's *fiancée*, as he has been accused of doing. He had been urged by Giorgio's mother, his sister, and even by Giorgio himself to prove his contention that Delia Morello was dishonest. His relations with her were prompted only by his desire to afford Giorgio the proof of her perfidy. Refusing to face the truth, Giorgio committed suicide. Diego gives an entirely different explanation of Rocca's actions: "He does not wish to have to confess that he has been a plaything in the hands of a woman—a little puppet that Delia Morello has broken by throwing it into a corner, after amusing herself by making him open and close his arms as in an act of prayer, by pressing with her finger on his chest the spring of passion. Now the little puppet is up again; his little face without a nose, all cracked, chipped. . . . The little puppet shouts that it is not true that the woman made him open and close his arms in order to laugh at him, and that, after laughing at him, she broke him. He says 'No, no.' I ask you if there is any spectacle more touching than this!"

Diego has gone to Francesco's house to tell him of Rocca's arrival. Francesco is busy training for his duel, practising with his fencing master and seconds. Both Delia and Rocca arrive. Delia has come to beg Francesco not to fight the duel with Doro. She begs him for her sake not to do it. She succeeds in enveloping Francesco too in her charm. Upon seeing Rocca, Francesco attacks him, insults him, defies him. He thinks that Delia is his, but he is wrong. Pirandello brutally uncovers the truth. As soon as Delia and Rocca see each other, they throw off the mask of their interest in Giorgio Salvi. The truth is that their blind passion has overpowered them since first they met. Placed face to face, they are unable to resist it, and they fall into each other's arms, while Francesco cries, "It is absurd, it is monstrous! There is between you the corpse of a man." Rocca acknowledges it. "It is monstrous, yes, but she must stay with me! She must suffer with me, with me." It is the logic of instinct, which is stronger than reason, and which uncovers and destroys all the false constructions of the intellect, leading these characters from the ridicule of self-illusion to the tragedy of reality.

In this play the æsthete and the moralist have come to the

help of the dramatist in order to project on the screen of art pitiful and tragic events. The æsthetic considerations and the moral concern, however, do not destroy the dramatic character and the pathos of the vicissitudes that we witness. Pirandello in building up the play has been very much concerned with the relation between art and life. He has introduced in two intermezzi the real persons from whose life he took the idea of the comedy: Delia Morello and Baron Nuti, who are in the audience, mingle with the spectators, and witness their lives reënacted on the stage. They represent life as it is in its actuality, while the Delia of the play and Michele Rocca represent the way in which man interprets idealistically his shameful acts. The former are tragic and crushed by their tragedy; the latter gesticulate and find solace in their bubbling, excited chatter, until they are compelled to return to the plane of reality, whence a social incident had removed them. When Delia and Nuti see themselves in the fixity of art, in which is reflected all the ugliness of their deeds, they become outraged and violent. Delia Morello leaps on the stage and slaps the actress who is impersonating her. None the less violent is Baron Nuti, with the result that a confusion arises in the theatre and an imaginary third act, so Pirandello informs us, is not played. The public, after either admiring or condemning the play, goes home.

Outwardly the play seems involved, gloomy, and pessimistic. When we single out the various strands that Pirandello has woven into it and look at the intimate texture of the work, it becomes clear and faintly illuminated by the light of his idealistic philosophy of humility. All those tortuous constructions are due to the fact that Delia Morello and Michele Rocca do not possess resignation—the gift of the humble of spirit. When we find ourselves in a world the only sure reality of which is death, where we are not sure of our own acts and of their reasons, of our opinions, of our conscience, when we know so little about ourselves, when we are one today and another tomorrow, when the only absolute certainty is that of the "little certitude of today," of our material possessions, of the fleeting existence of our bodies, when life is a continuous erosion of the most precious things we have, what armor will protect us other than humility? Do not ask for conclusions and solutions. Life is a conclusion and a solution unto itself. We are lost between the elusive and maddening fluidity of our ideas and the consoling gift of a gentle dream: "We advance sadly along a road already invaded by the shadows of the evening. It is enough to raise our eyes to a little loggia still illuminated by the setting sun, with a red geranium that glows in that light—and suddenly a distant dream touches our hearts." This sudden pure emotion is a true consolation for us humans. Pirandello is against pride and deceit: "Detach from yourself the little puppet that you create with the fictitious interpretation of your acts and your sentiments—and you will immediately see that it has nothing to do with what you are, or what you may truly be—with what is in you that you are not conscious of, and which is a terrible god, understand, if you oppose him, but which becomes immediately compassionate for every guilt if you abandon yourself to him and do not wish to find excuses."

There is a scene which reveals the intimate sentiment of Pirandello. As Francesco is preparing for his duel with Doro, and his friends are discussing the elusive meaning of all this ado between the two friends, Francesco is reminded of the countryside where he was supposed to go to visit his sister and his little niece when the unfortunate incident occurred. The beauty of the country and the charm of the little girl are made to float invitingly before the man who soon will either face or give death. Real life was there in that beauty, in that affection, in that charm!

The keynote of the play is given by the very title, *Each in His Own Way*, which refers to the duty that each has in creating his own reality. Reality is not a convention; it is not an object that everybody calls by a given name. Reality is something that we must create with our own souls, out of our own lives, in humility and candor: "Here we teach that you have to build the road on which you walk, singly, for every step that you wish to take, battering down what does not belong to you, because you have not built it yourself, and you have walked on it as a parasite." The only logical consequence of human volubility, of the ludicrous changes to which man abandons himself with wanton madness, is "the tragedy of a deranged and a convulsed soul that has lost its bearings." Delia Morello and the people who move around her in the play had not succeeded in creating their own reality, and for this reason they could only act as poor marionettes, guided by the arbitrary and violent hand of instinct and by the volubility of their minds.

XIV

The Beauty of a Lie

NAKED

(*Vestire gli ignudi*)

This play might be called the comedy of the unmasking of a lie if we did not feel that the false statement made by the heroine was so naïve and touching as to make us rebel at qualifying it with a term that bespeaks base deception. Since Ersilia Drei paid with her life for trying to die surrounded by an imaginary, romantic halo, it befits us to be kind to her and sympathetic with her experiences. She had always had an aspiration towards the beautiful, but life had constantly conspired against her. Her longing was for a modest sort of beauty, such as even an average person is wont to desire. Hers was in fact, a common species of sentimentality, but it held for her the promise of beautifying a life made up of commonplace events, of vain aspirations, and, alas, of shame.

Ersilia Drei, sick and wan, is presented to us by a comparison that Pirandello derives from his observation of the immediate reality: "It is as when a poor little beast in the street happens to fall into the midst of a group of nasty big dogs, and the gentler the small one is, the more they attack it and bite it and tear it apart." In desolate dejection, "shaking her head and slightly opening her hands that she holds in her lap" Ersilia Drei confesses, "I have never succeeded in being anything at all." She was a nurse, one of those continental nurses, girls of good family, refined, sensitive, and accustomed to move like shadows in wealthy households. "I was but a nurse's uniform, frayed, that is hung every night on a nail in the wall," she characterizes herself. She had charge of an exquisite little girl, Mimmetta, the daughter of Grotti, the Italian consul at Smyrna. One day a fine-looking naval officer arrived from Italy. There is an oriental background to the story: the sea, the sun, the oriental night full of palm trees and perfumes. Love sings for the first time in her heart. She becomes engaged to the naval officer, but it is a short parenthesis of happiness for her. Tragedy falls like a pall over the household. The little girl entrusted to her care falls from the terrace down to the street and is killed. Ersilia hastens back to Italy and finds that her *fiancé* is going to be married to another girl. She goes to a public park and takes poison. She wants everyone to know that she has died for love, a betrayed sweetheart.

Failing to die, however, she tells her story to a newspaper reporter when she is recovering in a hospital. Men have been cruel to her: by saving her they have proved the horrid truth about her and her life. They have torn the nice little dress that she made to cover her pitiful nakedness. Now that everyone has discovered the truth she will be taken around the town to be shown to the curious mob; the fiction with which she has given a look of decency and romance to her death will be heartlessly destroyed. The pitiful and romantic story of Ersilia Drei has filled the newspapers, and all of Rome has been stirred by it. A novelist, Ludovico Nota, becomes interested in the case of the poor young woman and writes a novel about her. When Ersilia leaves the hospital, he invites her to go to live in his apartment. His housekeeper, at first furious, upon learning that Ersilia is the romantic victim whose story covered the front page of the newspapers, becomes very maternal and puts herself at her disposal. Franco Laspiga, who jilted her, upon hearing that she has attempted suicide because of him, suddenly develops a feeling of responsibility and wishes to atone by marrying her. The subtle quality of Pirandello's mind reveals itself, here as elsewhere, by calling attention to the fact that in every dramatic event there is always an element of cool, planned, opportunistic consideration. Ersilia Drei did not try to die for love. She simply could not bear the heavy burden of her life any longer. Franco does not wish to marry Ersilia merely because she is a heroine. He has been jilted by his *fiancée*. Ludovico Nota is not prompted to be kind to Ersilia by a feeling of compassion. He has dreamt of a gay romance, as he reveals to the poor girl who is still frightened from having gazed upon death.

Franco, twenty-seven years old, tall, blond, slender, and elegant, rushes to Ludovico's apartment in order to throw himself at Ersilia's feet and ask her pardon. He is thankful to Ludovico for giving her shelter. Ludovico, who is very much irritated by all the publicity that he is receiving, answers sharply, "Are you grateful to me because I am no longer a young man?" This query reminds us of Pirandello's habit of portraying even out-of-the-ordinary events in an atmosphere where the common and ordinary sounds and modes of life are never absent. Franco is obsessed by his guilt: "How much harm I have done to everyone! It seems as if the whole world is full of the evil I have perpetrated. I am crushed by it."

The solution seems to be very close at hand. An optimist might say, Well, Ersilia Drei has succeeded. Now Franco will marry her and they will live happily ever after. This optimism, however, does not tally with Ersilia Drei's feelings. She refuses to have anything to do with Franco. She writhes in her bed and threatens to throw herself out of the window if he enters the room. She is frightened as she cries, "Is it my fault if they have saved me?" Indeed, she has to face a difficult situation when Franco goes to see her on the following day, speeded by idealistic ardor and zeal for redemption for himself and for her that is in sharp contrast to the reception accorded him by Ersilia. "Do not touch me, do not touch me!" she cries with fervor, as Franco tries to take her in his arms. She tells him that the situation has changed now, that it is not true that she has tried to commit suicide for him. She looks at him and states, "I have difficulty in even recognizing you."

Pirandello at this point stresses the change that even a brief time has wrought in Ersilia. How can she say that she hardly recognizes a man whom she has loved, to whom she has given herself, and for whom she has declared that she even attempted to commit suicide? The sharp contrast between the present and the past is determined by contradictory emotional states unrelated to each other and representing two distinct

moments in the life of the character. The life of a machine is
the best coördinated; that of man lacks coördination in an
inverted ratio to its richer emotional span. Ersilia Drei sees
Franco in a light that is totally different from the one by
which he was enveloped at Smyrna. That light was created by
the sentimental effervescence of her soul and imagination.
Now she sees him with the detached objectiveness of one who
is tied to this life against her will. Franco is most insistent in
his generous impulse and, in being so, he is cruel because he
forces poor Ersilia to destroy the beautiful iridescent shell
that hides a terrible truth—the life that she lived after the
young officer, having awakened love in her, left her in the
consul's house.

To persuade him that she will refuse any offer from him of
love, marriage, help or protection, she hurls at him the
ghastly spectacle of what happened the night before she attempted to commit suicide. "You must know that I offered
myself to the first man that passed," she says. Ludovico Nota
comments, "In desperation! On the eve of her suicide! Do you
understand?" This makes Franco more eager to atone for his
wrongdoing, since the greater Ersilia's misfortune, the greater
is the sense of responsibility that is awakened in him. Ersilia
is compelled to admit to Franco that after his departure she
yielded to the consul and was his mistress until by their neglect they caused the death of Mimmetta. The consul, who has
come to the apartment to demand an explanation of what had
been published in the papers, finds himself face to face with
Ersilia in what the author makes a very poignant scene. Each
accuses the other of responsibility for their wrong relationship. In what Ersilia calls her revolt at being contaminated,
Grotti sees scheming means of exciting him. She says: "You
caught me by surprise when I still felt the fire that he
[Franco] had kindled in my flesh . . . and, deny, if you
can, that I bit you. Deny that I scratched your neck, your
arms, your hands." Grotti answers, "You coward, you were
exciting me." They go over the days of lust and romance that
caught them in a deadly net, and they see unspeakable
miseries in them. Acts that once might have loomed in the

light of sentiment now exude filth and generate disgust. Grotti, like the Father in *Six Characters in Search of an Author,* rebels at Ersilia's attempt to summarize all his life in that stupid episode of his existence. He wishes to return to the fullness of his daily life that "you, cursed woman, have held in your sway for a moment, by confusing me. What! Do you believe that my whole self is contained in that moment of stupid idleness and of lust that I spent with you, for which I had to pay so dearly? With the unhappiness of my whole life: the death of my child." As many of Pirandello's characters do, Grotti tries to excuse his profligacy on the ground that he was unhappy with his wife. He had been as a father to Ersilia for a long time, and he was glad when Franco Laspiga gave evidence of an interest in her that culminated in their engagement. When he understood that she had given herself to Franco, his first reaction was a feeling of pity and sympathy. Then Grotti felt his attitude tinged with the sensuality that arose from the thought that she was no longer pure. Once, in days subsequent to Franco's departure, she had seemed to look at him in a way that betrayed her doubt as to his paternal feelings towards her. That glance marked their downfall.

Both Ersilia and Grotti are emphatic in their accusations. Pirandello does not accuse. He looks with eyes that flash with understanding, malice, and compassion, and says it was the blind force of instinct. Now that they are no longer bewitched by the enchantment of passion, now that passion is dead, they find only ugliness in it, and experience a revolt that leads to hatred and to nausea. It is especially so for Ersilia, who sees herself torn between the spirit and the flesh in expressing her complex detachment from the past that attracted her with its promise of happiness and gave her tragedy. "My flesh obeyed, but not my heart—never—I felt hatred for you, as my own shame! I never consented with my heart that bled because I had betrayed it like a shameless thief. I looked at my naked arms and I bit them! I yielded, yes, I always yielded; but I felt within me that my heart did not surrender!—Ah, infamous person that you are! You destroyed through vice the

only joy of my life—which I could hardly believe possible—
the joy of being betrothed." Passion has for Pirandello tentacles rather than soft, caressing hands. His characters throw
themselves into its fire, more out of desperation than because
passion lures them with its attractiveness.

Sudden changes take place when the truth is known. Franco
calls her a bad woman. Onoria, the housekeeper, who had
developed a great love for her, labels her an impostor.
Pirandello is amused at these sudden changes of sentiment;
particularly at Franco who now denounces the immorality
of Ersilia's action when he himself has been guilty of the
same wrong towards her. Has he not been engaged to a girl in
Rome and has he not proposed to Ersilia while at Smyrna?
Would he not have married the other girl had the wedding
not been postponed by the news of Ersilia's attempted suicide? However, Franco is right on one ground—in being
resentful at Ersilia's lie that she tried to kill herself for love
of him. She has no right to say that after her relations with
the consul. Even Ludovico Nota is puzzled by this strange lie:
"To be frank I fail to understand why she lied when she was
at death's door. Certain lies can be useful in life, but not
in death."

No one sees her real reason for the lie. Desolate and alone,
she takes poison again, and announces that she has lied not in
order to live but in order to die. She finds in her approaching
death calm and sweetness. She smiles and says, "If I had not
done this, no one would have believed me when I said that I
did not lie to live but to die." As she speaks "she makes a
gesture of disconsolate pity, hardly opening her hands, a
gesture that says without words the reason why martyred
humanity feels the need of lying." They have all lied, Franco,
Grotti, Ersilia. "It is," as Ersilia explains, "because we all
wish to appear at our best.—The more one is . . . the more
one is . . . [*she means "revolting" but she feels at the same
time loathing and so much pity that she is hardly able to say
it.*] the more beautiful we wish to appear. [*She smiles.*]
Well, yes, to cover ourselves with a decent dress. . . . I tried
to make a decent little garment for myself, at least, for my

death. That's why I lied. I swear it to you. I had never been able to have one in my life without having it torn by the many dogs that have always attacked me in every street; without having it soiled by the basest and vilest miseries. So I attempted to make myself one—a beautiful one—to die in—that of a betrothed, in order to die in it with a little sympathy and pity from everyone. Well, I have not been able to have even this! It has been torn from me, cast into the gutter and spurned. . . . Now go. Let me die in silence: stark naked. Go. Go and tell, you to your wife, you to your *fiancée*, that this poor girl has died naked." Pirandello has clothed her with his sympathy and with the beauty of his art. Now, Consul Grotti will return to his career; Franco will marry his *fiancée*; Ersilia lies dead. At least her desire is fulfilled. She is in our hearts clothed with the sympathy and pity that her creator has won for her.

The plot is very short and uneventful. The interest centers above all in the halo of human pathos that surrounds the gentle figure of Ersilia Drei and in the keen analysis that allows Pirandello to disclose the hidden motives, shades of unthwarted intentions, and deeds of the various characters. This appears in a vivid light in the analysis of the relation between Ersilia and Consul Grotti. Probing, but probing with a compassionate heart and a gentle hand into the diseased wound, Pirandello discovers that Grotti's paternal feelings were not less real and true than his infatuation and profligacy. Grotti says to Ersilia, "If you had believed in my disinterestedness in you, in my goodness which was indeed real, the beast would not have awakened in me, suddenly with all its desperate hunger." But all of Pirandello's sympathy goes out to Ersilia Drei. He is aware that her pitiful life, seen from the point of view of Grotti, of Franco, of the family of his *fiancée*, is horrible. It precipitated "the scandal, it snatched from people a pity that was undeserved, a universal commiseration," yet he insists that we must look at it from the point of view of poor Ersilia Drei who lied because she aspired to a life of decency. The contention of Consul Grotti that the Smyrna episode was a meaningless interlude in his life is even truer in the case of Ersilia. As she and her former lover stand face to face, passion is rekindled in the veins of the man, but Ersilia disdainfully rejects him because, to her, the dead child stands between them.

Pessimism forms a gloomy background to this play. Since the characters are morally hideous, they are compelled to clothe themselves with dignity while inwardly they are conscious of their misery. It is not a case of hyprocrisy. Nothing would offend poor Ersilia Drei more than this word. She was lying to adorn herself for death just as people are washed and dressed before burial. She did not lie to and for others. She lied to and for herself. She was conscious of her lie, but thought that if she paid for it with the modest token of her life, she would make enough amends. Indeed, the main *motif* that runs through the play with consoling effect is the power of a lie even though thwarted. What would life be without the ornaments and trappings of imagination? Why do we try to keep the natural color of our hair and the freshness of our complexion, fighting against the destructive power of time and of death? Are these not deceptions? Is not the whole of civilization a compassionate lie, when one realizes that at the end there stands the gigantic and gaunt specter of Death?

Pirandello feels unspeakably sorry for mankind, sorry for himself, sorry for the poor characters that have been brought before the public and have been made to reveal a truth that burns and destroys. He seems to say with sadness: What we have portrayed is life, and the only thing for these characters to do was to cover the shame into which they had fallen when instinct ruled them in the oriental, intoxicating beauty of Smyrna. Woe unto us if we did not call to our aid pitiful deception! When the shame of these characters is uncovered in broad and glaring light, despair and death follow. Had Ersilia died, enveloped in the romantic halo of a suicide for love, she would have added a sentimental, beautiful page to the many that have been recorded, even if only in the ephemeral life of a newspaper. But men insisted on discovering the truth, and tragedy made its entrance.

When we look in retrospect at the events of the drama,

they seem to be covered with a minute web in which the ironical is faintly visible in a predominating, pathetic tone. Irony takes here the form of the query: Who can determine the precise boundaries between goodness and hypocrisy, between heroism and necessity? They seem to merge into each other when one considers that Franco, Onoria, and even Ludovico Nota pass so readily from exaltation to condemnation of Ersilia. Pirandello pleads for human compassion. Is it necessary, after all, to imitate these characters in their sudden changes of attitude? Is it not better to refrain from passing judgment on poor dead Ersilia, and to let her sleep in peace, enshrouded in the veils of human sympathy that Pirandello has awakened in our hearts?

XV

Madness as the Only Refuge

HENRY THE FOURTH

(*Enrico Quarto*)

Henry the Fourth is pure tragedy and one of the greatest plays that Pirandello has written. Under the grandeur of history he has disguised an intensely touching human drama. When the Emperor Henry IV disappears and the man looms in all the agony that tortures him, his humanity is as complex and deep as the figure of the emperor was stately.

We find ourselves in the majestic throne room of Henry IV. The valets and private counselors of the German emperor are around the throne waiting for the monarch to enter. Historical names echo: Goslar, Worms, Saxony, Lombardy, the Rhine. A naïve reader or spectator might at first believe that this is an historical play. Pirandello, however, in the realistic trend of his art, has always focused his attention on life close at hand, on man as he lives on this planet of ours with his complications and tragedies. At the very outset, therefore, the author takes care to call us back from the lofty and stately region where our romantic minds may have wandered. We hear words that destroy the spell of our historical dream:

—"Give me a match."—

—"Well, you can't smoke a pipe in here."—

Men dressed in the costumes of the eleventh century are poking fun at a new courtier who, dressed as a man of the time of Henry IV of France, has come there, having confused the two Henrys. The confusion is truly a calamity because Bertoldo, the new courtier, has perused an entire library in order to prepare himself for the part of being a member of Henry IV's entourage. The great emperor asks questions of these noblemen of his court, and woe unto them if they do not give him the logical and proper answers! The intrigues of the time, wars, men, dynasties, prelates, popes, kings, rebellious princes, all live again as the life of Henry IV and his times is daily reënacted. But this is only the form of the life that surged in and around the emperor. The content is absent. There are, to be sure, the clothes, the throne, and the valets with halberds, but these men are playing their parts because they are paid to do so by a wealthy relative of the present Henry IV. For these men the tragedy that they represent is pure though lucrative comedy. They stand for the common lot of man with nerves well protected against being unduly sensitive, ready to react with broad laughter to any situation that may stir, and, therefore, disturb their contented apathy.

The only one for whom the dualism between form and content is destroyed by a tragic misfortune is Henry IV. One day, twenty years previously, during a masquerade in which he was disguised as the German emperor, he fell from his horse, struck the back of his head on the pavement, lost consciousness, and, upon coming to, he believed that he was Henry IV. His wealthy sister had him placed in a magnificent old castle where everything was arranged so as to make his pitiful illusion possible. He lives exactly as Henry IV did. He receives his ambassadors and the ambassadors of foreign countries; he rants against Peter Damian whom he blames for the tense situation existing between him and Pope Gregory the Great; he asks Countess Matilda to intercede for him. Very discreetly Pirandello confides to us that the extraordinary situation would be easier to understand if we knew certain details about the man. For months previous to the pageant Henry IV had prepared himself to play the rôle of the German emperor by reading the history of the time and by becoming saturated with its spirit, as do imaginative people who readily identify themselves with the man that they study. He had always been a great, genuine actor, and he used to transform the life and feelings of the characters that he portrayed into his own life and feelings. It had been easier for such a man to feel that he was Henry IV than it would have been for a matter-of-fact individual. To help make the

151

illusion perfect there is an entire wardrobe full of the costumes of that period, perfectly executed by competent theatrical supply houses. It is an expensive scheme, but there is an enormous patrimony, that of Marquis Nolli, his sister's son, at the disposal of the mad emperor. Valets and courtiers are thoroughly instructed in their rôles. They know that the Emperor's wife is Bertha of Sousa, a sister of Amedeo II of Savoy, and that the emperor wishes to repudiate her. They are versed even in the details of the life of the emperor and of the historical personages that mingled with him.

The only jarring notes in the midst of so much venerable antiquity are two modern oil paintings, one representing him as Henry IV, and the other the Countess Matilda. To Henry IV they are images reflected by a clear mirror from an indefinitely vague past where his life, after the fall, ceased to possess the flow of living things and became frozen in the idea that he was Henry IV. His likeness represents him as he was twenty years before. A servant, Giovanni, in a cutaway coat, enters and breaks even more the illusion that we are back in the eleventh century. The courtiers jokingly tease, "Man of the twentieth century, away! You demon, evoked by the magician of Rome!" Giovanni shouts to them to put an end to their nonsense since he has come to tell them that Marquis Nolli has arrived with a group of ladies and gentlemen. They come from the world of life where people move, love and hate, grow old and die, while others are born. They do not know what it is to be immobilized as is Henry IV, for whom time ceased to flow twenty years ago and who now believes himself to be still a youth of twenty-six. A sad plight this is, to be sure, but one that promises eternal youth, and, if the illusion be complete, blinds one to the flesh that withers, the hair that grows gray, the strength which ebbs away, in a word, to the inescapable and fatal disintegration of life which goes on for all and for everything. These visitors are old friends of Henry IV: Donna Matilda, her daughter Frida and her *fiancé*, together with a physician and a middle-aged gentleman, Belcredi.

Their conversation better informs us about the masquerade

and the queer individuals who took part in it. We are taken back to the time when youth and gallantry blossomed around the beauty and charm of Donna Matilda. She had two ardent suitors, the present Henry IV and Belcredi, who now enjoys her favors. Belcredi is a scoffing, cynical cerebralist, "slender, prematurely gray, a little younger than she; he has a curious head similar to that of a bird. He would be most vivacious if his agility (that makes of him a formidable swordsman) were not as if sheathed in a sluggish, oriental laziness that reveals itself in his strange voice, a little nasal and with a drawl." It is not correct to state that Belcredi and Matilda are lovers. There is hatred intermingled in their relation. Belcredi is a past master in antagonizing everyone with his insinuating remarks that reveal his perversity and the acuteness of his intellect. Donna Matilda is still beautiful, although she has to wage a gallant fight against ravaging time. Her mouth, "most perfect with a hint of sorrow," reveals in her a tragic person who has never found herself since that masquerade twenty years ago cut out of her life the man who is now fixed in the illusion of being Henry IV. He was a little odd, Donna Matilda confesses, but because he was full of life, temperamental. She had made the mistake of treating him as she treated all her admirers: "Among the many misfortunes that befall us women there is that of seeing before us, from time to time, two eyes that look at us with a restrained, intense promise of a lasting affection. [*She bursts out laughing, but her laughter is strident.*] Nothing is funnier than that! If men were to see themselves with that lasting promise in their eyes!" However, she did not laugh at her genial and temperamental admirer as she laughed at others, as she laughs at Belcredi. "When I laughed at him it was also for fear. Perhaps his was a promise in which one could believe. But it would have been most dangerous." He had impersonated Henry IV because she was disguised as Countess Matilda. Happiness had stood before her, but she had not seized it and made it hers. She had married another man, had had a daughter, Frida, the living image of her. Her husband had died. Belcredi had taken her body while her soul hated him.

153

Donna Matilda has come to the castle for the first time. Here she is now in this hall, a place of grandeur and of mockery and, therefore, of tragedy, where the man who had possessed the key to her rebellious soul has lived twenty years a living death, softened by illusion. She, the doctor, and Belcredi enter, disguised as personages of the eleventh century—Donna Matilda as Adelaide, Bertha's mother, the doctor as Hugo, Bishop of Cluny, and Belcredi, since he insisted on coming, as a monk of Cluny. He looks like "an ostrich dressed as a monk," according to Donna Matilda. When Henry IV enters, a broken man, a wreck of magnificent manhood, we are seized with the feeling of the tragedy of his life and perhaps of all life. He, as is to be expected, is typically Pirandellian in that his temperament bears all the marks of that mental state that the author calls "a sincere exaltation." Even Belcredi, his rival, is compelled to admit it: "Not that he simulated his exaltation. On the contrary, he became sincerely exalted, but immediately he saw himself, and that ended it." He saw himself and at once the warmth of sentiment vanished to be replaced by the cold process of reason that led him to exasperation and despair. Then he tried to distract his mind by doing strange things. He organized pageants, dances, and charity balls. He now confides to his visitors: "Life flows away from us and the man of yesterday stands before us men of today immobilized in such a hideous form that we cannot bear to look at it." He asks Donna Matilda: "Has that ever occurred to you, Madame? Do you really remember being always the same? Do you recollect that day? How could you have perpetrated that deed?" [*He stares so fixedly into her eyes that she almost faints.*] In Belcredi, he sees with hatred Peter Damian, his enemy. The courtiers try in vain to convince him that he is only a monk of Cluny.

Is it possible for a true madman to feel intuitively the presence of a mortal enemy and be sensitive to the atmosphere created by people who have played such a great part in his life when they come before him disguised as historical personages? Can a madman speak as poignantly of life, of its swift passing, and of its destructive quality as Henry IV does, addressing himself to Donna Matilda? Why does he speak so much of the need of a mask and implore that he be allowed "to live in its entirety this life from which he has been excluded"? Is he conscious of playing a game of tragic duplicity? The doctor, in his dogmatic, scientific certitude, believes that Henry IV is a genuine madman, while Donna Matilda, with feminine intuition, feels that he has recognized her and that he is pretending. She tells the doctor: "His words have appeared to be full of a sad longing for my youth and for his own, on account of this horrible thing that has happened to him and that fixed him there in that mask which he cannot remove from his face and of which he wishes to be freed."

As soon as the visitors leave, the astonished courtiers and valets hear words that show that Henry IV is conscious of his madness, and, therefore, in at least the current understanding of the word, he is no longer mad. Henry IV rebels when Landolfo, one of the courtiers, says: "I wish I had known that it was not true." Henry IV asks in a voice that betrays his inner anguish: "Does it seem to you that it is not true?" He tells them that his fiction is true because he lives it as true, and concludes: "Only so, truth is no longer a jest."

The doctor, persuaded of the normal madness of Henry IV, has a plan: To suddenly confront him with Frida dressed as Countess Matilda was on the fatal day. Frida is placed in the niche whence the portrait of Donna Matilda has been removed. Donna Matilda as she is today is to stand before Henry IV at the same time. The doctor thinks that the shock determined by the clash of two different stages of life will bring to Henry IV the realization that twenty years have elapsed, and will break off the threads that bind him to the fictitious image of himself. He will be cured; he will be a normal individual again. When Henry IV suddenly sees Frida, the past surges back to him, overpowering him. He stands there staring at Frida, the symbol of his destroyed youth. Emotion and terror make his whole body quiver. Belcredi, to whom the courtiers have revealed Henry IV's

confession, ironically and cuttingly mocks the whole performance. Vehemently Henry IV remonstrates and relates the story
of the tragic years that he has lived entombed in that castle.
For twelve years he had lived in a state of true madness which
had come upon him when he fell from his horse that Belcredi,
in his jealousy, had made rear by pricking him.

What was he to do when he knew that his madness had
left him and he was, once more, sane? Should he have told
himself: "Away with these trappings. Away with this empty
fiction. Let us go out. Where? To do what? To be pointed out
stealthily by everyone as Henry IV, no longer in the present
attire and setting, but arm in arm with you, [Belcredi] among
the dear friends of life? I should have arrived with the hunger
of a wolf to a banquet already over. I preferred to stay mad,
to live my madness with the most lucid consciousness and thus
avenge myself of the brutality of a stone that struck my
head. . . . I filled this solitude, squalid and empty as it
appeared to me when I opened my eyes, with the color and
splendor of that distant day of carnival."

As he goes over his solitary and lonely life, the only fact
of the past full of significance for him is his love for Donna
Matilda. There she stands now in Frida as true and real as
she was in that far-off day of dream and gloom, of beauty and
desolation—the day of the masquerade. He is swept away by
the poignant force of his vivid recollection. He rushes towards
Frida and tells her: "You have been frightened, my child,
by the joke that they have persuaded you to play on me—
without understanding that for me it could not be the jest
they intended, but this awesome wonder: dream that becomes
alive in you more than ever. There [in the picture] you were
an image. They have made of you a living person. You are
mine, mine, mine by right." [*He embraces her, laughing like
a madman, while all shout with terror.*] Belcredi dashes forward to take Frida away from him. Henry IV draws his sword
and wounds him mortally. Henry IV, "with his eyes wide
open, frightened by the life of his own fiction that suddenly
has forced him to commit a crime," surrounded by his
courtiers, cries out, clinging to his madness: "Now, indeed,

there is no other remedy. [*He calls them around him as if to protect himself.*] Here, all together—all together, and forever." Madness is his only refuge.

Pirandello has projected in Henry IV the desperate passiveness to which he resigned himself when haunted by the inescapable but crushing event of his poor wife's madness. In the words of Henry IV, there echoes Pirandello's feeling of powerlessness in his despair. "I believe that phantasms are nothing but a little unbalanced condition of our mind: images that we fail to hold within the boundaries of the kingdom of sleep. They appear even in the daytime; and they terrify. I am greatly frightened when at night time I see them before me—disorderly images that, having dismounted from their horses, laugh. I am sometimes afraid, even of my blood that throbs in my veins like the thud of steps resounding in distant rooms in the silence of the night."

The drama is a subtle study of the interplay of the conscious and the subconscious, the rational and the irrational, as they may be observed in human actions. To what extent are our acts conscious? If we, without being seen, should look at the valets as they stand around the throne of Henry IV, we should believe, judging by their actions and words, that they were true and real. What difference is there between seeing them and seeing ordinary persons moving in the realm of actual life? As with grave mien they discuss matters of state with the emperor, we have no proof that they are acting. Conversely, we cannot ascertain that they are not acting when they speak and act in their capacity of men of today. We can be led in a most convincing manner to these paradoxical extremes by a process of logical and complete subjectiveness. Pirandello goes more deeply into the question of the reality of human personality. For twenty years, these valets have lived as men of the eleventh century. It is highly improbable that they have not merged to some extent with that superimposed rôle, even so far as to have their identity obliterated for hours at a time at least.

This play makes us realize more than any other how unjust is the accusation of abstract and cerebral so often applied to

157

Pirandello. One feels constantly the author's reaction against those who lack spontaneity in life. He focuses his attention both on the worldly people of whom Henry IV, Donna Matilda, and Belcredi are the exponents and on the scientists, represented by the doctor. Pirandello finds himself at odds with both of them. The exaltation with which Henry IV lived before the tragedy speaks of a lack of real emotion and simplicity which led him to complicate life and to rationalize it. The doctor's stand is pure abstraction, and Pirandello ridicules him. The man of science is sure that the madman will react just as he expects and prescribes. It seems very peculiar to the author that the doctor, in his scientific dogmatism, has the courage to classify as demented one from whom he expects such a logical and certain reaction. Reasoning for Pirandello is a useless encumbrance that bespeaks man's inability to seize life in its essential points. The fantastic ravings of Henry IV before the accident were more cerebral and useless than his illusion centering around the belief that he was an historical character who lived eight hundred and eighty years before.

The power of the living reality is one of the strongest *motifs* in the play. What compelled Henry IV to leave the artificial groove into which he had gathered whatever débris of his life was left to him, was the call of the living life that reached him through the youth and charm of Frida. There was a violent clash between the desolate coldness of his solitude and the warm breath of the world that he had forsaken. That clash made it impossible for him to cling to his illusion and, therefore, it revealed the tragedy of his lucid madness. But it also made him feel that he was unfit to reënter the swift current of life that goes on and on, leaving behind all those who cannot keep pace with it. Tragedy stalks in, superinduced by this harrowing contrast. Critics are apt to put abstraction in Pirandello where it does not exist. If, upon seeing Donna Matilda as she is in the picture and as she is today, we should state that Pirandello conceives reality as existing on two planes, we might succeed in displaying brilliancy, but we should fail to feel what the author meant to be seen. The predominating element is the author's feeling of the swift passing of time with its transforming and ravaging power. The doctor thought and spoke of the two planes, but he is the butt of Pirandello's ridicule, and critics who follow him will share the same fate.

All the characters in the play are molded with that vividness and clear-cut contour that Pirandello lends to the creatures of his imagination. Henry IV, however, towers above them all. His madness is a case of lucid madness, a madness that is kinder than sanity; a madness to which one goes for shelter when life becomes crushing and unbearable. Were we to view Henry IV as an ordinary man, feigning madness, he would arouse indignation in us for his prolonged pretending. If we accept his conscious madness, we stand before him appalled by the greatness of the sorrowful and tragic existence of one who has willfully cut himself off from life because he knew that life held no promise for him. We see him as a tragic figure, enmeshed in the contradictions of life, immobilized in the merciless fate of his madness, but surrounded by the warm sympathy and pity of the author. He stands unforgettable before us as one for whom a conscious, planned madness is more tragic, harrowing, and devastating than one of which an ordinary individual is unaware. The madman as illuminated by the poet has eclipsed the one diagnosed by the physician.

XVI

Dualism of Personality

AS YOU DESIRE ME

(*Come tu mi vuoi*)

We have seen it repeatedly stated that Pirandello does not express the dualism of personality in the scientific and pathological sense. He deals with the tragic need of having to force upon ourselves a personality that we know with the utmost clearness is not ours. In the earlier plays this process was conceived with more objectivity and less sympathy. The author could laugh as he related the adventures of his characters, even if laughter was painful to him. As his feeling of sympathy has increased, the element of laughter has gradually diminished until, in the latest plays, it has disappeared altogether. The absence of laughter has elevated the tone of his drama, lending to it the grandeur of tragedy in the expression of all the pity that the author feels for life and man. This is especially true of *As You Desire Me*. In it the idealistic elements, which existed in the form of broken threads at times hardly visible in the earlier plays, appear now in a clearer form.

As You Desire Me is a play of absolute, exasperated, irrational idealism, indicting modern life with its ambiguity, its lust, its commercialized sensuality, and placing the sense of true reality in the beauty of the soul. In the avowed intention of the author, it is the story of the soul that has tried to live on this earth and could not. The soul that has been embodied in Cia, the beautiful wife of Bruno Pieri, one of those rare women whom Pirandello has placed high above the average— a luminous expression and a glimpse of an unattainable dream. Sharing the nature of a dream, she has illuminated the life of people around her and then has swiftly disappeared. She lives only in the memory of those who have known and loved her, and in a portrait by Boffi, a friend

160

who caught and immortalized her in the cold but merciful mold of his art. In the portrait she appears as the bride of Bruno Pieri in the days that were happy for them, before the last war submerged the world in blood and grief.

Ten years have elapsed. Between the dreary present and the beautiful past there is the invasion of Northern Italy during the War when the brutal invaders overran the Villa Pieri, violated Cia, and carried her away with them. Everyone has believed her dead: her husband, their friend Boffi the painter, Uncle Salesio, and Aunt Lena who, following the untimely death of Cia's mother, had brought her up as her own daughter. After years of fruitless search they have all resigned themselves to the belief that Cia is dead. Uncle Salesio and Aunt Lena have deeded their property from Cia to her sister, which act displeased Bruno very much.

This is the background, tragic, but truthful, when we think of what happened during the last war in the invaded regions. After ten years, life has resumed its normal rhythm in the villa. Time has added its unkind touches to all its dwellers, but Cia's villa, restored, is again beautiful with the house nestled in a restful, green, serene landscape. Man has temporarily won against the destruction and the victorious greed and lust of other men. Uncle Salesio is again busy attending to his flowers, and he has filled a large basket to arrange in exquisite vases in the house. He is, we are told, "a little thin old man, who would still be spry if his shoulders and the back of his head were not glued together." Aunt Lena, supervising what he does, and finding fault with it as of old, is a "stout and solid lady in her sixties, with a large masculine head all covered with strange, gray curls." She is direct, with an abrupt way of speaking, just as Uncle Salesio is timid, meticulous in what he does and says. These characteristics of the solid tangible reality serve the purpose of keeping the play on the plane of everyday reality. If the idealism of Pirandello is similar in its origin to that of the past, it is truly modern in that it places, side by side, both the negative aspects of life whence it originates and the luminous goal to which it aspires.

Cia, after ten years, has been found. Boffi, the artist, has discovered her in Berlin. He has never forgotten her. He was in Berlin when he saw a cabaret dancer who resembled Cia. He wired her husband and followed her home several nights, calling her by name while she turned and laughed at this new admirer with a strange, Mephistophelean look on his face, with a twitch that made him raise his head "as if not to drown." He feels disgust for the filth of life. The dancer, whose name is Elma, is in her thirties, most beautiful. There is a sort of scowl on her face as if to impose her will, in order not to yield and to let herself go to the very depth of abandonment, "where her soul, devastated by the storms of life, would almost be dissolved." Under a very elegant mantilla she wears one of the splendid and strange costumes of the character dances that she invents. She is the mistress of Carl Salter, a sensual and revolting German writer.

He and his daughter, Mop, are waiting for her to return. As is usual in Pirandello's love entanglements, only hatred feeds the passion of Salter and Elma. She is independent, reckless, impudent to him. She flaunts her scorn at him, discloses his weaknesses, the misery of his literary fame. That very evening Elma arrives in the company of four youths drunk with liquor and lust. They appear to Pirandello thus: "In the subdued light and confusion, those youths, one fat and pink, another bald, another with bleached hair, effeminate to an unbelievable degree, seem agitated marionettes with wanton, exaggerated, meaningless gestures." Boffi has defended her against them until they reached the apartment.

The richly furnished apartment and its occupants are the extreme embodiment of Pirandello's sense of revolt against the sensuality and inanity of modern life. Mop, in silk pajamas, crouched in a large armchair, is silently crying. Her father is angrily commenting on Elma's companions. There is rivalry between father and daughter, for both love Elma. Here is Salter's daughter as seen by Pirandello: "Her face is marked by something ambiguous which moves one to nausea, and at the same time with something tragic which perturbs one deeply." Here is Salter: "His face is puffed, pale, with clear eyes, almost white in the circle of dark pouches around them, clean-shaven, his thick lips standing out in sensuous prominence." He has a revolver in his pocket, determined to put an end to a life that is unbearable to all.

Elma is a little drunk, too, but one feels in her a superior person, a person who is not steeped in the lust that surrounds her; indeed, one who shrinks from a lust that exudes shame and awakens revolt in her. Her soul is not dead, since she is conscious of her own shame and she lives in torment. She affirms her right "to lie with the life that I live." She shouts: "There are no longer secrets today, nor modesty." Human beings are like beasts "with the difference that beasts at least are natural, endowed with the wisdom of instinct, while in man, to be natural is a sad, destructive, and also filthy folly. Woe unto us if reason did not serve as a strait-jacket." Pirandello has placed in Elma his tragic idealism. She turns to Boffi and says: "My name is Elma, did you hear, an Arabian name which means water." [*In so saying, she moves all her fingers, spreading her hands to signify the forced lack of consistency of her life.*] Life has passed through her fingers like water, a symbol of her bitter tears. That is the deep side of Elma, but she has been compelled to repress that side by being gay: "They made me drink so much wine! Oh! And five cocktails, champagne." She has thrown herself into the whirlwind of disgusting sensuality which for Pirandello forms the most salient characteristic of modern civilization. Elma bears the name of the "Unknown" in the play. There is a symbolic meaning in that name. She had been made unknown even to herself by the moral misery of her life.

The higher Pirandello's idealism rises, the greater relief lust takes in his play. This explains why he has embodied his idealism in a lost woman. Some might express astonishment at this combination and attribute it to Pirandello's humor. This is not humor. It is knowledge of the human heart. In order to see the serene countenance of good it is often necessary to know the ugliness of evil.

Boffi reiterates to Elma that she is Cia, Donna Lucia. She laughs. Boffi believes that she is feigning. What proof can he

163

have that she is not? He insists frantically. She denies, then affirms, to tantalize Salter, who shoots himself in her presence. She agrees to leave with Boffi on the strange adventure. She has but one alternative: either be the soul of Cia and go to Bruno, or be Elma, the Unknown, and stay with Salter. She chooses to be Cia. To a person like Elma, who is in the depths of despair, Boffi's offer is the only way of escape. She does it, as she says, "to flee from myself; not to have any remembrance of anything, of anything—to empty myself of all my life—here, look: just body—to be only this body. You say that it is hers? that it resembles hers? I don't feel myself any longer. . . . My heart beats and I don't know it, I breathe and I don't know it, I don't know any longer whether I am alive. I am only a body, a body in the expectation that someone may take it. There—if he can take me—if he can give a soul to this body that is Cia's body—let him take it and put his memories into it, his own; a beautiful life, a new life. I am desperate. . . ." She will live again now, reincarnating the soul of Cia. She sees in that possibility her own freedom, freedom of herself, freedom from Salter and Mop, freedom from the night life of Berlin. She will reach the unity of her life through her soul—through the soul of Cia.

Pirandello takes every care to show the possibility of this transformation. Our knowledge of the identity of a person rests on a very weak basis. I say that I am "X" and you believe me. If tomorrow a person comes and says that I am "Z" what logical grounds have you for refuting it? It is useless to say: After all, we know ourselves; we know who we are. Pirandello's aim here is to arouse our sympathy and understanding for cases in which the clearness of the identity is not possible, and in that lies the great pathos which rings through the play. We are before a person who is compelled to disavow herself in order to bear the weight of life. The greatest punishment for Dante's sinners was to have their human features obliterated or distorted. Their tragedy was forced on them. Pirandello makes his characters obliterate their own personality, leading them to a deeper and more pitiful tragedy. The author is entirely conscious of the new fate that he has decreed for his characters. He does not laugh any longer. He is tragic now.

So Elma, the Unknown, becomes Cia. She goes to the villa, as beautiful as the Cia of ten years ago, although now distracted, dismayed, and apparently unable to take complete hold of herself in her old environment. She is still the same Elma intimately, half ready to reform, half ready to reenter the inferno of life.

The difficulty on the part of her relatives to accept the physical Cia has not been great. The fertile imagination of Pirandello has succeeded in making the acceptance quite plausible by asserting that people seldom agree on the physical traits of a person. The same person will appear to one as the perfect image of the father, to another as the perfect image of the mother. Cia's eyes, for instance, are green to Aunt Lena, blue to Uncle Salesio, and gray to her husband. Why should they have difficulty in believing that she is their Cia after the changes that ten years make? The natural goodness that abides in every human being, in every woman, appears again in the Unknown, although at times the scowl of the old self suddenly reappears; then she speaks with uncontrollable vehemence, with excitement. She has found a diary written by Cia during the first year of her marriage. It is the diary of a noble person. She reads it passionately and with longing; she imbues herself with the soul of Cia, as she lives in that diary; Cia, a creature of exquisite beauty, purity, and goodness. The beauty of the Unknown acquires again the serenity that it had lost.

But the Unknown finds it infinitely difficult to have her identity, as existing in the soul of Cia, recognized. It is easier to make the body of Cia live again in her than it is her soul. From the very beginning she has had to struggle with all the human miseries that surround our bodily existence. She has had to hear stupid recriminations about the property which had been transferred to her sister on the assumption that Cia was dead, and that now must be returned to Cia. She cries out: "I did not want any of this, from the very beginning—nothing of all this." With harrowing insistence the doubt

165

comes to her whether Bruno is interested only in her or in the property that now will return to him: the villa, the fertile lands that he had reclaimed from the devastation of war, only to see them given to Cia's sister. She is perplexed by the fact that it is hard to draw a straight and narrow line between pure love and interest. She has to admit likewise that Bruno is more interested in her body than in her soul. There was a mark on Cia's body that the Unknown does not have. He is confused by that absence. The mark means more to him than the beauty of Cia's spiritual qualities. Who can draw the line between where love ends and passion begins?

The final test comes when Salter, who has not died of the self-inflicted wound, brings from a Vienna sanitarium to the villa the actual Cia, a wreck of humanity, both pitiful and revolting to look at. She is the Demented One in the play. The Unknown surprises Aunt Lena in an attempt to ascertain whether or not the Demented One is Cia. Aunt Lena "with a sudden resolution, conquering her own distaste, while all present are shuddering with horror, takes the face of the Demented One in her own hands and calls: 'Cia, Cia.' The Demented One remains passive with her mute, meaningless smile." The Unknown meanwhile, unnoticed, has come downstairs followed by her husband. She has the proof that they doubted. They did not have faith in her, the faith that she wanted. She is hurt. Her old self asserts itself again. She is defiant, haughty. She strikes back at those who have destroyed the possibility of her new life, who have made her realize the futility of her noble attempt. She has wanted true love and she has not found it. She says to the confused members of the family who have gathered in the house: "Many an unfortunate one, after years, has returned just like that [*she points to the Demented One*], with features obliterated, unrecognizable, without any memory, and sisters, wives, mothers, have fought to have the unfortunate one with them. Not because they have recognized him, no (cannot the son of one resemble that of another?), but because they have believed him to be their own, they have forced themselves to believe him to be their own. And there is no contrary proof that may be valid when one wishes to believe!—It isn't he? But for that mother, it is he; yes, it is he! What does it matter if it isn't he if a mother keeps him and makes him hers with all her love? Against every proof she believes him to be hers. Against any proof she believes him to be hers. Did you not believe me even without proofs?" Elma could only be the soul of Cia with Bruno, or her own body, her tortured and profaned body, with Salter. The end comes when, obeying the cruel logic of the premises, Elma returns to Berlin with Carl Salter.

No ascetic writer—not Saint Augustine in his *Confessions*, nor the author of the *Imitation of Christ*—has expressed the revolt against the flesh as violently as does Pirandello in this play. He has portrayed it in the Unknown with an exasperation that approaches frenzy. Modern civilization is reduced here to a brutal phenomenon incompatible with the need of the human soul. Pirandello's idealism is irreconcilable with the practical and material aspects of life. He is as unbending as the monks of old who believed life possible only in their little cells, or as the mystics who dreamed of a perfect life in the communion with Christ or with the Deity. Their upward flight was based on renunciation. Pirandello, like them, seems to be unwilling to recognize the necessity of the practical elements of daily life. On this ground the play embodies not only the tragedy of Elma, but it also tends to attract one into a gloomy circle where there is the feeling of the hopeless tragedy of all: the soul cannot live on this earth unless it accepts the limitations of actual life, limitations that are harrowing and dwarfing. Below the lofty level to which Elma tried to make Bruno and his family rise, there lies the stifling plane of petty considerations and concerns. Only the exasperated, irrational, idealistic mood of the author can explain such an attitude. It is irrational, to be sure, if looked at from the point of view of Bruno and the mediocre lot that compose Cia's family; but quite in accord with Pirandello's philosophy that life is only in the sentiment that permeates human acts.

Pirandello has now openly asserted his faith in sentiment

to which he has given positive connotations. He is very far from his initial position, where he identified sentiment with the cold construction of the intellect. Sentiment is no longer misguiding subjectivism. It is a luminous force that alone may redeem Elma's life. At an earlier stage of his thought Pirandello was placed between sentiment and reason, and mistrusted both. In a more serious mood, with a consciousness of life enriched by experience, he recognizes that sentiment is the only solution. If Elma's sentiment pointed to a height that defied what is grossly natural in man, it also afforded satisfactions and it held promises that were unknown to those who lived on the plane of everyday life. From this point of view Pirandello's idealism is quite rational and constructive.

The basic cause that made it impossible for Elma to transfuse herself into Cia's soul, to be Cia, was that both Bruno and his relations tried to recognize Cia by her body while she was only soul. The issue arises quite limpidly and poignantly in the play, whether the "real" part of the human personality rests on the physical characteristics of man or on the deeper qualities of his mind and soul.

There is not the slightest doubt in the Italian original as to which of the two women is Cia; that is, who is the pitiful body of Cia and who is the soul of Cia. The doubt concerning the identity, however, is ever present in the play; indeed, the whole play centers around this identity, which is kept a secret for Elma's antagonists but not for the spectators, who are given the opportunity to admire the cleverness of the playwright in mastering the situation with his subtle technique. Anyone in the play can with equal logic claim that Elma is Cia or the contrary. This actually happens with Salter and Bruno disputing with each other the material identity of the Unknown. The spectator, however, clearly sees the intentions of the author when he sees the Demented One stand near Elma, the Unknown. Cia, living only in her soul, is searching in vain for a shelter, for a new, pure body. The tragedy that has befallen Cia ten years before doomed her to an irreparable destruction. For this reason Cia is represented by the pitiful figure of the Demented One and by the

Unknown who tries in vain to make her soul live again in herself. The soul of Cia can live only in the memory of her dear ones and in the cold, distant life that Boffi's art gave to her when he saw her in all her beauty and loftiness.

The solution, leading to Elma's return to Salter, is befitting real tragedy. In the classical tragedy the solution was death. Our ancestors must have known less the torture of the soul if death, physical death, was to them the greatest calamity. Pirandello, a spokesman, in this, of the modern man who is more accustomed to death than were his ancestors, views the torment of the mind, the anguish of the heart, as being more fearful than the physical death. That is the reason why in his plays, as in many other modern plays, the climax keeps the characters in the living death of the torment of the mind. The ancients were more merciful and practical. Death ended it all. In modern tragedy there is no solution. Elma is left on the rack of having to go back to Salter after trying in vain to be as pure and lofty as Cia. There is no hope for her, and so she is reëngulfed by the nauseating and revolting life of the flesh, chained to the white-eyed man she loathes.

XVII

In the Realm of Mystery

ONE DOES NOT KNOW HOW

(*Non si sa come*)

One Does Not Know How [1] is the latest of Pirandello's plays. Its author looks upon it as one of his best dramatic works. It is derived from one of his most fundamental beliefs: his belief in the realm of mystery. Man moves in an impalpable atmosphere of dreams, whether he is conscious of it or not. Because of this he walks over the bleak planet of the earth as a bewildered stranger and a grieving vagabond. Beyond the boundaries of time and space, above the arched blue curve of the sky, there is life unformed and unfettered, life out of which a strange god has carved the earth and the universe. No laws, no limitations, no boundaries exist there. Life is a ruinous stream that roars into dazzling white stretches of infinite space. Woe to us if we have a glimpse of that primeval life! We become both terrified and deified by it. We cease to be human and our contact with the average man becomes impossible while there is born in us the irresistible urge to reënter the stream of universal life. This belief was implied in preceding plays but here it appears in a clearer form, and it affords the main *motif* of the work.

In *One Does Not Know How* the urge of the infinite and the presence of mystery are revealed under the form of the uncontrollable character of our emotions and acts. There are moments in life when something frightful and horrible happens and *one does not know how* it has happened. After the act which was brought about by the tragic absence of our will and consciousness, we are confronted by a brutal and clumsy truth and we are stranded on the desolate shore of

---

[1] This play has not yet been published in the Italian edition. The author most kindly gave me the German translation by Stefan Zweig, which I have used.

grief. Then we feel suspended halfway between our own world and that of primeval life, unfit for the former, unable to attain the latter. This is the form that the sense of personal isolation has taken in Pirandello, creating one of his most powerful and tragic characters in Count Romeo Daddi, the central figure of the play.

The drama unfolds in the beautiful villa of Giorgio Vanzi, a naval officer married to Ginevra. Intimate friends of theirs, Count Romeo Daddi and his exquisite wife Bice, are their guests. There is also another guest in the villa, Marquis Nicola Respi. The atmosphere is charged with uneasiness as if laboring under an impending storm. They all talk of the strange conduct of Romeo Daddi, who acts as if he were not master of his own acts. He stares with a tragic fixity which suddenly relaxes into a wan smile that makes one shudder. He utters strange words as he moves like a ghost in the Vanzi home. He keeps mumbling to himself: "What? Nothing. Everything is buried! Everything is sunk!" It seems that his whole inner world has been destroyed by a violent earthquake.

Romeo's unstable mental condition disturbs Bice, his wife, and Ginevra, the hostess. Bice confesses to Ginevra that at times one can see insanity in his eyes, but "he says things that frighten you because they seem to be taken out of your own soul, as if they were the thoughts that flashed through your mind a moment before." This fact makes it impossible or at least very hard to consider him insane, since logically one must infer that we are all insane if he gives expression to our own thoughts. He wonders why "so many seek in wine and drugs a refuge into an artificial paradise when actually we live so little in complete consciousness, when we are constantly snatched from ourselves through the indefinite element of our impressions, through the sun-induced drunkenness in the spring, through the awe of mysterious silence, when we get a glimpse of the sky and of the sea or of swallows darting in flight." Romeo has lost hold on himself through the realization of the uncontrollable character of his emotions, of his perceptions, and of his thoughts. Staring

171

with eyes that seem to come back from infinite distances, he says to his friends: "See, now it seems that I am looking at you, but who knows how you appear to me? I hear you, I answer you, I am with you, but deep within me I am at the same time elsewhere, in the wave-like play of impressions and perceptions that I could not represent to you without really appearing insane."

Less affected by Romeo's condition are the two men, Giorgio Vanzi and Marquis Respi. They are individuals who seek their goodly share of pleasure in life and have learned the ways of the world that teaches how to snatch forbidden fruit and to put the stone of forgetfulness over the act. The only price that life seems to exact from them is that of discretion, of stealthy steps, and then silence and oblivion.

Not so with Romeo Daddi, whom two tragic circumstances have robbed of the easy philosophy and limited sensitiveness of the average man. Once, when in his teens, by sheer accident he killed a peasant boy in a fight. As was his wont, he had gone into the fields where the free expanse of the country awoke the sense of similar endless distances within him. Suddenly he noticed that a peasant boy had caught a lizard in a sort of noose that he had made with a long stem of rye. As Romeo leaped forward shouting: "No, do not kill it!" the boy had crushed the poor creature against a stone. It was shortly after sunset. Romeo still remembers "the ghost-like shape of the moon that was beginning to be tinged with a pale gold against the gray of the sky that softened into the dying twilight." With unspeakable horror Romeo saw the eyes of the poor animal contract in pain; he saw its tender body quiver before it stiffened in the rigidity of death. He struck the stupid and brutal killer. There ensued a battle with heavy, moist clods of earth. Romeo, who was about to have the worst of the encounter, suddenly snatched a stone and struck the boy on his head. Dead! Romeo, still panting, his heart beating to the point of suffocating him, leaned against the wall and gazed with terror at the silent immobility of the fields under the moon, at the boy who lay there, his face half hidden in the earth. An increasing sensation of a formidable, eternal solitude swept over him: "It was not I. I did not mean to do that. I knew nothing about it."

From that day he had learned that there are acts which are beyond our control, acts the contour of which is blurred, fading into death and deceptions. Experiences of this sort are not easily blotted out from one's life. They do not pass like perfumed breaths of wind in a moonlit night. They are stones that weigh heavily on us, buried in the mysterious depths of our hearts; they are blows that make us open terrified eyes into the infinite. For thirty years that tragic secret had made an automaton out of him. And now, just a few days ago, Romeo had soiled his soul with another crime, the betrayal of his best friend, of Giorgio Vanzi, the man he loved like a brother. He had sinned with Ginevra, Giorgio's wife, a woman at whom he had never looked with covetous eyes. One morning Bice was about to leave the villa, and Romeo and Ginevra had gone to see her off at the end of the drive where an automobile was waiting for her. When Bice had kissed Romeo it had seemed to Ginevra that that kiss had touched her lips. After Bice drove away, Romeo and Ginevra walked towards the villa in the midst of the intoxicating perfume of flowers. They had gone into the house, they had been compelled to sit near each other. A mysterious force had thrown the woman into the arms of the man. The whole universe had been blotted out. Inhibitions, the social barriers that hold together our being, had fallen like dead dust, like nothing at all, and the two had felt the roaring torrent of life envelop them. They were snatched outside of the laws of man, outside of themselves, primeval beings again, unfettered and free.

But the awakening had come. Romeo had seen himself before a deeper and more tragic abyss: betrayal of his best friend. Ginevra had resumed control of herself more readily since, like most of Pirandello's women, she was very instinctive. She did not wish to speak of their fall. It had happened and that was all. She had very little remorse. She loved her husband too much to feel remorse. If she had yielded to Romeo, she had done so when she was too full of love for her husband. She was absent, at least her consciousness and her will were absent, when they sinned. Now she has no regrets and she wants to forget.

This reaction is quite in keeping with Pirandello's concept of womanhood. Women are more instinctive than men, in that love absorbs all of their being and they yield to it with a complete abandonment. Desire is born to women on the wings of dreams. Not so with men, in whom the more acute power of "reason" makes the experience of love more complicated and turbulent, even more theatrical.

Romeo cannot stem his remorse and his repentance. He has to talk about their sin; he must reveal it to his wife, goaded by a mysterious force before which his inhibitions are of no avail. The more he talks to Bice and to Ginevra about it, the more he feels unable to live on the same planet near care-free, happy, and instinctive beings like Respi and Giorgio. Only those who are practical can live.

Romeo feels the urge towards disintegration. He knows that he deserves a punishment, but his punishment must not be the one that the law of man metes out to offenders: prison. No. If, after the crimes that he has committed, he has felt face to face with the mystery and the infinite, his punishment should be freedom: "Away, away, where there is nothing firm, established, no houses, no relationship, no cause and effects, no contacts, no laws, no customs, nothing. Freedom as punishment! Banishment into dream, as saints go into the wilderness." He realizes with increasing and more harrowing clearness that we have lost touch with cosmic forces through our being "human," through the fact that we have become civilized and have encumbered the earth with houses and theatres, skyscrapers and churches. We have "built up ourselves" to the extent that we live as a world within a world, the "human" world separated from and hostile to the divine realms of life. This realization comes over Romeo and frightens him, especially after his experience with Ginevra. Had Ginevra and he yielded to instinct in the immense distances where life is unhampered by laws and customs, outside the artificial mold that man has imposed on it, all the complications and the tragic consequences of their sin would not have come in the wake of the lapse of their consciousness. He would not be confronted now by the brutal fact that he has betrayed his best friend. He would not hear within him the echo of a terrifying voice that calls him adulterer and traitor. But he has sinned in a man-made world where he has followed the call of the cosmic voice of instinct, and for this reason he is now lost and desolate.

A great problem looms before him, the problem of human responsibility: how and to what extent are we responsible for certain acts from which our sense of consciousness is absent? Near him lives a flower of perfect femininity, Bice, his wife. He is curious to know whether she too may be subject to these lapses of consciousness so that nature may also play on her its strange pranks. He pries into her soul, torments her until one day he wrenches from her the confession that once in a dream she had belonged to Giorgio. This seems monstrous to Romeo. Even Bice, the purest woman he had ever known, the one around whom everyone saw the halo of dream, was prey to the mysterious forces of instinct. She had sinned just as he had.

Romeo's torment is boundless. He is gradually drawn towards his fate by the irresistible force of his subconscious or unfettered self. He knows that Giorgio will kill him should he learn of his betrayal, but he has to confess just as he had to kill the peasant boy and just as he had to sin with Ginevra. He has become an automaton in the hands of Destiny. As he sees that Giorgio is about to go away with Ginevra without having become aware of what had happened, he cannot resist the impelling force that harasses him and urges him towards his doom. He unfalteringly tells. Giorgio does not understand and does not forgive. He draws his revolver and kills him.

Romeo, by telling, places himself outside the boundaries of practical life. It is logical that Giorgio, the practical man, should kill him. Romeo's last words are: "That was done in the human way," thus conveying what the author meant to emphasize: the victory of the average man over the indi-

175

vidual who is doomed to isolation and even to destruction.

Pirandello never loses his sense of balance between the divine afflatus of his cosmic aspiration and his grasp on the limited and concrete daily reality. Even in his seeming paradoxes there are fragments of truth that glitter and at times dazzle. His searching mind has discovered bitter and perplexing truths in the darkness and depth of the human soul. The author has not made of Romeo an abstract embodiment of the divine in man. Like all Pirandellian characters, Romeo possesses the tortuous element that their creator finds nestled in the dark folds of the human intellect. He can explore Bice's heart as a diver explores the mysterious depths of the sea. He even surreptitiously intimates that something deceitful and underhanded exists between Bice and Marquis Respi, who had been one of her admirers.

Although Pirandello places the theme of the uncontrollable character of our actions in the very center of the play, he is careful to contrast Romeo with the instinctive quality of Ginevra's temperament and with average men like Giorgio and Marquis Respi. Romeo had always felt the urge towards a life unfettered of all the restrictions to which men have subjected it. Often, as he walked along a country road, he would kick a stone, telling it as he did so: "Have a good time and fly wherever you desire." As a child, as he wandered in the fields, he used to envy his dog, Fox, who always knew what to do: to follow his master faithfully. Fox was pure instinct. Romeo was the prey of unknown forces that held an unbreakable sway over him and made a restless vagabond out of him. The boundless expanse of the country attracted him because his soul was thirsty for the infinite. When he had killed the young boy he had felt that he was outside the precincts of the everyday life. An unspeakable loneliness had seized him and poignantly a strange realization had come over him: "It was not I. I did not do it. It happened in a region that lay beyond my consciousness."

The solitude of Romeo is now increased a thousandfold by his sin with Ginevra and because of her attitude towards him and towards their fall. She does not understand why he torments himself so insistently and pitilessly. She frankly tells him: "All my desire was for Giorgio. I had never been like that before. All my blood was aflame in my veins." She vividly recollects that intoxicating morning as if to find an excuse for her weakness in the bewitching charm of nature and, therefore, to disclaim responsibility and to remove a personal character from her surrender. More practical than Romeo, she points out to him the way that one must follow if one wishes to continue to live: forgetfulness. The boundary line between virtue and deceit is not very clear-cut. In order to carry on one has to be like Ginevra who shouts: "I do not know you. I have loved only him, Giorgio." And she buries the past by obscuring it in her consciousness.

More striking and harrowing is the contrast between Romeo, sensitive and self-tormenting, and Count Respi, a debonair libertine who knows with scientific accuracy how far he can go with ladies even if they happen to be as lofty as Bice. Respi is an irritatingly happy average man. Romeo tells him: "I envy you, Respi. I don't praise you, but I envy you. Nothing has ever happened to you outside of your will. Because you don't look into yourself, you have perfect control over yourself. You *know* all your escapades, you fortunate man. You can be satisfied with or repentant of what you do, and for that reason you are to be envied." Romeo had never known the joy of satisfaction or of repentance, because his acts had always been beyond the range of his full consciousness. There was no merit nor demerit in all he did, and he was completely detached from his own acts.

Romeo analyzes also the average qualities of Giorgio's personality. Giorgio, too, is a "fine specimen of the man who *knows,* who is conscious of all he does, even of short-lived escapades which are no crime during such long absences." He refers to Giorgio's life on his cruises and to his love affairs in his short visits to various ports.

Romeo envies both these men because they possess full mastery of themselves, albeit, it is within the narrow boundary of their sensual life. They are creatures of the senses and they live happily in that realm, unmindful of the call of the infinite which torments Romeo. But is their life truly to be envied? Is it not dwarfed by the narrow range of their emotions, by all that cramps and limits the spirit of man that has been banished from the realm of things eternal?

The author has lent to Romeo Daddi the *cupio dissolvi*, the longing for disintegration, of the mystics. Pirandello does not like the present trend in Italian criticism represented especially by Pietro Mignosi, a professor at the University of Palermo, which tends to make a mystic, indeed a Catholic, out of him. Yet, unquestionably there is, particularly in the present play, a strong undercurrent of mystic thought, if by mysticism we mean the attempt to gaze on universal life through the trelliswork of the tangible world. In *One Does Not Know How* one is ever conscious of the author's concern over the boundless spaces that stretch "beyond the horizon," to use a phrase of Eugene O'Neill's, who resembles Pirandello in hearkening to voices that come to him from unknown distances. There is in Romeo a complete detachment from all earthly possessions, from all that man calls conquest and progress. He says: "Truth and reality abide in God alone. All that pertains to us is perishable and destined to die. Our will, our wisdom, our knowledge, all this is nothing." His vision enlarges as the end approaches. The divine overpowers the human in him, and we feel the ethereal quality of a pure spirit as he atones for his guilt.

At the same time we should not lose sight of the fact that Pirandello returns here to his meaning of reality which, to him, is based not on the crude apprehension of the outside world but must be vivified by our sentiment, and made alive by our faith and passion. It is not enough to know that the moon is in the sky and the forest is on earth. As such the moon and the forest are mere abstract concepts. We must let our "sentiment" envelop them, since only by our so doing "they acquire a full reality." This full reality is our possession when we are carried away, down the swift current of the sea of being, unaware of the ties that hamper us, one with the infinite.

Pirandello has humanized the drama of Romeo by allowing the complicating force of "reason" to have a certain hold on him. Romeo wavers at first and does not openly tell Giorgio of his sin. With the cunning of despair he tries to lead Giorgio into the intricate net of his reasoning: "Imagine that my wife had told me that she had dreamt of you and had been untrue to me in her dream." He tries to prepare him for the stark truth by asking him what he would do if his wife should tell him that she had sinned with another man in a dream. Giorgio, the average man whose practical sense always works towards making his life comfortable, states that a woman should not tell her husband of such a dream. In vain Ginevra deftly seeks to help and suggests that guilt is absent from what is done in a dream. (Romeo's wrong and hers had been a dream too.) Giorgio, with the inexorable logic of the average man, does not understand and, upon learning the truth, he kills.

The humanity of Romeo is also enhanced by the fact that we see him trying in vain to cling to the pleasurable aspects of life. He longingly says: "If we could only cling to the knowable things!" His failure makes us realize how great a misfortune and tragedy Pirandello has embodied in his character. Poor Romeo is carried to his doom by the same blind forces that the Greek dramatists felt in the obscure fate of man. There is nothing that he can do against his destiny. He must go on and on carrying the burning load of his guilt till death opens for him the portals of the infinite.

Pirandello has never revealed the tragedy of being human more powerfully than in this play. To be human is to know how to cope with the tricks of nature, of man, and of the daily existence. If successful, we are thus led to the dwarfing and satisfied happiness of the beast, leaving untouched the world of mystery that slumbers in the depth of our being. So we must choose: Either we must be satisfied brutes or unhappy spirits thirsty and hungry for a precious liquid and food that most human beings neglect. To the pure spirit in us, the whole of life, even nature is an artificial construction.

This play has a marked tendency towards pure lyricism in

179

that action is reduced to a minimum and the whole drama centers about the harrowing inner experience and mental anguish of Romeo Daddi who towers above the other four characters that the author has placed near him. Two short stories, *Cinci* ("Cinci") [2] and *Nel Gorgo* ("In the Whirlwind") [3] are the material source of the play. In the play, Pirandello has attributed to Romeo the experiences of two different characters that form the warp of the two stories.

If we look in retrospect at the plays contained in this section and which correspond to Pirandello's intuition of the "grotesque," we see that the drama is first created by the artificiality of the characters. As a result, the events that unfold before us are comedy, that is they are permeated by laughter, the laughter of Pirandello who notices and unmasks the complex artificiality of the characters. As time has enriched and deepened his thoughtful observation of life, a sense of tragedy viewed as one with life and permeating the very texture of human life has appeared in his drama. The complications and the isolation of man are not superimposed by lack of sincerity. They are there because they are part of life. There is no escape. It is the common fate of us all. If we were to ask Pirandello to what or to whom the process of "building up oneself" is applied in this play, he would answer that the average man and the average life have undergone this process. Laws, customs, inhibitions, nature, cities, churches, and statues are all prisons in which universal life is caught and suffers. The hero here is Romeo because he has freed himself of the artificial barriers of earthly life. He has joined the mystics of all religions and of all times who sought and attained their communion with the deity and were lost in it. Perhaps he has laid the foundation of the religion of a distant tomorrow.

In this fashion Pirandello has left the lowlands of mockery and has risen to the sublime and lonely heights of pure tragedy.

[2] *Novelle per un anno*, XIV, 199–212.
[3] *Ibid.*, VIII, 193–207.

Part Three

SOCIAL PLAYS

XVIII

Introduction

The social theme was implied in Pirandello's attitude of observer and critic of human acts. In analyzing man's actions he was logically and necessarily led to the consideration of the social environment.

Pirandello's social drama has distinct antisocial leanings. Influenced by his unhappy experience of life, he always viewed modern civilization in the light of corruption and profligacy. His exasperated idealism created an abyss between actuality and dream that never gave him the hope of a better condition. Even in the early play, *Limes of Sicily*, we have seen that the drama of Micuccio Bonavino, the symbol of good and old Sicily, rises from the contrast between a mythical perfection as embodied in country life in Sicily, and the corruption of modern civilization. The author accuses progress of having shattered the dream of the poor young peasant who looms gigantic in all his simplicity against the laughing and coarse, though elegantly dressed, friends of Teresina.

Pirandello's irreconcilable attitude towards modern civilization, and his antisocial outbursts are found as an undercurrent in many of the plays considered in other sections. His antisocial attitude forms the background of *As You Desire Me*, just as it assumes a sad note in *The New Colony*, where the author reaches the gloomy conclusion that an ideal society is possible only in the dreams of men like Plato and Tommaso Companella, who liked self-deception. In reality the restless and struggling instincts of men make a perfect civilization impossible.

Social implications are scattered in most of Pirandello's plays, although we are including in this section only the four in which the social element is in marked evidence. This social attitude takes the form of a pondering, at times humorous and at times idealistic, over the problems of marriage, the fate of human society, and the meaning of immortality, which themes are developed in the plays herein contained: *The Pleasure of Honesty; Think It Over, Giacomino; The New Colony;* and *Lazarus.*

These plays show the more solid part of Pirandello's thought, although the presence of serious ideas does not bear any relation to the æsthetic value of the works. This is particularly true of *The New Colony* and *Lazarus,* where Pirandello's idealism reveals itself in an evanescent form, failing to become embodied in strong personalities. On the other hand, *The Pleasure of Honesty* and *Think It Over, Giacomino,* are very solid and significant works, and can be ranked with the best that Pirandello has produced.

A social play has necessarily a moral intimation. Pirandello is a modern moralist who approaches moral problems with a smile rather than with a solemn countenance. Anyone who sets out to write a play about matrimony dealing with the validity and social significance of marriage takes upon himself a very hard task. It is easy to degenerate into senseless and vulgar recrimination, or into idealistic and sentimental exaltations. Pirandello has had the good taste to hide his moralistic tone behind a deceptive screen of humor and laughter, with the result that we are suddenly and greatly surprised when in the end we find ourselves before the serious countenance of moral life. The idea that morality is an integral part of the very texture of life acquires a deeper meaning when it comes to us from the original and brilliant paradoxes of a humorist. Morality is rendered palatable and artistic by making it lose its solemn and forbidding aspect.

The element that stands out in Pirandello's social plays and in the social implications of his drama is the moral inferiority of man, and, by way of a logical contrast, the superiority of woman. Pirandello, like most modern playwrights, has been very chivalrous with women and he contrasts the superficiality and fickleness of man's affections to the deeper feelings of woman. This attitude is the result of Pirandello's approach to the theme of instinct. He has never succeeded in overcoming a sense of loathing and revolt for sensuality. As people tie to a dog's neck the chicken it has killed in order to cure it of the habit, so Pirandello has never been able to free himself from the thought of the lowness of sexual instinct. He is not like Dante, who read in the book of experience that there are worse sins than lust, and consequently assigned in his Inferno a worse punishment to the traitors than to the lustful ones. Pirandello is constantly harassed by the presence of instinct in his characters. He seeks a refuge in the concept of purity that he has lent to women. In his social drama he shows that the loftiness of woman could make life different for his characters, but that these are made blind by the violence of their lust to the loftier life that is projected before them. This is the social implication that is found in *Diana and Tuda*, in *She Wanted to Find Herself*, in *Grafting*, and even in the tormented *As Well as Before, Better than Before*.

In his earnest and passionate attitude towards life, Pirandello insists that formality is not enough to give a meaning and rhythm to our actions. If he often presents characters who enshroud their deeds in the pomp of conventionality and formalism, he leads them to their doom when they refuse to heed his pleading that life is not an abstract concept nor a moral appearance, and that our acts are not meaningless, mechanical motions. His strong individualism has always led him towards a deeply felt mode of feeling and living, even if to do so was painful to the point that he had to call on humor and laughter to relieve the tension.

In many of Pirandello's plays there is a strong undertone of satire before the spectacle of social life. It would be wrong to characterize such a spectacle with the epithet of "miserable" or "sad," a natural characterization that social satire is inclined to give to human actions. Pirandello is too full of human compassion to justify such adjectives in reference to human events. Man advances to the best of his ability on the path of life, and if he falls we should not excuse him, but should feel pity for him. Pirandello reveals his attitude in words that are uttered by one of his most perfect characters, Baldovino, in *The Pleasure of Honesty:* "We are not alone. There are two of us: we and the beast. The beast

185

that carries us. There is no use to whip it; you can never compel it to act according to reason. Try to persuade a donkey not to walk near a precipice. The donkey will take blows, flogging, hard pulls at the halter, but it will go there because it cannot help it. And after you have beaten it soundly, look at the grieving eyes of that poor beast—tell me, don't you pity it? I say pity it—and not excuse it. Intelligence that excuses the beast descends to the lowness of the beast. But to pity it is a different matter. Don't you think so?" (*The Pleasure of Honesty*, p. 227.)

Pirandello is not the rigid moralist who formulates moral laws in his cold brain, stifling the voices and claims of his heart. Such a moralist carries a book in his hands, keeps his eyes fastened on it, and passes judgment based on the letter of the law that has no spirit for him. History has registered many unbending figures of stern reformers. One recalls in this connection Calvin and the judges of the Spanish Inquisition. Pirandello has never failed to be compassionate.

The analysis of social life that he affords in his plays is of the nature that is found in playwrights whose power of observation was greater than their gift of fancy. He is closer to Molière than to Racine, closer to Goldoni than to Metastasio or D'Annunzio. What he lacks in external fantasy is compensated for in him by a deep sense of human sympathy for the foibles of his fellow-men.

XIX

The Strange Adventures of Lady Honesty

THE PLEASURE OF HONESTY

(*Il piacere dell'onestà*)

In this play we find ourselves before a strange, quixotic treatment of the theme of honesty. Pirandello, following the spirit of his times, when morality is more practised than preached, does not give us a treatise nor an oration about it. Rather he approaches the problem with his usual quizzical smile. He seems to be at first uncertain whether honesty is an impelling force of life or just an empty word. As events develop, he and his readers are led to the conclusion that something powerful abides in honesty, something that man can momentarily cast aside, but to which he must eventually turn to give consistency and support to his life.

The moral problem which constitutes the very texture of the play arises from an immoral situation. Agata Renni, a young woman who is approaching the age when the possibility of marriage becomes rather doubtful, has had a love affair with Marquis Fabio Colli, a man in his forties who is separated from his profligate wife. Agata's mother, to prevent a scandal, decides to marry her to Baldovino, member of a noble family in dire financial straits.

Pirandello has looked with ironic and indulgent eyes on the mother who, in making arrangements for the marriage contract with Maurizio Setti, a cousin of the Marquis and a former school chum of Baldovino's, admits that she has played her part in the fall of her daughter. Grievingly and feelingly she confesses to Setti, "You cannot understand what torture it is for a mother to see her daughter advance in years . . . begin to lose the first flower of her youth. One does not have the courage to use the rigor that prudence suggests. Ah, honesty! What a mockery at times, my dear Setti! When the eyes of a daughter turn to you almost imploringly for a little love, the lips of the mother cannot utter a word, since she has known the world and had her big or little share of love." Agata's mother had actually steeled herself against interfering with Agata and Colli while they were in the garden on a starry night filled with the intoxicating perfume of flowers. "Outside, flowers and stars; within, anguish and the most heart-rending tenderness. And the mother cries within herself: 'Let all the stars and all the flowers for once be for my daughter,' and there, in the darkness, she stands, watching over a crime to which all nature invites, that tomorrow men and her own conscience will condemn. I cannot be excused, dear Setti, but I deserve sympathy."

The sin arises from this background of a mother's grief and from a wave of sentiment on the part of Agata Renni who felt unspeakably sorry for Colli whom she knew to be "unhappy, separated from his unworthy wife." "And you see," insists the mother, "this reason which should have prevented Agata from going to such a point has been the one that has led her there. When a woman has waited so many years for a companion without finding him, and at last meets a man who deserves all her love, and she knows this man to be ill treated, embittered, offended by another woman—believe me, she cannot resist the spontaneous impulse to show him that not all women are like that one; that there are some who know how to answer love with love and appreciate the luck that the other has spurned." Pirandello's characters do not sin for profligacy. Sentiment is their worst enemy. There is not in Pirandello the strong, elementary naturalism of Verga in his Sicilian stories. Agata sins because of sentiment, and because of sentiment her mother has relaxed the close watch that mothers once exercised over their daughters. But the problem is there, cruel and terrible in its stark reality: Agata is going to have a baby. So greatly ashamed is the mother that she even goes so far as to wish death for herself. "One ought to die afterwards, but death does not come. Life continues, life that to be and to endure needs all those things that in a moment we have thrown away." Woe unto Agata if the world should know that she, unwed, is going to become a mother!

Ridicule and shame would be heaped on her. There is only one thing to do: procure a husband for her in order to save appearances; to rectify the situation; to make it moral by draping over it the cloak of honesty. Here is the first lance that the serious ironist, Pirandello, breaks in favor of an old chatelaine, Honesty. Agata cannot reappear in the world without at least the appearance of honesty. Honesty that we cast aside when the voice of instinct and sentiment sings in our hearts is our indispensable possession, painful as its acquisition may be. Its acquisition is truly painful for Agata. She has to marry a man whom she does not know, Baldovino. But "sentiment must be restrained; it must recede in order to make place for reason."

Here is the drama. We are at its very portals where we meet Baldovino, a strange individual who, with his quixotic temperament, dwarfs everyone around him, although he was meant to enter the Renni household in the rôle of a humble understudy. A man like Baldovino cannot remain in the shadows of mediocrity. He has been tossed by the stormy waves of life; he has reached high towards the stars with his intellect, while he has known the mire of the very depths, dragged down by his instincts and passions. Setti has gone to interview him at his dilapidated villa in the town of Macerata. Following is the impression that Setti received from their conference. "It seemed to me that I was not on this earth any longer—but in a strange, fantastic land, lugubrious, mysterious, where he moved freely in the fashion of a master and where the most bizarre and impossible things could happen and seem natural and customary."

It is easy for Baldovino to accept the strange request of his old school chum, Maurizio, who proposes that he become the *pro forma* husband of Agata Renni. To a man constantly balancing on the seesaw of fantasy, the more absurd the adventure, the more acceptable. Baldovino, incapable of living a normal life, has found in his lucid abstraction resembling madness a means of compromising with life which helped him to bear his lonely and drab existence. In his daily suffering, condemned to a distracting solitude in that sluggish and somnolent provincial town, reduced to poverty, desperately alone, he cannot touch earth, so heavy in mental and almost physical pain is the price exacted by that contact. If one be allowed to describe it so, he has reached a sort of strange pragmatic wisdom, based on detachment from the aspects of a normal reality, which permits him to abandon himself to sudden wild flights into the realm of fancy where possibilities are endless.

It is necessary to have clearly in mind the tragically fantastic character of Baldovino's mode of thinking and living in order to understand the play. He has renounced all that side of life that we may call material and concrete and which centers about instinct and obeys the dictates of sentiment. Baldovino is only "intellect," not because he delights in floating on the fleecy clouds of the irrational, but because the circumstances of his life have forced him to take refuge in the lonely castle of his imagination. Imagination, so the idealists of all times say, is the last refuge of those whom a happy and joyous life has rejected. Under these circumstances Baldovino's intellectual wanderings into the realm of the absolute are tinged with grief and resentment, with hatred and longing for destruction, yet he holds them in abeyance by the purifying force of his idealism. In the fortress of his lucid imagination he can re-create the harrowing conditions of his existence, and contemplate them with a detached feeling, since his heart is absent and only his intellect functions.

The life of Baldovino must be envisaged through the absolute preponderance of his intellect and the exclusion of his heart. As long as we are ruled by the heart we are not capable of a detached attitude. Heart is to Pirandello instinct and sentiment, and to listen to its dictates is to live in the warmth and in the blind violence of living things. To be dominated by instinct means to Baldovino to cling to the pleasurable gifts of a natural life. How can he in his lonely superiority and his ghastly isolation entrust himself to the flow of a natural and instinctive life? He has become the perfect embodiment of a man living only through his intellect. He transforms facts into concepts, thereby depriving them of their power to hurt

him. The concept of sorrow is not so destructive as sorrow itself, nor is the concept of joy as delectable as joy itself. He
knows that, but he also knows that sorrow in his life far out-
weighs joy. Consciously he has to still his heart that claims
its share of joy, and cling to his intellect that creates for him
a world of formulas and concepts. He is penniless, for instance, but by the quick opening of the shutter of his mind,
he can see endless figures galloping towards the infinite, giving him the sensation of the possession of millions, billions,
trillions. Society has stupidly called him dishonest for not
paying back to a few thickheaded but tenacious *bourgeois*
the money that they had lent him. He has been denied credit,
condemned to penury. The mobile flight of those figures is
his vengeance. Setti's proposal is rather odd, indeed, unique;
but it does not shock a man accustomed to roam in the world
of the irrational. So he accepts.

What strikes Baldovino most is the fact that he whom society has always branded as dishonest, is now called upon to
save the honesty and good name of Agata Renni, of her
mother, of her lover, and of her unborn child. Following the
lucid sword of his logical mind, he becomes a sort of categorical imperative, a stern defender of honesty. Once a husband, he decrees that there will not be any compromise nor
half measures. He will be an unbending dictator. Since all
concerned must rally around honesty, they will have to be
honest, literally and intrinsically. This uncompromising
form of honesty is the easier since they all are assuming an
artificial rôle before the eyes of society. Artificiality, according to Baldovino, presupposes the absence of sentiment, making it possible for us to measure our words and deeds, to
"build up" ourselves, as the stage director of this drama tells
Colli. Baldovino insists, however, that they be sincere among
themselves by laying bare the facts, no matter how bitter.
Colli's sensibilities are shocked by the blunt: "Agata has been
your mistress." He rebels at that crude way of putting it, but
Baldovino has the cold logic of facts in his favor.

The scene between Colli and Baldovino is a powerful one.
Face to face, the two men are trying to stake their lives on a

situation that, when the fog of uncertainty and social hypocrisy is removed from it, gapes before them in all its shame and ugliness. The one who removes the fog is Baldovino. He asks Colli to speak "openly," but adds that openly means not only to talk frankly with others but to act sincerely with one's self. Baldovino is pitiless in his sincerity. "When I enter this house," he says, "I present myself to you in a form adapted to the relation that I must assume with you. You, in receiving me, must do the same. But, ultimately, behind our masks which are facing each other, behind the Venetian blinds and curtains of hypocrisy, are hidden our most secret thoughts, our most intimate sentiments, all that we really are for ourselves, aside from the relations that we wish to establish with one another." Baldovino hates these "constructions," the superimposed personality that he has to force on his intimate self. "I experience within me an unspeakable nausea for the self that I am compelled to build up and display in the relations that I must assume with my fellow-men."

This sense of "nausea" redeems Pirandello's characters from the charge of moral turpitude and from that of abstraction. In discussing the situation with Colli, Baldovino insists that their respective positions be clearly defined before he consents to play the rôle of formal husband. Colli must not think that he can continue to enjoy his dream of love with Agata. Everyone will have to be honest. All will live in celibacy. "I must become a tyrant," announces Baldovino to Colli, "and you must respect me, not so much me personally, but the form which I represent: that of an honest husband of an honest woman." Baldovino accepts the rôle of being only the "form," the "mold" of a husband. He will move like a concept among people who have known for years the richness of the gifts of life and nature. He will be as abstract as a concept, but he will possess by virtue of that form, its elusive, intangible, yet undeniable power.

The marriage ceremony of Agata and Baldovino creates a situation laden with grave possibilities. It seals a mask on Baldovino's face, a mask which burns and sears. Now, more than ever, to exist means to Baldovino to renounce sentiment, to replace it with cold reason. Here is a man living near a woman, a lovely woman like Agata, compelled to repress every feeling, every sentiment, condemning himself to an unnatural passiveness. From the outset, two distinct points of view clash in violent contrast: that of Colli and of Agata's mother, both of whom want to use Baldovino as a screen for the prolonged happiness that Agata finds in Colli's love, and that of Baldovino who accepts his rôle of defender of honesty with the enthusiasm of a crusader and the rigor of a logician. A problem arises: To what extent can the form be and remain a pure form, that is, a construction of reason, resisting the efforts of sentiment to break into it, to fill it with its turbulent strength? Baldovino's life is an abstract and cold form only on the surface. He knows that on that form depends his whole present existence, the respite from financial worries, and the petty material fetters with which life strangles the best part of an intellectual man. If he repudiates that form he will lose every contact with Agata and with the fictitious structure of life that he has erected which, painful as it is, possesses enough consistency to give a purpose to his existence.

For ten months under the apparent calm of the situation a great struggle goes on. Colli and Agata's mother have been planning to get rid of Baldovino as soon as the child is born. Colli, much to the astonishment of all, has founded a banking firm at the head of which he has placed Baldovino, who has displayed a real genius for organization and administration. Under him the firm has flourished beyond expectation. He has ruled with an iron hand. He has truly become a categorical imperative, and, reasoning as he does according to absolute principles, he provides a pattern of perfect life for all. He confesses, "Suspended in the air, I float as if resting on a cloud. I experience the pleasure of saints in the frescoes of churches." His pattern of perfect life applies both to the bank and to his home. If honesty in business is a logical necessity, then everyone has to be honest, and the same honesty must guide the actions of all the members of his household. His logic is so penetrating and convincing that no argument can resist its thrusts. Agata's mother, Colli, and the directors are all crushed by the power of his reasoning. This is so because he reasons as a categorical imperative, and he can do so because he lives in and thinks and orders from the lofty tower where he has enclosed himself.

Baldovino is aware of the effect of his rule on the people around him. "They complain, don't they? Tell me," he asks of Setti. "They shout—they champ the bit. . . . Well, I know it! I stifle them. I stifle anyone who comes near me. But you see; I cannot help it. For ten months I have not been a man . . . I am almost a deity. You should easily understand that. I have a body only for the sake of appearances. I am steeped in figures, in speculations, but they are for other people. There is not in them the gain of one *centime* for me, and I don't want there to be. I am here in this beautiful house, and I almost do not see, hear, nor touch anything. At times I marvel at hearing the sound of my own voice or the noise of my footsteps. I am living—do you understand?—de-li-ci-ous-ly in the absolute of a pure, abstract form." This is why Baldovino can be all that he is, honest even in handling millions. Everyone sees in him a mirror of perfection in which none dares look at himself. To listen to his order is to obey the cold and unchanging voice of righteousness. The strange fact is that Agata submits to his orders with respect and finds logical whatever he commands.

The situation becomes graver for Colli when a child is born to Agata and motherhood destroys the lover in her. Now Baldovino stands between her and Colli and acquires a deeper significance when she realizes that her son will bear his name. Colli is justified in remonstrating with Mr. Setti for choosing a man out of the ordinary. Baldovino is distinguished, even good-looking. His intellect is such as to dwarf into nothingness a placid and commonplace man like Colli.

Baldovino's rôle appears more and more important as time passes. He becomes conscious of the value of his presence in the Renni household as he realizes that Agata's mother and Colli are still determined to get rid of him. He ponders over the possibility of gratifying their wish by committing an unworthy action and thus affording them an excuse. He is forced to admit that that would be a perfect solution to the problem of eliminating him as a husband. Once the child is born he is no longer needed. But as a father he cannot so leave it. He has accepted the rôle in order to save the child too. "If as a husband I can go away without doing any harm to my wife, who will drop my name and resume hers; as a father my dishonesty would damage my son who bears my name. The lower I shall fall, the greater the damage that will be done him."

The crisis is precipitated by various formalities in connection with the child's christening. Baldovino has decided to give him the name of Sigismondo. He knows it is a burdensome name and that "the poor child runs the risk of being crushed by it," but he is adamant against the protests of Colli and Agata's mother. Sigismondo has been the name of his father and of his grandfather. It is absolutely necessary for a child who will bear the cognomen of Baldovino to be named after his ancestors. "It is not for me," says the logical Baldovino, "it is for form, and for form, since I must give him a name, I cannot give him any name other than this one." How strong is the form assumed by Baldovino! Pirandello is like a scientist who comes by chance across a new fact, a new formula, and marvels before the magnitude of his sudden discovery. Of greater moment is the question whether the child will be baptized in church or privately at home. The grandmother contends that the child should be baptized at home to lend more dignity to the ceremony. Baldovino counters with the argument that no rite can be more austere and meaningful than when performed in church. Even the curate who comes to the house ready to perform the ceremony has to admit that this is true "at least in principle." Agata, upon being called upon to decide, sides with Baldovino. This shows that she has been won over to him and has detached herself from Colli, ruled only by a mother's instinct.

Colli fights his last battle by attempting to set a trap for Baldovino whereby he will appear to have misappropriated

195

half a million *lire*. Baldovino shows Agata the proofs of his innocence. Agata stands by him. His innocence is the innocence and honor of her son. This fact plunges Baldovino into a frenzy. If Agata stands by him, then he can no longer play the rôle of a *pro forma* husband. He, by that very interest on the part of Agata, cannot continue to abide in the region of abstractions. He decides to leave Agata. Dressed as he was when he first went to her house, he is ready to go. He stands between the pure form into which he has walled himself and the old self of the days spent in his dilapidated villa at Macerata. That self is there, held in subjection by the new rôle he has imposed on himself. "You know," he says, "I have in me a horrible beast of which I have tried to free myself by chaining it to these conditions which were offered to me." He discovers that his greatest enemy is hidden in him: his own sentiment. It has been possible for him to be purely a form as long as sentiment was absent. Now sentiment has gradually flowed back into the artificial mold of the husband of Agata Renni. Baldovino has felt interest and love appear and grow in him: he has repressed and stifled them. When Agata sides with him, he must flee. He must be true to his promise to be only a form, an abstract concept. He gives Colli the proofs of his innocence. Let Colli accuse and ruin him. He can begin again the life of an intellectual rover, of a sentimental vagabond.

Contrary to their hopes, the plotters discover that the elimination of Baldovino will be a common disaster. The son's future, in which they are all interested, is so closely dependent on him as to make a continuation of the existing situation an impelling necessity. They all beg him to remain, the mother, Colli, Mr. Setti. Baldovino, however, has resolved to leave Agata. He thinks that his wife is clinging not to him but to the pure form that he promised he would be. Agata has learned to appreciate and even love Baldovino. She announces that he can leave if he wishes, but she will follow him. He is her husband. Baldovino capitulates when he feels that Agata's esteem for and interest in him have opened a new horizon to his desolate soul. Under the mask of husband

and father his real features have so asserted themselves **that** the nobility of the human profile has taken the place of the grotesque and painful mask.

There is an undertone of social satire in the very events that form the warp of the play. Pirandello views with grieving mockery the attempt to hide the illegitimacy of the child under the cloak of a marriage ceremony. The clear-eyed Baldovino saw very well that the mother and Colli wanted to use honesty as a means of perpetuating a wrong situation. They wanted to use him as a soulless tool and then cast him aside. The author, half ironically and half thoughtfully, makes Baldovino don the armor of honesty and fight gallantly for it against the machinations of his enemies.

Defending the pitiful and yet glorious plight of intellectual life, Pirandello chooses Baldovino, a man out of the boundaries of society and civilization, and contrasts him with the exponents of the more fortunate class, individuals to whom society has granted wealth, social status, and respect. The man who has been renounced by society is superior to his antagonists in everything, especially in honesty. He has an ethical concept of business, and his honest practices are resented by civilized individuals like Colli and the directors. When Maurizio Setti comments on the success of the concern of which Baldovino is the head, the latter calls his attention to the fact that he does not steal as many bankers do. He rejoices in the feeling of perfect aloofness from the miserable slavery of money. He says: "To see hundreds of thousands of *lire* pass through your hands, to be able to consider them just as cheap paper, not to feel the slightest need of them, is a divine pleasure." It is the pleasure of honesty realized to a perfect degree by one who is accustomed to roam in the realm of the absolute. To him, a perfect logician, it is equally absurd that wealthy people should have religious ceremonies performed at home. Baldovino informs the curate that rich and poor are alike in the eyes of the Lord. The curate agrees in principle with Baldovino that the child should be baptized in church, but sides with the family in agreeing that out of regard for custom the ceremony could and should be performed at home. This is the reason why life is as we see it around us, and why civilization often appears to be only a mocking name.

To Baldovino civilization does not mean order or progress based on the ending of the struggle waged by our ancestors in the jungle. Indeed it marks an intensification of it. He shows his fingernails to Maurizio and says, "Do you see to what a point we have arrived? We do not cut our fingernails to disarm ourselves. On the contrary we do it that our hands may appear more civilized, that is, more adapted to a struggle fiercer than the one that our ancestors in a primitive stage fought only with their nails."

This play, like many of Pirandello's works, could be and, indeed, has been attacked as being abstract and cerebral. The truth is that Pirandello has shown the defeat of the abstract and cerebral Baldovino before Baldovino the man, who finds a meaning to his life in the promise of Agata's love. Even in the mental aloofness of the days spent at Macerata and when he lived in the pure form of the concept of a husband, Baldovino is too conscious of his mask to be abstract. Abstraction is rhetoric, and Pirandello's characters feel too vividly and passionately the weight of their grief and tragedy to be rhetorical.

Pirandello is here a brilliant and ironical asserter of the power of honesty. As a genial and quixotic knight of Lady Honesty, he breaks his lance against those who preach of her in hollow voices and with solemn faces, while he attacks those who are inclined to think that honesty is just a prejudice of narrow-minded people. Pirandello the humorist begins by placing honesty in a man who lives outside the normal boundaries of life and by claiming that to be absolutely honest we must live as abstract formulas. Eventually he shows that honesty is imbedded in the very texture of social life to the extent that even when assumed as only a form it becomes a powerful reality and leads to the fullness that it is meant to afford to men.

XX

Where the Law Cannot Reach

THINK IT OVER, GIACOMINO

(*Pensaci, Giacomino*)

This play is built around old Professor Toti, who is the negation of a schoolmaster and the glorification of a compassionate man. He is old and tired, and his high-school pupils make all sorts of noises and play all kinds of pranks as he teaches them the sciences. One day a youth leaps through the first-floor window, much to the uproarious amusement of the pupils to whom the professor is trying to teach the various families of monkeys. The school principal, who has come to investigate the cause of the commotion, is furious. He tells Toti that he should retire, and that he will then receive a pension. Toti takes him at his word. He will not retire from teaching, but he will marry, and marry a young girl, just for spite, so that at his death his pension will cost the government dear. Toti is one of those old gentlemen who laugh because they possess a greater wisdom than so many who go around with a solemn mien, all filled with their importance. He enters upon marriage with a perfect understanding of the step that he is taking. Whimsically explaining to the principal the reason for marrying, he says: "A wife? What wife are you talking about? Just an act of charity. You, then, are like everybody else. You see the professor and do not see the man. You hear that I wish to get married, and you imagine a wife near me as a husband, and you begin to laugh. A wife at my age? That would be funny. I a husband? Just a profession, an appearance. In reality, nothing at all. I am and shall remain a poor old man who will have the company for two or three years of a person who will be grateful for the good I do her at the expense of the government."

The ridicule is turned on the principal as well as on all

those who wish to laugh at the old professor. Ridicule cannot touch him, for he knows the world and is intelligent enough to shield himself even against the ridicule that usually is cast on an old man when he is betrayed by his wife. "I count on that," he says. "That will touch my profession as a husband, but not me. Indeed, I shall see to it that the husband, as a husband, shall be betrayed. Of course. Otherwise, how could I, poor old man that I am, have any peace? But how could I be offended—if I am not a husband—nor can I be one—nor desire to be one? A charitable deed, that's all—and if all the imbeciles of the town wish to laugh about it—let them laugh. It will not worry me."

Toti marries Lillina, the young daughter of the school janitor, an arrogant, disrespectful fellow who hated Professor Toti and was in the habit of reporting him to the principal for the lack of discipline that he noticed in the science class. Lillina has been having an affair with Giacomino, the young man who leaped through the window of Professor Toti's classroom. Lillina has revealed to Toti the distressing fact that she is going to have a baby, and the old professor, touched by her tears and by the sadness of the situation, has married her with the one stipulation—that Giacomino, for whom he has a great fondness, continues to be her lover. Lillina is the ideal girl for Toti. She has a lover and she is very young, so the government will have to pay a pension for a long time. She will look after Toti. She will look after him, give him a home, and when the baby comes he will find great joy in the little child: "A little child whose hand I shall hold and with whom I shall take a walk. For an old man there is no better company to learn the way to the grave."

Two years have passed since Toti's marriage to Lillina. They live very happily in a home cheered by the little boy, Nini, whom Toti loves as if he were his own. The old professor has had the luck of receiving quite unexpectedly a considerable amount of money, 140,000 *lire,* from his brother who died in Roumania without leaving a will. The professor has invested his money in a city bank where he is the strongest stockholder. Thanks to him, Giacomino occupies a nice position in the bank. Toti still teaches, with no better discipline in his classes than before.

One day he receives a call from the school principal, who has come to tell him that he must resign because all the parents are protesting against having a man like Toti instruct their children. Toti rebels: "I expect to have someone, since you are not willing to do so, come to discuss with me not what seems but what is. I mean my conscience." Lillina, meanwhile, has become very morose; she cries constantly, is nervous, indifferent, and impatient with her little Ninì. Toti believes that it is due to the fact that people are protesting. "Well," he says paternally to Lillina, "that should not concern us at all, because you and I know that we don't do anything wrong and must think only of keeping together, waiting for time to show that I am in the right.—Not now, but at my death, when I shall leave you well provided for and without worry."

That is Toti's dream—to leave Lillina and Ninì all he possesses and have Giacomino marry her, rectifying a wrong situation. Giacomino, however, is thwarting his plans. For three days he has not come to the house nor has he gone to the bank. This is due to the intrigues of Rosaria, Giacomino's sister, and Father Landolina, who are trying to break up the relation between the two lovers.

Father Landolina, anxious and subtle, goes to see Toti. He intervenes because Giacomino's sister has appealed to him. "It is a question, my dear Professor, of a poor Christian soul who, whether rightly or wrongly I don't know, is hurt, offended by incriminating rumors that have spread over the town about her brother." Rosaria, who is a very pious woman and has been a mother to Giacomino, wishes him to marry. A girl has already been chosen for him. Giacomino has promised his sister that he will never see Lillina again. It is very convenient to have a logical and moral excuse for the instability of one's feelings. Father Landolina begs Toti to give him a written statement to the effect that all gossip about Giacomino and Lillina has no basis whatever. He and Rosaria want to show this document to the parents of the girl in order to calm their apprehensions about Giacomino's moral character. Toti is furious, but restrains himself and courteously sees Landolina to the door.

He decides that the only thing to do is for him to take Ninì to Giacomino and remind him of his duty towards his child and towards the mother. Old Toti, with his half sophisticated, half jovial laughter on his lips, is met by the cold politeness of Rosaria. He is told by her that Giacomino is not at home. He brushes aside her statement with his subtle laughter, and enters the house. That laughter is the worst weapon that she has ever encountered. She is powerless before it and goes to inform Giacomino of the professor's visit. In the meantime, Toti takes Ninì on his knees and sweetly talks to him: "Do you know who will come here now? Giami. You love him, don't you? He, too, brings you sweets and toys. But you must love me more, my child, because I am about to leave you. You cannot understand these things yet, and you will never understand them, because when you do you will have forgotten me—this man who has held you in his arms—clasped you so—so, and has shed tears for you."

Giacomino enters as old Toti is speaking so tenderly to his child. He is ashamed of himself; but he has promised his sister, he has been engaged a month to the girl that he is going to marry. Toti is very angry with the moral indignation of an old man who, having treated Giacomino and Lillina as his own children, has defied ridicule and now sees the fruitlessness of his effort. He pleads, but as Giacomino refuses to yield he threatens that he will go with the child to his *fiancée* and expose the whole truth to her. Then he pleads again: "Is it right to so ruin a home, a family, to break the heart of a poor old man, of a poor mother, and to leave without help and guidance a poor little innocent child, like this one, Giacomino, like this one! Don't you see? Have you no heart? Don't you see your child here? It is yours, yours." Giacomino is touched and clasps his little boy in his arms. Lillina is saved in spite of the protests of Father Landolina and of the sister. Giacomino returns with Toti and Ninì to his home, another example of the old saying that "the home is where the child is."

The play corresponds perfectly to Pirandello's concept of humor: it contains a situation that is ludicrous if looked at from the outside, and pathetic if the inner feelings are known.

The comedy has been characterized by Adriano Tilgher as the comedy of a husband who does not wish the lover to leave his wife.[1] It sounds like one of those characterizations meant to whet the appetite for immorality. *Think It Over, Giacomino* is a comedy built on elements that are illogical and immoral for those people to whom morality is only appearances. To Pirandello morality is the substance of life; it abides in the very grain of life, and as such it has to react on what is basic in human needs, and it encompasses the physical and spiritual sides of man. Toti finds the immoral situation, and since he is compassionate he tries to save Lillina from shame. The wrong situation is not created by him. It is brought about by the neglect of Lillina's parents and by nature.

There are bitter reflections on morality as it is usually interpreted by people like Lillina's parents and Giacomino's sister. Often morality is nothing but our own interests. We appeal to moral principles when they can strengthen our positions. We neglect them, we reject them when they oppose our desires. Pirandello unmercifully flays the bombastic arrogance of the janitor, Lillina's father, that hid a mean and despicable nature. He is equally unmerciful with the hypocrisy of Father Landolina and Giacomino's sister. Cinquemani, the janitor, had no scruples in prostituting his sixteen-year-old daughter by marrying her to a man in his sixties, yet he was ready to kill Giacomino and to turn Lillina out of his home when he discovered their love affair. Toti, in a voice that expresses the moral indignation of the author, shouts: "Where do you expect her to go, you old fool? You accuse her when the responsibility is yours, because you did

[1] *Studi sul teatro contemporaneo*, p. 139.

not watch over her and have kept her here among all the filth that pupils write on the walls and on the benches."

When the janitor and his worthy wife discover that by agreement of all concerned Giacomino has continued to be Lillina's lover, their moral sense rebels. They resent Giacomino's presence only because their plan was to enjoy a comfortable old age on Toti's money, with a widowed daughter. That is the value of their morality. Rosaria's moral sense is not loftier. She wants Giacomino to give up Lillina, but she hopes that he will be able to keep his position in the bank with Toti's protection. A written statement from Toti would have meant that the situation would have been quietly remedied by eliminating the elements that she did not wish while keeping those that were remunerative. Father Landolina represents the cold, moral law, and as such he is the target of Pirandello's thrusts. The law solves through marriage the problem of the relation between a man and a woman. But what of cases like that of Lillina's and Giacomino's? Had the matter taken the course that Lillina's parents had meant it to take, the girl would have become a prostitute and Giacomino a shifty, irresponsible man. Father Landolina stands for the categorical, unbending spirit of the law as is evidenced when he wishes the written statement from Toti. To him that document would be enough to destroy the wrong situation existing between Lillina and Giacomino. His action and attitude show the lack of reality of the law whenever it relies only on appearance, ignoring the truth and the substance of a situation.

The play carries also a feeling, a rebellion, on the part of one who believes in the pragmatic values of life against the formalized ones. It is not enough to go before the law in order to be husband and wife. Here the humorist comes to the fore. Toti and Lillina had gone before the law, yet they were not husband and wife. The humorist with glee shows that in this case the reverse is true. Those who had not asked the sanction of the law were actually husband and wife. At this point the humorist disappears, as Pirandello discovers that the real bond that binds them is a child.

The figure that stands out in constant relief is that of Toti. Since the moral question is continuously present, Pirandello makes him the arbiter of the morals of the characters and the one who, in his own erratic fashion, is willing to be a martyr in order to rectify the immoral situation between Lillina and Giacomino. He expects to die in peace in the belief that they will become legally married. In answer to the urge of his compassionate heart he had created a solution that benefited all concerned, even if he had to bear the brunt of ridicule. Toti, however, had the saving grace of laughter that became a formidable weapon against his enemies. It was laughter that led him to win his battle in favor of little Nini, whose soft hands had warmed his cold hands before death, obeying the law of nature of which he had an infinite understanding.

XXI

Impossibility of a Perfect Human Society

THE NEW COLONY

(*La nuova colonia*)

We are in a maritime town of southern Italy, in a wine shop where sailors, smugglers, and harlots have their rendezvous. The atmosphere is one of grimy poverty, of social injustice, and of powerless revolt. The chief characters are people who live by smuggling, and therefore have the police always at their heels. Among them stand out Spera, a poor lost woman, and Currao, a handsome youth, strong, daring, and rebellious.

These people have been brutalized by want and by the struggle that they have had to wage for the bare necessities of life. Their strong, bony features and ungainly limbs testify to the physical struggle, while in their words there is the echo of an internal hatred that partakes of frenzy. "Good—evil: you who have time and leisure can busy yourselves with the consideration of such things." So says old Tobba in whose coat there are more "patches than there were wounds on the flesh of Christ." Life is so unbearable for them that their only escape is to go to live on an island where penal prisoners used to be kept and which is now deserted because it is slowly, insensibly sinking. These people, rough and ill clad, are like broken molecules in the social body, ready to fly in every direction, goaded by the loathing for their life. Spera voices their sentiments: "Loathing, yes, loathing, you of your life, I of mine. I am quivering all over. I feel my bowels twisted like a rope."

Spera is a grotesque mask of womanhood, but she wants a different life because of the baby that she has borne to Currao. Currao, too, wants to live honestly, but he is helpless. When he goes out to sell fish that he received for help that he had given two fishermen, two guards arrest him, believing that he has stolen them. There is only one thing to do: to go away, to go to the island even if it sinks into the sea. Are they not sunk there, as Spera says? "And here, where you are; are you not sunk? You could not sink more deeply than you have here. At least there it will be God who will make you sink—not men more wicked than you! More wicked if they refuse to let you come up to the surface just to breathe. [*She presses her hands on her breast.*] An irresistible desire to breathe from the depths of my lungs has entered into me."

The situation in which these people are placed is such that moral desperation takes hold of their being, even physical being, and makes them writhe and sneer while a sudden thirst for a new life is born in them. Thirst is the word that expresses the parched feeling in their throats and in their withered souls, and the desire of their lips to touch something soothing, pure, and fresh. They will work. Spera "will serve them, mend their clothes, take care of them if sick, and she will work with them: new life, new life, and ours—made by us."

They rig Tobba's old boat and sail for the island. Spera will have her child with her, and as she goes to get him from his nurse now, after five months, her breast feels a sweet, warm flow of milk: milk for her baby. They all cry "Miracle! Miracle!" because in the beginning of a new life what is extraordinary has a powerful hold on man.

Life is at first very happy on the island. They find shelter in an old house, half battered down. Currao is their recognized leader. They set up a tribunal, since they have discovered the need of having to organize themselves under a law; they who have fled from the law of the land. Spera is a sort of queen and saint for them. She has become beautiful again, "so natural," so ennobled by the love of her baby and by the purity of life on the island.

Until now Pirandello has abandoned himself to the feeling of hope, of goodness, and of the idyllic in the crude form that it can take in the smuggler's heart; but now his penetrating and sophisticated mind sets to work Instinct looms again like a terrible and devastating god. All the men on the island desire Spera, the only woman in the place, but she is Currao's because she has had a baby by him. There arise violent questions of ownership as to whom this or that belongs, as to who is to occupy this or that room. One of them has left the group and has gone to live by himself in a corner of the island. Spera tries in vain to instill in them the beauty of her faith: "There is a way of being all for all; and do you know which it is? That of being nothing for ourselves."

Crocco, a despicable scoundrel, represents the forces that are for disintegration and destruction. He resents Currao's position, thinking it easy for him to be on the island. "It is easy for you to occupy your position," he remarks. "What does it cost you? You have her [*he points out Spera*]. You are the leader and you rule." It is of no use for Currao to tell him that he is "the servant of all, the first in giving, the last in taking"; that there must be a law, only "now, here, there isn't any longer the law of others; there is your own." To Crocco that is nonsense. It is the law of Currao, and for that reason Currao stands for it. Crocco is unfit to be social. Someone accuses him of being wicked, of having been born wicked. Spera quietly and understandingly suggests: "We are not born wicked. It is only that he no longer finds the way of being good to anyone—and no one helps him to find that way." In fact, everyone on the island is against Crocco. One day he rushes to the old boat that is moored in the bay and sails back to the land to avenge himself.

Crocco goes to see Padron Nocio, a rich fisherman, owner of many fishing boats, whose young son Dorò has gone to the island because he loves Spera. Padron Nocio sails with four boats to fetch his son. Crocco leads the expedition. They take with them wine and women, the symbols of the old civilization that will destroy the new one that Currao has attempted to build. The inhabitants of the island at first want to prevent their landing, and they threaten them with long poles and stones. Padron Nocio informs them that he has come for his son, and Crocco shouts, "Mita is here! Women are here! Women!" Mita is the beautiful daughter of Padron Nocio. Women were the bait for the hungry males. The old smug-

glers throw their weapons away, and run to the beach, shouting in exaltation "Women! Women! Women!"

Currao sees himself lost. He is attacked and menaced. To
keep his power he agrees to marry Mita, but he would also
like to keep his son, Spera's baby. How could she allow him
to have her whole life? She seizes her child and flees. She
flees to the rocky heights of the island and shouts that if
Currao touches her son the earth will tremble and the sea will
engulf them all.

The earth obeys the wrath of a mother. It quakes and the
waters submerge all the island except a last high spot where
mother and son have taken refuge. The love of a mother is
the only thing which is saved in the wreck wrought by human
passions. One sees here the wistful eyes of Pirandello focused
on the spectacle of human society with the same half amused,
half grieving expression as when he looked at the vicissitudes
of but one individual.

There is in this play a deep vein of philosophy and antisocial sentiment. Life as it is lived today, with its amusements, ambitions, envy, and intrigues, is evil, while there is
another life which glows in children's eyes: a life of which
men have a glimpse for a fleeting moment, but which they
forsake and crush. The aspiration of Spera and of the perse-
cuted smugglers has been a reflection of the divine life which
abides in the form of a faded remembrance in the soul of
man. Inevitably, actual life has come and has reached out
with its tentacles and has overpowered it. This has been the
fate of the colony on the island. Evil personified in modern
civilization has reached out there, too. The antisocial strain
is derived from Pirandello's belief in life as a primitive
entity, with candor, beauty, and original purity violated by
civilization. It is fatal that the everyday life should deface us
and leave us a prey to instincts.

Pirandello places his concept of pure life in the island
which represents nature. Spera finds her beauty and serenity
as soon as she is removed from the filth of the city and
plunged into the pure bosom of nature. She is the embodiment of Pirandello's idealism. Her philosophy is like that of

the great saints and mystics who spoke of complete annihilation.

The play reminds one of the adventurous flight back to nature of Robinson Crusoe; only Pirandello looks at life with more searching and disillusioned eyes. *Robinson Crusoe* was written when the world was about to make one of those titanic efforts in the creation of our industrial civilization. Pirandello wrote after the World War—the last chapter of industrial civilization in its extreme forms. He has no faith in our present civilization. The tragic thing is, however, that in this play—even Currao's civilization proved to be not better than the one he had fled. The only figure that is constructive is that of Spera, but her idealism is so lofty that it is a closed book to the average person and does not offer a pattern for the conduct of an average life. Life offers no solution. Disillusion and discouragement hold our temples as in a vise, while a gray, stormy sky hangs overhead. Only in the distance a faint light quivers. It is the dreamy idealism of Spera.

XXII

Resurrection and Immortality

LAZARUS

(*Lazzaro*)

Lazarus is a religious play with social implications. The author has expressed in it his religious beliefs, which start with a departure from the stereotyped idea of a theological God and end in a passionate, personal, and rather vague Christianity. In it Pirandello identifies God with the soul of man and looks upon the soul as merged with him, both during life and at our bodily death.

The question of life after death constantly occupies the mind of the author. Religions have variously and poetically depicted life in the hereafter. Pirandello sets this problem before himself: What would happen if a man should die and upon being called back to life by the help of science should realize that his eyes had gazed upon an empty and dark beyond? Science affords such a possibility, since it has discovered that an injection of adrenalin into the heart will cause life to ebb back into the body.

There are two distinct sets of characters in the play: one drawn with heavy black lines carries the author's dislike for theological religions; the other enveloped in idealistic veils and sympathetically treated gives us the dreamy concept of life that vibrates beyond the gloomy spectacle of human existence that Pirandello usually transports upon the stage. Here is Diego Spina, his chief antagonist and one of the central figures in the play: he is "a little over forty, tall, thin, with a pale, gaunt face, with hard, mobile eyes, always aglow like those of an excited maniac." Here is a monsignor: "Monsignor Lelli, mellow in appearance, not always succeeding in hiding with his glances and smiles all the bitterness that he has within him."

Against these figures Pirandello has projected those who

211

embody his own sense of religion and of an ideal of life:
Sara, Diego Spina's wife, who has left him because their
ideas on life and on bringing up children are so different as
to make their living together impossible; Arcadipane, a child
of nature, a strong, healthy, handsome, benevolent, and
serene peasant with whom Sara has gone to live on a farm
as his common law wife after having left her husband; Lucio,
Diego Spina's son who refuses at first to become a priest,
only to offer himself to Christ when a new sense of Christianity is born within him. On the fringe of the play there are
minor characters, drawn in accord with that sympathy for
characteristic persons of the lower classes for whom Pirandello has always had a particular and justified liking. There
is a sturdy old servant, Deodata, who takes care of little Lia,
Diego's crippled daughter, and who does not approve of the
excesses of her master. She is religious, but possesses the
practical and spontaneous feelings of women of her class for
whom religion is a safe investment for a moment of sorrow.
To her, Diego Spina's harsh religion is pure madness. Near
her there is Cico, a queer beggar, "a slender man, old, bizarre, with small blue eyes lucid as crystal, penetrating, cheer-
ful, and very expressive." He very much resembles Ciampa
of *Cap and Bells*. Instead of Ciampa's switch of madness that
compels men to make a clean breast of unpleasant and hateful thoughts, Cico is endowed with a little black devil that
lives within him and, according to him, says things that should
not be said.

Pirandello guides Diego Spina through the experience of
being brought back to life. He is a man whose religious beliefs are strictly orthodox, and is imbued with the indifference for the gifts of material life that has been the basis of
theological religions. Christ is to him the symbol of a suffering which is unmerciful, harsh, and cruel.

As the scene opens we see on the wall that runs around
the courtyard of Spina's house "a large, black cross with the
likeness of a squalid Christ all covered with blood." The religious beliefs of Diego Spina are not abstract propositions.
They are a guide for the conduct of his life. He believes in

212

sacrifices; not only the sacrifices that the Lord requires of us, but those which we must seek in order to offer them to him. This spirit of sacrifice—almost a reflection of the spirit that prompted man to sacrifice victims to the Deity—has brought conflict between him and his wife. "She loved her children with too passionate a love—as many mothers do," he tells Monsignor Lelli.

Diego Spina has had two children by Sara—Lucio and Lia. They were delicate and neurotic like their father. Diego sent Lucio to a seminary to prepare for the priesthood, and he put Lia in a convent where the child, her health neglected, was taken ill and ended by her legs becoming paralyzed. She is about fifteen, but looks like a child. Diego is sincere in his almost brutal belief that if we suffer we acquire merit before God. He refused to comply with Sara's wish that the two children live on their farm in the country where life would be more wholesome. Sara had recourse to the law; human justice decreed that the husband was right.

She left him, and went to live on one of their farms. It was not until two years later that she became the common law wife of Arcadipane, to whom she bore two children. She has cast away her expensive clothes and is now dressed like a peasant woman. Country life has kept her young and lovely, and she is beautiful in her simple attire. "Beautiful, yes, beautiful: she seems to be still in her twenties! As she passes by, radiant as the sun, everybody turns to look at her! A miracle!" So Cico expresses his admiration for her.

Sara's life on the farm has been very happy. She and Arcadipane live on the soil in a truly Franciscan fashion. They have cultivated every inch of Diego's farm and have made it wonderfully productive. They love the springs that bring fertility to their land and quench their thirst; they know suffering and joy through the travails and joy of the earth. Their two children, handsome and healthy, children of love and of nature, work with them. They live on the products of the land, and they send whatever part of the harvest they do not need to the town hospital, since Diego has refused to accept anything from them.

This is the situation when Diego suddenly decides to found a retreat for indigent people on the farm where his wife and her companion have lived for years. We learn of this plan through Cico, who comes to Spina's house saying that the devil must have told Diego to build that retreat. Cico, who calls himself "the Lord's tax collector," feels that his profession will now be ruined forever. He has been in the habit of going to wealthy people and asking them to pay to him the rent in advance for their home in the other world. He has been very successful as he has gone from door to door, reciting a long and monotonous poem, half religious and half humorous, in which his own poverty is contrasted to the wealth of the rich. As things are he will have to go to Diego Spina's retreat and people will say: "Now you, too, have a home. Why should we give you money?"

Cico voices in his queer, simple way Pirandello's perplexity over the problem of evil. In a theologically constructed universe, evil should have no place. Cico asks: "O Lord, but why? You give us teeth, and one by one you remove them; you give us eyesight, and you take it away from us; you give us strength and you take it away. Look, O Lord, how you have reduced me! Must we not bring back to you even one of the many beautiful things that you have given us? It will be a fine thing, a hundred years from now, to see before you figures like mine." Cico has been saying this in front of a mirror of a show window, giving utterance to the words of the little devil within him. Monsignor Lelli, who happens to pass, gives him the right answer: "You foolish one, God reduces you so that death may not be so hard for you to meet." But Cico retorts: "God could take away also our desire to eat when he takes our teeth away, and yet he doesn't!" Everybody laughs. Monsignor does not answer. This is Pirandello's way of putting a big problem in a small form.

The theme of resurrection and immortality is introduced in the play by the fact that Dr. Gionni brings back to life a white rabbit that belonged to little Lia. Diego, upon learning this, takes the animal away from her, in spite of her protests and tears, because it was evidence of something that clashed with his religious beliefs. Only God can give life or miraculously call us back from death to life. Dr. Gionni disclaims any power to perform a miracle, nor is he sacrilegious, for he says: "I can also consider science as an instrument of God. It is all a question of understanding each other."

That day Sara goes to Diego's house for the first time since they were separated. He still loves her. Only his stubborn nature and his unbending faith keep him away from her. Her serenity is in deep contrast with his excitement. The feeling of immensity that she had known through her contact with nature makes everything in that house appear dwarfed and old. The purpose of her visit is to tell Diego that their son Lucio has come back to her on the farm, determined not to become a priest. She begs Diego to relent. She too believes in Christ, but a Christ who gives life and not death and pain. She knows her children. Physically, they are like their father, but they have her temperament. They have been endowed with her spontaneous sense of life. When they lived closeted in the old, severe schools where Diego had sent them, they felt that they were being robbed of freedom and life, of sunshine and health. They are instinctive. Lucio has told his mother: "My life, when I was there in the seminary, was . . . smell, taste of incense, of wax, the taste of the holy wafer, and a fear of the steps that echoed inside the empty church."

Lucio's crisis is very scantily presented. It is clear, however, that the author wishes to bring out that a new faith has been born in Lucio's heart, which has urged him to go out into life and, following his mother's example, to earn his living by tilling the soil.

When Diego hears that Lucio has decided to give up the priesthood, he rushes out of the house to find him, is hit by an automobile, and dies. He has lain dead for three-quarters of an hour. Two doctors have certified to his death. Even an official death certificate has been issued. Dr. Gionni succeeds in resuscitating him with an injection of adrenalin.

Lucio, confronted by this portentous event, feels his faith grow stronger. The chief tenet of his new faith is his belief in immortality, but not in his father's sense. To Lucio, when the body dies it is only a bit of dust that returns to dust, but the spirit continues to live because spirit is eternal, and infinite, and it lives as such in us. The mistake that we make is to believe that the spirit may become ours during our existence. To Lucio God is "the eternal present of life."

Dr. Gionni wishes Diego Spina to be kept in ignorance of his death and consequent resurrection. He fears that the shock may be too great for him. Unfortunately, on the day that Diego Spina, Monsignor Lelli, and the notary go to the farm to dispossess Arcadipane and to deed it over to the new institution for the needy, the truth is revealed to the new Lazarus, quite accidentally. The notary jokingly asks Diego if his death certificate has been revoked. The whole truth comes out.

The effects of the sudden discovery of that truth are very serious. Cico is very severely jolted. If Diego does not know of his death, it means that beyond life there is nothing at all. So reasons the grotesque beggar, who throws his red cap on the ground and shouts: "Enough of your God, Monsignor. I'll keep my devil from now on. No one will fool my devil." As is to be expected, losing the idea of the traditional God makes him lose every sense of moral responsibility. Honesty, the law, the sacraments, everything falls with it. Even gentle Lia, with a wistful smile, as if talking to herself, says to her old servant: "What about the little wings, Deodata, that I was supposed to have in compensation for the feet of which I have been deprived down here? That's the end of my flight up there now."

In the town there is a great deal of commotion, and everybody looks upon the doctor as on a sorcerer. As to Diego, his reaction is stronger than that of the others because his faith was stronger. His whole world has crumbled and he finds himself standing angry and desolate on the brim of an abyss of nothingness. His neurotic temperament, formerly held in check by his religious beliefs and now a prey to murderous frenzy, leads him to attempt to kill Arcadipane, who is about to leave the farm. He and his little family were going to move to another place where they would find shelter and peace as before. Diego is half demented, and it requires the efforts of all to quiet him. It is only the personal, warm, deep religion of Lucio, together with the fact that he has again decided to become a priest, that changes Diego from violence to calm reasoning, and from reasoning leads him back to faith. "Where was my soul while I was dead?" asks the father. "In God, Father," answers the son. "Your soul is God, Father; and you call it yours; it is God, you see." Lucio explains that it is a miracle of science that Diego has been brought back to life again, but since "our soul is God in us, what do you expect a miracle of science to be except God's miracle when He wishes it to be performed?"

Lucio grows exalted as if a divine spirit has passed over him. He restores peace in the heart of his father. His mother continues to live with her companion and her new family. Little Lia is healed and she can move her paralyzed legs while they all stand in wonder before the manifestation of the new faith.

Lazarus is not a great play, although it is interesting as a document of the idealistic background of Pirandello's concept of life. There are two main themes in the play: one tortuous and torturing, represented by Diego Spina; the other calm and serene, represented by Sara. Had Pirandello stressed unduly the over-intellectualistic traits of Diego, he would have eclipsed or minimized the serenity of Sara, with the result that the play would have fallen short of the goal that the author, in a rare peaceful mood, had assigned to it. So Diego, who seemed destined to be an outstanding figure in the drama, remains half drawn and obscured by his antagonist, Lucio, when the author expresses through him his religious and idealistic feelings. Lucio, however, is an evanescent character, because the ideas he represents have a greater relief than his humanity.

The weakness of the play is in the flimsy theology with which Pirandello has replaced the old one. Lucio's beliefs are couched in terms not different from the many vague

217

terminologies that are used to express the unthinkable. Fortunately for man, for religion, and, to a certain extent, for the play, he veers towards a practical content of faith which merges with what is basic in every religious teaching: the pragmatic value of faith. It might seem at first that the author has given expression here to the usual clash between faith and science—faith represented by Diego Spina; science by Doctor Gionni. Knowing Pirandello's attitude towards the power of sentiment, which, even if illusory, is a great force in life, we cannot expect a glorification of science by a man to whom a simple faith is of paramount importance. The play steers away from any intellectual interpretation of religion, and points towards the ideal life that Sara had found in the simplicity of the fields and in her love for Arcadipane. As the play develops, Sara is differentiated from both the abstract idealism of Lucio and the cruel theology of Diego Spina. In the serenity with which Pirandello clothes the life of Sara and Arcadipane there is the halo of a rustic idyl that bespeaks pure dream.

Inherently the play carries with it Pirandello's indictment of modern civilization as represented by the townspeople, by Diego Spina, and, in its religious aspect, by Monsignor Lelli. Sara had to break its laws to find her happiness. She had to leave her husband in order to find the Franciscan peace and simplicity for which her heart longed. Sara stands between civilized and primitive life; between capitalism and a vague form of communism; between Diego and Arcadipane, and she experiences loathing for civilization, for capitalism, and for Diego, while she finds a measure and rhythm of a happy existence in the normal and loving life that Arcadipane has given her.

The keynote of the drama is this natural life, the ideal of which the author presents to his characters as a goal. In leading them there, he does not hesitate to break the law of man, proclaiming the law of nature and of God. For this reason Sara and Arcadipane are revolutionary souls in their elementary simplicity. Near the torment and complications of Diego Spina's mind and life, Sara and Arcadipane rise before

us as the symbol of a pure and noble life that the author
dreams for the few who have the courage to break the barriers
of convention when convention is tainted by insincerity and
denies us joy in the gifts of the earth.

Part Four

THE DRAMA OF WOMANHOOD

XXIII

Introduction

There logically arises at this point the question whether in the drama of Luigi Pirandello there are elements that interrupt his predominating pessimism, his tragic tension, his gloom, and the bitterness that transforms some of his characters into exalted marionettes.

Childhood is one of the fresh and fragrant flowers he has woven into the crown of thorns which he has placed over the brow of the mock king that is man. The voice of a child occasionally brings a soft and refreshing note into the din made by the excited words that echo in the plays; a soft hand steals into the tense hand of Pirandello's heroes, trying in vain to lead them to dewy meadows of asphodel where life is good and joyous. At times a child is presented in the light of an unfulfilled desire of a woman's life, and he opens a tantalizing vista before the person who longs to touch the velvety flesh of a baby or to hear the sound of a little voice that would have drowned all the harsh noises of life had her desire been realized. More often childhood is brutally crushed, as in *Six Characters in Search of an Author* or in *Tonight We Improvise*.

The theme of childhood naturally blends with that of womanhood, and they both belong to the constructive and positive stage of Pirandello's thought and drama. The naturalistic sketches present the author in the predominating rôle of a painter; the plays of "being and seeming" and the social plays emphasize Pirandello the humorist, as do some of the works considered in the section on "Art and Life." One notices, however, in some of these plays, that the author veers towards a more thoughtful and constructive outlook on life.

The aspirations of the heroines in most of the plays included in the present section are towards a life of purity which experience has denied them. It would be hard to prove that his earlier characters, the naturalistic Liolà and Micuccio, for instance, or the grotesquely exalted Father in *Six Characters in Search of an Author,* or the tragic emperor in *Henry IV*, aspired to a life different from the one which was assigned to them. The naturalistically conceived characters are not capable of imagining any state other than the one that nature and life have prescribed for them, while the characters treated with Pirandello's tragic sense of humor know only conscious exasperation of feelings, and to live in the inferno of their painful exaltation is the sole way by which life is made possible for them. Deprived of that exaltation, they are æsthetically maimed. In the plays of womanhood characters are no longer deformed by ludicrous postures and traits. The *motif* of building up oneself disappears, while illusion is given an idealistic and religious meaning.

This tendency is a direct derivation of the idealistic strain which we see encircling the gloomy and bleak waste of life, as Pirandello conceives it. There is in Pirandello's heart a hidden and repressed surge of sincere emotion and pathos, a longing towards peace and goodness, which he has succeeded in channeling into these plays. It is a natural reaction for a man who aspires—and a sensitive man aspires when he finds himself in a situation that oppresses him—to think of a life different from the one in which he is a tragic actor. If a man is deprived of imagination, he submits sheepishly to any abuse from life; if he is a highly sensitive and imaginative man like Pirandello, he reacts either by abandoning himself to bitter and broad laughter, or by giving himself to deep thinking. The result of this concentrated thought is the themes of womanhood and motherhood that have given life to the plays enclosed in this section: *As Well as Before, Better than Before; It Is Only in Jest; Either of One or of No One; Other People's Point of View; The Wives' Friend; Mrs. Morli, One and Two; Grafting;* and *The Life that I Gave You.* With the exception of Fulvia in the first of the above-mentioned plays, we find ourselves before constructive and positive personalities which mirror a less tormented state of mind than that we have noticed in previous plays.

The theme of womanhood centers predominatingly on

motherhood, the chord that has never lost its resonance in Pirandello's plays. No matter how perverted his women have become, how low they have descended, they have always kept in their hearts a little nook of purity and softness where abides the love for a child.

XXIV

The Turmoil of the Irrational

AS WELL AS BEFORE, BETTER THAN BEFORE

(*Come prima, meglio di prima*)

The play revolves around a husband who believed he could regain his wife's heart without appealing to the instinct of motherhood. The play takes us to a small town in Valdichiana, Tuscany, where one night a woman tries to commit suicide. Her husband, a celebrated surgeon from whom she has been estranged for thirteen years, is notified by the priest and arrives to find her near death. He also finds there a romantic lover who remonstrates at having an operation performed on her because he fears he will lose her if she is saved. The husband, using his rights as a husband and as a surgeon, operates on her and saves her life. Here a problem arises: Will she go back to her husband, or will she resume the irrational life that she has been living for thirteen years by passing from one lover to another?

The play is constructed on the interplay of rationality and irrationality in the life of Fulvia, the tragic woman whom we find convalescing in the Penzione Zonchi, her beauty ravaged by time and experience, her soul tortured and embittered.

Let us notice at the outset that Pirandello has built his play on very solid lines. He lays a great deal of stress on the accurate and detailed description of the setting with the suggestion of the Tuscan landscape with its stern fir trees, its peaceful green valley, and a winding road that leads to the boarding house at the summit of the hill. He also describes with a painstaking minuteness its interior, the furniture, its odd proprietor, Don Camillo, who at the same time is a priest, a school teacher, and the owner of the establishment; Roghi, a big, calm, well-to-do farmer, who has gone there to consult the famous surgeon about his sick little daughter; Don Camillo's sister-in-law and her daughter Giuditta. These people, representing just the average humanity, are set in sharp contrast to the striking individuals who are the characters enacting the strange drama that is to unfold before us. Fulvia and Mauri, the lover, are individuals who have left the quiet shore of an ordinary, monotonous life, and have gone on the open high seas, led there by passion, while tragedy swelled the sails and the roar of the storm echoed in their hearts.

Fulvia, tired of being tossed and bruised, had tried to find peace and oblivion in death. Her last lover has been Mauri, a magistrate in a little town in Umbria, to whom she had meant a new life, a sense of relief from the living death of his existence with his peasant wife, nine years older than he, and with his no less uncouth children, who called him not "daddy" but "your honor" in homage to the title of magistrate that meant so much to their mother. Mauri appears at the *pension* to claim Fulvia as his own, disputing her husband's right to renew possession of her. Mauri believes that Fulvia has attempted suicide for his sake. Now he has given up his position, his wife, and his children. He is ready to dedicate himself to music, the unrealized dream of his life, and Fulvia will be his forever. The whole presents a very romantic combination: music, love, and a hopeless, blurred future ahead.

Fulvia is partly amused and partly interested in the prospect of this sort of life for her. In sober moments she feels detached from Mauri. Actually, he has been just one of the many lovers she has had. When he enters the *pension* and violently clasps her in his arms, telling her that she is his forever, she looks at him, first with indifference, then with surprise, finally with scorn, and says, pushing him away: "Are you still here bothering me? . . . Why, I hardly know you. . . . Oh, stop talking like that." Mauri has just said that he has given her all his life. All his life when there has been only a short erotic interlude between them! In her lucid intervals he is to her nothing but an exalted sentimentalist, not different from the numerous lovers who had uttered those very words, leaving her uncertain whether they were deified by her guiles or she was duped by their sincere folly. In this case we cannot say that Fulvia is another woman now, and then draw a sharp line between the Flora as she was known when she lived as a prostitute, and Fulvia the redeemed woman.

Critics have played too high a stake on the element of double personality where Pirandello is concerned. Fulvia is tired of life, and she is disgusted with the filth that rises like a contaminating tide towards her and tries to stifle her. She has closed herself in a cynical coldness and aloofness. She is a pitiful and tragic human character. As such, she is very complicated, and Mauri has for her the appeal of the irrational, standing before her as the embodiment of the thirteen long years of wandering, gypsy-like life that she has lived since she left her husband. Therefore she is interested in Mauri too, since he stands in contrast with her husband who represents the rational life of a wife and mother to which she has to return if she forsakes Mauri.

Fulvia is presented as one "who has a visible disdain, and a true and deep hatred for her beautiful body, as if it has not belonged to her for a long time . . . not having ever shared, except with a fierce nausea, the joy that others have found in it." Her body has been the source of her tragedy. Her husband awoke in her perverted desires and made her feel unworthy of living in the purity of a home as a mother to a little daughter, Livia. She left him and wandered from city to city, passing from one lover to another, gradually lowering herself to the point of living with a mosaic worker who drank and beat her. Then she had known Mauri.

Here is Mauri: ". . . in his forties, dark, thin, with lucid and mobile eyes like those of a lunatic; almost joyous even in the deepest agitation, expressive. He speaks and gesticulates with that theatricality that is characteristic of an exalted passion, a theatricality warm and sincere, but which, at times, is conscious of itself to the point of almost seeing itself."

Life has also left deep marks and scars on Silvio, the husband: ". . . tall, in his fifties, bony, solidly built, wears gold-rimmed spectacles. He is smooth-shaven. The top of his head is almost bald, but long locks of blondish hair, discolored, fall in disorderly fashion on forehead and temples. He pushes them back from time to time and then holds his hands on his head, as if meditating. He has the air both distracted and turbid of a man who is going through a violent crisis of conscience, but wishes to hide it, so he stands there almost overcome by a deadly inertia, with a cold, empty, and resigned smile on his lips, and by an uncontrollable expression of mockery, a reflection of old, malignant passions not yet extinguished, although long subdued."

The background of the play is a tumult of passions that left these three human beings strewn on the bleak shore of disappointment and tragedy. Here again we find Pirandello's nausea for lust, a feeling that is reflected by the physical shuddering of poor Fulvia and the psychological incertitude of Silvio.

Fulvia is now forced to select either her husband or her lover. Her resolution to choose between them depends upon whether her husband can appeal to something noble and pure which still lingers in her soul, left unsoiled by all the filth that has contaminated her. In their masculine blindness both Silvio and Mauri advance only the arguments of responsibility and remorse, which are of no value to Fulvia because she does not recognize the validity either of Mauri's responsibility or of Silvio's remorse. She exclaims: "I am between a duty which I do not recognize and a remorse that I declare imaginary." She does not wish to be taken back by Silvio through pity. She spurns that pity. For thirteen years she has known what it means to be alone and unprotected against the onslaught of life. "I have lived for years day by day. I have lacked the most necessary things, and a tomorrow without certainty does not frighten me any longer. Destiny can try all its whims on me." There is only one feeling that links her to her past—her mother love for the little baby that she left when her revolt against her husband made her desert him and plunge into the whirlwind of a desperate life.

Pirandello at this point displays all the subtle quality of his art in presenting to us a Fulvia who inwardly is tender and delicate and passionately waiting for her husband to speak to her about her daughter, and outwardly appears in-

solent, daring, mocking, and cruel. She keeps flitting from
her husband to her lover, at times being ruthless with one,
at times with the other, flinging at Silvio's face his own shame,
and mocking the sentimentality of Mauri, until finally Silvio
mentions her daughter to her. Then she breaks down, with an
overwhelming outburst of love and pity. She cries with a new
voice, with desperate sincerity, almost dejectedly: "Alas! I
have been here so many days with him like the woman that I
used to be, with all my heart of long ago suspended there in
my home, my heart of a mother, all these days waiting for
him to talk to me about my daughter, saying to myself . . .
Stay here so . . . stay here . . . now he is good! He has
come, now he will speak of her to you. Now he will tell you
of her." But Silvio sees in her only the woman of his desire
and in his masculine blindness does not take hold of the only
link that might have joined again the present and the past:
Fulvia as a mother.

Following the dictates of his cold and calculating nature,
he suggests to Fulvia that the only way by which she can return home is to go back as his second wife. She cannot go
back as Livia's mother. He has told Livia that her mother
died when she was a baby; that her mother was a saintly
woman. The child has grown up worshipping the memory of
a dead, saintly mother, her childhood overshadowed by that
grief, in a home where celebrity and wealth did not bring
the warmth that a mother gives to her child.

Fulvia returns home to her husband, but not to her daughter as the logic of her sentiment would require. Her hypocritical husband has been blind to this important point. Her
tragedy begins as soon as she goes back under an assumed
name, as an intruder, a hated intruder to her very daughter
who worships the memory of her mother. The delicate poetry
of the anguish of a mother constitutes the central part of the
play. She cannot reveal herself to her daughter; she cannot
go over to her child and clasp her in her arms, lost in the
happiness of having found her again.

Livia is "serious, stiff. Her face clouds over every time she
makes an effort to look at Fulvia. She is a little over sixteen."

We see her dressed in the deepest mourning because that day is the anniversary of her mother's death.

Fulvia's situation in her home and before her daughter is relieved of its tragic character by ironical happenings such as the anniversary of her death. She has to see Livia in deep mourning and hear that three masses will be said for the soul of the departed Fulvia. She is told that her husband, out of consideration for his present wife, is unwilling to go to church. This cruel irony ripples over the play and makes suffering deeper and more human.

In all this tragedy and anguish Fulvia is not the redeemed, angelic person that a sentimental writer might have imagined. A woman who has gone through what she has endured for thirteen years of contaminated soul and flesh could not have suddenly assumed virtuous qualities. At every moment the old self, held in subjection, attempts to reappear. How can it be otherwise when Livia hates and despises her? Her hostility gives Fulvia the sensation of being dead. She has dreamt of a beautiful and perfect life, and now her life is more irrational than when folly held her in its sway. She has had to give to Livia the old furniture which the latter has claimed because it had belonged to her mother. She has had to give her even the layette that she had made for her with her own hands, and she tells us: "To find it together with my clothes of that time, was for me . . . well, I cannot tell you. I plunged my face in it; I breathed in it the purity of the past; I felt it tangibly in me, here, in my throat—as a taste—I wept in it, and those tears washed my whole soul."

But she reacts from this state of deep and pure emotion with a sudden, strange, and mocking laughter: "My name was Flora. An ugly name, to tell the truth! The name of a dog. He [Silvio] calls me Francesca, by my middle name." As Fulvia's existence becomes harder and harder she reproaches her husband for the imposture and lie under which he has brought her home. That lie has solved Silvio's difficulties to perfection, but has made Fulvia's life unbearable. She cries: "We must kill this lie because I am alive, alive, alive. I have reached the point of believing that she is the daughter of the

231

other one, of the dead one. It is fearful! A shadow that has become a reality, and what a reality! It has truly killed in me my maternal instinct for her."

The situation becomes more complicated when Fulvia discovers that she is going to be a mother again. This means a new life for Fulvia whose heart is starving for her child's love. Should, however, anything at all wound her in the love of her new baby, a gust of folly would seize her again. She soon finds out that Livia not only hates her but does not respect her as the mother of the unborn infant, upon whom she looks as an illegitimate child, the baby of a woman not legally married to her father. There had not been any need of a marriage ceremony when Fulvia had returned to her husband, so Livia, upon investigating the matter, through her faithful servant Betta, finds no record of her father's marriage. She conceives the greatest scorn for Fulvia, her own mother. When the latter returns home with her baby, Livia is more haughty, flippant, defiant, unconquerable than ever.

The appeal of the irrational comes on the scene again with Mauri, a wreck of humanity, nervous and dreamy, who has come to tell Fulvia that he cannot live without her. After a year of aimless wandering, feverish, almost near collapse, he has returned to the woman who has given him an unforgettable glimpse of what true love is, who has burned her memory into his flesh and soul. Mauri is determined to have Fulvia go back to him. He counts on her mother instinct that Silvio, the husband, had failed to take into consideration. His hopes are not in vain. When Livia, sure that Fulvia is nothing but a bold adventuress, bursts into a fit of rage and offends not only her, her own mother, but the little baby, Fulvia rebels and strikes at the one who has been responsible for that situation—Silvio. Fulvia leaves him.

The only tie between Silvio and Fulvia was Livia, but Silvio's fraud had destroyed the daughter in her. Having broken the formula that made Fulvia's presence in that house possible—her being unknown to her daughter—her life with Silvio comes to an end. Folly sweeps over her and carries her towards the open spaces where life is free and tragic.

When she is compelled to reveal to Livia that she is really her mother, she realizes that logically she has no place in that home any longer. She breaks away from the unnatural situation that her husband has created for her, and lets the irrational take her back into a life that she hopes will give her full possession of her motherhood: her newly born child. This time she will leave Silvio, but she will take her child with her. It will be "as well as before, better than before." She turns to Mauri and cries: "My baby! Go! In the other room! My baby!" And then she announces to Silvio: "I shall take Livia with me this time! Tell her!—Yes, I shall take her alive—and mine!—With me, alive!—We shall go towards life!—Defying fate!" The real Livia is the new child. The other was dead.

Had Pirandello allowed Fulvia, after revealing her identity to Livia, to continue to live with Silvio, the play would have fallen into the depths of commonplace. The inner logic of the situation compels Fulvia to abandon her husband and Livia, the puppet he had engendered, in order to punish Silvio for ignoring the tie that existed between mother and daughter.

As in many of Pirandello's plays we find here a strong element of social satire determined by the author's rebellion against anyone who attempts to establish a relation without sentiment and feeling. The villain of the play is Silvio, the husband, and not Mauri. Mauri had been capable of finding in Fulvia's love a source of nobler feelings than had the tortuous Silvio. The rebellion against cold, ironclad forms of life is voiced by Mauri when he wishes to unmask the stately composure of his rival: "You could teach me that all depends on the first time we take off before everyone's eyes the dress that society has forced on us." That dress stands for the veneer of civilization, for customs, habits, laws, that do not sink very deeply into man's consciousness. The playwright flays here the large part in our social behavior that is pure form with no adherence to our soul.

Pirandello calls this play a comedy, but it is a deep and stirring example of a tragedy on the theme of motherhood.

XXV

The Form and Substance of Matrimony

IT IS ONLY IN JEST

(*Ma non è una cosa seria*)

This play which is one of the most spontaneous and charming that Pirandello has written, takes us to a *pension* run by a self-sacrificing and self-effacing young woman named Gasparina. She is a gentle figure drawn from life. The dramatist has embodied in her the silent sacrifices of countless women who in running a boarding house follow their womanly instinct in making a home for the men who live in it. She is "very thin, a little worn, neglected. She would be most vivacious if suffering, anguish, and the sadness resulting from what she has gone through did not repress the spontaneity and liveliness of her temperament and personality, and did not give her a humility, smiling and resigned."

Pirandello has woven a lovely and touching story around her, enclosing it in the frame of a drama. Her youth and beauty have been painfully obscured by drudgery. There are devotions that wither, affections that enslave and destroy. She graphically but truthfully describes herself when she says: "I am an old donkey accustomed by now to whippings and to all the jerks of the halter." Some of the guests have taken advantage of her goodness, as they often do with submissive people, and she has often been in despair, not knowing how to meet expenses. Her life at the *pension* has been very difficult. Not that her lodgers ever tried to make improper advances to her, for no one had ever thought of her as a woman. She was only the person who prepared the meals with the cook, supervised the serving, attended to the bedrooms, bought food, and received the payments when they were made. Her youth—she is only twenty-seven—is vanishing, fading away like a useless gift, and she is no more preoccupied with it than are the bachelors around her. She says to one of the guests, a woman school teacher: "Do you think that I am a woman? I am a mop. Everyone can, if you will excuse the comparison, clean his shoes with it."

One of the guests, the irascible, gesticulating, and shouting Grizzoffi, even calls her "Gasparona" with the derogatory connotation that the suffix "-ona" gives to a person's name. She was too busy to mind that! Grizzoffi was always punctual in paying, anyhow! The one who resented any insult to Gasparina was Signor Barranco, "a middle-aged man still in his prime, wealthy, with a big nose, very devout, usually silent, rather gloomy, yet with shy and timid eyes." He protects Gasparina and has often paid out of his well-garnished pocket what other people owed the poor girl. His wife died a few months before and left him all alone. Who knows that he might not have some intentions concerning Gasparina, that model of perfection and virtue? For a wife of a man of his age she might do, after all.

The inhabitants of the *pension* are rather striking, and the author has made the most of their peculiarities, putting them into comic relief. There is a professor of pedagogy, who, believing that nicotine is harmful, delights in inhaling the perfume of an excellent cigar that is being smoked by another guest, the irascible Signor Grizzoffi. Curious and witty repartee is heard between the old professor and Grizzoffi, as well as between Grizzoffi the woman-hater, and Gasparina's defender, the dignified Signor Barranco.

On this day there is unusual activity in the boarding house. Flowers have arrived and have been beautifully disposed in the dining room. Several bottles of champagne are ready to contribute to the feast. The most important of Gasparina's guests, Memmo Speranza, is returning from the hospital after having been wounded in a duel by the brother of a girl that he jilted. Memmo, the life of the place, is happy, young, handsome, always in love, and always changing partners. Girls are his weakness; he sees them and he cannot resist them. What is worse, he takes them seriously, proposes, and becomes engaged. From the time that he was nineteen up to now, when he is thirty, he has been engaged twelve times. "They surround you," he confides to us, "envelop you, inebriate you, make you lose your head. . . . They make you swear that you will love them *forever*. They even force you to swear it before father and mother." That is very dangerous for a man like debonair Memmo. "I am like straw," he says. "I catch fire immediately, I am a big flame, then I am drowned in smoke. Marriage is not for me. Love, yes. Marriage, no." He has been thinking very seriously of the sad plight of man, who falls in love, thinks that he will love a woman forever, and then is not allowed to change his mind when he realizes that his love is dead. With the mortality rate of his love affairs, after the danger he had gone through, he has to find some method of preventing the recurrence of a situation as serious as the one the escape from which they are celebrating today in the *pension*.

The banquet is offered by him (to whom money does not matter at all) to announce that he has found a radical remedy. Since he has been at death's door because of his impetuosity in proposing to girls, he wants to put himself in the situation of not being able to do so again. His plan is to marry a woman to whom marriage will only be a formality. In the midst of the hilarity of the guests, Memmo announces that this woman is Gasparina. At first Gasparina laughs, and so do the guests. One of them wagers Memmo a thousand *lire* and a wedding party that he will not marry her. Signor Barranco, in his moral susceptibility, is highly indignant. So is Grizzoffi, but this is a natural reaction in a man who is separated from his wife and hates marriage. Memmo, after accepting the wager, declares, "I know that one cannot fool with marriage. I have risked my life to escape it and I marry Gasparina exactly for this: to guard against the danger of getting married in earnest." Memmo will mortgage his name so that he will not be able to dispose of it by offering it to women with whom he might fall in love in the future.

After all, why not enter this novel scheme of marriage? Gasparina will be taken away from the inferno of the boarding house. She will have a small home of her own, a little rustic villa outside of the city walls, a nice garden, vegetable patch and chicken yard, the little dream that consoles the heart of every city dweller. "You will live there very happily, with a nice allowance and entirely free to do as you wish," promises Memmo to Gasparina.

Barranco and Grizzoffi, indignant at this awful jest and mockery, leave the table. The others celebrate with champagne the promise of this strange marriage. After a final toast to the bride and bridegroom, Memmo and his friends go to the city hall to arrange for a legal marriage. Gasparina in her usual submissive way has yielded, but she knows that it is a joke, for she says to her faithful maid, Rosa: "It is only in jest, Rosa."

Two months have passed, and Gasparina, in her rustic abode, with rest and tranquillity, seems another person. The fresh country air and the warm sun have given her color. She dresses well with modest taste. She still has her humble air, but one feels that her natural vivacity begins to reappear, although still suffused with sadness. She goes to visit Memmo in his apartment in the city for the first time. She wants to tell him that he is free to break the contract if he wishes. She has heard that he is still in love with the woman whose brother wounded him. Indeed Memmo, having been told that the girl had taken his part against her brother and left her house as a protest against her family, has felt the old love rekindled. Sentiment, his congenital weakness, has flowed back into the empty shell in which he had enclosed himself and is disturbing him. As far as Gasparina is concerned, he can break that shell, be free if he wants to. Gasparina also tells him that Signor Barranco, the middle-aged guest of her former *pension,* who looked after her so carefully, has something to tell him. The tender-hearted, ready-to-weep Signor Barranco has decided to marry her. He studied the girl while in the boarding house and admired her honesty, her sweetness, and sacrifice. He is growing old. Who will look after him in his old age?

Gasparina is now divided between a prosaic marriage with Signor Barranco, which will save her dignity, and the continuation of this mock marriage which begins to weigh on her

237

because the youth, the looks, and the temperament of Memmo have wakened love in her humble heart.

After three months when the bonfire of Memmo's love for his ex-*fiancée* has died out, Gasparina sends for him. He arrives at the villa and is struck by the charm and beauty of Gasparina. That day she is truly beautiful. It is a June day. "Her face is flushed. She wears a large straw hat and is holding three beautiful roses and a pink in her hand; she is truly a flower." When Memmo suddenly realizes how beautiful his wife is and hears that Signor Barranco wants to marry her, he proclaims his love for Gasparina, and thereby the pure form of marriage becomes a full reality.

In its structure the play pivots on the idea of substance and form in marriage, but the soul of it, what gives beauty and life to it, is the gentle figure of Gasparina on whom the author has lavished his sympathy. Under the sadness of the voluntary beast of burden, he has found the woman, the grieving poetry of femininity. There is much pathos in her words: "Yes, I'm getting married, but it is only in jest."

Memmo Speranza's marriage, viewed in the light of what Pirandello calls logical, is a triumph of logic. What is human is voluble, changing, chaotic, and therefore illogical. What is logical is the result of abstraction from life, reducing life to a pure "case" in which you can arrange everything without the interference of sentiment, just as on the chess-board men and kings are arranged for a game. Pirandello humorously hints that from the standpoint of logic the perfect marriage is the one from which every emotional element has been removed. Such a marriage would come the nearest to the institution as it exists in the books of the law or of sociology.

Before the charm and goodness, even the beauty, gently veiled with melancholy, of Gasparina, the clever humorist disappears and the man with the gift of human sympathy takes his place. Then we see that Pirandello is fully conscious of the futility of abstractions because if we indulge in abstractions, we do not live. He knows that the great tragedy of man consists in the fact that he plans his existence according to logic, while he must live his life as sentiment. With a woman like Gasparina there is no need of abstraction. Memmo does not need to close himself in the chilly mold that he has artificially thrown around himself. Gasparina's charm and gentleness will teach him the way to the fullness of life. So the author lets Gasparina and Memmo be happy in the sway of sentiment, perhaps smiling like a father on his daughter's wedding day when the smile is not always entirely joyous.

XXVI

The Purifying Force of Motherhood

EITHER OF ONE OR OF NO ONE

(*O di uno o di nessuno*)

The *motif* that has often appeared in Pirandello's plays —that of conceiving motherhood as a purifying element in a woman's life—is deliberately and clearly resumed in *Either of One or of No One,* a comedy presenting an exquisite study of the soul of a poor prostitute. Apparently humorous, the play hides Pirandello's customary depth of mind and sympathy of heart for human misfortunes.

The play revolves around Melina, a poor young prostitute whom two young clerks, Carlino and Tito, invite to go from Padua, their home town, to Rome. They rent a room for her and gradually she becomes a sort of housekeeper and wife to them both. Having a little room of her own, being provided with food, with no worries, she blossoms again like a rose. She is like a mother to the two boys, darning their socks and keeping their clothes pressed. For four months the three have been very happy, quietly happy, because Melina has a halo of sentiment for them. But something has suddenly happened that has disturbed the rhythm of their existence.

Carlino, in his calmer temperament, and Tito, always ready to fly off the handle, have spent the whole night discussing this perplexing matter, and they are still doing so late in the morning. Their landlady, at one time very affable, is furious now that the hopes of marrying her daughter to one of the two young men have been shattered by the new development. That morning she takes the opportunity offered by the fact that the electric light is still lit in their room to express her resentment against them. It is a bad morning to start a quarrel, since the two young men are facing a situation unprecedented in their lives. They are expecting Merletti, a lawyer friend, to help them out of their difficulty.

The play hints that we should always go beyond appearances before we pass judgment on our fellow-men. Upon hearing that two young men have called a prostitute to Rome, our morals would be outraged. Pirandello, following the continental point of view that most young men have such contacts, wishes us to feel that those two have been prompted to call Melina to Rome not only by lust but also by a feeling of affection that redeems to a certain extent their passion. Sentiment, however, is what brings trouble to Carlino and Tito.

Merletti, the lawyer, represents opinion as formed from judging by appearances, which opinion, as such, has a generic character. He does not know what has prompted Carlino and Tito to act as they have, nor does he know anything about Melina, and yet he calls their action foolish. He has a theory of his own about matters of love; there is safety in numbers: "Four, eight, ten, if you wish. Why not? But not one, as you had," he states. Merletti, however, discovers very soon that those two poor boys had felt the need of a little affection, and that had prompted them to make their unusual arrangement. Merletti, a large man, healthy, boisterous, and jovial, coldly analyzes them: "Touch little birds under their wing; they keep there the warmth of the nest where they found shelter before they learned how to fly. You have not been able to detach yourself from your distant home town. That's why you live together, still bound by your memories of the intimacy of your homes up there. You are ashamed of those memories, as of a weakness that, once revealed, may make you ridiculous—so you put on a serious air."

Although the boys do not like to hear that, it is the truth. Carlino, the more spontaneous of the two, confesses that one night when they were all alone in Rome and very sad, the name and image of Melina floated before his mind. Why not have her come down from Padua? She was so good, so humble, so sweet. They wrote to her and the girl had come. She was very thankful to them for taking her out of her horrible and sordid life.

Merletti has to adjust a very grave case of conscience. Me-

lina has confessed to Carlino that she is going to become a
mother. Merletti breaks forth into an uproarious laughter
upon seeing the two boys caught in that difficult and really un-
solvable situation. He laughs at "the buffoonery of nature,
for the thing in itself," while Tito is furious and threatens
him with violence. Merletti tries to appease the menacing Tito
by explaining his mirth: "Don't you see? You thought that
you had fixed everything perfectly, wisely, but nature came
along and turned everything upside down. You believed that
you had thought of everything and, as if from a wonder-box,
nature suddenly springs up with a baby in its arms and sneers
in your face. Ha! Ha! Ha! You had not thought of this."

After the irresistible but sympathetic laughter of Merletti
subsides, the serious implications in the play begin to loom:
What are they going to do with that baby? Will they resort to
an illegal operation? Will they allow Melina to keep her
baby? And who is the father?

The latter question assumes an amusing tone when Carlino
and Tito attempt to solve the riddle on the biological basis
that the stronger of the two is the father. Carlino goes in front
of the mirror, looks energetic, feels his muscle, puts on a
scowl, puffs out his chest. Both he and Tito go out without any
overcoat, although it is winter, in order to prove which is the
stronger. The test costs Carlino a serious cold that keeps him
in bed for nine days.

Melina, not having seen him for such a long time, goes to
visit him. She is motherly and sweet. She has gone out to buy
something for the baby. She wants to buy everything herself.
She feels proud that she can provide for the child with the
money that she earns sewing for rich ladies. In her spare time
she has learned how to read and write, and she has bought a
sewing machine. It is a new life for her, full of intimate satisfaction and contentment. Carlino is loath to destroy her new-
found happiness, but he feels compelled to tell her that, since
the paternity cannot be established, the only solution is to
send the infant to an institution. Poor Melina rebels at that
idea: "But it belongs to me!" she cries. "That is out of the
question! The child will be born and I shall bring him up—

keep him with me—he is my child." Since neither Carlino nor Tito can assume the responsibility of the child, she will take the responsibility herself, completely. She cries desperately: "Don't you understand that now that I have learned how to live so, I cannot go back to my former life?"

In her tenderness for the child, who is her redemption, the girl stands higher than the two men, who are touched neither by the pathos nor by the moral force of the situation. They are only preoccupied with the responsibility of the child, responsibility they feel they cannot assume until it is known who is the father. As far as they are concerned, the child will have to go to an orphan asylum. Melina rises in defense of her baby: "Then in order not to feel that responsibility, to free yourself of it, what do you want to do? Throw him away? When I am here, his mother, who wishes to keep him for herself? Would you assume such a responsibility—which is a crime, a true crime towards a child who is yet to be born— merely because you want to take into consideration another responsibility that you do not have and that you cannot have, since it is impossible to know to which of you the child really belongs?"

Melina tries to make them realize that to condemn an innocent child to be the child of nobody is unjust and selfish. Their philosophy, cruel and unbending, stands out against the nobility and spirit of sacrifice of the mother: "I came to tell you that I ask nothing of you, that I do not wish anything at all." But the two men insist, appealing to the common practice of society, and demand for Melina's baby the penalty that society inflicts on innocent infants for the guilt of their parents. The title of the play echoes, fraught with an ominous meaning: *Either of One or of No One.* If it cannot be determined who the father is, then the child will have no father and will have to go where men herd the innocent victims of their lust.

To Melina the responsibility of the baby is a sweet burden; to them it is a punishment. Their punishment consists exactly in this: that they do not have a baby although each is tormented by the desire of calling Melina's baby his own. It is punishment meted out by a just and modern judge.

Meanwhile hostility arises between the two friends, occasioned by the jealousy centering about the natural pride of wishing to be the father of the unborn child. They end by separating and hating each other. They never see Melina, although they offer to pay for her maintenance.

Melina is all alone when her baby arrives. She accepts her fate, happy in the sweet right of her motherhood. Often one life in unfolding exacts the price of another life. Melina is near death. She does not have any milk for her little one. She gets up, as pale as a ghost, sustained only by prodigious nervous strength, goes to the cupboard, takes a little piece of bread and, after wetting it at the sink, covers it with a cloth, making a sort of nipple, and gives it to her hungry three-day-old baby to suck.

Merletti comes to see her. She has begged him to find Tito and Carlino whom she has not seen since the time she discovered that her baby was coming. She wants to entrust the baby to them: to make them swear before God that they will not send him to an orphan asylum. Death is good to Melina's baby and to her. She dies in peace, knowing that her child will be cared for.

In a neighboring villa, in order to save the life of a mother, it has been necessary to sacrifice the child. That bereft mother will have Melina's bereft baby. He will be happy with the happiness that Melina provided for him with her life. Tito and Carlino will go on, and they will not forget, it is to be hoped, the pale girl who had found in motherhood a source of the elevation that society had denied her. Melina had given her son her family name: Niní Franco. Now he will have Signor Franzoni's name. So nature unfeelingly gives and takes, and is not concerned with the heart that rejoices nor with that which writhes in pain.

This play to some extent illustrates that undercurrent of moral sensitiveness which is one of Pirandello's most distinct characteristics. Pirandello shows the immorality of the situation existing between Melina and the two men by forcing us to ponder over the fact that a child has been born out of that lax way of living. The impelling moral sense is quickly wakened in the girl. Neither of the two men can continue to consider Melina an instrument of pleasure now that she has been made holy by motherhood.

Pirandello has entrusted Merletti with the task of representing him. Tito says of him: "It is no use talking. He absolutely dissects me! He absolutely dissects me! I, who within myself feel sure of my judgment, of my sentiments, cannot communicate with him." Merletti does not possess the reserve that characterizes Pirandello, but he is as sympathetic with the two boys as Pirandello is with his characters. He understands perfectly their plight, although he is moved to laughter upon seeing them caught by nature in a trap that promises no freedom. Merletti's laughter is his salvation: "It may be that I am a buffoon—yes—but since I am one, and nature is one also, I burst out laughing at myself—of my own accord. You, so serious, get hurt and make people laugh at you."

There are two points of view contrasted in the play: that of Merletti and that of Tito and Carlino. Merletti is a crude and heartless fellow with his theory of safety in number where women are concerned. The other two strive very hard to clothe their deeds with sentiment and to appear loftier than Merletti. Yet, in a situation which was *ex-lege*, the method advocated by the carefree lawyer was saner and less harmful to all concerned. In the end we find Merletti near the dying Melina, and Pirandello makes him appear in a better light than do the two sentimental young men who had not the moral strength to solve the situation which they had created.

It would seem that at first the author is going to let events be shaped by Merletti's proposed solution of sending the child to an orphan asylum, but as the play progresses the ruthless law set by Merletti softens into the more human treatment that is accorded to Melina's baby by the sympathy that her author has felt for her.

XXVII

The Power of Passive Resistance

OTHER PEOPLE'S POINT OF VIEW

(*La ragione degli altri*)

This is the touching story of a woman condemned to barrenness, who bears in silence her husband's relations with a former sweetheart, of whose baby he is the father. For years Livia Arciani has known that her husband Leonardo has had another home with Elena and their daughter Dina, but she has refrained from any protest because she felt that she had no right to deprive him of being a father. The play pivots around the sentiment of motherhood which has been denied Livia and which spells tragedy for Elena when circumstances compel her to give up her child.

Leonardo is a superficial man with literary aspirations that are made possible by his wife's wealth and long-suffering nature. He is an art critic for a paper financed by a deputy who expects a political victory in the parliament. Leonardo has been engaged, not for his literary merits, but merely because he, as Livia's husband, is the son-in-law of a man whose help the deputy sought.

There had been quiet, happy days in the life of Livia and Leonardo until one day there came a letter addressed to him. They read it together. "He had no secrets from me," Livia tells her father, remembering those days with regret and longing. The letter was from Leonardo's cousin, Elena Orgera, to whom he had been engaged and who just for a whim had refused to marry him. Now she is a widow and, being in need, she has turned to him for financial help. "I myself insistently urged Leonardo to send it to her. How could I suspect? But not even he, not even he, suspected then what was to happen."

Pirandello gives a dismal picture of the events that led Leonardo and Elena to their wrongdoing; of the cold attitude with which their relationship began; of the feeling of recipro-

246

cal indifference that enveloped their lives as soon as the inevitable monotony set in.

Elena, in looking back over the past, realizes that she should not have asked Leonardo to help her. She herself does not understand how they have become lovers: "What joy can be found in what has been dead for so long, crushed under the weight of dejection, need, detachment? Everything is almost over before it begins." This is the attitude towards passion that Pirandello lends to many of his characters. It is a disillusioned coldness. The misfortune of Elena and Leonardo was due to the fact that a child came to them. Naturally that established between the lovers a strong bond of necessity and resignation. Even Livia, the wife, recognized this bond, and bore in silence the wound to her feminine pride. The situation had been accepted by all three, just as one has to accept certain inevitable conditions in life: deformity, misfortune, death. It was not a happy situation, but it offered at least an appearance behind which Livia, as a wife, could bear her existence without losing her dignity. The true substance of family life was absent from her home, but that was her punishment for her barrenness.

All three, however, suffered. Livia had a husband only nominally and, as difficulties had increased, Elena and Leonardo had grown indifferent towards each other. Leonardo supported his mistress and his child with the money that he made at the newspaper, but that was not enough, and he had deteriorated mentally and physically. He had reached the point of looking on Elena as his punishment. Even his little daughter was a punishment and, cruel as that was, he had to admit it.

One day Livia's father, an old gentleman with very clearcut ideas of right and wrong, and with the utmost respect for the letter of the law, goes to visit his daughter for a brief stay. Livia is determined to keep her unhappiness from her father. She does not do it for the sake of her pride, for the false pride of appearing contented when she was not. She is convinced of the futility of any attempt to remedy a situation that, to her, is incapable of solution.

She and Leonardo have moved for years in their aristocratic home without saying a word to each other, without mentioning the other woman, because they both have accepted the situation passively. The verdict of their lives is sealed.

Livia's father refuses to understand this when he becomes cognizant of the real situation. He blames Livia for her behavior from the very beginning, for her lack of suspicion of Elena Orgera, for having acquiesced so calmly, indeed supinely. He is likewise unable to understand Leonardo. Does he not have any conception of right and wrong? Does he not know that there is a remedy for everything except death? He, Guglielmo Groa, is ready to help him to rectify the situation—to give money to the other woman and make her disappear with her child, so that Leonardo and Livia can live together again.

There is in Guglielmo Groa the solid, unsophisticated, somewhat unfeeling type of the older generation—people with a clear-cut concept of a perfect universe created by God and, what counts more, guided by God. Death is their only unconquered enemy, and since they usually are long-lived they comfort themselves with the thought that they have even fooled death. They have established the independence of their country, they have improved it greatly economically, they have built roads and railroads. What is there that could stand in the way of a successful man? Guglielmo Groa finds himself for the first time before two human beings with an entirely different psychology and with a point of view that he simply cannot fathom. He concludes: "I must say that you are both crazy."

Here is the situation as it appears to Livia: "The wrong is over, paid for, and only its consequences are a punishment for him." Livia inwardly feels sorry for her husband. She has seen him slowly disintegrate. She cannot condemn him for not leaving his daughter to return to her: "If he had abandoned his daughter because convinced of not being able to keep her, and had returned to me, to the comfort of this home, he would have inspired in me loathing, horror. Do you understand now?" To her Leonardo went into that trap unwittingly, as a man falls prey to the tricks that nature plays on him.

She only feels sorry for him and she calls herself partly to blame for what has happened. Leonardo wanted a child. She could not give him one. That was why he had gone to Elena. Livia's reasoning is determined by her own longing for a child. The great tragedy of her life is not to have had a baby. All through the play she makes it clear to Elena, to Leonardo, to her father that when she married it was not for a husband, but for a baby. She lent her own feelings to Leonardo. It was not a stupid policy. She did not destroy that sentimental thread which at times is stronger than love and hatred.

Leonardo is utterly passive. He has reached the point of having to admit that it is useless to investigate human actions: "Right? I tell you quite frankly that for me there isn't any, that it is useless to accuse myself or excuse myself. I recognize my wrong, and since I have been punished I recognize that my punishment is just and I don't complain." He says this with cold sadness, convinced and resigned. Leonardo is tied to Livia by the tie of marriage, as a husband. He is tied even more strongly to Elena because of the child. Livia's father is the only one who refuses to admit that the situation is hopeless. Leonardo's conclusion as they discuss the matter is this: "Nothing, nothing. You can do nothing. It is entirely hopeless, believe me."

Livia's father still cannot understand. He gets a glimpse of the truth when Livia cries to him: "He has a daughter, father. He cannot listen to reason." Only then does the old gentleman realize that there are situations in which to reason or to follow the dictates of reasoning is perfectly useless, and he goes over to the point of view of Pirandello to whom reasoning is an element that normally precedes our actions. It is entirely useless to reason after the situation has come into existence. Right and wrong are splendid elements, but they are truly decorative and external when you face a situation that holds you in its deadly grip and does not let go.

Neither Livia nor Leonardo can see those elements in the surge of the events in which they are caught. It is no help to think that they are married, that Leonardo should not have left Livia to go with Elena. "Words, Father, words! I neither

defend him nor accuse him. I see myself, Father, what I have
lacked. Where children are, there is the home. And he, here,
does not have any children!" She is helpless towards her husband because of this belief. She cannot desire to have him
abandon his daughter.

The visit of the father has had only the effect of precipitat-
ing the crisis. It has been put up to Leonardo to choose between his wife and his daughter. Leonardo, as is to be
expected, has gone with his child. The father's visit was responsible for another situation—Leonardo's dismissal from
the newspaper. Now Leonardo is penniless, without any love
for his wife or for his mistress, alone with his little daughter
whom he adores but cannot support.

Leonardo goes home to fetch some papers and finds his
father-in-law ready to leave, alone. Livia has remained loyal
to her husband, faithful far beyond what he deserved. To
her a wife is always a wife. Leonardo, touched, tells her that
his gratitude to her is all that he possesses now. Livia stands
before him not as a crushing and bruising embodiment of perfection, but as a gentle, though firm, woman who is full of
understanding. "I know that you understand. You can spurn
me, but you understand why I am so." Elena has shown him
the door: "You are free to go whenever you wish—why not?
Let us put an end to this. There is the door." A mistress is
always a mistress, and when support is lacking, she will always turn the man out. There is no tie to keep them together.

Livia looms nobler and nobler before him. She has never
lost her dignity. Her silence under the blow that had crushed
her is a splendid display of courage. When she sees the plight
of Leonardo, especially of Leonardo as a father with a daughter he is unable to support, she decides to go to see Elena and
tell her that the only way out of the situation is to let her have
the child. The scene between the two women is a beautiful
one, for Pirandello has uncovered all the love and anguish
that nestles in the heart of a mother and has revealed how
deep is a woman's longing for a child.

Livia finds Elena and her daughter together in a poor,
shabby room. Little Dina wants to play "country" and her

father has gone to buy her toys; trees and sheep and a shepherd and his dogs. When, after a painful, tortuous introduction, Livia tells Elena the reason for her visit, the mother rebels: "What do you want? My child? I shall shout for help." Livia makes her realize that until now she has been the one who has taken into consideration other people's points of view—Elena's point of view. For that very child, for Dina, Elena's child, she had given up her rights in her husband: "I know too well that there is something stronger than any right of mine." She now appeals to the mother to give up her right as a mother. Livia speaks not only of right but also of duty, of necessity: "There is now a necessity that forces itself on everyone and denies the right of all: mine, the one that he may have to his child, your own right; to make us face only duty, his duty towards the child and your own, and the sacrifice that it imposes on all of us: including me, for the very reason that I have recognized it."

The solution is a terrible one, but it is the only possible one: she, the mother, must give up her little one, blonde and rosy, that the child may legally have her father's name and live in happiness, even luxury.

It is poor Elena's punishment. "Don't you understand that this is the wrong, the true and only wrong that you have done, not to me—leave me out—but to your very child, born here, in your sin? This wrong, with him the father, you the mother, this requires now a sacrifice that neither of you wishes to make."

Elena is skeptical as to the great interest that Livia takes in her child. She is resentful, even scornful. Livia then allows her to poor into her agonized heart. She has suffered the most cruel pain that a woman can suffer, the humiliation of barrenness. She has longed in vain for all that a child means to a mother. "I should be not a mother, but a slave to your child. Don't you understand that I am here before you, conquered, and that you win if you make the sacrifice? I should worship your child because she is the only thing I lack, and I should give her all of myself." Elena cannot understand, cannot see. It is her child: "I have given her life, my blood; I have given her my own breasts. Why don't you think of this? She has come out of my womb. She is mine, mine." It is a cruel folly, but Livia insists that she has borne all those years of silence and repressed grief only because she knew that he, Leonardo, was a father. Now Elena must give back to her, not the husband, as she wishes to do (she does not want a husband in him), but the father, and to do so, the child must go with the father.

Leonardo returns with Dina's toys. He sides with the mother. Livia leaves. She will remain alone. Leonardo will have to stay with his daughter. Elena is uncertain. There is a life of struggle, of cold darkness for the pretty Dina, and Elena's own heart is uprooted. She wavers. The idea tempts and frightens her. Finally she yields. She goes to fetch a pretty hat for Dina, for she wants her to look pretty when she goes to her new mother. Leonardo seizes the child and flees. Elena comes back into the empty room. She understands. "Then she runs to the window and tarries there for a long time, gazing. Finally she draws back silently as if bereft of her senses. She looks with astonished, blank eyes at the child's toys on the table, sits near the table, realizes that she has the child's little hat in her hand, looks at it, and breaks into desperate sobs."

The play stresses the victory of virtue and silence—Livia's victory. She is one of those rare and truly virtuous persons who can sympathetically transform silence into a mighty force that works for right.

The antisocial strain is clearly in evidence in the play. However, only apparently is Pirandello against society and marriage. He is opposed to them only when they clash with certain fundamental human needs, such as, in this case, longing for a child. Pirandello is not against right and wrong. He is against a specific right and wrong. Here he is opposed to Livia's father because he failed to see that the key to the situation was the little Dina. For the sake of the recognized form of marriage and for the sake of his own daughter, he would have brushed the little girl aside unmercifully. To Pirandello the situation should be unraveled through the little daughter who had been born outside of the home and had to be brought into the home, even if the mother had to be sacrificed.

As the play develops we witness a conflict between the forces of nature and the laws of man. Leonardo in following blind instinct has exposed his child to the brand with which society marks illegitimate children. Pirandello, although he has to sacrifice that bit of commonplace, Elena, solves the problem by taking the child to the father's home, to the legal wife, thereby making the forces of nature subservient to the laws of man.

The play is projected against the background of modern life, rendered through the intrigues of a newspaper director who supports a deputy and keeps Leonardo on its payroll only because the father-in-law is a friend of the successful candidate. Modern life is envisaged through city life as revealed by the words of Livia's old-fashioned father: "But what is the matter? Hush here, hush there. May a person not say a word? One can do anything at all. Actions do not offend here. But as soon as one opens one's mouth—hush, hush, hush. Do words offend you? It seems that in the city only your ears become sensitive."

The strongest *motif* that detaches itself from the play is that only a child can keep two people together. The saying: "Where children are, there is the home," is a sort of proverb in Italy, and it returns more than once in Pirandello's plays. The home of Leonardo and Livia was unhappy because no child had come to them. They become reunited only when little Dina, even if born of another woman, comes to make their married life perfect. Pirandello states without any shade of doubt that Leonardo belongs where Dina is. He vindicates Livia as a reward for her understanding soul, for the long, agonizing silence with which she concealed her unhappiness. She had considered the points of view of others, and that resignation had been her strength and had vindicated her.

There is no feeling of exaltation in Livia's victory since it must be envisaged through the misery of poor Elena. Livia's victory is a victory without the blare of trumpets and the roar of an applauding crowd. It is rather a victory reached by the author's intellect even against his heart that is full of human sympathy for Elena, the only real victim, who pays the wages of sin with the sacrifice of her child.

XXVIII

The Loneliness of the Lofty

THE WIVES' FRIEND

(*L'amica delle mogli*)

Italo Siciliano [1] has called *The Wives' Friend* a comedy of modern corruption. Pirandello's sense of perspective applied to immorality does not react differently when focused upon present day or upon historically ascertained past. He has faith only in a mythical age of purity which in its indefinite contour makes that faith possible, although it escapes analysis. Purity is, to him, only an aspiration of the soul, of some mysterious particle of our being. Around it there is the terror and storm of instinct. That is true today as it was yesterday. *The Wives' Friend* is not, therefore, a play of modern corruption.

On the contrary, it is a play dealing with the tragedy of one who has been doomed to loneliness by the loftiness of her nature. It is dedicated to Marta Abba, the great actress, friend of Pirandello. One feels that the author has wished to express his admiration of the actress by lending her name to the heroine, the woman who has conquered the hearts of all the wives, and whom at the same time the husbands love also: Marta, tall and stately, veiled in the seriousness that her virtue casts over her lovely countenance. Her nobility and beauty strike us from the very first scene when she appears with a large bouquet of flowers in her arms: "She is most beautiful, with auburn hair, deep, sea-blue eyes, liquid, full of life. She is twenty-four years old. Her manner, not stiff, but most reserved, does not interfere with the pure expression of the noblest feminine grace. She dresses with exquisite taste."

The setting is in the Rome of today, among a group of friends of the upper middle class. Those who contribute to the action are four young married couples who are, men and

[1] *Luigi Pirandello*, p. 10.

women alike, dominated by the beauty and charm of Marta. Her serenity is contrasted with the petty quarrels of husbands and wives who whirl around her, restless and dissatisfied.

Marta tries to keep peace among them. She had been the confidante of her male friends when they fell in love with their present wives; she had read their letters, often suggesting the answers. When they got married, she prepared their new homes for them while they were on their wedding trips, and after they had settled down she tried to compose their differences. Marta is the life of that circle of friends. Only she keeps them together, as peaceful as couples can be.

They all live in the light that emanates from her. Away from her, they quarrel, they are mean to each other, petty, even cruel. As soon as they draw near her they fall under the spell of her serenity. She is to look at; to worship also, but this feeling abides only in a little nook in the husbands' hearts that is unknown even to them. She is the one towards whom longing goes in the form of an elusive regret for not having married her. Most of the quarrels of these married couples are the result of the fact that they all look upon Marta as an ideal for the women to copy, for the men to compare with their wives. How could they copy a woman like Marta? They want to dress like her, to move like her, to act like her, and they fail pitifully. The husbands, placed before the beautiful original and the dismal and grotesque copies, laugh, criticize, make mean and cutting remarks. It is natural. One of the husbands tells her: "You believe that you make our wives more acceptable to us by inducing them to think, to act, to behave like you. They try to resemble you and they reveal themselves unworthy of their model, awkward, stupid, clumsy, miserable."

Why none of those men had not asked Marta in marriage is a mystery and a cause of secret regret to all of them. Their wives know it, and they all agree that the men showed very poor judgment in letting the charm of Marta's beauty and gentleness pass unheeded by them. Perhaps she had had no time to think of herself and of her youth, absorbed as she had been by her sincere and fervid concern for her friends' happiness.

The perfection of Marta is not of the stereotyped kind. She had reached the conclusion, very quietly within herself, that men and husbands do not seek what is noble and lofty in a woman, for she says: "I see very well how you want a woman to be! Well: just as you have dwarfed her—a monstrous shame. Your own vice and nothing else! Do not be surprised to hear me speak so. I am not one of those saintly persons who feign not to know anything at all. I am as I am, exactly because I know." She rebels at the fact that men see in a woman only the giver of sensual pleasure, blind to her deeper self: "Shouldn't this be a reward for you men, to have near you a woman, a real woman? The prize that no one must know, that is not revealed; that suffers, in the secret of her heart, of the joy that she gives, and in this suffering of hers is also a joy, a joy truly suffered from which life is born anew? The sweetheart and the mother, the sweetheart who becomes the mother, and who says, after patting the man's shoulder as one would a child: 'Enough now; be a man; do not see, in me and in you, only this.' "

That was the real reason why those men had never dared to propose to her. Marta was too lofty for them. Her reserve chilled their words on their lips. Each of the four husbands had found another mate, ridiculously inferior to Marta, and now they all bask in the lukewarm sentiment that bore resemblance to a flower that had not been allowed to blossom. Sometimes, this sentiment became tormenting because irreparable, and then there floated before them the picture of the life that might have been and had not been.

As is to be expected, Marta's four friends are differently affected. Two of them were resigned with the stupid composure of normal men in whom a wound of that kind is not constantly reopened by a vivid imagination. But one of them, Venzi, who is violent, restless, rather coarse, with a turbulent soul, loves Marta, and is as jealous of her as a person can be who can expect nothing.

Venzi, because of his irrepressible love for Marta, torments his wife and makes her very unhappy. Only Marta can place on the little heart of Anna Venzi the balm of her sympathy. Often Venzi tells his wife to put a new cosmetic on her eyelashes in order to enhance her eyes, and it hurts her so that she has to cry for pain. He laughs diabolically with laughter that shakes his huge frame, while in his eyes there is a dull light of desperation and hatred. He tells her to cut her hair short, only to laugh cruelly at her when she does so. Venzi is "about forty, of powerful build, especially in his chest, high shoulders, with a big curly head, a little gray at the temples, dark complexioned, clean shaven, still good looking, although too fat. He often grasps the lapels of his coat while dangling his head and rolling his turbid eyes almost in a childish way like a peevish or surly child. He dresses in black, carelessly."

Venzi is particularly upset now because Fausto Viani, a handsome, wealthy, distinguished, and amiable friend of Marta has just married, and while he was on his honeymoon she has prepared his home, revealing in every detail not only her exquisite taste but a personal sentiment for Viani that Venzi senses and resents.

Marta is very happy about the little nest that she has been able to prepare for her friend and his bride. A party is to be given in the new home to welcome back the newlyweds. Quite unexpectedly, Venzi goes to see Marta and disturbs the serene joy of her friendship for Viani.

Venzi in his usual diabolical manner makes the remark that the real mistress of the home is the one who has arranged everything with such perfect taste—Marta. They all agree that it is so and that it should have been so. Viani should have married Marta. There is a tense moment of uneasiness in the room, just as when a phrase or a word makes a deep impression on a person and may definitely influence his conduct, because it brings out into the clear light something that that person did not wish to confess.

It seems, in fact, that Viani had wavered between Marta and his bride for a long time; but then, like the others, had been too timid to propose to Marta. Marta laughs, blushes, denies, and resents the inference made by Venzi. She is happy only when they are happy, although, to be sincere, her rôle is not always without difficulties. It makes her happy, but there is also a tinge of sadness in her heart. Venzi has raised a little the veil that surrounds her soul.

Viani and his bride arrive. They are in quite a different mood from that to be expected of two young people returning from a honeymoon. Elena, the bride, is sick, terribly sick. She enters the home that Marta has prepared and refuses to see any of her husband's friends. She is nervous, upset, abrupt. She goes directly to her room. Marta is the only one who goes upstairs to her. As soon as Elena sees her she feels for her what all the other wives had felt— complete trust and faith. She is another addition to the choir of admiring wives that surround Marta.

Elena's illness is very serious. She is operated on, but her life is in danger since the removal of a tumor has not cured her. Her friends are worried. Her husband is distracted; Venzi is tormented.

Jealousy torments him. Suppose that she should die, then Viani would marry Marta. His jealousy suggests a diabolical plan to him: to make them all conscious of such a possibility. He sows a seed of suspicion in Elena's heart by making her consider what might happen in case she died. The house is ready, the house that Marta has prepared. Elena has to recognize that there is such a possibility. Her life becomes a torture because she has found herself capable of thinking such a monstrous thing of Marta and her husband; yet, she cannot remove that thought from her brain. Everything that Marta does for her, her attentions, her solicitude, her care, all is destroyed.

Venzi's is a novel way of vengeance and of torture: to transform into active forces the inner thoughts that everyone has at times when the irrational passes by us: black fluttering wings that touch our brains and leave a sense of cold in them. Venzi wants to take hold of the feeling of pure and noble friendship that exists between Marta and Viani and transform it into a conscious love, to make jealousy rise in Elena, to torment her and force Marta away from Viani.

Now that both Marta and Elena have been made alive to the possibility of an uncontrollable event that will take place after Elena's death, Venzi poisons Viani's mind, too, by making him see that deep in his heart he has thought of the possibility of marrying Marta, should his wife die. Why not? Marta is young, beautiful, exquisite. Now all three know. The stage is set for the tragedy of which his hopeless love for Marta makes Venzi the cruel stage director.

As Elena's sickness becomes more acute her torment increases too. She goes so far as to have Marta promise her that she will marry Guido Migliori, a handsome but uninteresting young man who has just asked Marta to marry him. She pleads: "Not for me! I believe you, I believe you! It is to remove from the head of that despicable man the thought that he has put here like a nail and which is driving me mad, killing me."

A few hours later she is at death's door. Pirandello places the husband before his dying wife and searches into his heart, and next to his grief for her agony, he discovers the nebulous, unrevealed thought entertaining without revolt the possibility of her death. It is a parallel case to the one already noted in *Each in His Own Way,* where a son confesses that after nine sleepless nights he has been led by exhaustion to desire that his mother were dead. In the case of Viani, it is not a question of his desiring Elena's death. He does not know whether her death would bring him a heartrending grief or the sense of freedom. As a matter of fact, he is distracted before the suffering of poor Elena. But a black wing, vampire-like, often beats in the endless abyss of human consciousness.

As long as Elena lives, Venzi hopes and waits, watchfully. If she dies, he will never allow Viani to marry Marta, never. As death is stealthily approaching, Marta and Viani are in a room adjacent to Elena's. Even their grief for the death of a human being so dear to them has been poisoned. Venzi enters the room unseen to witness his work of destruction. He moves like a thief. He is ready for anything. A few minutes pass. Elena is dead. Venzi shoots Viani and pretends that the latter has committed suicide. Marta goes over and a glance at Venzi reveals to her what has happened. She does not have any proofs. She can only weep and grieve over the only love of her life, a love that she would never have revealed to anyone, a secret sealed in her noble heart.

Venzi, with the intuitive power of jealousy, had surmised the truth. Marta loved Viani, but she would never have married him. A great confusion reigns in the house. The wives of her friends are determined to stay there with her, but Marta is a different person now. She turns to them and orders them to go out of the room: "I wish to remain alone. Leave me. I wish to remain alone, alone, alone." Such is the destiny of women like Marta, perhaps like Marta Abba, who are too lofty to be within the reach of man.

Pirandello's sympathy for Marta has led him to view the situation of modern women as a sad plight. They have to please men to get married. If they do not, even if they are as beautiful as Marta, they are doomed to loneliness. In this sense, Marta stands as an ideal of which her friends' wives are the ludicrous embodiment. It is natural that she should end as she did, sharing the lot of all ideals. Had she married Migliori, she would have been dwarfed into a placid nonentity.

This leads to another strong *motif* of the play: What will happen when something which might have been, that should have been, has not been? Tragedy can be the only result. Pirandello has made it arise from a natural, almost commonplace environment, in which Marta stands out very much as Beatrice, a dream of beauty and virtue, stood out among the women that Dante knew. Pirandello has here taken the place of Dante. May it be that Marta stands in the place of Beatrice?

XXIX

Where the Children Are, There Is the Home

MRS. MORLI, ONE AND TWO

(*La Signora Morli una e due*)

Mrs. *Morli, One and Two* is a comedy in which a woman, divided between the egotism of two men, finds again the unity of her life in her love for the little girl she had by her second mate.

The comedy is based on the idea that we are different with different persons. We are light hearted with some people, and as solemn as owls with others. This was the case with Evelina Morli who had only been joyous and carefree with her husband, Ferrante, while she had always been serious, silent, and subdued with her lover, Lello Carpani. Pirandello humorously and somewhat devilishly has inverted the rôles usually given to husbands and lovers. He has imagined Ferrante, the husband, full of life and mischief, always ready to take pleasure wherever he finds it, while he has fashioned in Carpani, the lover, a cold, stilted, and formal individual.

It may be accidental, however, since Evelina had married Ferrante when very young, and had been abandoned by him, leaving her with a little boy after five years of happy and almost irrational life. She had gone to a well-known lawyer, Lello Carpani, who saved her dowry and then made her his mistress. After the first stir of scandal, the best society of Florence had accepted Evelina because of her reserve, her gentleness, her seriousness. Lello had composed her as he had composed himself; he had made her over; he had taught her the correct etiquette, and thereby Evelina had won the respect of society.

Lello was one of those individuals who always assume a dignified air before the world for the sake of their profession. He had had the somewhat romantic youth usual in people who have literary leanings. Then the profession had come, and it had covered youth and poetry with the dignified robe of the law; not altogether, however, since because of Evelina he had defied the conventions of society. We are told that his almost conquered sentimentalism can "still be perceived through a peculiar little smile of his, and from the manner with which he passes his hand over his hair, which used to be very abundant and now is very scanty, but well arranged, with a part on one side and a little tuft on his forehead. His position! So many appearances that one has to put on and respect!" That is how a man becomes dwarfed by experience: "Alas! What are you going to do about it? This great seriousness of ours is necessary after all, although it contains so much hidden melancholy!" But what had Ferrante accomplished with all his good looks, his romantic outbursts, and his unbridled youth? He had left Evelina, had fled to America, and had not concerned himself at all with her fate nor with the fate of her son.

And yet it seems that it does not pay to be like Lello. Now Ferrante has reappeared upon the scene, has come to see Lello, and the perfect structure that the latter has erected around himself and his family life seems likely to totter and fall. It is true that Ferrante, although under an assumed name, has revealed that he has the best intentions in the world, but his very presence in Florence is an unbearable threat. Lello tells us that everything is confused and mixed up, for Ferrante who had disappeared and was as blotted out of his memory as if he were dead, now has reappeared. Pirandello seems to say to Lello: "Well, these things happen, my dear fellow. We plan our lives very carefully and the slightest change disturbs our beautifully laid plans "

Ferrante's return will most assuredly interfere with the quiet life of Lello Carpani. Now everyone will be reminded that Evelina is not his legal wife. Lello will no longer be clothed with the dignity of a husband. He will be looked upon as Evelina's lover. Everyone will say: "This woman has a husband and lives with her lover." Ferrante comments:

"That's correct, but it seems to me that as between you and the husband, this situation should be more upsetting to the husband."

The scene between the two rivals is a jewel of dramatic perfection and subtle humor. Lello, like people bent on appearing to be always perfect, reviews to Ferrante all his usefulness to Evelina from the time that she was abandoned by him. He wishes to cover with the glamour of the exceptional what is common decency and even self-interest. When he saved Evelina's dowry and legalized her husband's position, according to him he did so to make Evelina "entirely free of herself, not only without the preoccupation of every material difficulty, but free to rejoin her husband, if she wanted." Pirandello does not like people who want to appear perfect. He searchingly tells him: "You—forgive me for saying it— perhaps did not feel so much the need of honesty, as you did the need of appearing before her love adorned with honesty; as if to defy it by the comparison between the cowardliness of the husband who had fled, and your own abnegation." Lello boasts that he did not have the marriage annulled. Could it not be—so argues Pirandello through Ferrante—that he did not do so in order not to give to Ferrante the satisfaction of having it annulled in case he returned?

Now Ferrante and Evelina will meet again. To what extent has Lello been able to destroy the joyous nature of young and vivacious Evelina? Has he only concealed it under the composure that Evelina naturally assumed with him from the first day they met, he a famous lawyer, she a downcast and crushed woman of twenty-three with the care of a little boy, with her heart wounded by her husband's flight to America and by his lack of concern about her fate and his son's future? Has she forgotten the life of amusements, whims, and follies that she lived with Ferrante when first married? What has happened to the feelings that envelop those acts and keep them alive? It seems that almost nothing remains of the old Evelina. There is "a languor in her eyes, in her voice, in her smile," she is composed and dignified. In Evelina the fervor with which she and Ferrante have lived has gone into her love for her boy, Aldo.

Her first reaction towards Ferrante is one of open and violent hostility. She does not want Ferrante even to see Aldo. Aldo is hers. Ferrante has no right to him. She is the mother who wishes to have all for herself the son she has brought up. She cries: "Aldo is mine, only mine [*turning like a wild beast towards Ferrante*]. If you returned for this, you can go, because you have no right to him."

But Aldo interferes. He tells his mother that he is not a child, that he wishes to hear his father's side and know what reason he has to offer for his indifferent behavior. Ferrante has an excellent defense lawyer in Pirandello. After the financial crash that was brought about by others and in which his responsibility did not go beyond keeping the books in great disorder, Ferrante fled because, had he remained, he would have done a greater harm to his wife and child. By disappearing he took all the responsibility on himself, all the more that he knew the mother had enough money of her own on which to live comfortably.

Aldo sees that since his father is there, his situation is entirely changed. He must no longer remain with Lello where he feels like an outsider, crowded out by the seven-year-old half sister, Titti. Lello Carpani agrees with him. Aldo's presence in his house is absurd now that the father is back. As usual, logic was the handmaid of what suited him to perfection.

The mother is mortally wounded. She cannot let her child go. "Turning towards Aldo and embracing him and clasping him tightly with the fury of desperation, she cries: 'It is impossible. I shall not let you go. I could not live without you, my son. How can you think of abandoning me, abandoning your mother?'" Ferrante is calm. He tells her that he wants Aldo to decide. Aldo, obeying his own inclinations, and forced by circumstances, decides to go with his father. The mother may visit her son any time she so desires. Ferrante's strength is Aldo's presence. Evelina sees that the destiny of

Aldo is inextricably woven with that of Ferrante. If she gives up Ferrante altogether, she will lose her son. She has to compromise by allowing Aldo to go to live with his father, reserving to herself the right of visiting him.

Aldo and Ferrante are birds of the same feather. Aldo has his father's vivacity and love for life. They go to Rome as on a lark. They settle there. American money can do a great deal in Italy, and Ferrante lives in a princely fashion in a villa, and possesses servants and horses. There is only one thing missing—the mother, Evelina. Through a ruse, they succeed in having her go to Rome. They wire that Aldo is desperately ill. She arrives, is at first indignant, then threatens to return to Florence, and then to stay in a hotel. In reality she stays a week with them.

Events show that the past is not dead. Ferrante had thought that it was, years ago, when he had crossed the ocean and burned his bridges behind him, believing that he could start life over again. It had been impossible. He had to come back, urged by a force greater than his will. The life they had lived together had never lost its hold on him. He reminds Evelina of the happy days spent together and calls her again by the endearing name he used in their intimacy: Iviù. He calls her again, aloud, as he used to, with the same intonation of voice, and the whole past lives anew in the life that glows in that name. After her fright at being in the house of a man that she must forget, Evelina laughs. Ferrante later confesses: "I felt that laughter lacerate my inner self. Then our eyes met, and we were dismayed. No, the past was not dead."

In the atmosphere created by being together, just as once in a distant, yet vivid past, Evelina finds delight again in the most simple and almost childish pastimes. With little cries of fright and laughter she even goes on the seesaw while Ferrante and Aldo push her. She is young again, she is joyous, spontaneous, vivacious, happy. Father, mother, and son go on horseback; they laugh. It is happiness, such as none of them had thought could exist on this earth.

Pirandello seems to tantalize Ferrante by telling him how happy life would have been if he had not interrupted that happiness by fleeing to America! That is Ferrante's torment and punishment. As he sees Evelina as she used to be, the idea that she is his and no one else's rises in him, makes him hate Lello Carpani and revolt against the situation existing between him and Evelina. He knows that she is his. Why should she go back to Florence to be Lina (as she is called there) and not Evelina; Lina "the fierce little mother that she has become"; Lina serious and cold. How could she go back now?

Evelina has remained honest, in spite of the fact that the past has vividly risen before her and has tried to envelop her in its magic circle of slumbering, happy memories. But she has been strong because she "wanted to be able to return there again." With her renunciation she has bought the right to go back to Ferrante's house again in the only guise in which she could go back—as Aldo's mother. This is the argument that she advances against Ferrante who does not understand her in his rekindled love for her—the love of their youth.

In his masculine self-centeredness, Ferrante wants her to go there for him and not for Aldo. She gently tells him: "You cannot understand it, you cannot understand it, because only a woman can understand this." She is frank, open; "I feel that you are in him, in my love for him, while the love that I feel for my daughter, there in Florence, is for her alone." She had lived with Lello all those years, deriving strength from the life that Ferrante had always given her and that she found in Aldo. The reflection of that life had infused warmth into her existence. It had been a life of quiet duty to her son, to Titti, to Lello who had been good to all of them.

At the end of Evelina's week of happiness with her family, Armelli, a respectable law partner of Lello Carpani, arrives in Rome and discovers the truth. He wires to Florence the situation that he has found. He also brings the news to Evelina that Titti is constantly asking for her and that in Florence there is an epidemic of a children's disease. Titti has had a slight fever. That is sufficient to make Evelina strong enough to face reality and duty. She leaves for Florence immediately with Armelli. Ferrante and Aldo feel lost without her. They do not know what to do or what to say. Their silence in the sadness of the twilight shows that violence has been done to life and they are suffering for it.

We can easily imagine the scandal in Florence. Signora Armelli in her moral indignation calls Evelina's action "revolting." Miss Wright, the governess, leaves as a protest. In her innocence, Evelina cannot understand all this indignation. After all she has been with her son and in her husband's house. It is extremely hard to batter down the strength of an argument based on what is obvious to narrow-minded people. A lucid, sharp, and powerful argument appeals only to a few. A commonplace argument based on a usually accepted belief will rally the support of the many. In discussing the matter with Lello, Evelina had to face a man who was following the logic of the average person and using arguments based on those grounds. Such were the assumptions of Lello, and they were all the more irritating to him since he was powerless. Ferrante was Lina's legal husband. The ties of matrimony are strong; they remain so even after fourteen years.

The scene between Lello and Evelina after her return home conveys Pirandello's understanding of a woman's heart and of masculine blindness. Lello, in the rôle of a resentful and offended husband, thinks Evelina has betrayed him: "Ah, there! You admit it [that you have been in his house]. But like a brother, wasn't he? A brother who calls you Eva. Oh no, who calls you . . . what does he call you? . . . something like 'Ju,' the name of a mare." Evelina is perturbed by this sudden recollection of her life with Ferrante. She is offended by the crude and vulgar reference to the name by which Ferrante called her. Lello does not see this. He does not understand the delicate play of emotion that goes on in the exquisite soul of Evelina.

Evelina sincerely and firmly makes him understand that a woman like her knows how to protect her dignity, her honesty, and that "if I have returned it means that you may rest assured that I have felt that I could return." Had she yielded to Ferrante, as Lello in his frantic rage insinuates, she would not have returned to him and to Titti, her child. He is trying to go beyond the portals of her conscience, to investigate the natural and spontaneous feelings of Evelina over which she has no control and he no right of investigation. Lello's blindness and lack of understanding compel Evelina to tell him calmly and firmly: "If I have returned you must not believe that to return has not cost me anything." She has paid a high price for the right to return to him and to her daughter.

That might satisfy Lello's personal feelings, but what about the people and his reputation when everyone knows the scandal? It is a disaster. He is irritated by the idea of sacrifice, of what it cost Evelina to return to him. Her faithfulness becomes an insult. Evelina is compelled to reveal to him that the great factor in that moment of trial was her daughter. She had resisted temptation for her daughter's sake; for the right of holding her in her arms without blushing. Lello, blind with rage, counters: "What do you think I care about my daughter in such a case?" Evelina remembers that Ferrante had made the same remark: "He, too, there said to me: 'What do you think I care for my son if you come for him?'" She sees in a crude light the masculine aggressiveness and predatory attitude of the two men, and before it she affirms her right to lead her own life. She announces: "It is time that you both put an end to this, for my children matter to me if they don't to you. After all, you have Titti here; he has taken Aldo there. Each of you can be by himself in the fullness of his life, but not I, because Aldo there is his and mine. Titti here is yours and mine. He wants me for himself, you want me for yourself. I cannot divide myself, half there, half here. I am there and here, one, only one." In the name of this unity found in her children she is ready to break with Lello if he expects her not to see Aldo again, since she had repulsed Ferrante's advances in order to acquire the right to see her Titti again: "You are men, only men. I am a mother."

Titti appears. Pirandello advises: "From this point on, with a clear-cut differentiation, the scene must give the feeling of a life which resumes its rhythm on its natural basis." Evelina madly clasps her child in her arms: "You are right, my Titti. There is so much useless talk here, stupid and barren,

269

and you have been left there alone." She looks at her, caresses her, and kisses her hair. Titti seems taller now, almost up to Evelina's shoulders. She takes Titti in her arms and sways her very gently, while Lello looks at them both, serene and smiling. Evelina continues to hold her in her arms and says: "But I don't want you to become a little lady too soon, no, no, my little one."

Steering away from any sentimentality, Pirandello gives the play a solution required by the inner logic of the situation. Ferrante had offended life by fleeing to America. He had forfeited his right to have Evelina. Rather unwillingly, the author is compelled to be good to Lello Carpani by making Evelina go back to him and continue to be his accepted, if not legal, wife. He had to force himself a little to do so, but he has done so in the end. Certainly Ferrante was the more attractive man. Lello was too artificial to inspire any liking, but, after all, he had protected Evelina and the boy.

The usual undercurrent of serious and solid thought is found here as in most of Pirandello's plays. In a case in which a marriage has been broken, the author makes the one who has done so pay for it. Marriage is not to be trifled with. The author also stresses very cleverly the belief that morality does not lie in appearances. Evelina is pure in spite of the belief of the average person. Signora Armelli is guilty of a shameful entanglement with Aldo under her dignified appearance and behind the mask of her social position.

There are no intellectual complications in the comedy, only normal characters and events, and Pirandello's scintillating dialogue never lags but gives a deep insight into the human heart. If one should be so ill advised as to stress unduly the element of double personality, one would miss the central point of the play: the unity of personality that Evelina found in her mother love.

XXX

A Mystic Interpretation of Parenthood

GRAFTING

(*L'innesto*)

In *Grafting,* Pirandello is still steeped in that fantastic naturalism that can be recognized in so many of his plays. He has never forgotten the analysis of the instinctive forces of life, but his analysis has gradually become a philosophical, interpretative, or even mystic, musing.

In this play he ponders over love, and while being fully conscious of the power of instinct, he reaches a mystic interpretation given to love by a woman who has been brutally attacked and whose child, therefore, is not her husband's. To Laura Banti who loves her husband deeply and sincerely, the child who is to be born is his, his in her love, because she loves only him. It is the same thing that happens in the process of grafting trees.

In her villa where she goes after the frightful experience in order to recuperate and to regain a sense of moral and physical balance, she sees the old gardener Filippo grafting plants in the garden. He skilfully makes a deep cut in the plant, inserts the scion, and closes the wound. In the spring a new fruit will come. "But the plant," explains the old gardener, "must be in love, that is, it must desire to have the fruit that it cannot have by itself."

There is such an analogy between her case and that of the grafted plants. They, too, have been violated, cut, but they will bear fruit because God has wakened love in them. The plant through its own love makes the new bud its own, without knowing whence it has come. Her baby, too, will be made theirs by her love. She is sure of herself. She sees as never before the mystery which embraces all beings and things in the universe. Cold reason is not adequate to explain to her mother what she feels, but she says: "Nature knows it, my

271

body knows it, a plant, any of these plants knows it. It knows
that it could not have happened unless there were love. It has
been explained to me just now. I know this, that in me, in this
poor body of mine, when the thing happened, in this tortured
flesh of mine, there must have been love, and for whom? If
there was love, it could not have been but for him, for my
husband."

Laura had gone to the Villa Giulia in Rome to paint. She
was working on a landscape and she wanted to catch in it the
effect of light in the early morning. She had left the house
very early for three days in succession. She had been attacked
in the park by an unknown brute.

What will her husband feel? Giorgio had made a sort of
mistress out of her, so Laura's mother confides to us. He did
not want children. He was jealous of children. He wanted
Laura only for himself. His first reaction upon learning of
the attack is not one of concern about Laura, but a maddening desire to learn the details of the occurrence. Who was he?
He wants to kill him. Nelli, his lawyer and friend, tries to
persuade him that there is nothing to do. The unfortunate
thing has happened and that is all. If the man is apprehended,
he will get two or three years in prison. If Giorgio brings the
matter to court there will be a terrible scandal, since it will
get into the papers.

Giorgio sees his life enveloped by a dark circle. "Everything is over," he confesses. If he were to listen to his own
true impulse, he "would go there, to her bed, and he would
kill her, although innocent, for the very love that he feels for
her." A desperate jealousy stifles in him every feeling of
compassion for Laura. He refuses to see her, while she, in her
anguish, calls for him. He calls for his automobile in order
to go all alone to his country place. The only natural feeling
that he experiences is one of cruelty, cruelty to all, to his
wife, to himself. Just then Laura appears, a broken woman,
appealing to him, telling him that she wants to be near him.
Giorgio relents. "She raises her head in the tragic expectation that he may cancel her unbearable shame either through
death or through love. As he, overpowered by the intoxicating

feeling that emanates from her, always sobbing, seeks with his lips the wounds in her neck, she passionately places her cheek over his head." Will that passionate love of Giorgio give him enough understanding and sympathy when he learns that she is going to be a mother? Will he accept as theirs the baby that she is carrying under her heart?

Now she is alone at the villa of her husband's family, in the place where Giorgio has spent his youth and his adolescence. Giorgio was one of those young lords who used to think it quite proper to amuse themselves with young peasant girls at a time, not much removed from ours, when the world was free, just, and good, and the Golden Age reigned on earth, Italy included. Laura knows of an illegitimate child, the son of a peasant woman, of whom it was rumored that Giorgio was the father. Laura has sent for Zena, the peasant who had been her husband's plaything and nothing else. Zena comes to see her. She has quickly aged, and is already ugly and ungainly at twenty-five. She has had five children, and she works in the fields like a beast of burden. Laura wants to know from Zena the details of that gossip.

Zena is reluctant to recall a part of her life that is dead for her, but Laura is so gentle and kind that she overcomes Zena's shame and reserve. Zena was pretty, strong, and healthy then, and was engaged to her present husband. "Did he [Giorgio] know that you were engaged?" questions Laura.

"Yes, of course, but he, too, was very young," answers Zena.

What Laura wants to know is whether or not Zena surmised who was the father of her baby, Giorgio or her *fiancé*. Zena, with the candor of peasant folk, tells her that she was sure it was her husband's. She adds: "We peasants are sly. I see that you would like your husband to have had a baby by me. Well, I tell you this, that I, a peasant, gave the son to him who was his real father."

Giorgio arrives at that moment and hardly sees Zena. That episode of nine years ago did not mean much to him. He expresses surprise at Zena's presence there.

Laura, in the crisis that has gripped her whole life, feels

273

that she has never belonged to Giorgio as much as now: "If I belonged to you more, I should die. And yet death would be acceptable to me." She belongs to that man with a force and purity of which only a superior woman is capable. She cries to him: "I have only you! That's all: you, and nothing else which does not come from you counts. If I rejoice, if I suffer, if I die, it is for you. Because I am only as you desire me, as I desire myself: yours." She hopes that her husband will feel as she does about her baby, but she is bitterly disappointed.

Giorgio believes that he has been very generous in overlooking the misfortune of the attack upon her. But now it is the question of a child. He asks the doctor to tell Laura that he cannot accept a child that is not his with certainty. He requires that the child be eliminated through a surgical operation.

Laura firmly asserts her right of motherhood. She tries to make him see that. There is no guilt on her part, no wrong. She has given herself to him as no woman ever has, hoping that her love would wipe out the spot. Giorgio, in his lack of understanding, asks whether she did not "surround him with her love, envelop him in her caresses, to make him accept the situation." Laura is terribly hurt. She strikes back at him. After all there is as much doubt as to who is the father of her child as there was in the case of Zena's son. Giorgio is unbending.

Laura had hoped to lift him up to her. She wanted to save their love, to blot out a cruel misfortune, not brutally, as he had suggested, but with love and understanding. She cries to him: "I want you to see in your son all of me: he's yours because he's proof of all my love for you." Laura's passionate and noble love does not convince Giorgio. He is concerned about giving his name to a child that might not be his. Laura counters: "Do not be afraid of that. I shall have the courage that Zena had. It is a shame that, after the deceit, I cannot give him to his true father." Laura declares herself no longer his wife.

Giorgio realizes that he has opened an abyss between Laura and himself. Confronted by the certainty of losing her, he yields and love registers another of its victories. It is the victory of love over a purely physiological passion.

A very strong antisocial strain, as is to be expected, appears here too. Pirandello takes up again the defense of women and attacks the double standard that has been practised so long everywhere. Man, behind the stately appearance of the civilization that he has put up, has remained a brute. He has put on clothes, hats, fine shoes, and showy garments, but under it all there lurks the brute. Life "is still the forest! Still the forest! It is always the original forest!"

The play moves on the concrete and solid ground of everyday life. This permits Pirandello to prove convincingly his most idealistic and romantic thesis. Had he given a lyrical and fantastic treatment to the play, we would wander in the midst of evanescent characters. Laura is presented with traits that have at no time been exaggerated. She is a gentle, superior young woman, too lofty for her husband. Giorgio is a society gentleman who has never gone very deeply into the understanding of his wife and of life. He has not changed much from his love for Zena to that for Laura. Filippo, the gardener, and Zena stand for that directness and simplicity of instinctive life that is possible only in primitive beings such as are found in peasant life.

The drama sets a lofty goal before Giorgio: that of seeing the beauty of Laura's love and of lifting his own to a higher plane, rising above the intoxication of the senses. Here, as elsewhere, Pirandello qualifies this feeling that men share with lower animals as "sentiment." Giorgio says: "I am required to be generous, while here my sentiment roars like a wild beast." In later plays, the author gives a positive and constructive sense to sentiment.

Pirandello ridicules our individualism as fathers. We look at the child only as our own, as a proof of our personal value. We never think that we are either vehicles or tools and sometimes even puppets in the hands of nature. This is the real morality of the play: the power of nature and the universality of love. This feeling, in its unpretentious simplicity, lends to the play a cosmic sense of life.

XXXI

Only Illusion Can Conquer Death

THE LIFE THAT I GAVE YOU
(*La vita che ti diedi*)

This play appeared at the time when the author was interested in analyzing the value and proclaiming the necessity of the irrational as a means of escape.

We find here the tragedy of a mother who has to force on herself the belief that her son is not dead in order to stand the shock of that tragedy. Pirandello leads us to an understanding of the mother's grief and subsequent illusory process by calling our attention to the fact that in reality life is a constant death. As soon as life enters into us death beats the tempo of a silent funeral march with the same regularity as that with which the hands of a clock go on and on, while the time they mark never comes back. Is not that time, those minutes, hours, weeks, months, years, centuries, the road on which death has made its stealthy and inexorable advance? If you will look back into the centuries you will see death strangling life. In a collective sense life always rises again, but in an individual sense—and we live as individuals —it is death that ultimately overpowers life.

As her son lies in the death chamber, Donn'Anna Luna refuses to believe that he is dead. She talks to him softly with the composure with which mothers wait for their children to return when the latter have left them and have gone roaming over the world. She quietly says: "He has left. He will return." Had he not left their home when a youth and for seven years wandered after the woman whom he loved without hope of making her his? The corpse that is there before her is not he. She wants that body removed that she may live with her child as he lives in her memory, her real child. The man who came back to her, withered by life, disillusioned, sick, almost moribund, was not the child that she wanted.

Illusion is the last conquest of determination, and she must force herself to cling to the beautiful image that floats before her eyes on which was indelibly impressed the countenance of Fulvio as a child.

Her son had left her when very young and had gone to Florence to study. Here he had met an Italian girl who later married a Frenchman, Monsieur Maubel. The two went first to Liège, then to Nice. For seven years Fulvio followed her. She had two children by her husband, and for those children Fulvio and the woman, in spite of their great love, had restrained themselves and kept their love pure. For years the mother had remained shut up in her villa always thinking, gradually becoming detached from everything.

We have here the typical Pirandellian complex: a person given to absorbing and concentrated thinking, with thought acting as an acid on her material life, but affording solace to her mind and peace to her soul. The situation that confronts us in the play must be looked at through the mother's past, lonely life. Only so can we understand that her feelings are not arguments but real emotions. She had lived for long years in the solitude of her villa where "silence frightens one as he goes through the large, deserted halls. It seems that time falls precipitously into them." In this rarefied atmosphere Donn'Anna had waited while her thoughts followed her son, sympathizing with his great love, sacrificing herself for that beautiful passion.

It is natural that the average people who surround Donn'Anna fail to understand her. Don Giorgio, a complacent, fat country priest, not entirely uneducated, voices the belief that real life is in the beyond, and therefore the mother is not right in insisting that her son is alive. Donn'Anna retorts with an argument derived from the vague idealistic religion of the author: "I know that God cannot die when everyone of his creatures dies. . . . Not even you can tell me that my child is dead. You say only that God took him back with him. . . . Don't you feel that God is not there as long as he wishes to abide here, in me, in us; not only for ourselves but also that all those who have gone away may continue to live?" Without realizing how cruel they are, they strive to persuade her to see the truth that her son is dead, "and that if he lives in her he can only live in her memory." The curate, Donn'Anna's sister, the villagers, in their want of sensitiveness, insist on the actual truth as if the mother did not know it and as if she could accept it. She tells the curate: "I have never lived on anything else but memories. I have no other life but this one; the only one that I can touch— precise and present. But you utter the word 'remembrance' and immediately you make it recede from me, destroy it for me." The curate, by mentioning the words "memory" and "remembrance," destroys momentarily the perfect illusion in which the mother's heart and soul have found solace. She is perfectly aware that the physical life of her son is over, but she also knows that he can have another life, that he can be reborn through her love. She tells the curate: "God wants my son to continue to live. Not, of course, the life that he gave him here, but that which I have always given him! This cannot be taken away from him as long as life endures in me."

As the mother reënters the glow and flame of her illusion she forgets the actual and hurting truth and views the people around her as blind and powerless. She turns to Donna Fiorina, her sister, and gently tells her, as one mother to another, that for mothers the life of their children is only dream. They touch the tender flesh of their babies and they almost see it change under their hands. The images of their children are nothing but memories of dreams. Only a mother like Donn'Anna can understand that fully: "It takes seven years, I know, seven years passed in thinking of a son who does not return, and of suffering what I have suffered, in order to understand this truth that goes beyond every sorrow while there looms here a light which cannot be extinguished." She presses her temples with both hands. Had Donna Fiorina not noticed how her children, after one year's absence at the university, had changed? "They were young country shepherds a year ago, and now they seem two young lords," in the poetical but apt comment of Elisabetta, the maid.

Donna Fiorina is compelled to acknowledge the fearful truth uncovered by Donn'Anna. It was true. Her children had changed so as to be hardly recognizable; they look different and their ideas are no longer the same.

Donn'Anna lives quietly in the little closed world of her illusion, in a light that is artificial but consoling. The light that surrounds her is of her own creation, and she has to keep it burning with the oil of her human compassion and mother love. Only at times the tragic truth seizes her and overpowers her. She confesses to her sister: "What do you know of what I do when, upstairs, I abandon my head on the pillow and feel him, feel him in the silence and emptiness of these rooms where no memory suffices to animate and fill that silence, because I am tired? Then I too *know,* and a fearful shudder creeps over me. The only refuge, the last comfort, is in her, in the one who is to come and does not know yet."

The one who is to come is Lucia Maubel, the woman whom Fulvio has loved more than his youth and life. His death will be a test for Lucia's love. Will she continue to love him after she knows that he is dead? She comes to tell Fulvio that she is going to have a baby, his baby. She confesses to the mother: "Our love that had endured pure for so many years, conquered us in the end, stealthily." Upset and frightened, Lucia forced him to leave: "I could not meet my children's eyes," she says. Lucia is one of those women whom Pirandello has surrounded with the halo of nobility that every man sees around the quiet countenance of his mother. Pirandello does not need to make women erotic nor to complicate their eroticism to make them live in his art. Love, even if it breaks the barriers of the law, has a purifying effect on Pirandello's women, and rarely mortifies or offends their motherhood.

At first Lucia is hurt at Fulvio's absence. She does not understand the mother's words that he has left on a long journey. As she confesses the whole truth of their relation to the mother, she grows excited, almost distracted. She cannot go back to her husband now. Horror fills her at the mere thought of having to live with him again. She has suffered agonies that cannot be told while married to him. He is a profligate man, "fatuous and cold. He looks at life to laugh at it, at women to take them, at men to deceive them." Only Fulvio's love has given her courage and strength: "I have been able to stand living with him [her husband] only because I had someone to sustain me, to give me pure air to breathe, outside of that filth." Fulvio has made her feel that even the children she had borne to her husband were his: "Those children (it is true) are not love that has become flesh: they belong to that man—flesh—but the love that I had infused into them—I, I with my heart full of him—had transformed those two almost into Fulvio's children. Love is one." She regrets that their weakness had led them to sin after many years of brave renunciation: "We should not have soiled ourselves!" she cries to Fulvio's mother. The consciousness of having done wrong destroys even the pure joy of motherhood in her. She has come to Fulvio to see whether he could change that feeling and create in her the joy of being a mother.

Lucia is tired, excited, almost frantic. Sweetly Donn'Anna tells her: "I will teach you how not to go crazy, as I did for such a long time, as long as he was there with you. I used to feel him near me because I held him in my heart. He is there." [*She indicates his room.*] She admonishes Lucia, putting into words the bitter subjectivism that life had taught her: "Never seek anything that does not come from within you." Her strength must come from her heart, from her sentiment, that will conquer any obstacle, even death. Lucia insists on sleeping in Fulvio's room. She will be closer to him thus. "Yes," says the mother to her, "in your heart. Yes, in your heart." Lucia has been won over by the mother. Fulvio is alive.

On the following day Lucia's mother arrives. She is a perfectly normal and prosaic person. To her, Fulvio is dead and Lucia has compromised herself by going to his home. Donn'Anna pleads with her that Fulvio is not dead as long as he lives in the child that Lucia is bearing him. Francesca,

Lucia's mother, shouts: "Do you want to keep my daughter tied to a corpse?" The brutal question wounds Donn'Anna, but she finds in the very facts of the situation the strength to answer: "A corpse? Death for her is there, near the man to whom you have tied her: *he* is a corpse."

Lucia appears as the two mothers are talking, and discovers the truth: Fulvio is dead. As Lucia tragically cries her love and despair, the truth of the situation appears to Donn'Anna in all its cruel and ghastly light. Bitter tears fall upon her defeated effort to keep alive her illusion: "Oh my child!—here on your flesh—now indeed—I see him die—I feel his cold corpse here, in the warmth of your tears." Lucia is very close to her heart, as close as ever a daughter was to a mother. She is touched by Donn'Anna's anguish and tells her that her love for Fulvio is undiminished by his death and that she feels that he lives in the little life that is about to unfold through their love. She wants to stay with her. They will live together in this new joy as they have been together under the hand of grief.

Lucia's mother thwarts their plan. Lucia must go back to her home and to her two children. Donn'Anna sees the cruel logic of that thought, and resigns herself to be alone in the empty house no longer illuminated by illusion. She is truly dead now: "This is truly death, my child—things we have to do, whether we want to or not—and things we have to say . . . now a time-table to consult—then the coach to go to the station—to journey on . . . we are the poor, busy dead.—To torture ourselves—to console ourselves—to quiet ourselves—this is truly death." She is dead when the idealism of the author fails to keep her illusion alive.

The theme, as we have already noticed, is still that of illusion, but no longer a tortuous illusion, usually a consequence of wrongdoing. It is the illusion that we are forced to impose upon ourselves if we want to bear our human fate. In the face of a pessimism that has become complete, Pirandello's idealism has assumed a definite and pragmatic value.

The play is in a logical line of derivation from the author's tragic idealism. It is a passionate pleading for this idealism because it has been his own solace for many long years of torment. As is his fashion, having advanced the idea that life is a constant death as the basis of his play, he attempts to prove that actually it is so. What men call change is only death. It is the illusory comfort that words give us. Before the transformation of the boy into the man, only self-deception makes us speak of change: "Does that not mean that he is another than the one that he used to be? And if the one who was before is now no longer, what does that *change* mean?" It may seem strange that Donn'Anna should utter this categorical pessimism, she, the one who later soars to a dizzy idealism. Yet this explains the very nature of her illusion which is tragic and human.

At first we hesitate to agree with Pirandello's disconsolate philosophy. However, in the ultimate analysis, his thought is consoling, and his arguments are so pointed and so vivified by the real tragedy of the mother that we are carried away by his passionate logic. Pirandello convinces your intellect at the same time that he touches your heart. If life abides in our thought and higher emotions, is it not a mistake to give physical death such a great importance? Why should the mother have seen her son in the bald-headed, bent, used-up body that came back to her rather than in the gentle and exquisite boy who had left her seven years before? Closed in her impenetrable subjectivism she could call life only what she had known, what had been the flame of her eyes and soul before he departed, the flame of her lonely life after his departure.

The author is perfectly conscious of the desolate subjectivism of Donn'Anna, and feels compelled to distinguish between the common lot and the individual. To the average unfeeling mob "life has always put a stone on the dead in order to continue its march over them. But it must be our life, not that of those who have died. We want our dead really dead to live our life in peace. That's why we justify ourselves when we pass over the dead."

Pirandello has conquered an insurmountable difficulty in

making plausible a thesis that at first seems irrational and absurd. He has done so by embodying the mother in a woman who is above the normal and average person in sensitiveness and nobility. By so doing he places the problem on a personal basis that silences the recriminations of those who might deny the possibility of the psychological reaction that forms the very woof of the play. As Donna Fiorina tells us: "She has always been like that! She seems to be listening to what others tell her, and suddenly she comes forth—as if from a fantastic distance—with words that no one expected." Pirandello's contention is that if others fail to understand her, it is because they have not had her heart-rending experience nor have they been endowed with her sensitiveness.

With extreme skill Pirandello takes the problem from the height of a lofty, even ethereal idealism, and leads it to the ground of practical life. Only through sentiment was the mother saved; only through sentiment could Lucia endure her grief at not finding Fulvio; only through that sentiment could life resume for her in her husband's home, near her children, illuminated by reminiscences of Fulvio's beautiful and perfect love.

Part Five

ART AND LIFE

XXXII

Introduction

In this section are included the plays that have a distinctly intellectual genesis. The author contrasts here life and art in its diverse manifestations: dramatic art, sculpture, and poetry. The plays herein considered deal with the experience of a dramatist, sculptor, and poet as they place themselves before life and muse over the central character of art looked upon as life caught in the immutable eternity of form. As the result of this attitude, Pirandello has given us *Six Characters in Search of an Author, Tonight We Improvise, Diana and Tuda, She Wanted to Find Herself,* and *When One Is Somebody.*

In their inherent character these plays are the expression of Pirandello's experience as a man and as an artist. Although the two experiences may meet, they are often in sharp contrast, and from this clash arises the drama that Pirandello portrays in his plays. The author realizes that before him there are two alternatives: either to choose the life immobilized in the concept of his own unhappiness, or to abandon himself to the life of instinct that clamors for its rights against duty and sacrifice. This practical concern prevents the plays from being treatises on art in the disguise of drama, and infuses them with a deep note of human feeling.

One of the considerations that, as we shall see, affords to Pirandello a nucleus around which he builds his play, is whether or not life is more powerful than art; whether we enhance or stunt our emotions and feelings when we transform them into art. In the earlier years of his dramatic career he leaned towards life, life alluring and warm, strong in joy and strong in grief, a tide that carries us on the crest of its waves and fills us with the feeling of a power that nothing can equal. The power of life, however, was not conceived in the light of the orgies of the senses. As he lived in stoical resignation, broken by the outbursts of rebellion that he voiced through his characters, Pirandello realized with increasing clearness how much more powerful was the tragedy he lived than the tragedy he portrayed. What he sought was the reality of his inner pain reflected in his work. Every reflection of it was pale and inadequate when compared with the anguish that lacerated his heart. It was natural that he should proclaim life to be more powerful than art.

This state of mind is projected in *Six Characters in Search of an Author* and in *Tonight We Improvise* as well as in *Diana and Tuda*. Here art is looked upon as an inadequate means of expression which dwarfs life and robs it of its fire and glow. This longing for the pulsing throb of life originates in the thirst and hunger for life that nature has infused in every creature, animate and inanimate. Through this longing Pirandello reveals the torment of the artist as he is confronted by problems of dramatic technique. He rebels against the fact that there is a vast difference between actors and characters: actors as they are engaged by a stage director; characters as they have been created by the playwright. He also resents dramatic art's being laden down with conventional tricks of all kinds—division into acts, light effects, make-up—all elements that life in its actuality does not need in order to be dramatic.

It is but natural that a man who seeks the actual as passionately as does Pirandello, and who rebels with violence at any attempt to sentimentalize life or to cover it with rhetorical veils, should feel attracted by the *Commedia dell'arte*. One must not call the author's attention to the fact that the *Commedia dell'arte* also had its conventions and formalisms. We cannot call an artist from the region of poetry before the tribunal of logic.

The *Commedia dell'arte*, or improvised comedy in which only the plot was outlined and in which the actors filled in the dialogue, has had a marked influence on Pirandello. It was the closest approximation of art to life, and conventionalities of drama and stagecraft had no meaning for the actors of the *Cinquecento* who felt the passion of life and art with equal intensity. Pirandello found another bond of sympathy with them. They too knew the power of laughter, and they rendered life through it in all its power and violence.

Pirandello, however, pictures in other plays also contained in this section a state of mind of an opposite nature which was forced on him by the realization that art actually gave him a solace that he vainly sought in life. He turned to art with the same impetuosity with which he had aspired to life, and he saw that art gives stateliness and immortality to it. The keynote of these plays is the realization that a feeling if left in its own fluid state is truly alive, but doomed to change and eventually to death, while if given artistic representation at the cost of losing its vehemence, it can attain immortal existence.

Here Pirandello the naturalist has turned into the tragic idealist who assigns a solitary peak to the creatures of his imagination, where they abide in a suffering cheered by the cold light of art. If the true essence of life lies in reflection, then art outdoes actual life in that we can reach through it a fullness and a height unknown to those who entrust themselves to the chaotic and stormy violence of instinct.

The two antithetical moods are not created by the desire of changing technique for the benefit of entertaining the public as would a cheap juggler. Like all true thought and art, they come from within, and they are generated by the realization that life in its primeval attribute flows unattainable in the infinite distances that only our soul can picture. Life needs form in order to exist in the world of actual realities, and it becomes dwarfed by it. Pirandello approaches life when his senses urge him to reach out for its gifts, but his intellect has already withered the fruit that his lips long to suck. Then pessimism looms, and it stretches its destructive tentacles over the whole universe. For a man who had reached such a state of mind, to turn to art becomes a logical and deeply felt need. In the uncontaminated molds of art, life can be kept in all its purity and beauty. For a man who had so copiously drunk at the bitter spring of sorrow, it was natural to reach this point of detachment and of objectivity.

The need of rising towards the blissful heaven of perfect

forms is also derived from the identity that Pirandello discovers between the clear-cut contour of a statue and that of certain individuals who are so absorbed by a given painful or shameful thought as to become identified with it. He knew how clear and lucid, how terrible and agonizing was the fixity of one's body and soul. The fixity of his individuals and of all art bridged the distance between the drama of life that he always sought and that of art that opened a new avenue to his creative instinct. From portraying the fixity resulting from a moral wrong, he passed to portraying that due to the isolation to which all superior beings are condemned. Donata Genzi, in *She Wanted to Find Herself*, perfect embodiment of feminine grace and lofty womanhood, expresses this new mood of the author. We find in her a person who can look at herself in the mirror without experiencing the feeling of loathing and disgust that Pirandello has lent to earlier characters. The light of a higher ethical life also animates one of his latest plays, *When One Is Somebody*. Here Somebody is strong enough to keep his love for beautiful Veroccia on a high plane even when the voice of instinct sings for him the song with which the mermaids bewitched Ulysses' companions.

These plays, like those found in other sections, present a decided change in the inspiration and state of mind of the author. Pirandello has freed himself from the preoccupation of instinct, and his eyes have limpidly gazed on a higher life. As youth has forsaken him, he has seen more clearly behind the veil of material and instinctive life, and he has turned to art to express this new aspect of his drama. He sought a lofty region, the presence of which his soul had constantly felt even when gloom and pessimism weighed heavily on his outlook on life, and he found that region on the summit where abide the divine and luminous forms of art.

Art Does But Dwarf a Tragic Life

SIX CHARACTERS IN SEARCH OF AN AUTHOR

(*Sei personaggi in cerca d'autore*)

In *Six Characters in Search of an Author,* one of the most complex and baffling of Pirandello's plays, a stirring dramatic action is so closely woven with keen and almost erudite discussions of art that one is at first uncertain as to the central idea of the work. The fact is that the motivation of the play is essentially literary, since there run through it various æsthetic considerations such as: Is life stronger than art? What happens when we attempt to enclose life in the mold of art? Is its reality increased or diminished? Does not the artist owe the reality of his art to the torment and anguish which have gnawed into the soul and the very flesh of the man?

In a material sense the genesis of the play is found in a short story entitled *The Tragedy of a Character (La tragedia di un personaggio)* [1] in which Pirandello in an imaginary conversation listens to the plaint of a character who laments the rôle that has been assigned to him by the author of a book that Pirandello has just read. There is a page taken bodily from this short story and inserted in the play. In a more subtle and psychological sense the play is the projection of Pirandello's long-tormented life into the life and torment of the Six Characters.

As the title suggests, this is a play of characters. It is pertinent at this point to inquire who is a character in Pirandello's mind and in what way he differs from a normal man and an actor. We know Hamlet, Don Quixote, Don Abbondio, Sancho Panza. They are characters in that they represent a feeling, an idea, a supreme overpowering emotion. They have lived in the flame of this idea or emotion all

---

[1] *Novelle per un anno.* Vol. IV, pp. 237–46. Bemporad, Florence, 1922.

through the centuries and they still live in it, immortal in their impassioned immobility. As we look at them they are alive in spite of their fixity. "When a character is born," Pirandello informs us, "he acquires immediately such an independence from his author that we can all imagine him in situations in which the author never thought of placing him, and he assumes of his own initiative a significance that his author never dreamt of lending him." There are cases in life, Pirandello claims, in which man acquires the fixity of a character. Under the pressure of the unmerciful hand of misfortune and grief, man often reaches a point where he becomes so closely identified with that misfortune and grief as to be the embodiment of a passionate state of mind which crowds out, to an absolute exclusion, every other feeling and sentiment. Then he is a character.

Looked at in this light the Six Characters are the projection of that fixity in mental agony and pain which is a typical state of mind of the central figures that Pirandello has made live in his drama. The play is, intrinsically and ultimately, a keen study of human personality to which Pirandello has accorded a most brilliant treatment. He has called to his help his own anguish, his own experience as an author, his original intuition of the human side of art and the procedure of the *Commedia dell'arte*. The Six Characters oscillate with perfect balance between the artificial life of glorified marionettes and the moving, stirring existence of tragic human beings.

Pirandello's fatherly attitude towards the children of his imagination is reflected in these new Six Characters who clamor to be made to live. They are so overpowered by the passion that stirs them that they beg a troupe of professional actors to allow them to reënact their tragedy. They claim with emphasis and passion that, living their tragedy and pain, they are real characters. They are completely absorbed in their grief. In this they resemble the immortal characters to whom truly great artists have given life, a life which is immortal. "Man will die, the writer, an instrument of creation, will die; but his creatures will never die, and in order

to live eternally they need not possess extraordinary qualities nor perform prodigies. Who was Sancho Panza? Who
was Don Abbondio? And yet they live because, living germs,
they had the fortune to find a fecund matrix, a fantasy that
could nurture them, make them live through eternity." The
Six Characters, too, are immortal in the fixity of their pain.
Pirandello stresses their fantastic reality as well as their
physical traits which they share with all humanity. "A
strange, most feeble, hardly perceptible light is around them
as if radiating from them: a light breath of their fantastic
reality." They possess "a certain dreamlike lightness in
which they appear as if suspended, but which must not de-
tract at all from the essential reality of their forms and expressions." They are true human beings, but they do not
represent a heavy, solid, unwieldy humanity impervious to
deep feelings. Indeed, they are suspended in the effervescence
of the passionate desire to communicate to others the burning
truth which torments them within.

The Father has that uncertain and vague smile of those whom
life has baffled and disappointed. Outwardly he may be any
one of the many people we know, "rather fat, pale, especially
his wide forehead, with round blue eyes, most lucid and
penetrating; wearing light trousers and a dark coat; speaking
at times in a mellifluous tone, at times abruptly and harshly."
The Mother, as pale as wax, with downcast eyes, and dressed
in deep mourning, appears "crushed by an intolerable weight
of shame and dejection." The Stepdaughter, eighteen years
of age, is haughty, almost impudent. "Very beautiful, she
too wears mourning, but with showy elegance." Near her
are two other victims of the tragedy: the wan Adolescent,
timid, distressed, moving like a ghost among them; and the
Son, twenty-two years old, who is tall and stiff, and looks
disdainfully at them all. There is also a child of about four,
the only fresh, delicate note in so much gloom and hatred.

The Six Characters, representing life at its highest pitch
of intensity and depth, arrive on the stage at the moment
when a troupe of professional actors are about to rehearse
a play by Pirandello, *Each in His Own Rôle* (*Il gioco delle*

parti). As they appear, there is in them the afflatus of theatrical personality which urges them to go to the actors and make the strange request of being allowed to reënact a scene in which, as they say, their whole life has become crystallized. Pirandello brings into relief the prosaic traits of the actors as contrasted with the impetuous Six Characters. Everything is in disorder in the theatre; some actors are smoking cigarettes, some are reading a newspaper, others are going over their parts. Not so with the Characters. They are all tense, in a perpetually high and feverish tension. They have no need to rehearse their parts. They know them, all summed up in one tragic scene. They insist, above all, on their reality, which they contemptuously compare with that of the actors and that of the average man. Man thinks that he possesses an unchanging unity, while in him are intertwined infinite personalities which are in constant state of change. His illusions of today prove to have been the truths of but yesterday, and the truths of today will be the illusions of tomorrow. Not so with a character who is fixed in a definite mold, all through eternity, if a genius has made him live in the eternity of art. "A character can always ask of a man who he is, because a character has truly a life of his own marked with definite traits so that he always is a somebody, while a man generally speaking can be a nobody." As to actors, the reality of their lives is separated from the content of their art. They act; they do not live.

The story that the Six Characters relate is truly heart-rending. A strange mixture of pathos and shame envelops it. On the surface, it seems to be a drama of a divided family which includes a woman who has first lived with her husband by whom she had a son, and then with another man by whom she had three more children. There is nothing extraordinary in this, especially in modern times when divorces create even stranger situations. But our curiosity is aroused when we learn that all the misfortunes have been superinduced by the tortuous mental process of the Father. The Father is in fact an hyper-intellectual man who lacks that fluidity of feelings and sincerity of purpose that bring about a serene and quiet life. He speaks of the "complicated torments of my spirit." He himself informs us that he has always had an "aspiration for a certain moral character of life." This moral aspiration causes him to marry a woman of the people to counteract his own intellectuality. She is goodness and simplicity personified and lives only for her home and her child. Her husband, obeying his customary moral aspiration, takes the child from her and sends him to the country to be nursed by a sturdy peasant so that he may be in close contact with mother earth. There is in their wealthy home the husband's secretary, a silent, shadow-like, humble man like the wife. He and she, without even the thought of evil, understand each other because they are kindred souls. The husband, under the urge of his moral sense, makes himself believe that his wife cannot be happy with him. They are too different, he with his searching, subjective intellect, she with her humility and silence, her spontaneity and simplicity. He feels that the real mate for his wife is his secretary. He provides a home for the two of them and has them live together. He does this, urged on by the "demon of experience," one of the demons, popularized copies of the Greek *daimon,* so dear to the intellectual class of D'Annunzio's days. The "demon of experience" is just a phrase according to the Son and to the other members of the family. The Father rebels: "Phrases! Phrases! As if it were not everyone's consolation, before a fact that cannot be explained, before a disease that destroys us, to find a word which says nothing and in which we find quietude."

Both Pirandello and the family question the validity of the Father's acts because they are determined by his tortuous reasoning and not by real sentiment. How can one believe him when he says that he feels sorry for his wife's loneliness and therefore sends her away to live with the secretary? Does he not do it because he has tired of a woman with whom he has nothing in common? Does he not mention the "stifling atmosphere of his home life," mixing truths and lies and believing them all true? It is useless for him to put lofty motives into his acts after his poor and humble wife goes to live with the other man. He continues to watch over her out of a sense of responsibility, and, for the same reason, he is interested in the new family of three children. When the little girl grows up, he goes to meet her after school, taking her gifts as if she were his own. One day the family disappears from the town and does not return until after the secretary's death, many years later. The Father's torment and loneliness become greater. His Son is as if not his own; his house is empty and barren. The Stepdaughter voices Pirandello's revolt against the Father's attempt at philosophizing about human acts. "How sickening, how sickening, are all those intellectual complications, all that philosophy that uncovers the beast and then attempts to save it and excuse it. When we are compelled to 'simplify' life in such a beastly manner, casting away all the 'human' encumbrance of every chaste aspiration, of every pure sentiment, ideal, duty, shame, modesty, nothing moves us to rage and nausea more than certain remorses: crocodile tears!"

Some years later the Father visits a bawdy house where he finds himself face to face with the Stepdaughter, whom he does not recognize. The arrival of the Mother saves them from a greater disgrace. After the identification stamps their faces and hearts with burning shame, the Father takes the new family to his home and there they live under an evil spell, in a light of tragic exasperation.

Each has his own tragedy, and the tragedy of one merges with the tragedy of all. The Father refuses to have his whole life caught in that shameful moment as if his entire existence were summed up in that act. But he protests in vain to the Stepdaughter, who sees in him the cause of all her shame and misfortunes. The Adolescent is lost in that tormented life. The Son sees half-bred intruders in them all, and looks with cold, indifferent eyes at his Mother. She has belonged to another man. His Father is a libertine. The Son feels that his life depends on them "as a putrid shame which must be hidden." The Mother's tragedy is that of any mother who feels estranged from her son. All this shame and misfortune is summarized in that moment in which Father and Step-

daughter find themselves face to face as man and woman:
he a man nearing sixty, she a young girl of eighteen. Now,
the Six Characters are gathered in a tragic huddle around
that scene. This scene is a flame kept alive by hatred, rebellion, and remorse.

As the subtitle suggests, the comedy is yet to be made.
The rough copy is in them—in the Six Characters. "It is in
us, sir," announces the Father while the actors laugh. "The
drama is in us. It is we and we are eager to enact it, urged
on by the passion within us."

They present their drama to the Director. Why does he
not attempt to make of it a dramatic work? His task will be
very simple, since the characters are there before him. Instead of being written, the work will only be transcribed,
scene by scene. As the Characters enact their tragedy, the
professional actors will observe how real characters act, and
will attempt to reproduce their acting. The Director, with the
assistance of the Six Characters, gives a certain plan to the
action to which they are to give life.

The first act presents the fashionable establishment of
Madame Pace, where elegant garments are sold, together with
the honesty and youth of poor girls. The Stepdaughter insists
that the stage furniture be the same as that in Madame Pace's
room. The furniture is engraved in her memory, and it disturbs her to see anything different. The Father rebels because another person will play his part and the various
characters will receive names other than those which they
bear in real life. The Stepdaughter laughs at the thought of
the First Actress attempting to portray her passion. The first
scene is to bring together Madame Pace and the Stepdaughter.
The distance between the plane of life and that of artistic
reality is so slight that Madame Pace arrives attracted by
the divine afflatus of the tragic reality that the Six Characters are living. The Stepdaughter dashes towards her and
they talk in a low voice. The Director wants them to talk
loud enough for the public to hear. But can one utter aloud
the words that are used to persuade a girl to prostitute herself? Are these words said aloud in real life? Pirandello

makes Madame Pace speak in a queer mixture of Spanish and Italian to give a complete rendering of the actual reality. As the Mother sees her, forgetting that they are only acting, she shouts, "Monster, monster! Assassin! My daughter!" Reality refuses to be contained within the artificial mold of fiction. Madame Pace leaves, and the scene between the Father and Stepdaughter takes place. The play pivots around this scene as the life of the Six Characters centers around it. Pirandello lets their shame fall drop by drop over his sorrowing but steeled heart. The two characters are full of the impetus of reality. To them that scene is torment and life. They go through it word by word, stage by stage, partaking with cruel pleasure of the shame and nausea that it exudes.

After the Father and Stepdaughter enact their parts, it is the turn of the First Actor and First Actress to reënact them, but they fail miserably. How can it be otherwise when that scene is but mimicry to them? Small wonder that they indulge in exaggerated tones and conventional postures that create a banal uniformity. It is but natural that the Father and Stepdaughter are unable to recognize themselves in those puppets. With impatient, ill-restrained gestures, with half amused smiles, openly with words, they express first their astonishment, then their wonder, and finally their disgust. Both the Director and the actors are, by eliminating the truth, making of that tragic scene a romantic concoction: "Of my nausea, of all the reasons, one crueler and viler than another, which have made this of me, have made me just what I am, you would like to make a sentimental, romantic concoction." The Stepdaughter wants the truth. When she had told the man, her stepfather, that because of mourning she could not accept a charming little hat that he, with a lewd smile, wished to present to her, he replied, "Good! Then let us quickly remove that little dress." The Director does not want to have that phrase included. He wishes to replace it by making the man sympathetically inquire for whom she is wearing mourning. Pirandello is disgusted with this hypocritical sentimentality. The Director is afraid of the truth. Why hide the dregs of human lust when man is made insensitive to everything gentle and human, to the youthfulness of the victim, to the nausea of her paid flesh, even to her heart bleeding for a recent death? "I," shouts the Stepdaughter, "with the wound of a recent death in my heart, went, you see, there behind that screen, and with fingers that faltered with shame and repugnance, I undid my dress, my corset."

There is a greater moral lesson in this scene than in a hundred volumes of tiresome moralists. Pirandello does not shrink from the truth, no matter how bitter. He wishes to have faithfully reënacted to the very end the scene in which the Stepdaughter is shown standing before the man, her head resting on his chest. In presenting the scene the Stepdaughter wants her arms bare because "while standing so with my head resting on him and my arms around his neck, I saw a vein throbbing here in my arm and then, as if only that pulsating vein awoke repugnance in me, I looked at him wantonly and buried my head in his chest! [*and turning towards her mother*] Shout, Mother, shout! [*she buries her head in the Stepfather's chest with her shoulders hunched as if not to hear her mother's shout; then she adds in a voice vibrating with stifled anguish*] Shout as you shouted then!" The Mother, carried away by the power of truth and reality, cries, "No, my daughter, my child! [*and after having separated her from him*] You brute, you brute, she is my daughter! Don't you see that she is my daughter?" "Good," exclaims the Director. "The curtain can fall right here." The stage hand is so gripped by the reality of the drama that he actually lowers the curtain.

The next act presents the two families living in the home of their father a life of unspeakable tragedy that weighs on them like a leaden cloak. The Father stares with lucid eyes into the darkness of his studio at the heavy, useless burden of his life. The Stepdaughter is still haughty and arrogant; the Mother is crucified by the indifference of her Son who continues to be silent and disdainful. The Adolescent, meditating suicide, moves like a ghost in the spacious and beautifully furnished rooms of his stepfather. That thought absorbs him and destroys him. The only delicate note is afforded by the Little Girl, who can wander in the lovely gardens, a flower among flowers. As the act progresses, the Little Girl is drowned in the pool which has been placed in the garden scene. The Adolescent stares at her, and shoots himself.

The tragic end of the play reintroduces the original theme of the relation between art and life. Life enclosed in the artificial mold of art breaks its narrow walls, sweeps away fiction, and rules with tragedy and grief. In the wake of a tragic life there lurks death.

Outwardly we find ourselves before a play within a play, a situation that has often been resorted to by playwrights. Actually it is a cleverly constructed play in three acts in which the first act gives the background, the second reënacts the ghastly scene between the Father and the Stepdaughter, and the third presents the life of the Six Characters in the home of the Father where tragedy overtakes them.

What makes the play difficult to understand and most difficult to act is the fact that Pirandello has unveiled before us his secret concern as an author, together with his sympathy for the pitiful plight of the Six Characters. "Authors usually hide the travails of their creation," departing from their custom he tells us through the lips of the Father. He has dramatized the life of a character by portraying him as he is when he leaps into existence in the imagination of his creator, and what he becomes when he is presented by professional actors. The reality of the actor's rôle is fleeting. At best it lasts as long as he plays, and it changes from one actor to another and even from day to day in the same actor. But, in a true character, his reality is the same forever. The rebellion of the Six Characters is that of Pirandello, the playwright, who sees the reality of his characters offended by the interpretation of the professional actors. Characters, as characters, live in the mind or in the book of the author, not in the interpretation given by actors.

Pirandello has also expressed here the feeling of resentment that an artist experiences against the limitations of dramatic art. Why should characters utter aloud what is meant to be a terrible secret between them? Here art offends life, which is truth, in that, for the sake of the spectators, it makes actors proclaim aloud what should be only whispered. All through the play the acting of the Six Characters is closer to real life than that of the professional actors. There is also the resentment of the artist against his inability to take the tangibility of life and transport it into his art. Life as life is, and as such it needs no artistic representation. As soon as we translate it into art we can render but a pale reflection of it. The Father is the spokesman for Pirandello's anti-intellectualistic trend when he says, "You know that life is full of infinite absurdities which have no need whatsoever of appearing verisimilar because they are true. It is really madness to toil in doing the contrary, that is, to invent verisimilar situations and attempt to make them appear true." He contrasts life and art, identifying life with the vehement, maddening passion of the Six Characters, and voicing disdain for the art of the actors which is but form with no real human content. Pirandello feels that the concern of the verisimilar is a hypocritical contrivance, centuries old, to justify the lack of true creation. Men have created always verisimilar situations in the hope that they may seem true.

There is in the play the clash between reality and the perfect illusion of reality. If art is a perfect illusion of reality, then it is not reality; indeed, the more perfect the illusion, the more removed from reality it is. At the same time, if art is perfect reality, it identifies itself with the living actual reality, and it is no longer art. Pirandello has broken the impasse by widening the boundaries of what we call reality and giving a paramount place to imagination. "Nature uses the instrument of human fantasy to continue, even in a higher form, her creative work." Confronted by the angular, solid, unwieldy, prosaic reality of material facts and by the vain, empty life as portrayed by the artificial art of the professional actors, he takes refuge among the Six Characters and entrusts to them his own meaning of reality, which is life lived with passion illuminated by fancy, made immortal by true art.

These æsthetic considerations constitute the background

against which Pirandello has projected a highly dramatic life. It is truly a *tour de force* to have been able to keep the intellectual genesis of the play from crowding out or weighing down the emotional element centering about the pitiful and great figures of the Six Characters.

XXXIV

A Play in the Making

TONIGHT WE IMPROVISE

(*Questa sera si recita a soggetto*)

The *motif* of the closeness of art and life is ever recurring in Pirandello. It takes a strange form in that the man in him longs for life lived as actual experience, while the artist is fully conscious of the great power of art considered as a reflected activity.

The framework of *Tonight We Improvise* is constituted by showing a play in its making. The author contrasts the passion of the characters with the artificiality of the stage director in presenting a slight dramatic event that the latter has to stage. In its procedure and structure it bears a marked resemblance to *Six Characters in Search of an Author*, with the fundamental difference that it does not possess the striking characters that create the strength of that celebrated play.

The *deus ex machina* of the play is Dr. Hinkfuss, a stage director who in his physical traits and mannerisms has all the marks of a grotesque character. He is presented as a tiny man "who vents his rage for being short by wearing incredibly long hair. His hands are delicate with small, pale fingers as hairy as caterpillars."

Pirandello places before Dr. Hinkfuss a simple short story and bids him make it into a play. He wants to amuse himself in seeing how the stage director will acquit himself of this task. He patiently listens to the tiny, but fiery doctor who shouts that in the theatre he, as stage director, has a greater rôle than the playwright, in that he makes alive the stilled life that the playwright has enclosed in his written work.

The theme of the play is that of jealousy, the most fearful kind of jealousy, that of the past, felt by a husband who feared that his wife, no longer young or attractive, may still dream of the days when she was both young and gay. Before such a jealousy and before the events that accompany it, what will an artificiality-loving stage director do and what will real characters do? Pirandello does not trust Dr. Hinkfuss. Instead of allowing the dramatic action to weave itself naturally into the atmosphere created by the presence of the public and by the expectation aroused by the long prologue, Dr. Hinkfuss, obeying his instinct for systematized division, breaks it into various tableaux which are to take the place of the traditional acts. In his desire for novelty he has a new scheme—that of introducing the actors by their real names, although they are disguised as the characters that they are to impersonate.

The first actor, who is to play the rôle of the jealous husband, comes on the stage at the bidding of the director but rebels at hearing his name: "You must only believe that here, under these trappings, there is no longer Mr. [*he will say his name*]. He must live the character of Rico Verri, be Rico Verri: and he is, he already is." As Dr. Hinkfuss continues the presentation of the other actors, these, urged by the passion with which they live their rôles, begin to act independently of the director's plans. These actors are characters and not merely paid mannekins. They refuse to give a well-arranged and preordained action. Life in its impetuosity will present men and events better than the cold wisdom of a playwright or a stage director.

The setting is in a small provincial town in the interior of Sicily, where "passions are strong and they smolder in darkness till they flare up violently: most ferocious among them all, jealousy." People live a sluggish life there and they are ready to gossip, especially about a middle-class family whose actions are not very exemplary.

The family is composed of the father, the mother, and four daughters: Mommina, Totina, Dorina, and Nenè. The father, Signor Palmiro, a mining engineer, is a small man. They call him Sampognetta (little bagpipe) because he falls into lapses of absent-mindedness and whistles. The mother, Signora Ignazia, is an enormous woman who beats her husband and instructs her daughters in modern ways of making life pleasant and easy. She comes from Naples and is generally known as "the General." Her four daughters are "very beautiful, plump, sentimental, vivacious, and passionate." Their mode of living is in sharp contrast with the rigid watch that Sicilian families used to keep on their daughters. Pirandello, a Sicilian, has made Signora Ignazia come from Naples.

There are five young aviation officers who play with Signora Ignazia's beautiful, free-and-easy daughters. Only one, Rico Verri, is ill at ease among them. Where women are concerned he is not used to the freedom of the continent. He is shocked upon hearing the mother's ideas: "Do you expect me to keep them in a convent to learn the catechism and embroidery? That time is gone forever." In spite of their worldly ways, the daughters possess the virtues that they will need when they have homes. Mommina knows how to cook; Totinạ how to mend, how to make dresses, how to keep a budget. The daughters do not want people to know that side of their life; they keep it carefully hidden under another side: the theatre, opera, music. How they love music! Music opens new vistas for them, especially for Mommina. She sings *Trovatore* very beautifully, and as she sings she weeps.

Are there not enough dramatic elements in this simple setting? For Pirandello there are, but not for the stage director who wants his play to be highly melodramatic and picturesque. What would Christmas be without the customary tree, the lights, the gifts, and wishes? Since the story deals with Sicily, Dr. Hinkfuss thinks that "it will be appropriate to have in the beginning a small religious procession—a synthetic representation of Sicily. It will add color." There will be four choir boys in black cassocks and white cottas; four girls dressed in white and enveloped in spotless veils; then a canopy carried over the Holy Family represented by three people who impersonate Saint Joseph, the Virgin, and the infant Jesus.

A small portion of the stage is to be occupied by the entrance to a cabaret. Against the intention of Dr. Hinkfuss the events pertaining to the drama crowd out the sentimental and

305

picturesque setting which really has nothing to do with it.
What part can a formalized procession take in an atmosphere where the most violent and barbaric passions are
smoldering and are ready to burst into flame? In the cabaret
a great confusion arises, brought about by a jest of very
questionable taste played by some youths on poor Signor
Palmiro who had gone to hear a chorus girl who touched him
deeply because she sang like his eldest daughter and cried
while she sang, just as Mommina did.

Verri becomes more gloomy and more intractable as he
comes to know the ways of those girls better. He resents the
liberties that they allow the boys. It makes "his nasty Sicilian
blood" boil in his veins. He is not like the other officers. To
these, fooling with one is the same as fooling with another.
He is attached only to Mommina, who is the wisest of the
four girls. She is the one who has been sacrificed, "she has
always prepared amusements and parties for the others, and
has always been excluded from them." Mommina must be
his, only his, and although not even engaged, she must not so
much as look at the other officers. One day he finds Mommina singing the second act of *Trovatore*, surrounded by the
aviation officers and her sisters. Verri goes into a rage, quarrels with his comrades, beats one of them, and justifies his
conduct by asking Mommina to marry him.

As Dr. Hinkfuss continues to arrange his tableaux, almost
in despair in his inability to match the impetuosity of events
as lived by the characters in their assumed, yet real, life,
Signor Palmiro is brought home mortally wounded. Dr. Hinkfuss had planned a dramatic entrance for him. The maid was
supposed to shout: "Oh, the master is wounded! The master
is wounded! They are carrying him upstairs wounded!" Signor Palmiro enters, carried by the chorus girl and a gentleman. He had gone again to the cabaret to hear her sing,
because he found sympathy in her while at home there was
only that big woman, his wife, with her violence, and his four
daughters with their questionable conduct. A man in the
cabaret had offended the chorus girl. Signor Palmiro had
taken her part, and the thug had wounded him mortally. All

the dramatic effect that Dr. Hinkfuss had planned is absent. There is nothing but death, with Mommina crying real tears. Death is not dramatic. It is ghastly.

Now there is want at home, and want does not encourage virtue in four girls with a mother like Signora Ignazia. What else can Mommina do except marry Verri, even knowing what sad fate awaits her? He will be more jealous than before. Everybody in his home town knows the reputation of his wife's family, and he will show all whether she is modest and virtuous or not.

If what is being enacted does not have all the impetus of life, it is because Dr. Hinkfuss interferes with his "cursed theatre that may God destroy." He only cares about effects when life is roaring in the characters, in their blood, while passions ride gigantic black horses with them; and their bodies are all aquiver and their souls are in fever and agony. Mommina and Verri must remain alone. Their grief must be stripped of any veneer to be seen in all its pathos and tragedy.

The characters insist that Dr. Hinkfuss go away. Since it was the final scene, and since it was their passion, while he was doing his part merely for art's sake, they cannot stand his presence there. Mommina is now about thirty; has been married to Verri for several years and has two little girls. Dr. Hinkfuss would have used powder in her make-up in order to give the impression of age. There is no need of make-up for Mommina. She is already old; she is pale, disheveled; some of her teeth are out; her body has been made ungainly by motherhood. Her husband is violent, forbidding, gloomy. His jealousy continues; he forbids Mommina to go out, and since he cannot be jealous of the present, and no man ever sees her, he torments her and himself with the jealousy of the past. He tries to pry into her secret thoughts; he wants to know what she dreams. It is useless for Mommina to tell him that she does not have dreams; that if she did, when she opened her eyes again, her present life would be more unbearable to her; that he wants her death; that he does not want her even to think or to dream. That infuriates Verri more. He moves like a beast in a cage: "It is that, it is exactly that! I bar doors and windows and to what avail if I am betrayed here in this very prison? Here in her, within her—in this dead flesh of hers which makes her betrayal alive, alive, if she thinks, if she dreams." Verri is powerless: "Even if I blinded you," he says, "what you have seen, the remembrances which you have in your eyes would remain in your memory; and if I should tear your lips, these lips which have been kissed by others, you would continue to feel the pleasure, the taste, that they experienced in kissing, to the point of dying of this pleasure."

Now poor Mommina is dying, but not of the pleasure derived from the remembrance of the kisses she has received. She has heart trouble, and Verri is killing her with the savage fury of his jealousy. The images of her mother and sisters float before her, and they assume a tangible existence on the stage.

After Mommina had married, they had continued to live the same life. Totina had become a great opera singer; Nenè, a fashionable harlot. Now Totina is singing in the town where Mommina and Verri live, so a program has announced. Totina will sing in *Trovatore*, the opera that Mommina sang so beautifully.

Verri knows that his wife's family is in town. The past has surged like a polluted tide over him, and is stifling him. He goes to Mommina's room and reproaches her again for the liberties that the girls took in her house before they married. In his over-excited mind, he sees again how those aviation officers embraced her, how they kissed her. He is like a madman; he kisses her, bites her, sneers at her, pulls her hair. Mommina calls for help, and her two little girls hasten to her side in their long nightgowns, pale, frightened, while Verri flees, shouting: "I am going mad! I am going mad! I am going mad!"

The past, her love for music, the thought of Totina and of her mother are so vivid in Mommina's mind that her mother and sister appear before her. Reality is obliterated by her dream. Drawing her daughters close to her, she tells them how Totina has come to sing in *Trovatore*. She tells them of the beauty of a theatre on an opera night, as she had always dreamt of it in wishing to dedicate herself to singing. Had she not married Verri, she would have sung in *Trovatore*, because her voice was more beautiful than Totina's. Now Totina sings while Mommina's heart is giving way. But she clings to life, happy in her music and in having her little daughters near her, loving her, all three happy, at least for a moment while the little girls' eyes shine like stars in their pale faces. She feels that life is ebbing away. She sings her favorite aria desperately, with all her voice, and dies.

This is the play as we have laboriously reconstructed and interpreted it. The dramatic events are stifled by the technique that occupies a paramount part in the play. The constant clashes between Dr. Hinkfuss and the characters interrupt the action and prevent that unity which is so often admired in Pirandello and which is a direct derivation of the intense passion that stirs his characters. In reality there are two centers in the play: one that of the author who rebels against the artificiality of the stage director, and the other that of the pitiful story of Mommina, her family, and Verri. These two centers, often clashing and interfering with each other, rob the play of unity.

The play would not please a modern audience. The differentiation between actual life and life in the passionate characters is so slight that events can happen on each of the two planes without jarring the author who wishes to stress this closeness, but naturally they would jar the onlookers. What remains with us after reading the work is the drama of Pirandello, the playwright, in the torment of creating his play, rather than the drama of Mommina and Verri. One feels, to be sure, the pitiful condition of that poor human being tortured by jealousy, and the self-tormenting hatred of Verri, but one sees them in the distance, as if looked at through the wrong end of the opera glasses.

The author's mind is returning with excessive insistence to the theme of the making of a play, a theme which attracted his attention both in *Six Characters in Search of an Author* and in *Each in His Own Way*. In the endless series of æsthetic

recriminations, the stage director calls the playwright artificial; in turn, the characters call the stage director artificial,
and Pirandello seems to suggest sadly that life calls all of
them artificial. In doing it he attacks himself, and his auto-
criticism explains the weakness of the play. He has shown all
the tricks of the trade, just as in *Six Characters in Search of
an Author* he has shown the tormented travails of dramatic
creation.

As in everything that Pirandello has written, there are
beautiful pages and situations, and there stand out his beautiful and exquisite thoughts on art.

In spite of the negative reactions that the play has inspired
in us, we see in looking at it in retrospect that the play has a
prologue that is followed by a first tableau introducing the
characters and giving the situation as it stands when the
drama begins. Then new tableaux give the death of the father,
the marriage of Mommina, and the rage of the jealous Verri
that leads to Mommina's death.

Over the æsthetic consideration, over the tragic life of
modest and romantic Mommina, there floats the infinite sadness of the author before the mystery of life: "Life must
obey two necessities that, because they are opposed to each
other, do not allow it either to assume a definite form or to be
forever fluid. If life moved eternally it would never acquire
consistency; if it acquired consistency, it would never move.
And yet life must have both consistency and motion." Still he
realizes that life has ebbed away from the art that encloses
Mommina's tragedy. Nothing will ever equal nor make live
again the anguish of the poor girl who sang so beautifully the
aria of *Trovatore* and shed real tears as she sang.

XXXV

Life Rebels Against the Fixity of Art

DIANA AND TUDA

(*Diana e la Tuda*)

Diana and Tuda is another play dedicated to Marta Abba. The heroine, Tuda, has auburn hair like Marta's in *The Wives' Friend*, and is as beautiful as Donata Genzi in *She Wanted to Find Herself*.

Reduced to the main threads that the author has woven into the play, *Diana and Tuda* is the delicate and pitiful story of a young model who could not bear to be only a model, a statue, for the artist she loved. Her life wavers between two men: Nono Giuncano, an old and celebrated sculptor, and Sirio Dossi, his pupil. Giuncano is one of the many characters created by Pirandello to represent his absolute and irrational idealism. In his long and glorious career the old sculptor has made numberless statues, but he has always been tormented by the thought that his statues, since life is really fluid, voluble, and chaotic, were lives fixed unto death.

As an artist who lives his art in his very flesh, as an intimate part of himself, he has suffered before the stony silence and immobility of his statues as before something that was once throbbing with youth and is now cold and stiff. It has been tragic for him to take the life of a model and imprison it in clay or marble. A feeling of revolt has spread its cold tentacles over him as he has realized that death too makes a statue of a man. His own body is the model that death is using to transform him into a statue. The process is slow but fatal. As the years have passed, his hands, his face, and his limbs have been assuming the stiffness of what is dead. As this realization grew in him, a gust of folly passed roaring by him; it enveloped him; it compelled him to break and shatter his own statues to which he had dedicated his youth.

311

He saw his own death in them. He shouts to Sirio Dossi, the great believer in art: "It will make of you as well as of me a statue, when you lie on a bed or on the naked earth, stiff." The two artists are perfectly described in these words of Giuncano: "When I hear someone talk, when I look or go somewhere, in the words I hear, in what I see, in the silence of things, I have always the suspicion that there may be something unknown to me from which my spirit, though present, runs the risk of remaining excluded. Then I stand there with the longing that, if I could penetrate into it, my life would open to new sensations that would give me the feeling of living in another world.—This man [Dossi], on the contrary —I don't know—he is just like that; with blinkers on. He does not feel, he does not see anything. He wishes only one thing."

The all-absorbing interest of Sirio Dossi is a statue of Diana that he is molding. He wants it to have the same winged beauty and the same posture as the one attributed to Cellini that is admired in the Brescia Museum. He is using beautiful Tuda as a model. Behind a curtain which extends across the stage Dossi is working and Tuda is posing. Before the curtain is seated Giuncano. He is "gloomy, restless. He is in his sixties; powerfully built, with his white beard and hair in disorder. His face is haggard, but his eyes are very young and full of life. He dresses in black." He loves Tuda, but he would never reveal his feelings to her because he would not want to contaminate her life and youth. Dossi is feverishly working while Tuda is begging him to stop because her posture is very tiring and her arm is absolutely numb. He refuses to stop; the hour is not up yet. Giuncano violently demands that Dossi allow Tuda to rest. To Giuncano the art of statuary appears futile and sinful before the supple beauty of Tuda's body; and he resents Dossi's so torturing her exquisite limbs. But Dossi is deaf to his voice. At Tuda's slightest movement he shouts and threatens her. He has made four sketches of his Diana and has thrown them away. Now he hopes to have the statue as he sees it in all the purity of

its contour and in its perfection. A fever for work burns
in him.

Dossi is tormented too, as are all true artists, but his torment is brought about by reasons that are antithetical to those
of his master. While Giuncano is haunted by the immobility
of death, Sirio Dossi is harassed by the mutability of life.
The body of Tuda appears to him in all its changing forms as
he works at his statue. That is life which is never the same.
In his rebellion he wants to give to that body the immortality
of the unchanging and divine character of art.

Tuda suffers in being only a perfect, cold, and distant
body towards which Dossi often has a sort of hatred. She is
presented to us in the glory of her loveliness as follows:
"She is very young and marvelously beautiful; auburn hair,
curly, arranged in the Greek fashion; green eyes, long, large,
and luminous, that at times, in a passionate mood, gaze
limpidly and sweetly like a dawn; at times, in sadness, they
have the grieving, opaque character of a turquoise. Her lips
often have a sorrowing expression, as if she views life with
a disdainful bitterness; but if she laughs, she is suddenly
enveloped in a luminous grace that seems to spread light and
life on everything."

The play moves on two planes, one serving as a background formed by Giuncano's and Dossi's ideas about art and
life, another where the dramatic action develops. The main
characters, with the exception of Tuda, who is a model with
a soul that Pirandello has lent to her, are people who live in
the storm of a sensuous social life out of which they must
come because in their soul there is an aspiration to something higher than social intrigues and love affairs. The higher
life is represented in the play by art, much as in the old days
religion was the beacon that led men out of the stormy waters
of sensuality.

Dossi has a mistress, a society woman, Sara Mendel. It is
one of those relations that are obscure, especially to those
who writhe in them; filth that sticks, loathing that gurgles in
one's throat.

Tuda tries to remove Dossi from the abstract and rarefied atmosphere where he lives with his statue of Diana. She wants him to see that she is alive: "Alive! eyes, mouth, arms, fingers, legs, look at them. I move them, and this is flesh, feel it: warm." Dossi cannot see the living being in her. She must serve only his art: "But what have you to do with me, as a living being?" he says. "What counts is the statue—not you. Marble; it's matter; not your flesh."

A mere chance gives Tuda the opportunity to force Dossi to give her more attention. Another artist, Caravani, has decided to make a painting of Diana with Tuda as a model. It has been a scheme of Tuda's to compel Dossi to marry her. She has already had a few sittings with Caravani. The picture is half finished. Dossi, upon learning of this, is furious. In her free way Tuda says to him, taunting him: "When an artist wants a model all to himself, do you know what he does? He marries her, my dear." In her words, however, there is more than a caprice and a challenge. She loves Sirio Dossi, even if her wounded vanity and pride mingle with her feelings.

Dossi agrees to marry her. He will marry her to compel her to be a model for him only. There are so many erratic arrangements and situations under the cloak of matrimony, especially among people of Dossi's social circle, that at the most his friends will but laugh. He and Tuda will be free to live as they wish, since he marries her only as a model. To prove to his friends and acquaintances that Tuda is only a model to him, the model for his statue Diana, he continues his relations with Sara Mendel. Dossi is blind to the humble offer that Tuda has made of herself. He does not see the woman in her. She longs for a bit of real affection. She wants to be alive for him and to give him joy, but she is rejected and spurned.

As soon as Tuda is married she becomes more and more hurt and despondent. Her dressmaker, who has gone to her house to try on new dresses, finds her very much thinner. She is pale and haggard. The wife is taking her revenge on the model. Having assumed the form of a wife and not living as one, it is natural, human, and logical that she should suffer.

She even abandons herself to grotesque acts. She goes to the studio and puts her numerous dresses on the various statues that Dossi has created of her. She is a statue like them. "Very well," she says, "I shall see to it that he will find them so. You can imagine how he will shout that I have desecrated them! As if what he is doing to me were not worse than this! Must I be only a statue here? Like a sister to these? Well: I am dressed, but I want them to be dressed too." People around her laugh at this outburst, but there is in these words an anger that lacerates something in the human breast, the resentment of a woman scorned, whose love gradually turns to hatred.

The chief sufferer in this situation is Dossi. It is his penalty for trifling with a human heart and with a life. His Diana is not finished, and whatever there is of it is not the copy of the beautiful, young, and happy Tuda of former days. Dossi has uncovered the human being in her, has wounded her, and in so doing he has destroyed the model in her. In the features of the statue Tuda sees herself as she has been made to suffer by Dossi and her rival, Sara Mendel. She sees in the eyes "hatred for the torture that they have given me. Before, it did not have eyes like these—its eyes were different, quite different . . . and that hand that touches its side—do you see it?—that hand was open before! Do you see now? It is closed tight like a fist. . . . It is no longer the one that he wanted to make. It is I now there, do you understand?"

One day poor Tuda finds Sara Mendel in Dossi's studio and learns that he has given her the key. She rebels with a violence that the other woman cannot understand, but which is clear to the logical mind of Pirandello, who sees in Tuda the model only. Since she had failed to be a woman, a wife, to Dossi, and had to be reconciled to be a model, the studio is her kingdom and Sara should not violate it with her presence. She can go to Dossi's rooms, if she wishes, since Tuda is not really his wife, and he is completely free. But there in the studio, no; Tuda has a right there. She sees the subtle scheme of Sara Mendel. She has succeeded in keeping Dossi

chained to her, thus defeating Tuda as a wife. Now she wants
to defeat her also as a model, wound her in the only prerogative she has before the man whom she loves.

How can Tuda remain in Dossi's home now that he, by
giving a key to her rival, has offended her and destroyed her
even as a model? She offers herself to Giuncano in a fit of
desperation, and also because she feels sorry for the man
who has borne in silence and with reserve his love for her.
The old master nobly refuses because he knows that behind
Tuda's offer there is only "a little compassion" for him. His
soul is still young, for he remarks: "I stir too—yes, within—
I still feel, I still feel. I feel with all the forces of my soul;
but here, now—do you see? I have this body that I hate, in
which I was never able to recognize myself." He reveals to
Tuda the tragic story of his life. His father had been a profligate man, and no tie of affection had ever existed between
father and son. He had been the cause of the death of
Giuncano's mother. Giuncano hated himself, his body, because it resembled his father's: "It is horrible, yes," he says.
"It grows old, and it becomes his more and more as my features become more pronounced and the lines of my face
deepen." Giuncano has placed himself outside of life, like
so many of Pirandello's characters to whom life has been too
unkind and cruel, but he has the strength to shout to himself and to the woman who has offered herself to him: "Life
must not take hold of me again! It must not take hold of me
again!"

Tuda has decided to leave Dossi at any cost. She has written to Caravani that she is ready to be his model that he may
complete the painting of Diana that was left unfinished because of her sudden marriage. Caravani accepts, all the more
that a gentleman from Chile wants to buy the work. He goes
to Dossi's studio and finds Tuda steeped in deep thoughts imbued by Giuncano's tragic confession. He tiptoes over to her
and tries to kiss her. A slap reveals to this modern Don Juan
that love redeems Pirandello's women from the baseness of
the flesh. She tells Caravani: "Woe unto you if you touch me.
I come only to be your model." And she leaves Dossi's house.

Dossi is frantic. He cannot finish his Diana without Tuda. He has attempted to work with other models, but in vain. He has fought a duel with Caravani and has wounded him. Now he is seeking Tuda everywhere because he must have her, only her, to finish his statue. After many days he finds her, worn out and haggard, the shadow of her former self. Dossi, Giuncano, and Tuda enter the studio. She tells Dossi that she cannot be the model for his Diana any longer. She tries to go over to the statue. Dossi, thinking that she wants to destroy it, threatens to kill her. Giuncano, like a wild beast, leaps on him and strangles him. Now Tuda is nothing at all; neither wife nor model; just nothing.

There are several situations that make one wonder whether Pirandello had not in mind D'Annunzio's *Gioconda* when he was touched by Tuda's sad plight. The similarity, however, is only in elements concerning the plot, since Pirandello's characters do not possess the Olympian calm nor the æsthetic nature that D'Annunzio has given to those who create the drama of Gioconda. It is very interesting to note the contrast in the development of the plays by two authors so strikingly dissimilar as D'Annunzio and Pirandello. The different treatment of the love theme constitutes the basic difference between them. In D'Annunzio, eroticism makes the long disquisitions about art empty and cumbersome; in Pirandello, the tormented concern about life tinges with sincerity and pathos the art and love *motifs*. Passions play a large rôle in Pirandello's play, too, but only as a vital part of life and not for their own sake.

Critics may accuse Pirandello of being abstract in this play. Often the concept has obscured and overpowered the poetic element in the situations. Often the distance between the background and the action jars the audience, as when one passes from Giuncano's or Dossi's beautiful discussions of art to the petty jealousies between Tuda and Sara. However, it should not be forgotten that Pirandello has never failed to endow his characters with a sincere thirst for life. The lucid lucubrations of these people, excluded from a normal existence, constitute all their life, and it is pitiful to see them suspended in a harrowing emptiness. Giuncano and Dossi are both perfectly aware that before them lies the possibility of letting themselves be engulfed by the muddy marshes of a commonplace existence or of living in the torment of their intellect. Referring to what people call "living," Dossi asks: "What is it? To travel, . . . to gamble, to love women, a beautiful home, friends, fine clothes, to listen to the usual gossip, to do the usual things? To live for life's sake?" They refuse to live such a life, and they naturally find themselves in a world of lucid concepts where the intellect is forced to take a paramount rôle.

The gloom of Giuncano is not cerebral. One feels a real and genuine flame in his utterances because they reflect the thoughts of Pirandello. Man is caught in a trap—the trap of life. "Call it life," says Giuncano to Tuda. "As a child you moved more easily; you darted here and there—now a little less—always less, always less, till—do you think that you have lived?—You have finished dying." It is the thought that life is a slow, continuous, but inevitable death—a thought so dear to those who have been excluded from the feast of life, be they ancient philosophers or solitary saints. Giuncano, too, re-echoes the feeling that the author has expressed through other characters: "I am thus: with my wide-open eyes that would not like to know what they see: things as they are that bear the punishment of being as they are and of not being able to be otherwise."

Pirandello's ideas of art and life pass over the play like luminous beams moving in the night, but the sad plight of poor Tuda is never obscured before us.

XXXVI

Renunciation

SHE WANTED TO FIND HERSELF

(*Trovarsi*)

The thought of the effect of dramatic acting on personality has often appeared in a veiled or open way in Pirandello's theatre. The problem can be briefly stated thus: When we act we assume, be it but temporarily, a personality different from our own. To what extent does it become ours? Does it have any lasting effect on us?

She Wanted to Find Herself is dedicated to Marta Abba, whose dramatic art Pirandello admired very much. What would be the effect of an assumed dramatic personality on the life of an actress like Marta Abba or of Donata Genzi, if you prefer to disguise her under that name? Pirandello presents the thesis that a true artist such as Abba must deny herself her own personality, must give up the fullness of her natural existence for her art. When she lives entirely absorbed by the present reality, as a perfectly normal human being, constantly and deeply herself, she cannot be a true artist. To be truly great she must live in the characters that she impersonates, and if she does, she necessarily renounces her own personality and life. It is natural that a person who has had such a great interest in the theatre, who has known and lived among actors for years, should consider such a problem.

Donata Genzi bears the characteristic traits, both physical and mental, that Pirandello lends to his typical characters: "She is pale, perturbed, with a grieving expression on her strange, tragic lips. In her large eyes with very long lashes there is something gloomy and lost." She is one of the great individuals before whose depth and beauty Pirandello ceases to be a humorist and becomes a tragic writer in the loftiest and best sense of the word. It is due to this afflatus of his art that he sought his setting and characters in an aristocratic place and among distinguished people whom he uses to express his new mood. The tone of the conversation is higher than in earlier plays; as brilliant as ever, but more contained and reserved. We are led to the Villa Arcuri on the Riviera. Modern life has entered the play without Pirandello's recriminations, and its exponents are sympathetically treated. Nina, who represents a modern girl, athletic and outspoken, Giviero, a distinguished psychologist, and Count Mola, a friend of the hostess, Elisa Arcuri, are all presented in a favorable light in accordance with the distinction and good taste that are often found among people of their class. There are also among the guests two writers, Salò and Volpe. Volpe stands for the narrow, meticulous "realist." He is a great believer in experience, a convinced follower of instinct: "dark, untidy, he often pulls his lower lip with two fingers." Salò expresses the author's belief in imagination that dwarfs experience: "under his flying hair, long and gray, he has a penetrating, luminous, youthful countenance."

These members of the best society that crowd the Riviera are gathered at the Villa Arcuri to meet the great actress, Donata Genzi, who is visiting the hostess. Donna Elisa Arcuri and Donata had gone to school together. When Donata became famous, Donna Elisa had written to her. They had remembered each other, and a warm friendship had begun. Now, Donata is tired, almost sick. She has come to spend a few weeks with her friend to restore her health.

Elj Nielsen is the only guest who has not arrived. He is a blue-eyed youth, son of a Swedish sailor and of Count Mola's sister; now an orphan entrusted to the Count's care. "He is twenty-six years of age, very blond, but bronzed by the sun, with clear eyes and an exotic countenance. He is dressed as people dress at a summer resort; he is simple mannered, abrupt, and yet dreamy." He passes his days in his sailboat, roaming over the sea, happy in its blue immensity. Nina hopes that he does not come. She is desperately in love with him, as love flares up among the free, unconventional young people of today. She is afraid that Donata and Elj, upon seeing each other, will fall in love. It will be fatal, because they are two creatures of perfection.

We are introduced into the drama by the curiosity of the Marchioness Boveno, another guest, who asks what sort of woman Donata Genzi is. She is informed by Salò that she is not one of those persons who act in life, too, not one of the common, hateful variety that can be easily defined as "a woman who acts even off stage." To Salò an actress, a true actress like Donata Genzi, lives on the stage "and as such she does not act in life. She is not one woman, one person— but many, as many as are the women whose rôles she takes." He ends: "And perhaps—for herself, no one." When she becomes a woman like all others, and makes a life for herself and enjoys it, she will cease to be an artist in the same measure as she allows life to absorb her. An artist, according to Salò, must "deny herself, her life, her person, give herself and her life completely to the character that she impersonates." Volpe, the one who believes in experience, wants to know how an actress could enact a love scene if she had never loved in her life. Salò, furious, retorts: "Oh, I had forgotten that you believe in experience—that in order to know, you must experience. I know, on the contrary, that I have always experienced only what I imagined beforehand." Experience is to him a synonym of disillusionment. Facts are disillusioning because they do not correspond to the idea that we have formed. It is the same with love. Those who love are not conscious of their emotion. Sentiment is blind. In the depth of love we close our eyes.

The guests are interested in this discussion when Donata arrives. They ask her opinion. She agrees with Salò. It is enough for her to project herself intuitively into the characters that she impersonates. She confesses: "I am each time as my rôle wants me to be, with the greatest sincerity." Since they are talking of love, that devilish chap Salò points out to her that if some day she falls in love, she will copy herself as she was when enacting her love scenes. Donata Genzi admits that. She is conscious of the fact that to deny herself a per-

sonal life is the penalty for the privilege of living her many
lives on the stage. She has always lived a lonely and secluded
existence; the warmth of love has never cheered her heart. Art
is not fiction for her: "It is life that is revealed to us. Life that
has found expression. It is no longer feigning when we have
made this expression our own to the point that it becomes
fever in our veins, tears in our eyes, smiles on our lips." Art
is to her exaltation, but also renunciation.

As she becomes more and more conscious of the limitations
that her art has imposed on her personal life, a deeper light
gathers in her eyes. Her inner torment becomes clearer as she
clothes it in sharp, lucid words before the guests, and she sees
it in the transparent consistency that words give to ideas. She
knows that an artist cannot have secrets, that she belongs to
the public, that all claim the right to fall in love with her, while
her heart is lonely and cries for a bit of warmth that she
knows she must deny herself. She knows that to really live,
fully, instinctively, one has to throw oneself headlong into the
abyss of life. She is aware that it is not really living to be suspended as she is, caught between the powerful mirror of art
and the swift river of life, "ready to answer in her mind the
call of every sensation, of every impression, of so many
images that a sudden longing may kindle." Her life is as
evanescent as that of one who wanders among memories. She
is like a flower that has not been able to blossom. She knows
it, yet she has denied herself to love in order to offer all the
thirst of her whole self to her art.

After this sincere and dramatic outburst, she is too excited
to have dinner with the other guests. She begs to be excused,
and retires to her room, only to come downstairs after a while
to go down by the sea, seeking solace in its immensity for the
torment of her soul. In the hall she meets Elj Nielsen, who has
arrived in the meantime. He has preferred to stay there,
alone, glancing at a magazine, while the guests are having
dinner. His plans are to wait until his uncle goes to bed, then
sail his boat, defying the roaring, stormy sea. Donata asks
him to take her with him now on his sailboat, to face danger
in the storm that is growing worse. Elj is at first surprised;

the request, the look of the unknown lady, and her daring spirit move him from his customary indifference. He tells her that he has "courage for himself, but fear for her." Donata insists. They go. Elj's sailboat is too fragile to withstand the mighty waves which batter its slight hull to pieces. Elj saves Donata by a miracle. They fall in love.

Elj is the very antithesis of Donata. She has the restrained consciousness of acts, postures, even ideas that her art has given her. He is fluid, spontaneous. He has in his blood the adventurous spirit of his father. He confides to her that he does not like commercialized sport: "I detest it as it is practised: imposture, mania, or speculation. I want my eyes to remain eternally new. I live with nature. I keep away from every intimacy as from a plague. I don't want disappointments. I want other people to remain new for me. Everything new. Only what is sudden is beautiful for me—what does not seem true—the continuous surprise that overtakes us. If I look closely at something and think of it, I am lost." His spontaneous temperament is revealed more clearly now that he is in love with Donata. She is convalescing in his studio where he had taken her on that harrowing night. He wants Donata and himself to be always new to each other: "You must never know what may come to you from me: acts, thoughts, surprises; things do not seem true to you in one like me." He paints. To be out at sea before the always different aspect of nature is to him a moment of supreme joy in which he finds the best in him: exaltation, rapture, courage to conquer all difficulties. His painting falls short of his expectations and desires because life appears to him a bursting shell, a continuous blossoming, a stupefying miracle. Donata, too, is new to him, and he is lost in her love. Elj knows that his instinctive, complete abandonment to her is the secret of his joy.

Donata is not less happy than Elj. She confesses to him that she has never belonged to herself. "But now that is over, all over. This is life and I want to see and feel my life only in you. To touch it in you, so: the light of your eyes [*she passes loving hands over them*], the taste of your lips [*she passes her fingers gently over his lips*]. Now I live, now I

live." She wants to find herself—her real self—not the one
that she has transfused into her acting. She hopes to find
her deep self and offer it to Elj. This is the meaning that "to
find herself" has for Donata Genzi. Will she find herself in
Elj's love? Will that love be greater than her art, absorb her
so as to make a new being out of her, a perfect being not only
in the eyes of others but before herself in the light of her own
limpid eyes?

One day while caressing Elj's hair she becomes conscious
that her caress is exactly the same as that which Giviero, one
of the guests, had told her he had noticed in her acting. She
is horrified. She begs of Elj: "Don't let me think of how I
am, how I move, how I look at you, the gestures I make. I
don't want to see myself. I know my face too well. I have always made it up. Now I want mine as it is, without my seeing it."

She, too, would like to be entirely new, but she cannot. She
must use the same voice, the same words, the same gestures
that she has so many times used in her love scenes. She becomes more and more conscious of the futility of her attempt
at being as spontaneous as Elj. She has thrown herself blindly
into life just as that night she threw herself into the slashing
fury of the storm. She has realized that that is the way of life
and of love: to close her eyes; and she has obeyed. She now
awaits with fear the moment when her eyes will be open, when
a man as spontaneous and rebellious as Elj will see her on
the stage. She tells him: "You are like a child who perhaps
will be frightened as many children are when they see
masks."

She considers giving up her career, but she realizes that it
would be too great a sacrifice. Elj's love cannot fill her life.
He represents only instinct, fluidity, even gentleness and
purity of instinct, but that is all. Grievingly she admits that
she has not found herself in that love. Life is still to her the
beating of quivering wings, the aspiration towards a goal
which is never attained. It was that feeling that made her acting so beautiful and appealing. Perhaps all in the darkened
theatre recognized themselves in the passionate expression of

her vain aspiration. She sees her failure in the light of the struggle that goes on in the whole universe when what is unformed is constantly striving to take shape, to be something definite, unaware of the fact that at the end of that transformation lurk death and destruction.

Through this realization her faith in art is strengthened. She reaches the conclusion that only art affords a perfect creation, finished unto itself, yet not dead but gloriously living. She is terribly unhappy now. Before she met Elj the thought had often come to her mind that her unhappiness was due to the fact that she had denied herself the experience of actual life, love, and passion. She has to confess that it is worse now: "It is worse, worse to have a life of your own. If you abandon yourself completely to it, you can no longer understand anything at all. You reopen your eyes, and if you don't wish to be engulfed by all that is commonplace, by all that becomes habit, a rut, monotony without color or taste, everything is again uncertain, unstable. With this difference that you are no longer as before, but you have tied yourself, compromised yourself, through what you have done without having succeeded in finding yourself." Love has been a disappointment to her because it has fallen short of her imagining —the imagining that art had enriched for her.

Uncertain, trembling, almost groping, she returns to the stage. The first time that Elj sees her act will be the crucial test. What she feared happens. Elj goes to the theatre and sees her as she had been with him in their intimacy. He feels that his love cannot stand this. He leaves the theatre before the play is over, and returns to his sea, to his nature, away from the painted masks that make him shudder. Donata too had suffered. In the first two acts she had felt lost. She confesses: "I felt dragged down by the public with which I had lost contact. What silence! What emptiness! I sweated blood—a torture, a torture!" But all of a sudden in the third act she really found herself: "A sudden jerk, here, within me, and freedom was mine. I forgot everything. I felt myself taken, carried away. Life flowed back into all my senses, my ears could distinguish sounds again, and everything was again clear and sure, sure. I possessed life again and so full, so full, and so easy—in such complete intoxication of happiness that everything glowed, burned, lived, and grew with me."

Donata had found herself in her art, but through Elj's love. She had fled to his room without even changing her costume to offer to him her triumph. He had already left. She had hoped that he would understand that it was possible for her to have her experience as a woman merge with her experience as an artist. Only so could she have the complete experience of his love. That night she had felt that she had "found not only the fullness of her art as an actress but the fullness of her life as a woman." Elj had not understood. His blindness condemned her again to the painful loneliness, the haughty disdain, and the isolation on the lofty peak where she nurtured her art with the sacrifice of her womanhood. She realizes that she cannot find herself in instinctive and complete life as she had longed to do. She accepts her hard but luminous destiny: to create, to re-create in her acting the lives of the great heroines of drama.

In this play we find the same *motif* as in *Right You Are if You Think You Are*, but accorded an entirely different treatment. Here, too, echo the words of Signora Ponza, "I am no one for myself." Donata Genzi had condemned herself to an impersonal life, to the negation of her identity, for the sake of her art. After the brief interlude of her love for Elj, she returns to the stage, grieving as Signora Ponza did but, being an actress, with more theatricality.

In humble terms, the problem of Donata and Elj is that of people who want to reconcile marriage and career. Pirandello has naturally made it more complex according to the nature of the two characters around whom the drama pivots.

The play is also a defense of the life of an actress against the stupid, current opinion that imagines that every actress must be corrupt: "The normality of a chicken cannot understand the flight of a crane. The chicken stands for current morality, *bourgeois* morality with all its preconceived ideas and prejudices," explains the humorous Salò.

Donata Genzi shares Pirandello's lofty idealism which at

times becomes exasperated and tormented, bordering on irrationality. She revolts against the limitations of the everyday
life and looks on her body as on a clumsy impediment: "Seeing myself called back to reality by certain glances directed
at my body, finding myself a woman—well, I don't say that
it displeases me—but it seems an almost hateful necessity,
in certain moments, and I feel the impulse to rebel against it.
Candidly, I do not see the reason why my body should be for
me my most personal possession." The author has placed in
her not only his admiration before an exquisite and perfect
embodiment of womanhood, but also his tragic wavering between art that has consistency and life that is fluid. Life is
Elj Nielsen; art is Donata Genzi.

The idealism of Pirandello before alighting on the blue
waters of the Riviera and tarrying for a brief moment on the
love of two perfect creatures, has soared to a dizzy height.
Pirandello has voiced here his rebellion at the very fact that
we are who we are because this fact precludes the possibility
of our being innumerable other beings: "Once life has become caught in this mold, in us, that's the end. It is fixed."
Pirandello is tormented here by the fixity of universal life.
He has revealed his grief through Donata Genzi's words:
"When we perform an act, it is not our whole being which
performs it, all life which is in us—but only what we are in
that moment—and yet that act, once accomplished, immediately imprisons us—stops us with obligations and responsi-
bilities, in that given way and in no other, irreparably."
Every possibility of action is precluded from us then: "and
of so many germs that could create a forest, only one germ
falls there, the tree grows there, and will not be able to move
from there, there in its entirety forever."

We hear in this play many of Pirandello's ideas on art in
general and on dramatic art in particular. There are clever
and witty statements such as the one that Salò voices: "Art,
being eternal, should have no age. But the trouble is that, being a woman, it loves fashion." There are also exquisite pages
in which Donata Genzi reveals the exaltation and solace that
she found in art.

The ever recurring *motif* in the play is the author's wavering between yielding to the fetters of a dwarfing experience and entrusting himself to the freedom of a daring imagination. He has revealed his idealistic mood by leading his heroine to a lofty region where only a few superior beings such as Donata Genzi and Marta Abba can abide.

XXXVII

The Misery of Fame

WHEN ONE IS SOMEBODY

(*Quando si è qualcuno*)

The keynote of *When One Is Somebody* is the misery of literary fame. The author studies the life of a poet who has found that respect, admiration, and glory are "all things that kill." His family, his admirers, the whole country have immobilized him in a given image that has blurred his real features by sealing them in a painful fixity. Although in his fifties, he seems to have lost the possibility of looking any age. They have molded him much in the fashion in which a puppet is made. He is almost embalmed alive. His life is no longer his own, nor are his acts or his feelings. He is tired of being followed by the eyes of the public: "They are as many mirrors before you, those eyes that stare at you. They make a statue of you, always composed in a fixity of perfection that is very tormenting."

His literary fame has established a certain form and style in his art from which he cannot depart. His head with his long hair brushed sweepingly back from his forehead in the fashion of all poets has become "of public ownership like the head on a coin." But he suffers, since behind that stereotyped image there is a soul that rebels: "No other image of me is admitted. I have expressed what I have felt, and there—crystallized—I cannot be different. Woe unto me if I am! They do not recognize me any longer. I must not move from the precise, definite concept which they have formed of me: there, that one, motionless, forever!" He confides his sorrow in these terms: "How many times, at night in my studio, do I feel oppressed beyond endurance: a puppet, to be left there, before my desk, in the light of the lamp, with its wig, its wax face, its wax hands, its lifeless eyes—there, motionless."

Pirandello has derived his theme and feelings partly from

329

his own experience, and he embodies the misery of greatness
in a character that has even been deprived of a name. His
speeches are marked by three asterisks. (We shall follow the
author's procedure in using them.) Fame has destroyed his
identity. It is natural that he should have no name.

When we meet his family we do not wonder why he has
assumed his stilted and statuary coldness, his unchanging im-
passivity that makes one think of a mask. "Giovanna, his
wife, is a large-boned woman, a rigid personification of the
official glory of the husband; she has a very low forehead,
austere oval eyes, a solemn look, a strong, imperious nose, a
firm chin; she dresses pompously in black and silver." The
children, Valentina and Tito, are as formal and hollow as
their mother. Tito basks in the glory of his father, and he
always has the words "Papà, papà," on his lips. We learn
that "when he has said 'Papà' he has said everything." Valentina, the daughter, already in her thirties, seems unapproach-
able, like a figure descended from a picture. She is painted
with painstaking artifice. She has an air of supreme absent-
mindedness. These people have solidified the father's fame
into a block of marble.

The poet lives in an ancient house, and his library "smells
of the musty air of old prints and of the closeness of churches.
It gives a stagnating sense of solemn oppression." When one
sees him seated before his desk, he looks as if crushed by the
artificiality of his life. He is not as alive as the pictures of
four great men of letters that he keeps in his library: Dante,
Ariosto, Foscolo, and Leopardi. They are the only people with
whom he can communicate, but they do not give much encouragement. Pirandello has treated their four figures sym-
bolically and when * * *, the man without name, is in the
library, they move from the panels where they are portrayed
and they enact a sort of mute scene in which they appear in
the typical postures that tradition has attributed to them.
They, too, have been immobilized by their fame: "In an absolute silence, they will, all four at the same time, gesticulate
most excitedly: Foscolo, all aquiver, with his arm raised and
his palm up, invites Dante to speak of the new destinies of

Italy, as he would like to; but Dante, forbidding and disdain-ful, shakes his shoulders peevishly and with an outstretched finger says, 'No, no,' most energetically. On the other hand, Leopardi disconsolately shakes his head and opens his arms in desperation, as if to say that everything is useless and vain; while Ariosto, with a smile of knowing indulgence, makes to the unhappy poet gestures of exaltation with his head and arms, as if to say: 'Well, find solace in yourself.' " The ad-monition is lost on the downcast poet, as it is lost on Leopardi.

The sudden return from the United States of a nephew of * * *, Pietro, with his wife Natascia, a beautiful Russian girl, and her sister Veroccia, leads * * * to the realization of his living death. Pietro, Veroccia, and Natascia represent youth, the youth of the new continent where races by intermingling are creating a new human type: "Russia, America, humanity that is blossoming anew."

Pietro, in his thirties, is blond, "speaks with great vim, then suddenly closes himself in a watchful silence of expectation while his eyes dart here and there." Only Natascia knows how to calm him with her beautiful, strange eyes. "Natascia is ter-ribly calm. The strange ideas that pass through her mind are visible only in the designs of her embroidery, which no one can understand at all. That's the way in which she finds relief in order to play the part of a wise little wife and affectionate sister" to Pietro and Veroccia. The latter is hardly in her twenties, with auburn hair. She is the very embodiment of vivacity, youth, and life.

Invited by Pietro, * * * has gone to the latter's villa as a guest in order to rest, and he has found a great and beautiful love in Veroccia. She has discovered that under the dead crust there is a living soul. The poet tells her: "A moment was enough for you to search into my eyes and see that I was alive." That love has brought a new youth to him, a love that he has kept on a spiritual plane only because it would have seemed to him, a man in his fifties, to contaminate her pure and supple youth, had he yielded to his passionate desire. His whole self seems changed. He dresses in sport clothes; he moves with agility; he knows again the beauty of being natural, the joy of laughing and hearing other people laugh, especially if in their laughter tinkles the joyousness and freshness of youth. Veroccia is joy for his eyes and delight for his soul.

Since knowing Veroccia, he has written poetry permeated by the fire that she has awakened in him, waking the dreams of the poet. Near her, it was natural for that fire of youth and for those dreams to flame into poetry. It was a new poetry, a reflection of the thoughts and sentiments that Veroccia had awakened in him.

The poems in which * * * has expressed that interlude of love and youth have been collected in a volume under the pen name of Délago. The book has been an editorial venture of Pietro. He has followed the clamorous and striking methods of American advertising in presenting the volume to the public. He has designed a gorgeous and varicolored poster with two portraits of the author. On the right there is the familiar one of * * * "in his posture, famous because thousands of times reproduced in books and prints of every kind; at the left that of the imaginary Délago, a fine-looking youth in his twenties who might even be a distant image of * * * when young, unknown to all and unrecognizable." Pietro has disguised the identity of * * * under that of a young American poet of Italian extraction.

The book is a real event in the world of Italian letters. The young generation feels that it has found in Délago "its own voice; . . . a voice that Délago has found for all of us there in America, in the clash of new forces." Three representatives of this new generation go to Pietro's villa to make inquiries because they have heard that Délago has arrived at Genoa on the steamship *Roma*. Quite frankly they contrast the glory of Délago with that of * * * in his very presence. He suffers unspeakably.

He cannot reveal the truth; he cannot tell that he is Délago. Délago, fantastic and unreal, is crushing him, the real author. There is a mocking irony in that fact. "You," remarks * * * to Pietro, "deprive me of my life to clothe another man with it."

Veroccia wants the truth to be known: "I want you to be

332

Délago for all," she says. "You feel this impossibility because you have chosen to be hidden in him, and now you feel that he stifles you, and you rebel."

Can the old poet reveal his young soul to his admirers? If he should tell them that he is Délago, he would kill Délago; "I am not nobody. I am somebody. I am I, as I am for everybody, and I cannot be another. If I say that I am Délago, if I shout that I am Délago, Délago is done for. He becomes just my mask, don't you understand? A mask of youth which I put on for mockery." To his dismay there rises clearly before him the vision of his self unnaturally divided into two beings, contradictory and hostile. Either he agrees to be Délago or the old Somebody. Veroccia is not his. She is Délago's, and to Délago belongs that brief moment in which youth and love have flared again. Veroccia granted him a short interlude in which he was allowed to bask in the warmth of her youth, but there was to come a sad end to that short-lived dream.

In fact, his family goes to Pietro's villa to interrupt this midsummer night's dream of poetry and youth. His wife and children have come to protest against the fact that * * * wishes to publish a new volume of verses that show a decided similarity to Délago's poetry. Even Giaffredi, a minister of state and friend of the family, has gone there because the Italian Government, on the occasion of the fiftieth birthday of the poet, wants to bestow on him the title of count for his literary merits, and could not do so if his poetry changed. Glory, especially if officially consecrated, is of one kind and one only.

A difficult choice lies before * * *: either he must be young with Veroccia or he must reënter the groove of his stilted existence with his family and with his glory. He yields to the pressure of his family and friends, and returns to the musty atmosphere of his home. He appears "as if he has reëntered his immutable image, universally known to all. He is pale and as if dulled into the rigidity of a stone."

He also agrees not to publish the manuscript of the new lyrics that he had put in Pietro's hands. Pietro, however, against his wishes, publishes them as new lyrics by Délago and reveals that Délago is one person with the old poet. The new generation turns against him: "For us, the poet—it is well that you know it—is no longer the wise man of letters, one who can amuse himself by appearing young when he is not. Knowing that you are Délago is enough for us to disown you. The poet for us must be above all a man." Délago has been killed by Somebody. * * * has to confirm even to the press that Délago is only a mockery; a mockery, and it was his whole life, the purest part of his soul. He had wanted Délago to obscure his previous fame. He had wanted to live in Délago because Délago was still alive and represented the eternal youth of his soul.

His friends and his family see only the mockery in his literary hoax. They insist on finding mirth in it, and they are blind to the fact that it is only tragedy to the poet. He sadly comments in despair: "The hoax! The hoax! You only see the hoax, you! It is incredible to you that I may still feel alive; evade this prison of myself! I am closed in, walled in! And I stifle! I stifle! I die!"

The celebration of * * *'s fiftieth birthday is a national event. They have reproduced his voice on phonograph records that all in the land may hear him. It is a tragic sensation for him to hear that voice which awakes a feeling of hatred in him. Photographers arrive to take his picture and flash it all over the country. They celebrate the rebirth of the old poet, and they do not realize what that rebirth has meant to him. He submits to everything, even to the torture of having to pose several times with his editor, with his friends, with his dignified family.

Pietro, Natascia, and Veroccia go to see him. They have read in the papers his statement about Délago. Veroccia is deeply hurt that he has declared that Délago's poetry and person are nothing but a joke. Had she been to him nothing but a jest? She leaves him indignantly, while he is unable to say a word, petrified in his grief. After Veroccia leaves, he talks to her tenderly and sadly as if she were present. He cannot be alive as she wanted him to be alive. She was only the youth of his spirit and he would have contaminated her young body had he accepted the offer of herself that she made to him: "You have not understood this restraint in me, of my shame in being old before your youth."

* * * is ready to accept the final humiliation: the official conferring of the title of count. A solemn festival is given in which high dignitaries of the political and literary worlds take part. Giaffredi is the official orator. * * * listens to his own funeral oration. "He is dead." So cries Veroccia as she gets a glimpse of him, moving as an automaton. After the official ceremony is over, he wanders in the garden alone and sits on a bench, a living statue of his useless and empty glory.

Is it indiscreet to ask whether this is one of the plays conceived and written when the beauty and charm of Marta Abba illuminated the pages of the playwright? Veroccia, in whom * * * found the last flare of his soul, has auburn hair like other noble heroines that have appeared in Pirandello's theatre. Has the author meant to silence the stupid innuendoes of people who surmise wrongly in their inability to feel the presence of something finer and loftier than the crude sensuality to which they reduce life?

Perhaps Pirandello has also tried to express humorously here the contrast between the new and the old generation. Newspapers in Italy a few years ago often used to carry attacks, and even do today, against the writers of the last century while exalting those of the present. To a superior mind like Pirandello's this literary clamor is foolish and amusing because he is not ready to countenance artificial divisions that are meaningless in the serene world of poetry. Only in this way can we interpret the benevolent irony towards the young generation, irony that is found behind the literary hoax of Délago. Pirandello seems to say to the younger generation: "Do you see? You believed that Délago was one of you, and the truth is that he was a man of the older generation." To Pirandello great art is life, and life in its cosmic reach does not know this or that generation.

Resuming the theme of *Diana and Tuda*, he has forcefully, but with greater pathos and serenity, expressed the tragedy of a man whose body begins to wither while his heart is still

335

young and warm. The attitude assumed by * * * towards Veroccia, and his behavior, are proofs of Pirandello's deep sense of humanity and of the nobility of his art and life.

In this play, which is one of the latest and finest, every trace of self-deception, of intellectual dishonesty, has disappeared. At an earlier stage of his development Pirandello would have accused the poet of having contributed with his tortuous intellectualism of his own fixity. Here the family, his friends, and life, are responsible for that fixity. Pirandello, sobered by experience, deepened by it, is no longer capable of laughing, albeit sadly, at his characters. He is completely penetrated by the tragedy of * * *, a man who has lost his identity to the point of having even his name obliterated.

CONCLUSION

Conclusion

In the course of this study of the dramatic works of Luigi Pirandello we have emphasized the tragic character of his life and have identified it with his art rather than stressing either his humor or his idealism. Both humor and idealism are the forms assumed by the grief that oppressed him. Critics are likely to take one outstanding characteristic and to insist on it to the exclusion of all others, thus neglecting what is basic and stressing unduly what is external and formal.

I have passed several months steeped in the dramatic works of Pirandello. It was as if I lived in the intimate communion of his soul. I met the characters that he has created, I learned how to look into their hearts, to suffer with them, and I feel that they have allowed me to penetrate into the heart of their creator. Those characters are now around me. They look at me with a resigned and sad air, and they tell me the secret anguish of the man who has mirrored himself in them. In our intimacy, I see no longer the grimace and the painful tic with which nature has marked them. They are human, deeply human beings, especially in their tragic grief.

Many people find Pirandello's pessimism excessive, and they resent it. They must belong to the class of those who think of man as a being endowed with eyes, nose, mouth, and a clear-cut profile, who quietly passes through life like an engine of which they definitely know the horsepower and the output. It is possible that they have the luck—if it is luck—of seeing themselves in the concept of a perfectly normal man. But let us suppose that another individual does not feel himself normal; that in place of his intellect there is a hostile force, a kind of motor whirling at terrific speed, and that his heart is full of rebellion and of tumult, that his brain is cold and sharp like a blade. Would we then have the courage to reproach this individual for seeing himself in characters to whom life is unbearable and who aspire in vain to free their

339

wings from the mire that weighs them down? Would it not be cruel to deny such an individual the possibility of finding in art the solace that life has so cruelly denied him? Who could reproach Leopardi his pessimism? Pessimism is as natural in him as optimism is in a healthy and happy individual. It is equally natural for Pirandello who, in the name of the agonizing torture of his life, can claim the right to present characters that have not been blessed with the gift of joyousness.

Pirandello is a modest man, given to thought. A few years ago he came to New York, and the Chamber of Commerce invited him to be one of the guests at a banquet where former Mayor Walker was present. Both Pirandello and the debonair mayor were called upon to talk. Pirandello said a few words and modestly sat down. Mayor Walker engaged in a humorous speech that brought on applause that rocked the house. Pirandello, so an eye-witness has related, sat quietly by, his chin resting in his hand and his arm propped on his crossed knee, gazing in amazement as if he could not understand. In that perplexed and thoughtful attitude there is a great deal of his personality and of his art.

It may be that someone will scoff at certain facts that form the plots of Pirandello's plays. Yet life offers stranger vicissitudes than those presented by him. In August 1934, the Philadelphia papers spoke of a boy in whom nervousness had taken the form of constant singing that could not be stopped for nine days and nights. The same papers in the same month spoke of a former beauty queen who felt such revolt for the physical side of love that she had lived for three years in a kissless marriage. Imagine the sensual clamor of Atlantic City on the night that she was crowned queen, and then see her and her husband struggling in a situation that no one could easily project against such a background. Of such cases as life offers unrequested is made up the grotesque element in Pirandello's plays.

As I look at the crowd of characters who gesticulate and move in a frenzy in the perspective afforded by Pirandello's dramatic works, I think of the forest where Dante enclosed those who committed suicide. Dante created in it one of the most ghastly and powerful scenes of the *Commedia*. The poor human soul has been caught in the texture of the tree, becoming one with it, and writhing in it. On the judgment day those souls will reclaim their bodies, and they will hang them on the branches from which they will dangle all through eternity. Dante has been more compassionate than Pirandello. He has punished his characters after they have committed suicide, thereby dividing life and his inferno; Pirandello has denied his characters the interlude of a peaceful existence, and has obliterated the boundaries between life and suffering.

I have tried to present the forms that the thoughtful and deep humanity of Luigi Pirandello has assumed in his theatre. By his intellectual aloofness, by the creations to which his sense of grieving isolation has given life, by his art that is as serene as it is unadulterated, Pirandello deserves a prominent place among the great spirits who have honored Italian letters and, indeed, since art is universal, the literature of the world. He has written in one of his short stories: "The characters of my fiction are spreading all over the world the rumor that I am a most cruel and heartless writer. I need a sympathetic critic who will show how much understanding there is beneath my laughter." [1] Nothing would give me greater joy than to have succeeded, no matter in how small a degree, in rendering justice to the great mind and to the great heart of Luigi Pirandello.

[1] *Novelle per un anno.* Vol. IV, p. 236.

BIBLIOGRAPHY

Bibliography

PIRANDELLO'S WORKS USED IN THIS BOOK

In a Sanctuary. Bemporad. Firenze. 1925.
The Other Son. Bemporad. Firenze. 1925.
The Patent. Bemporad. Firenze. 1926.
The Jar. Bemporad. Firenze. 1925.
Limes of Sicily. Bemporad. Firenze. 1926.
At the Exit. Bemporad. Firenze. 1926.
The Vise. Bemporad. Firenze. 1926.
The Duty of a Physician. Bemporad. Firenze. 1926.
Liolà. Bemporad. Firenze. 1928.
Cecè. Bemporad. Firenze. 1926.
The Imbecile. Bemporad. Firenze. 1926.
The Man with a Flower in His Mouth. Bemporad. Firenze. 1926.
Man, Beast, and Virtue. Bemporad. Firenze. 1925.
Cap and Bells. Bemporad. Firenze. 1925.
All for the Best. Bemporad. Firenze. 1923.
Each in His Own Rôle. Bemporad. Firenze. 1925.
Right You Are If You Think You Are. Treves. Milano. 1918.
Each in His Own Way. Bemporad. Firenze. 1926.
Naked. Mondadori. Milano. 1927.
Henry IV. Bemporad. Firenze. 1923.
As You Desire Me. Mondadori. Milano. 1930.
One Does Not Know How. Verlag. Wien. 1935.
The Pleasure of Honesty. Treves. Milano. 1918.
Think It Over, Giacomino. Treves. Milano. 1918.
The New Colony. Bemporad. Firenze. 1928.
Lazarus. Mondadori. Milano. 1930.
As Well as Before, Better than Before. Bemporad. Firenze. 1923.
It Is Only in Jest. Bemporad. Firenze. 1926.
Either of One or of No One. Bemporad. Firenze. 1929.
Other People's Point of View. Mondadori. Milano. 1925.
The Wives' Friend. Bemporad. Firenze. 1927.
Mrs. Morli, One and Two. Bemporad. Firenze. 1925.
Grafting. Bemporad. Firenze. 1926.
The Life That I Gave You. Bemporad. Firenze. 1925.
Six Characters in Search of an Author. Bemporad. Firenze. 1928.
Tonight We Improvise. Mondadori. Milano. 1930.
Diana and Tuda. Bemporad. Firenze. 1927.

345

LUIGI PIRANDELLO

She Wanted to Find Herself. Mondadori. Milano. 1932.
When One Is Somebody. Mondadori. Milano. 1933.

TRANSLATIONS OF PLAYS

Sicilian Limes. *Theatre Arts Magazine* 6: 329–44. Oct. 1922.
Three Plays of Pirandello. E. P. Dutton and Co. New York. 1923.
  Six Characters in Search of an Author. Tr. by E. Storer.
  Henry IV. Tr. by E. Storer.
  Right You Are if You Think You Are. Tr. by A. Livingston.
Man with a Flower in His Mouth; dialogue. *Dial* 75: 313–22. Oct.
  1923.
Each in His Own Way and Two Other Plays. (The Pleasure of
  Honesty and Naked.) Tr. by A. Livingston. E. P. Dutton and
  Co. New York. 1925.
Three One-Act Plays. Tr. by Elizabeth Abbott, Arthur Livingston
  and Blanche V. Mitchell. E. P. Dutton and Co. New York. 1928.
As You Desire Me. Tr. by S. Putnam. E. P. Dutton and Co. New
  York. 1931.
The New Colony. Tr. by S. Putnam for the Shuberts. Not yet pre-
  sented. 1931.
Tonight We Improvise. Tr. by S. Putnam. E. P. Dutton and Co. New
  York. 1932.

TRANSLATIONS OF OTHER WORKS

The Late Mattia Pascal. Tr. by A. Livingston. E. P. Dutton and Co.
  New York. 1923.
Fly. Story. Tr. by R. Wellman. *Forum* 71: 220–8. Feb. 24, 1924.
Shoes at the Door. Story. *Living Age* 323: 371–5. Nov. 15, 1924.
Goy. Story. Tr. by A. Livingston. *Menorah Journal* 10: 15. Feb.
  1924.
The Outcast. Tr. by Leo Ongley. E. P. Dutton and Co. New York.
  1925.
Mere Formality. Story. *Golden Book* 2: 399–410. Sept. 1925.
Shoot. (Si Gira). Tr. by C. K. Scott Moncrieff. E. P. Dutton and Co.
  New York. 1926.
Reserved Coffin. Story. Tr. by J. G. Harry. *Golden Book* 3: 122–7.
  Jan. 1926.
The Old and the Young. Tr. by C. K. Scott Moncrieff. E. P. Dutton and
  Co. New York. 1928.
Portrait. Story. *Living Age* 337: 300–6. Nov. 1, 1929.
Horse in the Moon. Tr. by S. Putnam. E. P. Dutton and Co. New
  York. 1931.
Two Double Beds. Story. *Spectator* 151: 764–6. Nov. 24, 1933.

Through the Other Wife's Eyes. Story. Tr. by J. Redfern. *Fortnightly Review* 139: 503–10. April 1933.

Here's Another! Story. Tr. by J. Redfern. *Fortnightly Review* 140: 599–606. Nov. 1933.

One, No One and a Hundred Thousand. Tr. by S. Putnam. E. P. Dutton and Co. New York. 1933.

Sicilian Limes. Story. *Golden Book* 21: 1–9. Jan. 1934.

Truth. Story. Tr. by J. Redfern. *Fortnightly Review* 141: 658–65. June 1934.

Dinner Guest. Story. *Golden Book* 20: 50–7. July 1934.

Miss Holloway's Goat. Tr. by J. Redfern. *Golden Book* 19: 586–9. May 1934.

Better Think Twice About It. Stories. Tr. by Arthur and Henrie Mayne. E. P. Dutton and Co. New York. 1934.

Naked Truth. Stories. Tr. by Arthur and Henrie Mayne. E. P. Dutton and Co. New York. 1934.

CRITICISM

United States

Two Noisy Roman School Masters. J. Collins. *Bookman* 51: 410–16. June 1920.

Grotesques of Pirandello. E. Storer. *Forum* 66: 271–81. Oct. 1921.

Luigi Pirandello. J. C. Grey. *Theatre Arts Magazine* 6: 317–28. Oct. 1922.

Six Characters in Search of an Author. S. Young. *New Republic* 32: 335–6; 33: 97. Nov. 22, Dec. 20, 1922.

Floriani's Wife. S. Young. *New Republic* 36: 207. Oct. 17, 1923.

Luigi Pirandello and His Writings. B. Crémieux. *Living Age* 318: 123–6. July 21, 1923.

Luigi Pirandello, Dramatist. *Review of Reviews* 68: 440–1. Oct. 1923.

Six Characters in Search of an Author. J. Crawford. *Drama* 13: 130–1. Jan. 1923.

Six Characters in Search of an Author. E. Wyatt. *Catholic World* 116: 505–7. Jan. 1923.

Eleanora Duse, Actress Supreme. Luigi Pirandello. *Century* 108: 244–51. June 1924.

Living Mask. B. De Casseres. *Arts and Decoration* 20: 32. March 1924.

Living Mask. S. Young. *New Republic* 37: 287. Feb. 6, 1924.

Living Mask. H. Kellock. *Freeman* 8: 544–5. Feb. 1924.

Luigi Pirandello, Dramatist. E. Storer. *Fortnightly Review* 122: 227–41. Aug. 1924.

Pirandello Hacks at Life. *Current Opinion* 76: 457–8. April 1924.

Pirandello's Warning. A. Rotre. *Forum* 71: 791–4. June 1924.

Portrait. *Theatre Arts Magazine* 8: 149. March 1924.

And That's the Truth, if You Think It Is. J. Crawford. *Drama* 16: 51. Nov. 1925.

Italian Letter. R. Piccoli. *Dial* 78: 43–50. Jan. 1925.

Pirandello on Writing Plays. *Living Age* 326: 473. Aug. 1925.

Plays of Luigi Pirandello. J. Palmer. *19th Century and After* 97: 897–909. June 1925.

Some Plays of Pirandello. B. Causton. *Contemporary Review* 128: 229–36. Aug. 1925.

Pirandello Confesses . . . Why and How He Wrote Six Characters in Search of an Author. Tr. by L. Ongley. *Virginia Quarterly Review* 1: 36–52. April 1925.

Luigi Pirandello. Walter Starkie. Dutton and Co. New York. 1926.

Naked. J. W. Krutch. *Nation* 123: 539–40. Nov. 1926.

Pirandello Interviewed. *Living Age* 331: 80–1. Oct. 1, 1926.

Pirandello, Man and Artist. E. Storer. *Living Age* 329: 415–19. May 22, 1926.

Jesting Pilate. J. W. Krutch. *Nation* 124: 295. March 16, 1927.

Luigi Pirandello. D. Rops. *Living Age* 332: 1001–7. June 1, 1927.

Masks: Their Use by O'Neill and Pirandello. G. Anschutz. *Drama* 17: 201–2. April 1927.

Pirandello and the Italian Stage Crisis. *Literary Digest* 93: 36–8. April 23, 1927.

Pirandello, Prophet of Unreality. *Review of Reviews* 76: 212. August 1927.

Pirandello's Plans. *Living Age* 333: 365–6. Aug. 15, 1927.

Right You Are, if You Think You Are. S. Young. *New Republic* 50: 141–2. March 23, 1927.

Pirandello's Humor. M. Y. Hughes. *Sewanee Review* 35: 175–86. April 1927.

La Nuova Colonia. *Living Age* 334: 955–6. June 1928.

Pirandello, Paradox. T. V. Blankner. *Theatre Arts Monthly* 12: 891–902. Dec. 1928.

New Pirandello in Diana e la Tuda. F. Blankner. *Poet Lore* 40: 215–22. June 1929.

Modern Italian Novel. Domenico Vittorini. University of Pennsylvania Press. Philadelphia. 1930.

Pirandello Quits Europe. *Living Age* 339: 317. Nov. 1930.

Pirandello Without Honor. *Living Age* 337: 544. Jan. 1930.

As You Desire Me. *Living Age* 338: 290–1. May 1, 1930.

Pirandello on America. *Living Age* 339: 541–2. Jan. 1931.

Actor Looks at Pirandello. H. Miller. *Canadian Forum* 12: 78–9. Nov. 1931.

As You Desire Me. *Commonwealth* 13: 415. Feb. 11, 1931.

As You Desire Me. *Nation* 132: 198. Feb. 18, 1931.

BIBLIOGRAPHY

As You Desire Me. *Catholic World* 132: 721. March 1931.

As You Desire Me. *Arts and Decoration* 34: 84. April 1931.

As You Desire Me. *Drama* 21: 9. April 1931.

As You Desire Me. *Theatre Arts Monthly* 15: 277. April 1931.

As You Desire Me. *Theatre Magazine* 53: 26. April 1931.

As You Desire Me. *New Republic* 66: 209. April 1931.

As You Desire Me. *Outlook* 158: 36. May 13, 1931.

As You Desire Me. *Bookman* 73: 409–10. June 1931.

Broadway to Date; Whither Masks? B. De Casseres. *Arts and Decoration* 35: 82. Oct. 1931.

Six Characters in Search of an Author. *Arts and Decoration* 35: 46. June 1931.

Six Characters in Search of an Author. *Theatre Arts Monthly* 15: 450–1. June 1931.

Tonight We Improvise. S. Young. *New Republic* 71: 44–6. May 25, 1932.

Pirandello in Search of Himself. *Literary Digest* 114: 18. Oct. 1, 1932.

Only Women Will Challenge the Mailed Fist; interview. R. Bercovici. *Pictorial Review* 35: 4. Oct. 1933.

Award of the Nobel Prize to Pirandello. *New Republic* 81: 30–1. Nov. 2, 1934.

Awarded Nobel Prize for Literature for 1934. *Publishers' Weekly* 126: 1749. Nov. 10, 1934.

Nobel Prize. *News-Weekly* 4: 42. Nov. 17, 1934.

Nobel Prize Author. *Commonwealth* 21: 120. Nov. 23, 1934.

Nobel Prize for Literature Awarded to Pirandello. *Nation* 139: 577. Nov. 21, 1934.

Nobel Prize Winner. G. A. Borgese. *Saturday Review of Literature* 11: 305. Nov. 24, 1934.

Portrait. *Rotarian* 46: 21. Jan. 1934.

Wins Nobel Prize. *Literary Digest* 118: 8. Nov. 17, 1934.

Tendencies of the Modern Novel. *Fortnightly* 141: 433–40. April 1934.

Pirandello, Italy's Man of Letters. G. J. Lux. *Richmond Times Dispatch,* Sunday Magazine Section 3, Dec. 16; 8, Dec. 23; 9, Dec. 30, 1934.

Conversation with Pirandello. A. Rousseaux. *Living Age* 347: 512–14. Feb. 1935.

Nobel Prize Winner. S. D'Amico. *Theatre Arts Monthly* 19: 114–21. Feb. 1935.

Pirandello in Search of an American Theatre; interview by S. Putnam. New Hope. Aug. 1935.

Metaphysics and Pirandello. E. C. Knowlton. *South Atlantic Quarterly* 34: 42–59. Jan. 1935.

LUIGI PIRANDELLO

England

Letter from Italy. M. Praz. *London Mercury* 6: 35–7. Sept. 1922.

Something New. D. MacCarthy. *New Statesman* 18: 618–19. March 4, 1922.

Luigi Pirandello. D. Williams. *Cornhill Magazine* 55: 268–83. Sept. 1923.

Henry IV. F. Birrell. *Nation* (London) 35: 379–80. June 24, 1924; Reply. F. Birch. 35: 407–8. June 28, 1924; *Rejoinder* 35: 437. July 5, 1934.

Henry IV. H. Wolfe. *Spectator* 132: 954–5. June 14, 1924.

Pirandello. F. Birrell. *Nation* (London) 34: 634. Feb. 2, 1924.

Henry IV. F. Birrell. *Nation* (London) 37: 399–400. June 27, 1925.

Henry IV. D. MacCarthy. *New Statesman* 25: 309–10. June 27, 1925.

And That's the Truth (If You Think It Is). *Outlook* (London) 56: 202. Sept. 26, 1925.

And That's the Truth (If You Think It Is). I. Brown. *Saturday Review* 40: 334–5. Sept. 26, 1925.

And That's the Truth (If You Think It Is). W. J. Turner. *New Statesman* 25: 694–5. Oct. 3, 1925.

Henry IV. N. G. Royde-Smith. *Outlook* (London) 56: 57. July 25, 1925.

Henry IV. H. Shipp. *English Review* 41: 437–40. Sept. 1925.

Six Characters in Search of an Author. D. MacCarthy. *New Statesman* 25: 282–3. June 20, 1925.

Pirandello. N. G. Royde-Smith. *Outlook* (London) 55: 429. June 27, 1925.

Pirandello. M. Waldman. *London Mercury* 12: 396–405. Aug. 1925.

Pirandello Season. I. Brown. *Saturday Review* 139: 670–1. June 20, 1925.

Plays of Signor Pirandello. *Spectator* 135: 11–12. July 4, 1925.

Man With a Flower in His Mouth. N. G. Royde-Smith. *Outlook* (London) 57: 393. June 1, 1926.

Pirandello, Man and Artist. E. Storer. *Bookman* (London) 70: 8–11. April 1926.

Naked. F. Birrell. *Nation* (London) 40: 924–5. April 2, 1927.

Naked. H. Horsnell. *Outlook* (London) 59: 330. March 26, 1927.

Naked. D. MacCarthy. *New Statesman* 28: 732–3. March 26, 1927.

Six Characters in Search of an Author. H. Shipp. *English Review* 47: 113–14. July 1928.

The Life That I Gave You. R. E. Roberts. *New Statesman and Nation* 1: 425. May 16, 1931.

Secret of Power. *Saturday Review* 152: 554. Oct. 31, 1931.

What is genius? *Bookman* (London) 81: 6–7. Oct. 1931.

BIBLIOGRAPHY

Luigi Pirandello. A. Wareing. *Bookman* (London) 81: 190. Dec. 1931.

Portrait. *Bookman* (London) 84: 62. April 1933.

The Life That I Gave Him; adapted by C. Bax. D. Verschoyle. *Spectator* 153: 521. Oct. 12, 1934.

Italy

Bibliografia di Pirandello; edited by Manlio Lo Vecchio Musti. A. Mondadori (Milan). Idem. Bibliografia di Pirandello. A. Mondadori (Milan), 1952.

APPENDIX

PIRANDELLO AND THE ITALIAN THEATRE*

By Domenico Vittorini

T HIS brief essay on Luigi Pirandello as a dramatist has been written with the conviction that the task of criticism follows two parallel lines of investigation. One is objective and aims at singling out the aesthetic and ethical principles shared by the author; the other is subjective and enjoins the critic to state whether or not, in his opinion, without the slightest shadow of dogmatism, the author has reached the goals that he assigned to his art, and whether or not his works have attained artistic significance.

This is the modest task that I have set before me in sketching the outwardly quiet and inwardly tormented figure of the man who in our lifetime called the attention of the entire world to the literature of Italy. The Nobel Prize that he received in 1934 was a clear recognition of the universal appeal and significance of his art.

Born in Sicily in 1867, Luigi Pirandello lived through two very different epochs of Italian history; one represented by the civilization that appeared after Rome became the capital of his unified country, the other encompassing the years in which Italy, following the urge of the "sacred egotism" of nations, grew of age, expanded economically and politically with that mixture of good and evil that is inherent in all change and growth. Pirandello died in 1936, before his country was engulfed in the tragedy of the second World War. Had he lived, I feel confident that he would have raised his stooped shoulders and, faintly smiling, with arms outstretched in the manner so peculiar to many of his characters, would have said: What can you expect, life, history and man being what they are?

*Read at the Casa Italiana of Columbia University on Saturday, April 19, 1952.

Culturally speaking, Pirandello bridged the Verismo period and our own age. The critic has two main sources at his disposal among Pirandello's writings: his *Umorismo*, published in 1908, and the preface to *Sei personaggi in cerca d'autore*, penned in 1925, as well as the numerous passages in the dramatic works of this period.

The basic aesthetic ideas expressed in *Umorismo* link Pirandello with the Verismo movement. His later utterances show that he departed altogether from the tenets of that school in order to veer towards an art more universal, complex, and psychological.

It is unquestionably true that Pirandello had definite links with Verismo, the main, but by no means the only, stream of literary life in Italy in the nineties. Nor was there any reason for Pirandello to resent this. He learned from that movement how to use in his fiction a landscape that he knew intimately, his native Sicily, and how to adhere to the human traits of his characters, two basic characteristics that served him in good stead, as he reflected in his art his own quixotic temperament and the strange vicissitudes of his existence. Let us not forget that he lived for years with a demented wife and that he greatly resented the indifference of the Italian public.

Yet, Pirandello's protest had a basic justification in the fact that he had not slavishly followed the footprints of Giovanni Verga, his master and friend. He had, instead, created a type all his own of realistic fiction by injecting humor into the material that the Verismo of his Sicily offered to him. He had transformed the objective and wistful naturalism of Giovanni Verga into a more searching and subjective study of man and life.

His *Umorismo* clearly documents the new treatment that he accorded to the realism of his age. Art, so he tells us, appeared to him in the light of contrast between being and seeming, between life as a cosmic force and human existence as a personal experience. But that critical essay on humor shows also, or rather, leads one to conclude that the world of naturalism was not suited to Pirandello's philosophical temperament. Who would ever have surmised that behind the grotesque figures that moved in the early works there was a deep philosophical intuition? The average reader only laughed at the vicissitudes of those little men and women whom the author paraded before him with the only purpose, so it seemed, of ridiculing them. How could the average reader, or even the critic, correlate the events of Pirandello's early fiction with such statements as these: "Life is a continuous and fluid entity that we try to stop, to fix in unchanging and definite forms, inside and outside of us, because we all are fixed forms, forms which move along others equally fixed." We are, he continues, the result of concepts reached through an infernal machine called logic, which pumps our sentiments from our hearts up to our brains and reduces them to lifeless abstractions. Only now and then, in rare moments of inner illumination, do we resume contact with real life, life as a cosmic flux that suffers in being enclosed in its human molds: rocks, plants, animals, men. Then we experience a terrifying shock, as we see ourselves live suspended in the inner void created by the contrast between cosmic life and its earthly and human forms. Pirandello's fiction reflected in his puny and strange-looking characters the ludicrous embodiments of this ideal life-concept. We must not wonder that this fiction was never popular.

We can appeal directly to him to prove that he considered himself a philosophical author. In the preface to his *Sei personaggi in serca d'autore*, he wrote: "I have never been satisfied with representing the figure of a man or of a woman for the sheer pleasure of representing it; nor with narrating a specific event, gay or sad, for the sheer pleasure of narrating it; nor with describing a landscape for the sheer pleasure of describing it." He attributes to such authors the quality of being "historical" or "descriptive." But he points out that there are other writers for whom "a human figure, an event, a landscape become enriched with a peculiar life-sense that lends to them a universal value. These are writers of a nature strongly philosophical." He adds: "I have the misfortune of belonging to the latter type." It was but natural that an author, who took his art so seriously and who had studied himself so clearly, should seek a more congenial medium of expression.

In his first attempts Pirandello did not abandon the themes dear to Verismo. His *Lumie di Sicilia* testifies to this. Indeed, he often returned to that small, yet unforgotten world, even in later years, when he dramatized short stories previously written. These plays constitute a very readily distinguishable section of his dramatic work. Many of the one-act plays belong to it. Most of them are characterized by a Sicilian setting, a language that achieves effectiveness through a restrained and consciously simple vocabulary, by elementary passions as material for the plot. *La patente*, *La giara*, *L'altro figlio*, *Liolà* are typical of this activity. Many of them can be very successfully staged, but they all show a deep contrast between the simple figures that move in them and the philosophical utterances that they are made to voice. Imagine Ciampa, a small-town bookkeeper, the hero of *Il berretto a sonagli*, who suddenly sallies forth with these words: "We are puppets, dear Mr. Fifi. The Divine Spirit enters into us and it becomes dwarfed." And, as if this were not enough, Ciampa proceeds to refer to that processs of "building one's self up" which plays such a large part in the major works of our author. The thoughtful reader cannot help noticing the dualism that besets this and similar plays, gems of dramatic art as some of them are. Of this contrast, the author himself must have been conscious, for he changed to a new dramatic form in which this jarring discrepancy was eliminated. Of *L'uomo, la bestia e la virtù* he said: "It is tragedy stifled by the traditional Italian comedy." Pirandello uncovered the limpid stream of his creativeness when in his major plays he forsook the realm of comedy and entered the precincts of stately tragedy. Then he penned such works as *Sei personaggi in cerca d'autore, Enrico IV, Come tu mi vuoi, Quando si è qualcuno.* His fame is especially evidenced in these works, the most significant of modern Italian dramatic literature. As a result of these plays, he was recognized as the dominant figure of the European stage from 1920 until his death.

He expressed the torments of the intellectual men of our time more fully than any other contemporary playwright. His characters became the lucid and perfect projection of the same tragic sense of life that he had expressed less perfectly in the works of his youth. In this sense, he was right when he insisted that his art had never changed. It had changed only in that now his new characters were possessed of a rich personality and of a stature that was consonant with the message that Pirandello entrusted to them. The author himself states that he gave to the unforgettable Father of *Sei personaggi in cerca d'autore* the task of conveying the impossibility of human comprehension, of the multiple character of human personality and the "tragic conflict between life as a fluid entity and life as a fixed and immutable form." The main characters of his plays have absolved this function with a perfection that assigns to Pirandello a place among the great dramatists of all times.

The theme of "costruirsi," of building oneself up, rises with a clearcut contour in these major plays and it conveys with compelling force the conviction of the author concerning the tragedy of being human. The plight of the characters has become one and the same with that of the author, and the reader is carried away by the passionate pleading of the latter. The conscious madness of Henry IV is not conceivable in a less complicated character, for complication presupposes a great wealth of psychic power, even if misdirected. Henry IV, like Mrs. Morli in *La Signora Morli, una e due* or like Baldovino in *Il piacere dell'onestà*, is an exemplification of "costruirsi," but what a difference from Ciampa, Cecè, or even Mattia Pascal! What tragedy and what agonizing torment Pirandello has been able to create in him, a man who, masquerading as Henry IV, becomes unconscious as the result of a fall from his horse, and wakens into the belief that he is actually the German Emperor. For fourteen years he vegetates in the neutral state of his madness, when suddenly he reopens his eyes on the horrible spectacle of his true identity. His cry of terror conveys with an overpowering impact the tragedy of being himself. Seldom have imaginary tortures been made so real in the limpid mirror of art! Henry IV, too, like Mattia Pascal, has remained excluded from life but his loneliness is of a different nature and is conveyed in a different style with a different poignancy. The Unknown woman in *Come tu mi vuoi* is also a "costruzione" when she tries to live again in herself the soul of Cia, but what a difference from the wanton women of earlier works who, "built themselves up" in deceit and perversity! The soul of Cia cannot live again on this earth because, upon her return, her husband and relatives are more interested in her body than in her soul and so the Unknown goes back to her destiny of worldliness and tragedy. Did the literal identity of the Unknown really matter since she was bringing back to them the soul of Cia? Had the literal identity really mattered for mothers who during the first World War, fought over a torso that each believed to be her son maimed on the battlefield?

One of the best exemplifications of Pirandello's intuition of "costruirsi" is found in *Quando si è qualcuno* in which the author reflects his own reaction to the literary fame that the world accorded to him after his plays were given both in Europe and America. Pirandello's hero had reached the conclusion that respect, admiration, and glory are "all things that kill." His family, his admirers, the whole country, had immobilized him in a given image that had blurred his real features by sealing them in a painful fixity. The main character concludes that he has been embalmed alive and confesses: "They make a statue out of you, always composed in a fixity of perfection that is very tormenting." He had to dress, to wear his hair long, to speak, even to write in the form that his contemporaries associated with the idea that the public had conceived of him. Was that living? He adds: "How many times, at night in my studio, do I feel oppressed beyond endurance: a puppet, to be left there, before my desk, under the light of the lamp, with its wig, its wax face, its wax hands, its lifeless eyes — there, motionless." Pirandello presents the speeches of the hero by marking them with three asterisks, since he has not given him a name in the play. He is a Somebody, a shadow entity which gradually has become synonymous with Nobody. When the Italian government, on the occasion of the hero's fiftieth birthday, decides to honor the poet by making him the spokesman of the regime, the latter passively acquiesces. His passiveness is so complete that it becomes very plausible when he is seen rising with the stand on which his statue was supposed to rest. This play constitutes one of the last expressions of Pirandello's meaning of "costruirsi." He embodied in it the most personal and fullest idea of the tragedy of not being oneself. His last words have a poetic and human resonance which is not easily forgotten: "Puerizia — arcana favola — ombra chi a te si avvicina — ombra chi da te s'allontana — " ("Childhood — mysterious fable — a shadow is he who draws near you — a shadow is he who draws away from you.") These are the words which, as the hero speaks, become engraved on the stone that contains his epitaph. What greater tragedy for fluid life than that of becoming petrified, for a living man to become "the statue of himself!"

Playwrights are generally remembered because of the dramatic forms which they have introduced, for the novelty of the material used, for the characters that they have created. Pirandello deserves to be remembered for these reasons, too. But, as time passes, I believe that he will be remembered, at least by thoughtful readers, for the many pages that he has dedicated to man who feels lost before the mystery and wonders of the universe, to the study of the real meaning of living on this planet, to the singling out of quiet moments in his existence in which, against and beyond the social hypocrisies that surrounded him, he reached the simple truths, spontaneous feelings, and unadulterated sentiments that represented for him a true pattern of living. Here is one of the passages that reveal the basic character of Luigi Pirandello: "We advance sadly along a road already invaded by the shadows of the evening. It is enough to raise our eyes to a little loggia still illuminated by the setting sun, with a red geranium that glows in that light — and suddenly a distant dream touches our hearts." This passage is taken from *Ciascuno a suo modo*, one of the most tormented plays that he wrote; a play in which characters are shown as deceiving not only others, but themselves; a play in which everything is tortuous, spasmodic, torturing and tortured, because there is no basis for the thinking and acting of those who, though they proclaim very vociferously and excitedly their sincerity, are deprived of opinions and beliefs, even of conscience. The title is at first very baffling, until one reads passages like the following: "Detach from yourself the little puppet that you create with the fictitious interpretation of your acts and your sentiments — and you will immediately see that it has nothing to do with what you are, or what you may truly be — with what abides in you without your being aware of it, and which is a terrible god, understand, if you oppose him, but which becomes immediately compassionate of every guilt if you abandon yourself to him, and do not wish to find excuses." With these words comes the admonition that everyone of us has to create his own reality through spontaneity of feelings and through humility.

Other memorable words in their human resonance are those of Ersilia Drei in *Vestire gli ignudi*, the forlorn and forsaken heart that longed so for a bit of love that she, through a lie, prepared to take her life by poison in order to replace with the tinsel of her story the white garland of orange blossoms that she had so desperately hoped would one day rest on her brow. But everyone refused to see the reason for her lie. So, desolate and alone, she took poison again and announced that she had lied not in order to live but in order to die. "Well, yes, . . . I tried to make a decent little garment for myself, at least, for my death. That's why I lied. I swear it to you. In my life I had never been able to put on a little dress without having it torn by the many dogs that have always attacked me in every street; without having it soiled by the basest and vilest miseries. So I attempted to make myself one — to die in — that of a bride, in order to die in it with a little sympathy and pity from everyone. Well, I have not been able to have even this! It has been torn from me, cast into the gutter and spurned . . . Now go. Let me die in silence: stark naked. Go and tell . . . that this poor girl died naked."

Allow me to quote from *Come tu mi vuoi* and let us take notice of the deep chords that Pirandello reached in justifying the Unknown for assuming the personality of Cia: "Many an unfortunate one, after years, has returned just like that (she points to the Demented One, the pitiful body of Cia, once beautiful and all perfection of soul and mind) ; many an unfortunate one has returned with features obliterated, unrecognizable, without any memory, and sisters, wives, mothers, have fought to have the unfortunate one with them. Not because they have recognized him, no (cannot the son of one resemble that of another?), but because they have believed him to be their own. And there is no contrary proof that may be valid when one wishes to believe! Is it really he? But for that mother, it is he; yes, it is he! What does it matter if it isn't he, if a mother keeps him and makes him hers with all her love? Against every proof she believes him to be hers." And yet, the author of such passages has been called cerebral and abstract!

In his concept of the impersonality of love, Pirandello joins Plato who, in his ideal republic, wanted a communal possession of wives and children, that one would love all the children in the state and not only one's own. If we preface the reading of *L'innesto* with this thought, we shall understand better the theme of mystic parenthood that is the kernel of the play. We shall, at least, heed the pathos of the words of the woman who, loving her husband in an absolute way, couldn't conceive that the child that she was bearing as the result of a brutal attack by an unknown individual, should be considered the child of any man other than her husband. These are her words: "I want you to see in your son all of me; he is yours, because he is proof of all my love for you." Naturally enough, Giorgio, the husband, does not understand. Pirandello condemns him to losing Laura, who proves too imaginative and too lofty for his practical mind.

Time does not permit a discussion of Pirandello as a social critic, of his theme of conscious illusion that makes the wearing of a mask so painful for his characters, of his abstract idealism that leads him to justify even adultery as he does in his last play, *Non si sa come*, to mention only a few of the many aspects of his art.

However, consideration, be it brief, must be given to Pirandello's place and role in the Italian drama of our time. It was certainly the impact of his work that caused a large section of Italian drama to forsake the modes as exemplified by Giacosa, Bracco and Sem Benelli and to replace them by a fantastic setting whose dimensions and rhythm are not regulated by ordinary logic. The "Teatro del Grottesco" that flourished during the first World War and in the interlude between the two wars was closely connected, historically and culturally, with Pirandello's intuition of life and art. In fact, Pirandello was an intimate friend of Luigi Antonelli, one of the leading figures of the group of the Grotteschi, which looked upon *Umorismo* as its guiding light. Pirandello did not belong officially to this group. His position was somewhat like that of Alessandro Manzoni who influenced Italian Romanticism, although he refused to be officially linked with the movement. Pirandello's influence on the revival of Italian art in the 1920's was very effective, and was carried out through the formation of his own troupe with which he toured both Europe and the Americas.

It is more difficult to single out what specific influence Pirandello had on playwrights of other nations. He exemplified the interest of our time in probing into the psychological and the subliminal, and contributed to the popularity of such themes. More than of influence, I believe it is proper to speak of similarity of intuitions between Pirandello and Eugene O'Neil, Fernand Crommelynck and Jean Sarment. They all used themes to which they were attuned by the history of their time, their personal experiences, and, above all, by their oversensitive temperaments.

Pirandello's work was far from done, so he felt and confided to his friends, when death overtook him in his sleep. He was buried without pomp, as he had requested. With him disappeared the most significant Italian literary figure of our time.

Criticism has not stressed enough the intimate note of admonition that lies very unobtrusively but deeply in the art of the Maestro. We know so little of ourselves, of the Universe, and of our fellow-men; life is so fleeting, indeed, so ruinous that only humility and sentiment can save and console us. The world of his art is populated by strange-looking characters whose eyes are wide open, whose nerves are tense, whose hands are contracted as if in fear of losing control over themselves, and who, nevertheless, manage to look normal, and walk with seeming indifference and even dignity among other men sharing their lot and feigning with equal success. Pirandello still lives in the creations of his fancy, possessed now of a peace that he never knew on this earth.

LUIGI PIRANDELLO AS I SAW HIM*

Domenico Vittorini

University of Pennsylvania

T HE following are recollections of my meetings with Luigi Pirandello in New York during the months of July and August, 1935, offered here as an historical document of what he said in many hours of intimate conversation. The term "historical" is used advisedly, in humble awareness of the tenuous data upon which the historian is often compelled to rely for his reconstructions of the past. That Pirandello belongs to the literary history of the last fifty years, there is no doubt. He created such a stir in the dramatic circles of our time as to cause his name to be widely known outside of Italy; and enough playwrights were influenced by his intuitive grasp of human personality that "Pirandellian personality" has become a byword in our generation.

I first met Luigi Pirandello at the reception that was accorded him aboard the steamship *Conte di Savoia* at the 18th Street dock on July 20, 1935, when he arrived in New York for a three months' stay in the hope of having his well-known play *Sei personaggi in cerca d'autore* (Six characters in search of an author) made into a film. As I stepped on the ship, the thought that I was shortly to see the man whose work I had always admired keyed me to a nervous tension. When I confided my nervousness to a young colleague of mine, he, with characteristic modern indifference toward greatness, exclaimed, "For heaven's sake, man, do you think that Pirandello is a god?" Being aware that reality is something very subjective, I did not answer and hastened toward the other end of the hall where the

* From SYMPOSIUM, Vol. VIII, No. 1. Syracuse University, Syracuse, N. Y.

smiling and wistful countenance of the playwright had appeared. He was accompanied by the ship's officers and the New York City dignitaries who had gone to meet him at quarantine.

Pirandello was of medium height, rather heavy-set, with an oval face and a short, pointed, gray beard. Although sixty-seven years of age, he was quick in his movements, and his person bore the marks of a robust manhood. What attracted me more than anything else were his mobile eyes. They had a way of their own of converging on you as if to penetrate your innermost thoughts, and then they suddenly became hidden by an impenetrable veil as he relaxed his attention and withdrew within himself. Introspection was not a pose with him. It was an instinct and a habit reflected in many of his characters. Shy and timid, he stood in the midst of the reception committee. While grateful for the recognition accorded him, he seemed to have to force himself to listen to the oratory lavished in his praise.

As I stood a little to one side, interested in seeing his reactions in meeting people, I saw him turn and beckon to me with his finger. He must have been told that I was eager to have an interview with him. He was very cordial in thanking me for my interest in his writings and expressed gratification at the manner in which I had presented him in a long article that had recently been published in the *Ateneo veneto* of Venice.[1] He gave me an appointment for the following day at the Waldorf-Astoria.

The next morning, as I waited in the lobby of the Waldorf-Astoria, it was hard for me to picture Pirandello, who had always indicted the splendor and the hustle of modern civilization, on the forty-first floor of a hotel that has no rival anywhere for size and luxury. He received me in the large living-room of his apartment. He seated himself in a rather high armchair against the open window, and I was happy to look up to him. As we discussed his art and plays, he seemed gradually to recede miles and miles from the luxury that surrounded him. I had with me the page proofs of a volume that was to appear a few months later.[2] I submitted to him my plan of work, my interpretations of his plays, and my main conclusions. He was very interested and eager to hear what I had written. I translated into Italian the passages in question, because he confessed that, although he could read English, he found it difficult to understand when spoken.

My first interview almost went awry at the very outset when I showed him the index of the various chapters of my book and told him that in the first chapter I dealt with his contacts with naturalism. Pirandello was very indignant. "My art has no connection whatsoever with naturalism," he almost shouted. "Giovanni Verga, the great representative of that movement, wrote me that there was a new force and a new light in my art. I have a letter written to me by him after the publication of my novel *L'esclusa* (The Outcast). Indeed, I feel that I am at the opposite pole from naturalism. I have battered down blind faith in clumsy, tangible reality. My characters, through imagination, conquer and break the fetters of everyday reality. I have shown the stupidity of placing our sense of reality in this material world of ours, which was the pivotal point of the art-mode created by the naturalists." I pleaded that I considered naturalism only as a point of departure for his art, and that my book aimed at showing how he had developed later into the artist so uniquely psychological that we all admired. I cannot say that the Maestro looked convinced, but he became more approachable.

"Certainly, it was due to naturalism," I continued very cautiously, "if your early characters are small figures caught in the ebb and flow of everyday life. Indeed, I feel that they are not capable of carrying the intellectual motivation of your art as are the more complex personalities that one finds in your later works." I referred to the dramatization of early short stories that are typically naturalistic, and I singled out *Liolà* (Liolà) and *L'uomo, la bestia e la virtù* (Man, beast, and virtue).

"Yes," agreed Pirandello. "These are developed along the lines of the traditional comedy of the XVIth century." Of *L'uomo, la bestia e la virtu* he said, "It is tragedy stifled by comedy."

The reason that Pirandello was so resentful about my mention of his contacts with naturalism was that Benedetto Croce, in an article published in *La critica*, had reduced Pirandello's art to the form and substance of the naturalism of the eighties.[3]

"Croce, in his obtuseness," said Pirandello with ill-repressed anger, "has failed to see the human strain that runs through my art. He has always been unable to see that I have been and am an enemy of formalism and hypocrisy. Basically, I have constantly attempted to show that nothing offends life as much as reducing it to a hollow concept. My idea of *costruirsi*, of building oneself up, is the fundamental tenet of my art. Marriage, fatherhood, motherhood, and personality have no meaning except that which we give to them. In my plays I have shown how unreal marriage is, if held together only by civil and religious ceremonies. I have shown couples who quarrel at home but stroll through the city streets arm-in-arm as the embodiment of marital perfection. Such people are not alive nor real. They are self-constructed, empty concepts. I have compared one such man with a cigar that has smoked itself out, keeping its shape but being only ashes." He was referring to Lello Carpani, an important character in *La Signora Morli, una e due* (Mrs. Morli, one and two).

I told the Maestro that I had taken the liberty of pointing out in my book the anti-social undercurrent of his thought. A slight expression of resentment passed over his face as he replied, "Society is necessarily formal, and in this sense I am anti-social, but only in the sense that I am opposed to social hypocrisies and conventions. My art teaches each individual to accept his human lot with candor and humility, and with full consciousness of the imperfections that are inherent in it."

Pirandello was very happy when I showed him I had strongly stressed the positive side of his thought, quoting especially from the interludes of *Ciascuno a suo modo* (Each in his own way). "All true art contains a philosophy of life that tends toward sound and noble living," he concluded.

"What about the 'drama of mirrors' as your drama has often been characterized?" I asked on another occasion. "It is an exaggerated view of a situation that exists in many of my plays," he answered. "If we present ourselves to others as artificial constructions in relation to what we really are, it is logical that upon looking at ourselves in a mirror we see our falseness reflected there, made galling and unbearable by its fixity. That is all that I mean by placing my characters before a mirror and making them say that they would like to spit at themselves." Pirandello had a very intense manner of speaking in discussing his plays. One could see that he lived for his art.

He complained of having been misunderstood, or not understood at all, especially in Italy. "How many do really understand what I have tried to do and say?" he asked, raising his shoulders and closing his eyes in the typical Italian fashion that expresses resentment and mortification, as well as a bit of contempt. I called to his attention how much the criticism of Adriano Tilgher in *Voci del tempo*[4] and in *Studi sul teatro contemporaneo*[5] had contributed toward blurring the clear profile of his drama. Pirandello seemed unwilling to dwell on Tilgher, undoubtedly because he had accepted Tilgher's presentation of his art as final in the early twenties. However, he agreed with me that Tilgher had unintentionally misrepresented the philosophical content of his drama by stating that his art pivoted on the obliteration of reality and of human personality. He also agreed that dramatic art is not conceivable without a clear-cut personality, and that the conscious madman that appears so often in his plays is a well-defined dramatic character. He added with a gesture of resignation, "Tilgher is not the only one." Yet, I had a slight suspicion that at least his managers, if not he himself did not regret the quibbling and shouting that accompanied the performance of his early plays after the first World War. It certainly helped theatre receipts. One finds an echo of those disputes in two of Pirandello's plays: *Sei personaggi in cerca d'autore* and *Ciascuno a suo modo.*

Pirandello departed from the discussion of Tilgher to inform me that what he thought of life and art had been expressed by him in a book that bears the title of *L'umorismo* (Humor)[6] published back in 1908. He insisted that neither his life concept nor his art had substantially changed, and he plunged into a wonderful discussion of what life was to him. He said with a force that bespoke his inner conviction: "Man moves in an impalpable atmosphere of dreams, whether he is conscious of it or not. Because of this he walks over the bleak planet of the eacth as a bewildered stranger and a grieving vagabond. Beyond the boundaries of time and space, above the arched, blue curve of the sky, there is life, unformed and unfettered, life out of which a strange god has carved the earth and the universe. No laws, no limitations, no boundaries exist there. Life is a ruinous stream that roars into dazzlingly white stretches of infinite space. Woe to us if we have a glimpse of that primeval life! We become both terrified and deified by it. We cease to be human, and our contact with the average man becomes impossible. My art is the expression of what happens to universal life when it becomes individual existence."

I showed him various passages in my page proofs that brought out the tragedy of being human as he had expressed it. He added, "There are four great forces in life whose urge man constantly feels: love, hate, mystery, and the acquisitive instinct." He turned toward the little table near which we were seated and grasped a small and exquisite ash tray that was there: "We say as fiercely as in the days of the cave man, 'This woman is mine!' As to mystery, this is to me the greatest force of all. Man speaks, and he does not know whence his words came. We are the prey of forces that emanate from a world that we feel moving beyond time and space, a world whence all the forces of instinct issue."

This was a golden opportunity to have Pirandello explain his concept of personality. Here are his very words as they survive in my notes: "That last generation looked upon nature and man as something existing in unchanging, clear-cut, and solid form outside of us. To me, reality is something that we mold through the power of our imagination. I have given a quixotic treatment to this concept, especially in *Cosi è, se vi pare* (Right you are if you think so); but this idea is fundamental in my art and it enlivens most of my work." He insisted on the reality of the split shown in *La Signora Morli, una e due.* "Hasn't it ever happened to you," he queried, "that you feel one way with one person and another way with another?" Fully in agreement with him, I showed him what I had quoted from his *Umorismo*s "Man does not have an idea, an absolute concept of life, but rather a changing and varied sentiment according to time, cases, and circumstances."[7]

With a slightly ironical smile, Pirandello countered: "You see that I said that long ago, and that applies also to my idea of personality. We say 'I am one,' and we look upon ourselves as well as upon our fellowmen as solid and clear-cut personalities, while in reality we are the juxtaposition of infinite, blurred selves. Take the case of Mrs. Morli in the play we have mentioned. Yes, she was one while in the company of her husband Ferrante and another when she was with her lover Lello Carpani. That is an experience we all have." He was so serious as to seem almost aggressive. "Those who deny the reality of Mrs. Morli are deprived of understanding and feeling," he stated with explosive emphasis.

"The strange thing in that play," I added, "is that she is carefree with her husband, and serious, almost sullen, with her lover."

With a gleam of mischief in his eye, Pirandello said, "That's a trick of the trade!" He went on, "My idea of personality is clearly presented in my latest play *Non si sa come* (One does not know how)."

I had not read the play and felt lost. I thought that I had perused all of his plays. He informed me that the play had been given in Germany before being performed in Italy. Stefan Zweig had beautifully translated it. Pirandello gave me the German translation that I might add the analysis of that play to my book.

"Yes," continued Pirandello, "we pass most of our time outside of ourselves rather than in a state of full consciousness. We constantly lapse into subconscious reveries that detach us from our surroundings. It is the call of primeval life. How can our personality be one when so suddenly we are capable of reentering primeval life and of being absorbed by it?"

When I told him that this seemed a sort of flimsy mysticism that clashed with the central theme of the play in question, which represents a strange case of adultery, he exclaimed, "Sexual instinct in its origin is a cosmic force, yet when it enters individual life it leads to the most terrifying complications. It makes us betray our friends, break moral laws, and disregard conventions."

"But you thus destroy the moral code," I interjected.

Pirandello was on the defensive. "I cannot help it," he said. "There are emotions and acts that are uncontrollable because of the blurred character of our personality. It is so, and I should not be honest with myself and with my art if I did not say so."

"You actually reach the same conclusions as D'Annunzio," I added.

Pirandello was furious. "No, no," he shouted. "D'Annunzio is immoral in order to proclaim the glory of instinct. I present this individual case to add another proof of the tragedy of being human. D'Annunzio is exultant over evil; I grieve over it."

I remained silent and convinced in the face of this rebuke.

This discussion brought us to Pirandello's religious point of view. He stated that Pietro Mignosi of the University of Palermo was trying to make a Catholic mystic out of him, but he added that he could not recognize himself in that role. "In my system of thought," he said, "there is no place for any organized religion." Then turning sharply toward me, he added very seriously, "Don't you see that even God has built Himself up?" I must have looked puzzled, for he continued, "I am not sacrilegious. I mean that God is a universal concept existing outside the partial constructions of Him that each religious sect makes. When this universal concept is enclosed in the Christian God, the Hindu God, and in as many gods as there are tribes in Africa and peoples on this earth, the universality of that concept is necessarily offended and dwarfed." I understood and, by way of comment, added that there was the same relation between the concept and the many gods that man has fashioned as between universal life and individual existence.

"This relationship exists also between the ideal state and the actual realization of a form of government, whether you call it democracy, fascism, or communism," said Pirandello another day in telling me of a request that he had received to grant an interview to a group of American newspapermen who wanted to know what he thought of the Ethiopian campaign. In spite of his political relativism, he took the defense of Italy with the result that the American press assumed a very hostile tone toward him. He explained to me that, since he was a member of the Fascist party and traveled with the permission of the Fascist government, he had no alternative. I could see, however, that his political faith was not very deep.

He was actuated by the same practical considerations in refusing to see Samuel Putnam, the translator of *Come tu mi vuoi* (As you desire me), who had recently joined the Communist party. Pirandello had the deepest affection for

Samuel Putnam, whom he had known many years before in Paris, but he confided to me that he could not see him because of his political affiliations.

Concerning *Come tu mi vuoi*, he was indeed provoked upon hearing that in the version offered on the American stage the identity of Cia and Elma had been purposely blurred. In the Italian original, there is not the slightest doubt about the identity of the actual Cia and of Elma, who consciously sets before herself the task of reincarnating the soul of Cia. I told Pirandello that I had set the question right in my book, and he was very grateful.

Another play on which his comments should be recorded was *Come prima, meglio di prima* (As before, better than before). In my analysis of it, I had failed to see the point in the dénouement of the play. Fulvia, the heroine, leaves the home of her husband, a famous surgeon, but a man of very low moral principles, and lives as a common-law wife of Marco Mauri, a quixotic dreamer who can offer her only an existence of passion and torment. When she returns home after many years, she discovers that her husband has poisoned the mind of their daughter Livia by distorting the truth about his wife. He has molded her into the conventional figure of a saintly woman who died when Livia was born. It was quite natural for Fulvia to be treated as an intruder by her daughter who hated her as much as she loved the false image of her saintly mother. When a new baby was born to Fulvia, she decided to leave her hated husband, but this second time she took with her the child, something she had not done the first time. What I had not perceived was the significance of her taking her child with her. Pirandello explained, "Don't you see? The first time she had left her daughter Livia with her husband who, not desiring to tell the truth of the situation, allowed Livia to grow up in the belief that her mother was a saintly woman now dead. Fulvia rebelled at the idea of having lived in this conventional and false concept in the memory of her daughter. That was an imposture, and had made a puppet out of the living Fulvia. This time her husband will not have the chance to contaminate her child's mind and falsify her personality." As to Mauri, Pirandello said, "I actually met that man in a small town in Umbria. I transported him into my play as I studied him in real life."

He spoke at length of *Sei personaggi in cerca d'autore*. He did so especially one afternoon after having had a long conversation the previous evening with Mr. Selznick concerning the possibility of filming the play. Pirandello was highly excited. "I could not convey to him, no matter how hard I tried, my idea of the three planes," he kept saying. I read to him what I had written in my book, after having asked him whether I was correct in believing that the nucleus of the play was the clash between actual reality and reality in art. I translated for him: "The six characters oscillate with perfect balance between the artificial life of glorified marionettes and the moving, stirring existence of tragic human beings."[8]

"Yes," interrupted Pirandello, "but it is more than that. I have portrayed their life on three planes that could be expressed in the cinema even better than on the legitimate stage."

I agreed, and I added that to me the three planes were that conveyed by the six characters portraying the solid and angular reality of actual life, that of the actors who take the roles of the six characters in re-enacting their tragedy, and finally that of imagination that bridges the former two, thus creating a new reality which is "life lived with passion, illumined by fancy, made immortal by true art."[9]

Pirandello commented that this sort of three-dimensional art was the salient feature of that play, and expressed disappointment that I had not read this to him before his meeting with Mr. Selznick. From his rather bitter reference to his conversation with Mr. Selznick, it was evident that he had no desire to re-open his negotiations with the motion picture magnate. In fact, *Six characters* was not filmed.

Pirandello also commented on *La vita che ti diedi* (Life that I gave you), that had failed even in England where his plays had usually been very well received. "They do not understand the fact that for that poor mother who had lost her son the only reality was the image of her son as a child that she held in her memory. After all, that was all that was left of him."

In reply to my question as to which of his plays he considered the best, he showed his preference for *Enrico IV* (Henry IV).

It may be of interest to record what he had to say about Italian literature in general and about criticism. When I asked him to give me accurately the date of his plays, he was quite impatient. "What does it matter?" he asked. I told him that one could thus trace better the development of his art. He retorted, "Dates do not count. An author should stand before the critic as a complete whole." He added that he would soon write an autobiography, the title of which would be *Of my unasked-for visit on this planet*. He continued to speak animatedly and even volubly of his future plans, but I never got the dates of his plays.

He was very happy when I told him that I had presented him, in the introduction of my book, as the antithesis of D'Annunzio, and he added, "In the whole course of Italian literature, one constantly finds such contrasts: Dante and Petrarch, Ariosto and Tasso, Goldoni and Metastasio, Leopardi and Monti, and today myself and D'Annunzio." He had words of deep contempt for D'Annunzio.

Of contemporary writers in Italy who had significance for him, he mentioned Alberto Moravia, author of *Gli indifferenti* (The indifferent ones), and his own son, Stefano, who writes under the pen name of Stefano Landi in order not to exploit the renown of his father. He spoke with great admiration of the American authors Edgar Allan Poe and Mark Twain. He referred with a lack of admiration to Sherwood Anderson's play *If this be treason,* whose first performance he had seen the previous evening.

Of his personal life he said little. He appreciated greatly my defense of his relationship with the actress Marta Abba in a conversation with ex-ambassador to Italy Washburn Child. It happened in 1927 at a luncheon at Buck Hill Falls, where I had lectured on modern Italy and had presented Pirandello as the embodiment of the new consciousness that had emerged from the tragedy of the first World War. Mr. Child, with cynical humor, warned me not to be so sure about the new consciousness as embodied in Pirandello, and added, "He is having a good time just now with a young and beautiful actress."

Pirandello interrupted me, "Why didn't you tell him that Pirandello has never had a good time in his life?" In those words I felt the moral texture of the art of Luigi Pirandello as never before. He then confided to me, "She is like a daughter to me. She is younger than my own children. She is twenty-seven years of age and I am an old man, nearly seventy."

I told him that I had singled out the plays in which I had felt the presence of Marta Abba: *L'amica delle mogli* (Their wives' friends), *Trovarsi* (To find oneself), *Quando si è qualcuno* (When one is somebody). He confessed that he had written them thinking of her, and a smile shone in his brown eyes that were now soft and affectionate.

I never realized more clearly than in those conversations the close relation that exists between Pirandello the man and Pirandello the artist. I felt it again when with grief I read in our newspapers that in December, 1936, Pirandello was taken to his last resting place in a coffin of plain wood, in accordance with his request that he be buried without any pomp and ceremony whatsoever.

1. Vol. 117 (1934), 81-94.
2. *The drama of Luigi Pirandello*, University of Pennsylvania Press, Philadelphia, 1935.
3. Republished in *La letteratura della Nuova Italia*, Bari, Laterza, 1949, VI, 359-377.
4. 2nd ed., Rome, Libreria di Scienze e Lettere, 1923, pp. 92-102.
5. Rome, Libreria di Scienze e Lettere, 1923, pp. 135-193.
6. Venice, La Nuova Italia, 1908. It is now included in the volume edited by Manlio Lo Vecchio Musti and published by Mondadori of Milan in 1939.
7. *L'umorismo*, p. 138.
8. *The drama of Luigi Pirandello*, p. 202.
9. *Ibid.*, p. 301.

PIRANDELLO AND THE CONCEPT OF REALITY*

Domenico Vittorini

THIS short article is primarily concerned with the meaning that such terms as *real, reality,* and *realism* assumed in the mind and art of Luigi Pirandello.

The meaning of these terms has varied throughout the ages. One of the first to focus his attention on the relationship between life and art was Aristotle, one of the great men of Antiquity. In his famous booklet, *Poetics,* he defined poetry as "mimesis or imitation of nature." By nature, however, he meant the immutable and eternal pattern that underlies the phenomenical world. He followed the Platonically conceptual point of view that had blossomed in the perfect creations of the Classical era, represented by Homer, Phidias, and Sophocles. Not much was added to this investigation during the centuries of the Renaissance, when the term *verisimilitude,* as applied to art, reflected the same attitude as that of the author of the *Poetics.*

Pirandello, as a teacher of Italian literature in the *Istituto Femminile di Magistero,* a sort of Teachers' College in Rome, was very much interested in aesthetics and reacted against the Renaissance sense of realism as well as that of the naturalism of the late nineteenth century. He pronounced himself, with unmistakable clarity, against both the humanistic trend in the Italian literature of the Renaissance and against the narrow sense that the naturalists of the late nineteenth century gave to the term *realism.*

Luigi Pirandello was born in Sicily in 1867 and died in Rome in 1936. He was awarded the Nobel prize in literature in 1934, a clear recognition of the universal appeal and significance of his art. Pirandello lived his not too happy life astride the last century and our own, bridging two very

* From *Pennsylvania Literary Review,* Vol. 5, No. 4, 1955.

distinct ages, that of the objective naturalism of the late nineteenth century and that of the imaginative or subjective naturalism of our own. His early literary work, short stories and novels, bore marked traits of the objective naturalism of the last century. His later works, most in the field of drama, were and still are an outstanding exemplification of the literature of our epoch.

Pirandello's major and significant plays can be best understood if viewed as the projection of a theory of art that has distinguished modern aesthetics from those of the Ancients and from those of the late nineteenth century. He has contributed to both the modern concept of art and its reflection in works in which we men of today can recognize ourselves in ideas, feelings, and passions.

Pirandello was so deeply concerned with the creative character of art as to believe that the influence of Classical Antiquity on the Romance literatures had been very obnoxious. In 1906, he wrote a critical study that serves as a preface or introduction to a novel by an Italian humorist, Alfredo Cantoni (1841-1904), whom Pirandello admired very much. Regretting the vast role that rhetoric had played in Italian literature, he stated: "The harm that it (rhetoric) has caused in every age, not only to our literature but also to Latin literature and, hence, in varying degrees, to all Romance literatures, is incalculable." The pages that follow this statement insist on the necessity of originality in art. Condemning imitation, he stated: "In imitating a preceding model, one denies his own identity and remains of necessity behind his pattern. The best is to affirm one's own sentiment, one's own life." He believed that each work of art has in itself its own laws and rules. There are no "eternal principles" in literature. The task of criticism consists in "discovering the principle that determined and gave a personal character to the specific work of art." And again: "The work of fancy is a work of nature, an organic and living whole. . . . A work of art is nature itself that makes use of the instrument of human fancy in order to create a work of a higher order, more perfect because elements that are too common, obvious, and fleeting have been pruned away. A work of art lives by its own essential ideality."

As to the attitude of Pirandello towards the aesthetics of the Naturalists, to hear himself classified as a Naturalist was enough to cause him to explode with typical Italian vehemence. His art, he believed, was a complete departure from the aesthetics of the Naturalistic School as exemplified by his personal friends and predecessors, Giovanni Verga and Luigi Capuana. He was wont to quote from Verga who, upon reading his novel *L'Esclusa* (The Outcast), had written to him that with his novels a new light was shining in contemporary fiction.

Pirandello, in his aesthetic views, resumed contact with Gian Battista Vico (1688-1744), who ushered in the Romantic Age with a fundamental distinction between the role of logic and fancy in art, a distinction that is still the corner-stone of modern aesthetics. Vico proclaimed in his *New Science* (1725) that art is the product of fancy and, if so, by inference, art is not conditioned by actual life. A character is not *real* simply because it is modeled on a man actually existing, actually known and studied in the world close at hand. If art is the product of fancy, Pirandello felt, a complete definition of aesthetics should embrace not only the use of Greek myths (Classicism), not only historical material (Romanticism), not only material observed in the society and environment in which the artist lives (Naturalism), but also whatever dreams and enchanted or awesome places the artist evokes from his imagination (Contemporary Art). *Reality* resides not in the material used, but in the life that the magic power of imagination can awaken in it.

In many of Pirandello's plays, *Six Characters in Search of an Author, Henry IV, Tonight We Improvise, When One Is a Somebody, To Find Oneself,* and others, one reads beautiful pages dedicated to his art concept. I quote at random a passage from *Six Characters,* that echoes the very words of the essay on Cantoni: "Nature uses the instrument of human fancy to continue, even in a higher form, its creative work." Art rests on a higher plane than actual life. It is capable of giving to the creative artist a completeness of existence that actual life does not give him. The vision and realization of this more complete and different form of life constitutes *realism*.

Realism is an aesthetic category and not the material that some artists have used. An artist can reach realism either by using ideal patterns or actual ones. He is completely free in his choice that is dictated only by his own temperament, mood, and experience.

The clash between Benedetto Croce and Luigi Pirandello that started with the publication in 1902 of the *Aesthetics* of the Neapolitan philosopher, ultimately rested on the fact that Croce, through his definition of art as expression of a subjective intuition of reality, still clung to *objective reality* as the model or pattern of art. Pirandello felt that *imaginative reality* is as real as the tangible, solid, and angular reality of the world close at hand. Hence, the insults and recriminations that each heaped upon the other until the very end of their lives.

The new meaning of reality in art is more than a theory in the late Pirandello. It served as the fertile seed from which developed the new drama that our age has admired with almost universal consent.

Pirandello was a very patient and stubborn worker. He worked very slowly, and his plays clearly show the moment when he departed from the Naturalism of his youth, as exemplified in his short stories, *The Old and the Young*, and even in *Mattia Pascal*, in order to rise towards a type of realistic drama, the glory of which is a more searching and subjective study of man and life. His essay on humor, written in 1908, can only serve as a basis for his fiction and for the section of his drama formed by plays that were the dramatization of previously written short stories. An attentive study of the two sections would show how close Pirandello was, in inspiration and technique, to the tenets of

Naturalism, and how different and new are such plays as *Henry IV* and *Six Characters*. Naturalism, with its precepts of closeness to actual life, hindered and fettered Pirandello in realizing an ideal of art that had loomed even in the days when he wrote his *Umorismo*. How is it possible to correlate the events in Pirandello's early fiction and old plays with statements such as the following that are found in these critical works? Here we read: "Life is a conscious and fluid entity that we try to stop, to fix in unchanging and definite forms, inside and outside of us, because we all are fixed forms, forms which move along others equally fixed." We are, he continues, the result of concepts reached through an infernal machine called logic, which pumps our sentiments from our hearts up to our brains and reduces them to lifeless abstractions. Only now and then, in rare moments of inner illumination, do we resume contact with real life, life as a cosmic flux that suffers in being enclosed in its human molds: rocks, plants, animals, men. Then we experience a terrifying shock, as we see ourselves live suspended in the inner void created by the contrast between cosmic life and its earthy and human forms. Pirandello's fiction reflected in his puny and strange-looking characters the ludicrous embodiments of this ideal life-concept. We must not wonder that this fiction was never popular. It was this intuition of life that was developed in the works written after the First World War. He uncovered a new and deeper stream of creativeness only when he forsook the tenets of Naturalism and entered the precincts of stately tragedy. Then he penned such works as *Henry IV*, *Six Characters*, *As You Desire Me*, *When One Is Somebody*.

A perusal of the Preface to *Six Characters*, written in 1927, seven years after the play which had sent the name of the author all over Europe and South America, can serve as a document to illustrate the art concept that led to the new art. Here Pirandello differentiated between "historical" or descriptive authors and "philosophical" ones. He ranked himself as one of the latter type. Art had become

for him the medium of expression of the unspeakable loneliness of his soul, as befitting a man who had lived for years
in the company of a wife who was demented and in a period
of history made up of wars, hatred, and destruction.

Such an intuition of art as Pirandello revealed in his new
plays helps us to understand our contemporary art or, at
least, that section of it that refuses to accept the principle
that art must be molded on models found in actual life.

Pirandello's theoretical attitude, as exemplified in works
that men will never forget, shows how limited is the current
use of the term *realism*. If realism is associated with the
idea of art as the closest approximation to actual models,
then the significance of art rests on accuracy and not on
creativeness. In a way, such a restricted view of realism
proclaims the uselessness of art in that it is unquestionably
true that no reflected object is more similar to itself than
the very object that the artist wishes to represent. Why
waste time in reproducing imperfectly in art what exists
perfectly in life?

In our discussion, it became clear that the term *reality*,
as used in his works, was often confusing. Drawing on what
I had learned from him more than from any other author,
I suggested to him that in order to distinguish between
reality in life and *reality* in art, one could use the term
actuality for the former and *reality* for the latter. Art transforms the actual into the real. The actuality of life is outside
the realm of art until the fancy of a poet gives to it the new
life to which Pirandello constantly referred. The logic of
life is different from that of art in the same way as that of
primitive peoples and children is different from that of
highly civilized beings. "Vico discovered this long ago,"
interjected Pirandello, looking very wistful.

Our conversation resumed its usual pleasant character
when we returned to the discussion of *Six Characters*, and
I told him, much to his satisfaction and even joy, that, to
me, the three planes were conveyed by his consideration of
the characters as actual human beings in the snares of

nature, by their resentment upon seeing themselves represented by professional actors when the stage director decides to use their tragic case as art material of an improvised play, and, finally, as they live now in Pirandello's play.

To understand fully Pirandello's art one must be aware of the efforts through which his characters are made to replace their actual existence by one created through illusion and fancy. The two planes are constantly and clearly visible in his best plays. To restrict ourselves to *Naked Masks*, a collection of his plays translated into English and now available in the Everyman's Library edition, one finds a great variety of situations, all characterized by this pitiful attempt to put on a mask that covers a scarred human countenance, seared by shame and contorted by suffering.

The central nucleus of *Henry IV* is precisely this: an imaginative and hypersensitive gentleman who, while impersonating the famous emperor, Henry IV of Germany, falls from his horse, strikes his head, and, when he opens his eyes, he has lost the consciousness of his actual personality, as a man of today, and feels that he is the historical character of the eleventh century, who lives again in his mind the struggles against Pope Gregory VII, the other rulers of the time, and the intrigues of Peter Damian. A wealthy sister places him in a palace and surrounds him with counselors, guards, and pages who keep that illusion alive. One day he recovers consciousness of his actual identity. Never has human fancy so exploited the artistic possibilities of the clash of the two planes, the actual and the fantastic, and seldom have the two planes merged into a more tragic and heart-rending unity of artistic reality than in this play.

In *Naked*, the contrast between the actual and the self-imposed illusion is projected into the attempt of Ersilia Drei to fabricate the tale of a little romance in a life that has never known the joy of love. When the iridescent bubble of the fiction that has become her whole life is destroyed, she commits suicide.

In *The Pleasure of Honesty,* Baldovino, at the end of his resources financially and intellectually, decides to become the husband of a young woman with social position and wealth who has had to hide the fact that she, unwed, is going to give birth to a child. Baldovino is fully conscious that he wears only the mask of a husband, and that he lives in the home of Agata as a phantom. Pirandello makes him take his role as a husband so seriously and with such telling effect that eventually the form of the husband in Baldovino becomes the reality of the husband of Agata Renni.

The nucleus of Pirandello's dramatic art lies precisely in the transformation of the *actual* into the *real.* It represents one of the most beautiful and perfect embodiments of realistic art, as the playwright understood realism. He was so successful in presenting this to his readers because existence and art in him became fused into one. Confronted by the angular and hard existence that was his because of his temperament, sensitivity, and the circumstances that surrounded his life, he took refuge in the reality of art, just as his characters took refuge in the reality of illusion. He lived the last years of his life believing that true art portrays life lived with passion, illumined by fancy and solidified in the joy of creative art.

It was an unforgettable experience to have been privileged to know one of the greatest men of our time. In my personal life it has been an even greater gift to have been able to study the work in which he still lives, the only kind of survival in which he believed.

PIRANDELLO IN EVERYMAN'S LIBRARY*

T HE recent publication of five of Pirandello's plays edited by Eric Bentley (*Naked Masks*, Everyman's Library, 1952) is truly a happy event for those who are interested in dramatic art in general and in Pirandello's drama in particular.

In this book, the best of Pirandello's works are made available to the average reader in England and America, while the introduction and three apendices, with their carefully checked biographical and bibliographical data, are of particular interest to scholars. The first appendix contains an accurate and lucid translation by Eric Bentley of Pirandello's preface to *Six Characters in Search of an Author*, which is a major declaration or the dramatic principles that apply to Pirandello's late plays, just as *Umorismo*, written in 1908, casts a revealing light on the earlier works that show the author's contact with, and departure from, the Naturalism of Verga and Capuana.

There are two statements in Appendix II (p. 379) that are open to question. One refers to the *New Colony*, a play that, according to Mr. Bentley, shows a "definite fascist mentality," just as *Lazarus* is "miracle mongering." Since both Fascism and Christianity are positive and dogmatic systems, they could not be accepted by Pirandello who believed that the essence of Life is unfettered and fluid, and, therefore, every "form" that encloses it gives to it a fixity that dooms it to disintegration and death. This is the basic and unchanging principle of Pirandello's system of ideas. Accordingly, he presents in the *New Colony* the thesis of the impossibility of realizing a perfect government and society on this earth. Likewise, in *Lazarus*, since all religions are "constructions" of the universal concept of God, Pirandello

---

* From Yearbook of Comparative and General Literature No. 2, Chapel Hill, North Carolina.

rejected the Christian belief in the personal survival of the soul. For Pirandello, the soul longs to re-enter cosmic Life, whence a strange God detached it to make it live on the bleak desert of this life. Personal form is for him the chief factor in the tragedy of being human.

The second statement of Mr. Bentley to which I take exception refers to Pirandello's *grande passion* for Marta Abba. My exception is based on Pirandello's own words when he expressed to me, in 1935, during an interview with him in New York, his great resentment against the misconception of his relationship with Marta Abba. I had mentioned to him that the ex-ambassador to Italy, Washburn Child, had cynically referred to that relationship. Whereupon, Pirandello exclaimed, "She is younger than my own children. She has always been like a daughter to me."

The major contribution of Mr. Bentley in this book is his translation of *Liolà*. It is an entirely new translation and it has been beautifully and accurately done by one who knows both Italian and English perfectly. Moreover, Mr. Bentley has a truly lyrical temperament, and he is in love with Sicily. Only a poet can describe the Sicilian landscape as beautifully as this: "Sicily is like that: the African sun shines, the hard rock takes on the soft color of honey, the trees are laden with almonds and oranges, and vagabonds sing." (ix). However, again, I must be allowed to courteously disagree with Mr. Bentley as to the central interpretation of this play. He states that *Liolà* is "Pirandello on holiday. . . . truancy on Pirandello's part, an exception to the rules of the maestro's art" (ix-x). To us, *Liolà* presents the positive aspect of Pirandello's central intuition of life. Liolà, the main character, is primitive, spontaneous, fluid, and, is close to primeval life, and capable of living with joy. He is not so tortuous and "cerebral" as many, although not all, of Pirandello's characters. According to Pirandello, by applying the "infernal machine of logic," man forsakes sentiment and offends life in its very essence. Thinking is not a "gift" for man. Since it implies objectivity and consciousness, it leads to our "constructing ourselves," and, hence, is a negative force. Pirandello, while of necessity indulging himself in thought, punishes his characters by showing their tortuous thinking through which they "immobilize the continuous flux of life through concepts" (*Umorismo*, p. 214). By denying to his characters the gift of logical thinking, Pirandello reaches the absolute in his system of tragedy, the essence of which lies in incomprehension of others as well as of ourselves. In his plays, it is primarily the incomprehension of the characters of the plight in which they find themselves that creates tragedy.

In *Liolà*, the main character is the opposite of being "constructed." The characters that are "constructed," although they are too elementary to be aware of it, are Zia Croce and Zio Simone. Zia Croce conceives the scheme of attributing to Zio Simone, her wealthy cousin, the fatherhood of the baby that her unwed daughter Tuzza is going to have by Liolà. She not only wants to save appearances but also hopes to get her cousin's money. The latter, since he has not been able to have a son from his young wife Mita, agrees to the base pact in order to save his masculine pride. Liolà realizing that this offends and ruins Mita, a former sweetheart of his, intervenes and spoils the scheme. Unsuspectingly, Zia Croce and Zio Simone have thrown Liolà and Mita into each other's arms. Mita, too, is soon expecting a baby by Liolà. Zio Simone will now appear to be the father of two children who are in reality of Liolà. The only person who is left defenseless and exposed is Tuzza who in the very end tries to stab Liolà, but in vain. All this is very far from being an idyll, "the last Sicilian pastoral" (x). Indeed, *Liolà* bears a marked resemblance to the traditional Italian comedy and particularly to Machiavelli's *Mandragola*. In both works, the plot is basically the same and the two dishonest husbands, Ser Nicia and Zio Simone, are punished through the triumph of the romantic lovers Callimaco and Liolà.

An objective and critical reading of the text makes it questionable whether this play can be included among those that deal with the contrast of truth and appearance. It is difficult to agree with Mr. Bentley that in *Liolà* Pirandello wanted to prove that "reality is not more real than appearance" (xii)' (Tuzza would not grant this) and that Zio Simone "only appears to appear to be the father" (xii). Basically, Zio Simone wants to appear to be a father, but Pirandello unmasks him and holds him up to ridicule. This is all. More simply, *Liolà* belongs to that section of Pirandello's drama that is closely related to his early contacts with Naturalism. Even in technique, like many plays of this group, *Liolà* has been given a solid background, and its characters possess traits quite different from those so effectively described in the above-mentioned preface to *Six Characters*. The theoretical roots of *Liolà* are in *Umorismo*, just as those of the later play are in the preface of *Six Characters*.

In discussing *It is So (If You Think So)*, the term "reality" is rather misleading. In Pirandello, what exists in the observable and tangible world is an *actuality* that the artist uses in order to transform it, first into a psychological, and then into an artistic reality. The epilogues of many of Pirandello's plays contain in a very living and human manner the result of this transformation. The playwright is not at all interested in the actuality of the situation presented. It does not matter to him whether Ponza's wife is Lina or another person. Indeed, if this be ascertained, the play would lose its *raisin d'être*. What counts is the nobility of the veiled wife who proclaims that she is, to Ponza and to Signora Frola, what each wants her to be, and she is nobody to herself. With infinite compassion she has obliterated her own identity and consciously has lent herself to be whatever the two want her to be. This is a new type of "construction" in Pirandello. It possesses positive connotations and it is distinguishable from that of the comedies conceived under the guidance of the artistic principles contained in *Umorismo*. Tragedy shuns laughter and this is the ancient principle that Pirandello followed only in the later period of his *(If You Think So)* is "outside the boundary of realism" artistic career. In this context, the statement that *It Is So*

(xviii) clashes with the deep significance of the play. Pirandello's system of ideas, far from being abstract, is full of human understanding. Life being what it is, only simplicity, humility, kindness, and, especially, illusion, help us to bear its burden.

One of the merits of Mr. Bentley is to have championed the reality of Pirandello's ideas. This is precisely what Adriano Tilgher had failed to do in his essays written in the twenties. Pirandello was fully aware of this when he came to the United States in 1935, at which time he, in accepting my own analysis of his dramaturgy, repudiated Tilgher's theory to which he had previously given official sanction.

The greatest praise that can be rightly and gladly given to both Mr. Bentley and Everyman's Library rests on the fact that this new volume serves the average man as well as the scholar. This combination is befitting democratic society that constantly aims at raising the intellectual level of its citizens.

DOMENICO VITTORINI

University of Pennsylvania

EPIC AND ROMANCE
by W. P. Ker

This classic work by a great Medieval scholar is a fascinating description of the principal forms of narrative literature that emerged from the Middle Ages. Focusing upon Epic and Romance as products, respectively, of the "heroic age" and the "age of chivalry", the author examines these forms in general and then proceeds to a specific discussion of the contributions of three major schools — the Teutonic Epic, the French Epic, and the Icelandic Histories.

The Teutonic Epic is considered in the light of its tragic conception, scale of treatment, and style. A list of extant poems and fragments in the older Teutonic languages is included. **Beowulf** is discussed and analyzed separately. Then, moving on to the Icelandic Sagas, the author examines Iceland's place in the heroic tradition, matter and form in the sagas, tragic imagination, comedy, the art of narrative, northern prose romances, and other like topics. He follows this with a discussion of the Old French Epic (chansons de geste) and Romance and the Old French Romantic Schools. Competition of epic and romance in the 12th century, comedy, "humors", romantic additions to heroic styles, blending of classical and Celtic influences are among the subjects covered.

Besides the Homeric epics and **Beowulf,** this volume considers such works as **Maldon, Roland, Albein,** the **Helgi** poems, **Volocpa, Laxdaola, Roman de Troie, Tristram, Flamenca, Troilus and Criseyde,** and many others.

Index. xxiv + 390pp. 5⅜ x 8.

T355 Paperbound $1.95

THE GIFT OF LANGUAGE
by Margaret Schlauch

THE GIFT OF LANGUAGE (first issued as THE GIFT OF TONGUES) is a middle-path book about languages and their study. Written by a first-rate linguistic scholar, it avoids both superficiality and technical ponderousness.

The author will make interesting for you family relationships among languages; grammatical processes—illustrated from such colorful languages as Aztec, Maya, and Ewe; the formation of words—their wanderings, disguises, dresses before they reached modern English. She also analyses historical changes in sounds—whereby Shakespeare, to the modern ear, would sound as if he were speaking Irish dialect.

THE GIFT OF LANGUAGE will show you that linguistics need not be confined to dry-as-dust inscriptions, but can consider modern literature. The author analyses with great sensitivity the word-formations and deviations from modern English of such writers as James Joyce, Gerard Manley Hopkins, Gertrude Stein, E. E. Cummings and others.

Finally, you will find a discussion of the social interests of language: linguistic taboos in civilized societies; the magical uses of language by the children of modern New York; why Wodehouse's butlers speak impeccable English while their masters speak bad slang.

The author will show you the color latent in even our commonest words. This is a book designed for the reader who is interested in the romance of words, as well as for the sociologist, anthropologist, or student of language.

Revised edition. Index. Special index of 805 English words discussed. 62 thought-provoking puzzlers, exercises, diversions. 223 bibliographic notes. viii + 342pp. 5⅜ x 8.

T243   Paperbound   **$1.85**

FOUNDERS OF THE MIDDLE AGES
by E. K. Rand

This well-known study by the late E. K. Rand, Professor of Latin at Harvard, discusses the transformation of Latin pagan culture into the first stirrings of medieval civilization. It is not only a first-rate historical study in a little-known yet very important culture period; it is also a brilliantly written, easily followed account which will interest and be of value to almost every student of philosophy, comparative literature, religion, or history.

Dr. Rand begins with an intensive study of the interrelations between the early Christian church and pagan culture in the first centuries of the Christian era. Symmachus, Gregory the Great, Prudentius, Tertullian, Minucius Felix, Lactantius and others are carefully evaluated. Chapters on St. Ambrose, St. Jerome, Boethius, St. Augustine are then followed by discussions (with extensive translations) of Latin poetry of the 4th and 5th centuries, and survey of new educational theories, as in Martianus Capella, Cassian, St. Benedict, Cassiodorus, and others. Continual reference is made to the medieval understanding of Aristotle, Plato, Porphyry, Cicero, Horace, and Virgil, and the pre-medieval cultural scene is depicted with unique charm and clarity. Later emergences from these early medieval roots are traced, and modern historians are copiously quoted and evaluated.

"Thoughtful, beautifully written . . . a work of popularization by a ripe scholar," AMERICAN HISTORICAL REVIEW. "Extraordinarily accurate," RICHARD McKEON, THE NATION. "Recommended to every student of letters," TIMES (London). "Recommended as a work of importance for its additions to our knowledge of a little-known time," YALE REVIEW.

60 pages of notes include extensive Latin quotes, and an enormous bibliography. Index. ix + 365pp. 5⅜ x 8.

T369 Paperbound $1.75

MASTERS OF THE DRAMA

by John Gassner

This enormous half-million word volume is the only up-to-date history of world drama in English, the best introduction to world dramatic literature. It is unmatched in scope, ranging from the pre-historic religious festivals ancestral to the modern play, to the psychological and social drama of the 1950's in America. It describes in full detail the life and works of every major dramatist in history, from Aeschylus and Sophocles to Tennessee Williams and Arthur Miller.

This one-volume library of history and criticism is unmatched in its coverage of dramatic traditions not generally known to the American reader: the Japanese theatre, Chinese theatre, Classical Sanskrit plays, Italian Renaissance plays, and dozens of other areas. It is entirely adequate in its coverage of major dramatists, and unique in its coverage of minor plays and playwrights of interest—more than 800 authors, more than 2,000 plays!

Gassner's MASTERS OF THE DRAMA is not a bald summary of dates and plots. Brilliantly written, it demonstrates chains of development in dramatic history, analyzes recurring dramatic needs of each epoch, and examines the cultural and social environment of each dramatist. You will find it an unsurpassed reference work; a most useful introduction to new fields of exploration in the drama; a necessary commentary to the modern stage; and, itself, a fascinating classic of modern literature.

PARTIAL CONTENTS: 1. Primitive drama. 2. Aeschylus. 3. Sophocles. 4. Euripides. 5. Aristophanes. 6. Menander, Plautus, Terence. 7. Hebrew, Sanskrit drama, Kalidasa, etc. 8. Chinese, Tibetan, Japanese. 9. Medieval drama, religious and secular. 10. Italian Renaissance—Tasso, Bardi, Ariesto, Machiavelli, etc. 11. Lope de Vega, Calderon. 12. Marlowe. 13. Shakespeare. 14. Jonson, Beaumont & Fletcher, Webster. 15. Corneille, Racine. 16. Moliere. 17. Goethe, Schiller, etc. 18. German, French romanticism, Hugo, etc. 19. Ibsen. 20. Bjoernson, Strindberg. 21. Zola, naturalism, Maeterlinck, etc. 22. Pirandello, etc. 23. Hauptmann. 24. Sudermann, Schnitzler, etc. 25. Chekhov, etc. 26. Gorky. 27. Synge, etc. 28. Shaw. 29. O'Neill. 30. Modern Americans. 31. Post war theatre in Europe. Appendix: Jewish, Polish theatre, etc.

3rd enlarged edition. Bibliography of 30 pages; index of 50 pages. xxi + 890pp. 5⅝ x 8⅜. Clothbound, **$5.95**

LANGUAGE AND MYTH
by Ernst Cassirer

In this important study Ernst Cassirer analyzes the non-rational thought processes that go to make up culture. He demonstrates that beneath both language and myth there lies an unconscious "grammar" of experience, whose categories and canons are not those of logical thought. It shows that this prelogical "logic" is not merely an undeveloped state of rationality, but something basically different, and that this archaic mode of thought still has enormous power over even our most rigorous thought, in language, poetry and myth.

The author analyzes brilliantly such seemingly diverse (yet related) phenomena as the metaphysics of the Bhagavat Gita, the Melanesian concept of Mana, the Naturphilosophie of Schelling, modern poetry, Ancient Egyptian religion, and symbolic logic. He covers a vast range of material that is all too often neglected in studies of human thought.

THE MYTHIC NATURE OF LANGUAGE

These six essays are of great interest to the student of philosophy, of philosophy of science, the historian, or anthropologist. They are also remarkably timely for students of literature, what with the enormous emphasis placed upon "myth" in modern literary speculation. This book is not superficial speculation by a dabbler, but a penetrating study by one of the most profound and sensitive philosophic minds of our time.

CONTENTS. The Place of Language and Myth in the Pattern of Human Culture. The Evolution of Religious Ideas. Language and Conception. Word Magic. The Successive Phases of Religious Thought. The Power of Metaphor.

Translated, with introduction by Susanne K. Langer. Unabridged. Index. x + 103pp. 5⅜ x 8.

T51 Paperbound **$1.25**

ARISTOTLE'S THEORY OF POETRY AND THE FINE ARTS

edited by S. H. Butcher

This book contains the celebrated Butcher translation of Aristotle's POETICS, faced, page by page, with the complete Greek text (as reconstructed by Mr. Butcher from Greek, Latin and Arabic manuscripts). The editor's 300-page exposition and interpretation follows.

In his classic commentary, Butcher discusses with insight, sympathy and great learning Aristotle's ideas and their importance in the history of thought and literature. His scholarly remarks cover art and nature, imitation as an aesthetic term, poetic truth, pleasure as the end of fine art, art and morality, the function of tragedy, the dramatic unities, the ideal tragic hero, plot and character, comedy, and poetic universality. A new 35-page introductory essay, "Aristotelian Literary Criticism" by John Gassner, discusses the validity of Aristotle's ideas today and their application to contemporary literature.

"No edition with commentary can be recommended to English readers with such confidence as Butcher's," George Saintsbury. "One of the finest treatises on aesthetic theory — neither the literature nor the criticism of the past 40 years has rendered Aristotelian criticism irrelevant or obsolete," MODERN SCHOOLMAN. "An intellectual adventure of the most stimulating kind," NEW YORK TIMES.

Fourth edition. Bibliography. New introduction by John Gassner. Indexes. lxxvi + 421pp. 5⅜ x 8.

T42 Paperbound **$1.95**

THE UNIVERSITY OF WISCONSIN
PUBLICATIONS IN MEDIEVAL SCIENCE
Marshall Clagett, *General Editor*

JOHN PECHAM
AND THE SCIENCE OF OPTICS

JOHN PECHAM AND THE SCIENCE OF OPTICS

Perspectiva communis

EDITED WITH AN INTRODUCTION,

ENGLISH TRANSLATION, AND CRITICAL NOTES BY

DAVID C. LINDBERG

The University of Wisconsin Press

Madison, Milwaukee, and London

1970

Published by
The University of Wisconsin Press
Box 1379, Madison, Wisconsin 53701

The University of Wisconsin Press, Ltd.
27–29 Whitfield Street, London, W.1

Printed in the Netherlands by
Koninklijke Drukkerij G. J. Thieme N.V., Nijmegen

ISBN 0-299-05730-5
LC 72–98122

To Greta, Christin, and Erik

Contents

Contents

Preface

The history of medieval optics has progressed significantly during the past century. The pioneering studies on Islamic optics by Eilhard Wiedemann, beginning about 1880, were followed at the turn of the century and during the next twenty years by the work of J. H. Bridges, Ludwig Baur, A. A. Björnbo, Sebastian Vogl, and Joseph Würschmidt on various aspects of Islamic and European optics, and by the work of Pierre Pansier, Julius Hirschberg, and Max Meyerhof on medieval ophthalmology. After a pause of some thirty years, medieval optics again began to attract attention in the late 1940's, and in the past twenty years specialized studies of great value have been published by H. J. J. Winter, A. C. Crombie, Carl B. Boyer, Matthias Schramm, G. F. Vescovini, and others. But despite such activity, huge gaps in our knowledge remain, particularly with regard to European optics between the thirteenth and sixteenth centuries. With few exceptions (most notably Vescovini), historians of optics have leapt from Roger Bacon or Witelo in the thirteenth century to Maurolyco or Kepler near the beginning of the seventeenth century as though nothing (or at least nothing of importance) occurred in between; what has made the leap inevitable is the lack of modern editions and the resulting inaccessibility of the basic optical texts. If we are to fill the gaps, the vast medieval optical literature still in manuscript must be organized and edited.

The early activity in the history of medieval optics, outlined above, produced a considerable number of editions and translations of optical texts. But since World War I, textual work has slowed to a trickle. Vescovini has recently given us partial texts of the works of Dominicus de Clivaxo and Blasius of Parma from a single manuscript (in the case of the former, the only manuscript known), and Franco Alessio has added more of Blasius of Parma, also from a single manuscript. But aside from Albert Lejeune's edition of the medieval Latin text of Ptolemy's *Optica*, no critical edition of a medieval Latin optical text has appeared in the last fifty years. Thus one of the most pressing needs of the history of medieval optics is intensive attention to the original texts, and until this need is met, our understanding of medieval optics will remain limited. It is my hope that the present edition, translation, and analysis of John Pecham's *Perspectiva communis* will constitute a beginning.

There are good reasons for beginning with the *Perspectiva communis*. It is broad in scope, touching upon all the principal topics of medieval optics; moreover, it was among the most popular medieval texts on optics, and it became the standard introduction to the subject in the universities of the later Middle Ages. It is my belief that the very characteristics that made the *Perspectiva communis* a good introduction to optics in the Middle Ages will enable it to serve equally well as an introduction to the history of medieval optics in the twentieth century. In order to enhance its value as a general introduction to medieval optics, I have included, in this edition, numerous cross-references to other medieval works treating the same topics; such references, however, make no pretense of being exhaustive.

This study began as a doctoral dissertation at Indiana University under the direction of Professor Edward Grant, who not only suggested the topic but also involved himself wholeheartedly in its execution; for his generous counsel and friendship and his many detailed criticisms I am deeply indebted. Appreciation is also due my former colleague John Eadie and my graduate assistant Nicholas Steneck, who read the introduction with great care, Bruce Eastwood, who made a number of valuable suggestions regarding the translation and notes, Jeremiah Reedy, who checked all the variant readings, and Frederick Gregory, who proofread the entire manuscript. My wife, Greta, not only has offered encouragement and understanding, like the spouses of all other authors, but in addition has twice proofread the entire Latin text and has cheerfully evaluated my translation of scores of passages.

The universities with which I have been affiliated have all made their contributions to this edition, and European libraries have been generous with their resources. In particular, I express my appreciation to the following libraries for granting permission to reproduce pages from manuscripts in their possession: Wissenschaftliche Bibliothek, Erfurt; British Museum, London; Bodleian Library, Oxford; Biblioteca Apostolica Vaticana, Vatican City; and Herzog August Bibliothek, Wolfenbüttel. Special thanks must go also to the National Science Foundation, which has supported my work throughout—first with a graduate fellowship, then with two postdoctoral research grants, and finally by subsidizing the publication of the present volume.

Finally, I must acknowledge my debt to Professors A. Rupert Hall and Marie Boas Hall, now of the University of London, and Professors Edward Grant and Richard S. Westfall of Indiana University, who taught me the meaning of intellectual history.

D.C.L.

Madison, Wisconsin
February, 1969

Editorial Procedures

As I explain more fully in my introduction following, the *Perspectiva communis* is extant in two versions—unrevised and revised, both by Pecham himself. However, since Pecham made relatively few revisions for a work of such length, I have considered it unnecessary to reproduce the entire text and translation for both versions. Rather, I have interpolated Pecham's revisions into the unrevised text and thus have presented a single combined text and translation. I have chosen the unrevised version as the basis for the combined text and translation because it is the version that circulated, influencing the subsequent history of optics; moreover, the revised text cannot be accurately reconstructed because it exists in only a single copy and because that copy is incomplete.

Different sorts of revision by Pecham have required different methods of interpolation, but in each case his revision is distinguished from the unrevised text and translation by enclosure in braces {}. The most common revision consists of the addition of a few lines within or at the end of a proposition; in such cases the revision is enclosed in braces and inserted directly into the unrevised text and translation at the appropriate place. For example, Proposition I.43{46} begins as follows:

Operationem visibilis in visum esse dolorosam. {Idem siquidem immittitur in sensum et in contrarium. Nichilominus} hoc probatur [sic], quoniam operatio visibilis in visum est unius generis.

The phrases within braces being Pecham's additions in his revised text, the unrevised version thus reads:

Operationem visibilis in visum esse dolorosam. Hoc probatur, quoniam operatio visibilis in visum est unius generis.

And the revised version reads:

Operationem visibilis in visum esse dolorosam. Idem siquidem immittitur in sensum et in contrarium. Nichilominus hoc probatur sic, quoniam operatio visibilis in visum est unius generis.

However, when an entire proposition or a substantial portion of a proposition has been revised, I have included the revised text and translation separately, immediately after the unrevised text and translation (Propositions I.5{7}, I.6{8}, I.7{9}, I.12{14}, and I.29{32}). Occasionally it has been awkward to follow either of these procedures—for example, when a small segment of a proposition has been replaced by a brief and nonsubstantive revision. In such cases the revised text appears only in the variant readings and can be distinguished from scribal errors by its enclosure in braces. Finally, when Pecham's revision is merely a brief deletion, the deleted words appear in the variant readings followed by {*om.D*}, the braces distinguishing these words from scribal omissions.

Square brackets [] have been employed in the text and the translation to enclose my editorial insertions Angle brackets ⟨⟩ within the Latin text enclose expressions that I believe were in the original text but that are found in none of the collated manuscripts; such expressions appear in the translation without any bracketing.

Since the unrevised and revised versions differ in the numeration of propositions of Part I, I have included both numbers for each proposition, the revised number being enclosed in braces. I have arranged the propositions, however, according to the unrevised numeration. Occasionally a manuscript includes all the propositions but skips a proposition number, thus making all subsequent proposition numbers too low by one; I have made no attempt to indicate this type of variation in the variant readings. Proposition numbers appear sometimes as cardinal numbers, sometimes as ordinal numbers, sometimes as roman numerals, and I have not recorded these differences in the variant readings. I have, however, recorded differences between ordinal and cardinal numbers when they appear in the body of the text but have ignored discrepant expressions for the same numbers (e.g., the ordinal numbers *prima* and 1ᵃ or the cardinal numbers *una* and 1). In all cases, the collated text follows the majority reading of the manuscripts.

I have followed the medieval orthography of the manuscripts, including the use of *e* to replace the classical *ae*. Where the manuscripts differ among themselves on the spelling of a word, I have generally adopted the majority reading and have standardized the spelling in the variant readings. For example, the variant readings do not distinguish between *reflectio* and *reflexio* or between *dyaphanitas*, *dyaphaneitas*, *dyaphonitas*, and *dyaphoneitas*. The capitalization and punctuation are entirely mine, and I do not note variants of either one.

The margins of the manuscripts contain many figures, some of doubtful relevance. I have reproduced only those figures referred to by the text or required by it. I have had to correct or reconstruct many of the figures, and where rectification has been extensive or precarious, I have included a note to that effect. Where additional figures contribute to the understanding of Pecham's argument, I have inserted them in the notes to the translation. Letters representing geometrical magnitudes have been written in capitals in the text, translation, and figures, regardless of the manuscript treatment.

My primary concern in preparing the English translation has been to communicate Pecham's ideas faithfully and readably. Therefore I have departed from close cognates and a parallel syntax when doing so has allowed clearer and smoother expression of Pecham's thought. Because the Latin text accompanies the English translation, I have on rare occasions taken liberties with passages that I would otherwise have translated more conservatively. On the other hand, the complexity of an idea has occasionally forced me to remain very close to the medieval mode of expression.

The variant readings include all variations in the manuscripts except those of *ergo* and *igitur*, which appear to have been used interchangeably, alternative forms of the same word, such as *nichil* and *nil*, and variations in spelling, figures, and proposition numbers as discussed above. In the first folio of *A* (see the list of manuscripts and their sigla, below), which has been extensively annotated in a later hand, I have ignored marginal and interlinear notes that have no relevance for the actual reading of the text.

Only manuscripts *V*, *B*, *A*, *F*, *H*, and *D* have been collated in their entirety. Variations in these manuscripts have been expressed by means of a negative apparatus; that is, the notation provides readings only for those manuscripts that depart from the preferred (textual) reading. Thus "18 apprehensio: comprehensio *BFH*" indicates that, in line 18 of the given page, manuscripts *B*, *F*, and *H* substitute "comprehensio" for the preferred reading, "apprehensio"; it is implied that manuscripts *V*, *A*, and *D* agree with the textual reading. Whenever the preferred reading and the first variant given are sufficiently close in form that the note can be taken to refer to only one word in the particular line of the text, the lemma has been omitted. Hence, instead of "18 apprehensiones: apprehensionem *BFH*," I write "18 apprehensionem *BFH*" if line 18 contains only one word of which "apprehensionem" could be a variant. A superior number follows the lemma (e.g., "18 apprehensiones²") when the word appears more than once in the line, and indicates the particular instance of the word to which the variants belong (in the example above, the second occurrence of "apprehensiones"). A more complicated notation serves most other cases; for example, "6 equales sunt *tr. B et {om. D}* equales sint *H*" indicates that in line 6 the words of the preferred reading, "equales sunt," are transposed by *B* and omitted by *D* (the braces indicating that I regard the omission as a true revision), while *H* substitutes the expression "equales sint" and *V*, *A*, and *F*, by implication, follow the textual reading.

On occasion I have collated additional manuscripts: *L* or *W* or both have frequently been collated along with *V*, *B*, *A*, *F*, *H*, and *D* when those six basal manuscripts diverge widely from each other or contain doubtful readings; *O*, *P*, and *N* have been collated for a few propositions where several of the basal manuscripts contain long omissions. Whenever I have used such extra manuscripts and two or more manuscripts have departed from the preferred reading,

I have listed the readings of all the manuscripts collated (but if only a single manuscript has varied, I have retained the negative apparatus). Manuscripts *F* and *D* alone contain Propositions I.{80} and I.{87}, and I have again considered it desirable, in those instances, to record the readings of both.

Note that all italicized words, letters, or abbreviations belong to the apparatus used to express textual variations; all words or letters in roman type are readings of the collated text or individual manuscripts. The following abbreviations have been employed in the variant readings.

add.	=	addidit	*obs.*	=	obscuravit
alt.	=	alteravit	*om.*	=	omisit
corr.	=	correxi, correxit	*rep.*	=	repetivit
hab.	=	habet	*scr. et del.*	=	scripsit et delevit
mg.	=	in margine	*tr.*	=	transposuit

For works cited frequently in the notes, I have used the abbreviations that follow. Citations of proposition numbers unaccompanied by the name of the author or work (e.g., "Proposition II.20") refer to the present edition of the *Perspectiva communis.*

Alhazen, *Opt. thes.*	*Opticae thesaurus Alhazeni Arabis libri septem, nunc primum editi a Federico Risnero* (Basel, 1572).
Bacon, *De mult. spec.*	Roger Bacon, *De multiplicatione specierum*, included in vol. 2 of *The "Opus Majus" of Roger Bacon*, ed. J. H. Bridges (3 vols.; London, 1900). (No volume number is given in references to *De mult. spec.*, vol. 2 being understood.)
Bacon, *Opus maius*	*The "Opus Majus" of Roger Bacon*, ed. J. H. Bridges (3 vols.; London, 1900).
BGPM	*Beiträge zur Geschichte der Philosophie des Mittelalters.*
Björnbo and Vogl	Axel Anthon Björnbo and Sebastian Vogl, "Alkindi, Tideus, und Pseudo-Euklid. Drei optische Werke," *Abhandlung zur Geschichte der mathematischen Wissenschaften*, vol. 26, pt. 3 (1912), pp. 1–176.
Grosseteste, *Phil. Werke*	*Die philosophischen Werke des Robert Grosseteste*, ed. Ludwig Baur (*BGPM*, vol. 9 [Münster, 1912]).
Reg. epist.	*Registrum epistolarum fratris Johannis Peckham archiepiscopi Cantuariensis*, ed. Charles T. Martin (3 vols.; London, 1882–85).

Witelo, *Optica*   *Vitellonis Thuringopoloni opticae libri decem. In-
staurati, figuris novis illustrati atque aucti:
infinitisque erroribus, quibus antea scatebant,
expurgati a Federico Risnero* (Basel, 1572).
(Bound with the *Opticae thesaurus* of Alhazen.)

Introduction

Biographical Sketch of
John Pecham

Birth and Early Life

Fr. John Pecham, Archbishop of Canterbury, was one of the most important men in late-thirteenth-century England, and yet of his origins we know almost nothing.[1] The date of his birth can be inferred by counting backward from the years of his regency in theology at the University of Paris, 1269–71/72. Judging by the customary length of time required for a student to proceed through the arts and theological curricula to the doctorate in theology, one may conclude that Pecham was born in the early or mid-1230's.[2] Nevertheless, some biographers have inferred an earlier date from a reference by Pecham to Thomas de Cantilupe as "our scholar at Paris and our principal benefactor."[3] Assuming that Pecham's reference is to the arts course, completed by Thomas prior to

1. The best source for biographical information on Pecham is the recent biography by Decima L. Douie, *Archbishop Pecham* (Oxford, 1952). The following sources are also of value and have been employed in the composition of this biographical sketch: A. B. Emden, *A Biographical Register of the University of Oxford to A.D. 1500*, vol. 3 (Oxford, 1959), pp. 1445–47; Walter Farquhar Hook, *Lives of the Archbishops of Canterbury*, vol. 3 (London, 1865), pp. 327–66; Charles L. Kingsford, "John Peckham," in *Dictionary of National Biography* (Oxford, 1949–50), vol. 15, pp. 635–42; David Knowles, "Some Aspects of the Career of Archbishop Pecham," *English Historical Review*, vol. 57 (1942), pp. 1–18, 178–201; P. W. Lampen, "Jean Pecham, O.F.M., et son office de la S. Trinité," *La France franciscaine*, vol. 11 (1928), pp. 211–29; A. G. Little, "The Franciscan School at Oxford in the Thirteenth Century,"

Archivum Franciscanum Historicum, vol. 19 (1926), pp. 803–74; *Registrum epistolarum fratris Johannis Peckham archiepiscopi Cantuariensis*, ed. Charles T. Martin (3 vols.; London, 1882–85); D. E. Sharp, *Franciscan Philosophy at Oxford in the Thirteenth Century* (Oxford, 1930); P. Hieronymus Spettman, O.F.M., "Quellenkritisches zur Biographie des Johannes Pecham," *Franziskanische Studien*, vol. 2 (1915), pp. 170–207, 266–85; and A. Teetaert, "Jean Pecham," in *Dictionnaire de théologie catholique*, vol. 12, pt. 1 (Paris, 1933), cols. 100–40.

2. Cf. Douie, *Archbishop Pecham*, p. 3. On the time required for degrees, see Hastings Rashdall, *The Universities of Europe in the Middle Ages*, ed. F. M. Powicke and A. B. Emden (Oxford, 1936), vol. 1, pp. 471–73.

3. "...scholarem nostrum Parisius et benefactorem praecipuum" (*Reg. epist.*, vol. 1, p. 315).

1245, Lampen has fixed Pecham's date of birth between 1210 and 1220.[4] However, the only evidence that has ever been set forth for a regency, by Pecham, in the faculty of arts at Paris is a *Commentary on the Ethics of Aristotle* no longer attributed to him.[5] Moreover, Thomas is known to have studied theology at Paris during the years of Pecham's regency in theology.[6] Consequently there is no reason to date Pecham's birth from Thomas de Cantilupe's period of study in the faculty of arts in the 1240's, and we may determine the date (as above) from Pecham's regency in theology thirty years later.

The evidence for Pecham's birthplace is equally scanty. The most significant scrap of evidence is a letter written by Pecham in 1285, in which he remarks that the Priory of Lewes remains close to his heart "because we were nourished in its vicinity from childhood, and we have received comforts and honors from its teachers."[7] Upon this statement the majority of Pecham's biographers have based the conclusion that he was born and raised in the village of Patcham not far from Lewes in the County of Sussex;[8] Pecham's surname would then identify the place of his origin. This conclusion could be considered adequately established except for the claim of the contemporary chronicler Bartholomew of Cotton (d. 1298) that Pecham was born in Kent; thus at least one modern biographer has been led to conclude that Pecham came from the town of Peckham in Kent.[9] However, as Douie has indicated, the surname *Pecham* was common in Kent— indeed, there were Pecham's in both Kent and Sussex claiming to be related to the archbishop[10]—and it is not unreasonable to suppose that Bartholomew of Cotton erroneously ascribed Pecham's birthplace to Kent. In any case, the consensus among recent biographers is that Pecham was born near Lewes in Sussex.

John Pecham's surname was spelled in a variety of ways during the Middle Ages, as the general lack of uniformity in medieval orthography would predict. Early records contain the forms Peccanus, Pechanus, Petzan, Pisanus, Pescham,

---

4. Lampen, "Jean Pecham," pp. 212–14. Cf. Knowles, "Career of Archbishop Pecham," p. 3, and Teetaert, "Jean Pecham," cols. 101–02.

5. Victorinus Doucet, "Notulae bibliographicae de quibusdam operibus Fr. Ioannis Pecham O.F.M.," *Antonianum*, vol. 8 (1933), pp. 433–48, has argued against attributing this work to Pecham. Cf. Douie, *Archbishop Pecham*, p. 3.

6. On Thomas de Cantilupe's Parisian career, see Lampen, "Jean Pecham," pp. 212–14. Lampen has argued that because Thomas was a secular, he must have studied under Pecham when the latter was still a secular, i.e., during an earlier regency in the faculty of arts; but a master-pupil relation-

ship between a friar and a secular was not as irregular as Lampen assumes.

7. "...quo in ipsius vicinia coaluimus a puero, et ab ejusdem professoribus solatia recepimus et honores" (*Reg. epist.*, vol. 3, p. 902).

8. Douie, *Archbishop Pecham*, pp. 1–2; Sharp, *Franciscan Philosophy*, p. 175; Little, "Franciscan School at Oxford," pp. 852–54.

9. "...in Cantia natus" (*Bartholomaei de Cotton monachi norwicensis historia Anglicana; necnon ejusdem liber de archiepiscopis et episcopis Angliae*, ed. Henry Richards Luard [London, 1859], p. 371). Cf. Teetaert, "Jean Pecham," col. 101.

10. Douie, *Archbishop Pecham*, pp. 2–3.

Pecheam, and Pecham—but not Patcham or Peckham.[11] Perhaps the most common medieval orthography was Pecham, and I, along with a number of other recent authors, have adopted this form.

Education

Pecham's earliest education may have been obtained at the Priory of Lewes; this is suggested by the letter, quoted above, in which Pecham recalls his "nourishment from childhood" in the vicinity of Lewes. We know nothing further of his youth except that he received his training in the liberal arts at the Universities of Paris and Oxford. Pecham's study in the arts faculty at Paris can be inferred from a letter in which he recalls his education in France "from tender years,"[12] while his training at Oxford is attested by a letter of Adam Marsh referring to the need for a new tutor to replace "dominus Johannes de Pescham," who had recently entered the Franciscan order.[13] This letter was obviously written no later than 1259, the year of Adam's death, and probably belongs to the period of Adam's most active concern with the affairs of the Franciscan school at Oxford, 1247/48–53.[14] From the same letter we learn of the "illustrious conversation and advanced learning" displayed by Pecham at Oxford. Some time after entering the Franciscan order, probably between 1257 and 1259, Pecham returned to Paris and began the study of theology.[15] In 1269 he was awarded the doctorate in theology at Paris and for the next two years served as regent master in theology and lector to the Franciscan friary in Paris.

The years in Paris were those during which Pecham reached intellectual maturity. Many of his writings date from this period, including Biblical commentaries on *Lamentations*, *John*, *Hebrews*, and *Mark*, and a commentary on Peter Lombard's *Sentences*. Douie thinks Pecham's *Tractatus de anima* may also

11. Teetaert, "Jean Pecham," col. 101; Lampen, "Jean Pecham," p. 211; *Adae de Marisco epistolae*, in *Monumenta Franciscana*, vol. 1 (ed. J. S. Brewer; London, 1858), p. 256 (cited hereafter as "Adam Marsh, *Epistolae*"); *Joannis Duns Scoti doctoris subtilis ordinis minorum opera omnia editio nova*, vol. 7 (Paris, 1893), p. 233. On the relationship of the name *Pecham* to the villages of Peckham and Patcham, see the preface to *Fratris Johannis Pecham quondam archiepiscopi Cantuariensis Tractatus tres de paupertate*, ed. C. L. Kingsford, A. G. Little, and F. Tocco (Aberdeen, 1910), p. v.

12. "Nos in Francia ab annis teneris educati" (*Reg. epist.*, vol. 3, p. 874). Cf. Douie, *Archbishop Pecham*, pp. 4–5.

13. Adam Marsh, *Epistolae*, p. 256. Martin points out that the title "dominus" implies a degree in arts rather than in theology (*Reg. epist.*, vol. 1, p. lix).

14. On the chronology of the relevant periods of Adam Marsh's life, see Little, "Franciscan School at Oxford," pp. 835–36.

15. The years 1257–59 for Pecham's migration to Paris are suggested by Douie, *Archbishop Pecham*, p. 8. Knowles, "Career of Archbishop Pecham," p. 4, points out that Pecham may also have studied theology at Oxford before his transfer to Paris. For a refutation of the often-stated opinion that Pecham studied under Bonaventure at Paris, see Teetaert, "Jean Pecham," col. 103.

have been written during the Paris years.[16] Another index of Pecham's intellectual stature is his role in the philosophical and theological movements in Paris during the 1260's. He was a leader in the conservative opposition to certain Thomistic novelties, strenuously attacking Aquinas's teaching on the unity of form, though he later defended Thomas against extreme censure.[17] While in Paris, Pecham was also active in the power struggle between the seculars and the mendicants. With Bonaventure and Aquinas, he championed the mendicant cause in three pamphlets, *De perfectione evangelica, Canticum pauperis,* and *Defensio fratrum mendicantium.*[18]

Pecham's philosophical outlook was typically Franciscan. Indeed, Douie points out that "his significance in the history of medieval scholasticism is that his thought shows the beginning of the transition from the eclecticism of the early Franciscan thinkers towards Duns Scotus's...criticism of the whole Thomist position."[19] Accordingly, Pecham accepted the body of psychological doctrines usually considered characteristic of medieval "Augustinianism," such as the divine illumination of the intellect, complete hylomorphism, and the independence of body and soul.[20] As a philosopher and theologian, according to Knowles, Pecham

16. Douie, *Archbishop Pecham*, p. 11. However, Melani (*Tractatus de anima Ioannis Pecham*, ed. P. Gaudentius Melani, O.F.M. [Florence, 1948], pp. xlix–l) dates *De anima* to the 1270's, probably 1277–79. On Pecham's writings in general, see Doucet, "Notulae bibliographicae"; P. Glorieux, *Répertoire des maîtres en théologie de Paris au XIIIe siècle* (Paris, 1933), vol. 2, pp. 87–98; Pecham, *Tractatus tres*, ed. Kingsford, Little, and Tocco, pp. 1–12.

17. On the struggle between Pecham and Aquinas, see Knowles, "Career of Archbishop Pecham," pp. 12–15; Theodore Crowley, O.F.M., "John Peckham, O.F.M., Archbishop of Canterbury, versus the New Aristotelianism," *Bulletin of the John Rylands Library*, vol. 33 (1950–51), pp. 247–55.

18. Knowles, "Career of Archbishop Pecham," p. 8. Portions of the first of these three treatises have been edited by A. G. Little in Pecham, *Tractatus tres*, pp. 13–90.

19. Douie, *Archbishop Pecham*, p. 18.

20. As a number of historians have argued recently, the doctrines that have conventionally been considered most typically Augustinian actually drew their main inspiration from Aristotle, although they contained also an admixture of Islamic, Jewish, and traditional Christian elements. Crowley ("Peckham vs. Aristotelianism," p. 254) has pointed out that, whereas the doctrine of the divine illumination of the intellect (i.e., God as agent intellect) is considered "the hallmark of medieval 'Augustinianism', Peckham confirms [it] by an appeal to Aristotle." See Fernand Van Steenberghen, *Aristotle in the West* (Louvain, 1955), pp. 126–30, 145–46, for similar views. However, in his book *The Philosophical Movement in the Thirteenth Century* (London, 1955), p. 103, Van Steenberghen argues that "the true founder of neo-Augustinianism was John Peckham: he was the first to take up a position against Thomas on the ground of philosophical and theological controversy; he was the first to denounce the philosophical innovations of Thomas as an infidelity to St. Augustine." On Pecham's psychology, see Knowles, "Career of Archbishop Pecham," pp. 5–6; P. Hieronymus Spettman, O.F.M., *Die Psychologie des Johannes Pecham* (*BGPM*, vol. 20, pt. 6 [Münster, 1919]).

stood in the full stream of tradition, and in his latest years gloried in this. His works show him to have had a capacious and versatile mind and great industry, but he was not a profound speculative theologian, nor was he a great metaphysician, like his predecessor at Oxford, Thomas of York. His high reputation among contemporaries would seem to have been due to his gifts of exposition, and perhaps also to his very lack of profundity and the eminently "safe" character of his teaching.[21]

Later Years

Only Pecham's later years are well documented. He departed from Paris sometime during the years 1271–72 and returned to Oxford as eleventh lecturer to the Franciscan school. In appointing Pecham to replace Thomas Bungay, who had resigned to become provincial minister, the Franciscans at Oxford selected a man of European-wide reputation and one of the leading figures of the Franciscan order. At Oxford, as at Paris, Pecham was a member of the theological faculty, though, as Douie has suggested, "the greater interest at Oxford in science and mathematics would both have increased his reputation and given scope for his special tastes."[22]

Pecham resigned his post at Oxford in 1275 to assume the provincial ministership of the Franciscan order. He retained the post of provincial minister when he was appointed master in theology to the Papal Curia in 1277. Pecham's appointment to the papal court clearly reveals the high reputation that he had already acquired; it also served to advance his reputation in high church circles.[23] As provincial minister and professor at the curia, Pecham became known for his austere and correct personal habits, illustrated by his celebrated journey on foot from England to Italy to attend the general council of the Franciscan order in Padua.[24]

In 1278 Robert Kilwardby, Archbishop of Canterbury, was elevated to the College of Cardinals. Edward I secured the election of Robert Burnell to the empty post of archbishop, but Pope Nicholas III rejected Burnell and nominated John Pecham instead. Both Edward I and Pecham were apparently dubi-

21. Knowles, "Career of Archbishop Pecham," p. 5.

22. Douie, *Archbishop Pecham*, p. 35. On the organization of the Franciscan convent in Oxford and its relation to the university, see A. G. Little, *The Grey Friars in Oxford* (Oxford, 1892); and Rashdall, *Universities*, vol. 3, pp. 66–70.

23. Pecham's lectures were attended by bishops and cardinals, who, according to legend, arose when he entered the lecture room, as a mark of respect. See Kingsford, "John Peckham," p. 636; Douie, *Archbishop Pecham*, pp. 45–46. On the nature of the Papal University, see Raymond Creytens, O.P., "Le 'Studium Romanae Curiae' et le Maître du Sacré Palais," *Archivum Fratrum Praedicatorum*, vol. 12 (1942), pp. 5–83; Creytens disputes the traditional Franciscan opinion that Pecham was "first lecturer" in theology.

24. Kingsford, "John Peckham," pp. 639–40; Douie, *Archbishop Pecham*, p. 42.

ous about the appointment, the latter because of his own ill-health; but Nicholas prevailed, and Pecham was consecrated as Archbishop of Canterbury on the fourth Sunday of Lent, 1279. As archbishop he was exceedingly energetic—the very characteristic for which Nicholas had nominated him—with perhaps a tendency to lay too much stress on the dignity of the episcopal see. His intentions were above reproach, but his ecclesiastical policy was "marred by blundering zeal."[25] Pecham's ardent preservation of ecclesiastical rights is illustrated by his order that Magna Charta be posted in all cathedral and collegiate churches, though subsequent conflict with Edward led to withdrawal of the order.[26] In 1279 Pecham instituted a campaign against clerical abuses by summoning a provincial synod at Reading, where he attacked pluralism and nonresidence. Two years later he summoned another reform council at Lambeth.[27]

Pecham never lost his interest in retarding the spread of "dangerous" philosophical novelties, particularly the doctrine of the unity of form. In 1284 his visitatorial duties took him to the University of Oxford. In the course of the visit, not only did he renew Kilwardby's decree of 1277 proscribing a number of Thomist doctrines, but he also explicitly condemned the doctrine of the unity of form.[28] During the subsequent controversy, Pecham expressed the following thoughts, which clearly reveal his conservative attitude toward philosophy and the philosophical novelties that were appearing in the latter half of the thirteenth century.

...we are far from condemning philosophy, in so far as it serves the cause of theology; what we condemn are the unsanctified and novel terms that have these last twenty years been introduced into the treatment of high theology, to the manifest contempt and rejection of the tradition of the saints of old. Which of these two doctrines, we ask, is more sound and solid, that of the sons of St. Francis, Alexander of Hales and Bonaventura of blessed memory and their like, who in their treatises take for authorities saints and philosophers above criticism, or that newfangled system opposed to this at all points, which strains every nerve to demolish the teaching of Augustine on the eternal prototypes, on the divine illumination of the intellect, on the faculties of the soul, on the radical potentialities of matter, and on numberless other points, thus filling the whole world with the strife of words? Let the doctors of old, the truly wise, regard this; let God in heaven regard it and punish it![29]

Pecham's rich and varied career as a theologian, philosopher, educator, and

25. Kingsford, "John Peckham," p. 637.

26. Douie, *Archbishop Pecham*, pp. 113, 119.

27. *Ibid.*, pp. 95–104.

28. On Pecham's visit to Oxford, see Knowles, "Career of Archbishop Pecham," pp. 183–91; Crowley, "Peckham vs. Aristotelianism," pp. 250–53.

29. Quoted by Knowles, "Career of Archbishop Pecham," p. 189; for the Latin text, see *Reg. epist.*, vol. 3, pp. 901–02. On Pecham's attitude toward the philosophical innovations of the late-thirteenth century, see p. 6, above; cf. Van Steenberghen, *Philosophical Movement*, pp. 94–103.

ecclesiastical administrator was terminated by his death on December 8, 1292. Several qualities of his personality are summed up in the analysis of his character by the Dominican Nicholas Trivet: "He was a zealous promotor of the interests of his Order, an excellent maker of songs, of pompous manner and speech, but of kind and thoroughly liberal heart."[30]

Scientific Interests

The breadth of Pecham's scientific outlook is revealed by his writings, which include the *Perspectiva communis, Theorica planetarum, Tractatus de sphera,* and *Tractatus de numeris.* In addition, his *Tractatus de anima, Questiones de anima,* and *Questiones de beautitudine corporis et anime* contain a great deal of material that is properly classified as scientific.[31]

30. Quoted by Little, *Grey Friars,* pp. 155–56.

31. On Pecham's writings, see Doucet, "Notulae bibliographicae"; Glorieux, *Répertoire,* vol. 2, pp. 87–98; Pecham, *Tractatus tres,* ed. Kingsford, Little, and Tocco, pp. 1–12. The *Tractatus de numeris* is not what would today be classified as pure mathematics. It consists of arithmetic and number theory accompanied by a heavy dose of theology and number mysticism. Its first five chapters have been edited as *Arithmetica mistica* by Melani (appendix to *Tractatus de anima,* pp. 138–44); see descriptions of this work by Martin in the preface to *Reg. epist.,* vol. 3, pp. lxix–lxxiv; and Lynn Thorndike, "A John Peckham Manuscript," *Archivum Franciscanum Historicum,* vol. 45 (1952), pp. 456–58. Martin's preface also contains brief descriptions of *De sphera* and *Theorica planetarum* (pp. lxv–lxvii). Thorndike reproduces fragments of Pecham's *De sphera* in his *The Sphere of Sacrobosco and Its Commentators* (Chicago, 1949), pp. 445–50. On medieval treatises entitled *Theorica planetarum,* see Olaf Pedersen, "The Theorica-planetarum Literature of the Middle Ages," *Actes du dixième congrès international d'histoire des sciences* (Ithaca, 1962), vol. 1, pp. 615–18.

A number of other scientific works have been attributed to Pecham. Thorndike ("Peckham Manuscript," pp. 459–61) and Doucet (pp. 312–14) argue that an anonymous optical treatise contained in Vat. lat. cod. 5963 and Florence plut. cod. XVII sin.8 should be attributed to Pecham. A preliminary examination of this treatise, which is variously referred to as *De perspectivis* or *Tractatus de perspectiva et iride* (and which I shall call *Tractatus de perspectiva*), has persuaded me that its author was indeed Pecham. Lynn Thorndike and Pearl Kibre, *A Catalogue of Incipits of Mediæval Scientific Writings in Latin* (revised ed.; Cambridge, Mass., 1963), col. 1036, attribute to Pecham a *Perspectiva particularis* (Cambridge, Gonville and Caius College MS 506/384, fols. 246–49); Glorieux (p. 97) lists this as a doubtful work of Pecham. Some listings of Pecham's works refer to a treatise entitled *Mathematicae rudimenta,* but this is merely the revised version of the *Perspectiva communis* contained in MS Digby 218 and edited in this volume. Glorieux (p. 88) also attributes to Pecham a *Tractatus de animalibus* contained in Florence, Bibl. Nazionale, MS G.IV.853, fols. 77r–191v, but Doucet (p. 448) denies that this attribution has any foundation. Spettman has shown that *De oculo morali,* containing substantial anatomical and ophthalmological information and frequently attributed to Pecham, was actually written by Peter of Limoges (d. 1306); see Hieronymus Spettman, O.F.M., "Das Schriftchen 'De oculo morali' und sein Verfasser,"

The awakening of Pecham's scientific interests may have occurred through his connection with the University of Oxford, where Robert Grosseteste (d. 1253) had initiated a vigorous tradition of mathematical science. There was obviously no direct master-pupil relationship between Grosseteste and Pecham, since Grosseteste ceased lecturing in 1235 (about the time of Pecham's birth) to assume the episcopate of Lincoln. However, the tradition of learning established by Grosseteste seems to have persisted after his departure. Adam Marsh, who lectured in the Franciscan school until 1250, received Roger Bacon's praise for his mathematical abilities: "For there are exceedingly renowned men, such as Bishop Robert [Grosseteste] of Lincoln, Brother Adam Marsh, and many others, who are able to explain the causes of all things by the power of mathematics."[32] Bacon himself has properly been looked upon as one of the luminaries of the Oxford scientific tradition, and although it seems clear that Bacon did not study directly under Grosseteste—or, indeed, develop his interest in optics and mathematical science until long after he had completed the arts course at Oxford—Grosseteste's influence was doubtless exercised through his writings and his library, which he bequeathed to the Franciscans at his death.[33] These same writings were available to Pecham as a member of the Franciscan order, and they, along with the general orientation at Oxford toward mathematical science (of which Bacon speaks in the quotation above), may have been factors in Pecham's intellectual development.

Of Roger Bacon's influence on Pecham there can be no doubt. Even a superficial reading of their works on similar subjects reveals that Pecham drew heavily on Bacon. Douie has concluded that Pecham's "scientific writings, particularly

Archivum Franciscanum Historicum, vol. 16 (1923), pp. 309–22.

Douie notes that the *Questiones de beatitudine* "reflect the keen interest of Pecham and his audience [at the Papal University] in scientific problems and the Baconian theories; for the main subject was merely a pretext for the discussion of the laws of gravity, motion, and space, or the rarefaction of air when it entered a vacuum, or the action of the planets on the formation and composition of the precious metals" (*Archbishop Pecham*, p. 44). For modern editions of this work and the two treatises dealing with the soul, see Melani, *Tractatus de anima*, and *Johannis Pechami Quaestiones tractantes de anima*, ed. P. Hieronymus Spettman (*BGPM*, vol. 19, pts. 5–6 [Münster, 1918]); the latter work includes the *Questiones de anima* and the *Questiones de beatitudine*.

32. *Opus maius*, pt. IV, dist. 1, chap. 3 (ed. Bridges, vol. 1, p. 108). There is no inconsistency between the date given here and the years 1247/48–53 assigned earlier to Adam's most active concern with the Franciscan school; Adam ceased to lecture in 1250, but remained active in the affairs of the school until 1253 (see Little, "Franciscan School at Oxford," pp. 835–36). Stewart Easton has expressed reservations on the mathematical and scientific learning of Adam Marsh, but if Bacon is guilty of exaggeration, it is still true that Adam possessed sympathy and acquaintance with the scientific legacy of Robert Grosseteste; see Stewart C. Easton, *Roger Bacon and his Search for a Universal Science* (Oxford, 1952), pp. 91–93.

33. Easton, *Roger Bacon*, pp. 22–23, 90–91.

the *Tractatus de Sphaera*, were obviously strongly influenced by Bacon's *Opus Majus*," and this judgment could be broadened to include the *Perspectiva communis*.[34] But, once again, the question is whether Bacon exerted a *formative* influence on Pecham's scientific thought. To find the answer, we must consider the several occasions when Bacon could have exercised an influence on Pecham. It is possible, as Douie suggests, that Pecham studied under Bacon in the faculty of arts at Paris in the 1240's.[35] It is possible, also, that both were residing in the Franciscan convent at Oxford in the mid-1250's, after both had joined the order but before Pecham departed for Paris.[36] However, a significant influence on either of these occasions seems improbable, for Bacon's thought had not yet acquired that mathematical and optical stamp characteristic of Pecham's works and of Bacon's own later work. Therefore, it appears that contact of significance from a scientific standpoint could have occurred only in the 1260's, after Bacon had become interested in mathematical science; moreover, during this decade, both were residents of the Franciscan friary in Paris, where Pecham was studying theology and Bacon had been sent by his Franciscan superiors for closer supervision and possibly some sort of quarantine.[37] By this time, however, it was a mature John Pecham, studying and teaching theology. Moreover, one must question how close Pecham's relations with the disfavored Bacon would have been. As Bacon describes his situation, "my superiors and brothers, disciplining me with hunger, kept me under close guard and would not permit anyone to come to me, fearing that my writings would be divulged to others than to the chief pontiff and themselves."[38] It is unlikely, under such circumstances, even allowing for Bacon's tendency to exaggerate his persecution, that Pecham would have become his protégé. Nevertheless, since both were residents of the same house and since, as Bacon points out, his brothers had access to his writings, Pecham must have known what Bacon was doing, and it is possible that Bacon's tutelage was a force of significance in awakening Pecham's interests in optics and in mathematical science in general.

34. Douie, *Archbishop Pecham*, p. 5; Sharp, *Franciscan Philosophy*, p. 175. On the *Perspectiva communis* and its relation to Bacon's optical writings, see pp. 26–27, below.

35. Douie, *Archbishop Pecham*, p. 5. However, there is no evidence that Pecham was in fact Bacon's student.

36. We have no evidence for the exact date when either Bacon or Pecham joined the Franciscan order; all we can say is that both did so in Oxford during this period. Bacon had returned to Oxford from Paris probably about 1247 (and no later than 1250); Pecham left Oxford for Paris probably during the years 1257–59. The relevant chronology on Bacon has been convincingly set forth by Easton, *Roger Bacon*, p. 87, and by Theodore Crowley, *Roger Bacon: The Problem of the Soul in his Philosophical Commentaries* (Louvain-Dublin, 1950), pp. 27–31. On Pecham, see Douie, *Archbishop Pecham*, p. 8.

37. Easton, *Roger Bacon*, pp. 134–39.

38. *Ibid.*, p. 134. This passage is from a fragment of Bacon's *Opus minus* not extant in published form, but quoted in Wood's life of Bacon; see *Fr. Rogeri Bacon, Opera quaedam hactenus inedita*, ed. J. S. Brewer, vol. 1 (London, 1859), p. xciv.

Composition and Influence
of the *Perspectiva communis*

Title

The conception of a "proper title," assigned to a book by its author, was nonexistent in the Middle Ages. Titles were merely descriptive captions attached to books for the sake of convenience in referring to them or to distinguish them from one another. Since the only requirement for such a title was that it should provide an appropriate description of the contents, the same book obviously might circulate under several different titles. If, eventually, a particular title became standard, the selection was made not by the author, but by tradition.

The title *Perspectiva communis*, by which Pecham's treatise on optics is now universally known, seems to have made its first appearance during the fourteenth century. Early versions of the work generally circulated either with no title or with the title *Perspectiva*. For example, Vat. lat. MS 5963 and Florence MS plut. XVII sin. 8, assigned to the thirteenth century by Thorndike and Doucet respectively, bear no title at all;[1] nor do Wolfenbüttel MS Guelf. 38.6 Aug. 2° and Dresden MS Db.86, from early in the fourteenth century. The title *Perspectiva* appears in two early fourteenth-century manuscripts (Oxford, Digby MS 218 and Ashmolean MS 1522) and several manuscripts from later in the century.[2] The title *Perspectiva communis* is found in six fourteenth-century manuscripts, none of them particularly early.[3]

---

1. Thorndike, "Peckham Manuscript," pp. 451–52; Doucet, "Notulae bibliographicae," p. 309. Needless to say, one must be cautious about such an early date. Bernhard Bischoff of Ludwig-Maximilians-Universität in Munich, who graciously dated several manuscripts for me on the basis of photographic reproductions, has indicated in a private communication that Vat. lat. MS 5963 is in all probability from the thirteenth century, though possibly from early in the fourteenth century. Squadrani (see p. 54, n. 3, below) prefers a fourteenth-century date for Florence MS plut. XVII sin. 8. It is clear, in any case, that these two manuscripts were written no later than the early fourteenth century.

2. The portion of the Ashmolean codex containing the *Perspectiva communis* was evidently written not long after 1303, for the codex is all in a single hand, and earlier portions are given that date. Digby MS 218 is the revised version.

3. The six are Basel MS F.IV.30, Erfurt MS Q.387, Prague MS 1272, Prague MS 1284, Vienna MS 2433, and Vienna MS 5210.

Pecham's only reference to his own treatise is found in the opening sentences of the preface to the revised version; there he merely notes having written, sometime earlier, "certain unpolished mathematical essays," which he will now correct for the sake of students.[4] The earliest citation of Pecham's optical treatise by another author is, to my knowledge, in Duns Scotus's *Questiones subtilissime super libros metaphysicorum*, where reference is made to "*Pecheam Perspectivae.*"[5]

The earliest instances of the expression *perspectiva communis* that have come to my attention (aside from manuscripts of Pecham's work) are in two late fourteenth-century manuscripts of the *Questiones super perspectivam* of Henry of Langenstein (d. 1397), in the requirements for the M.A. degree at Prague in 1390, which include "sex libros Euclidis, sphaeram, theoricam, aliquid in musica et arithmetica, perspectivam communem," and in the lectures of Nicholas of Dinkelsbühl at Vienna in 1395 on *perspectiva communis*;[6] but although the degree requirements at Prague and the lectures at Vienna were undoubtedly based on Pecham's treatise, it is not necessary to interpret the expression *perspectiva communis* in the Prague and Vienna records as the title of a book.

The title *Perspectiva communis* became firmly established only in the sixteenth century with the appearance of printed editions. Eight of the eleven editions so entitle it, and a ninth refers to it as *Perspettiva...vulgo communis appellata....*[7] It has rarely been cited by any other title since.

If *Perspectiva communis* eventually became the accepted title of Pecham's work, we must inquire into its origin and meaning. *Perspectiva* requires little explanation; it is the medieval Latin equivalent of our term "optics," and Pecham's book clearly deals with the subject of optics. The adjective *communis* was frequently applied to the standard text on a particular subject, and this is undoubtedly why it was added to the title of Pecham's book.[8] Sędziwój von

Obviously, I can speak only for those thirty-two manuscripts that I have been able to examine (see the list of manuscripts, below).

4. Below, p. 61.

5. Bk. 5, chap. 7, *Opera* (ed. Vivès), vol. 7, p. 233. On the authenticity of this work, see Duns Scotus, *Philosophical Writings*, ed. Allan Wolter, O.F.M. (New York, 1962), p. xx.

6. Questions 1 and 9, in Paris, MS Arsenal 522, and Florence, Bibl. Nazionale, MS Conv. soppr. J.X.19. Rashdall, *Universities*, vol. 1, p. 449, n. 3. Alois Madre, *Nikolaus von Dinkelsbühl, Leben und Schriften* (*BGPM*, vol. 40, pt. 4 [Münster, 1965]), p. 10.

7. See the list of printed editions, pp. 56–57, below.

8. Manuscripts containing the most common version of the *Theorica planetarum* are sometimes entitled *Theorica planetarum communis*; see Pedersen, "Theorica-planetarum literature," p. 615. The expression *arithmetica communis* appears repeatedly in the statutes of the University of Leipzig in the fifteenth century, not (it seems) indicating the title of a book, but meaning simply "elementary arithmetic"; see Rudolf Helssig, *Die wissenschaftlichen Vorbedingungen für Baccalaureat in artibus und Magisterium im ersten Jahrhundert der Universität*, in *Beiträge zur Geschichte der Universität Leipzig im fünfzehnten Jahrhundert* (Leipzig, 1909), pp. 17, 36–38, 55. On the widespread use of the *Perspectiva communis* as an elementary text, see pp. 29–31, below.

Czechel, who lectured on the *Perspectiva communis* at Cracow in 1430, makes that very point in some remarks inserted immediately before the *Perspectiva communis* in Cracow MS 1929:

...the title, according to some, is "*Perspectiva communis* of master John of Pisa," thus called from the city;[9] and it is called "*Perspectiva communis*" by contrast with other perspective treatises, namely, those of Vitulio, Bachon, Allacen, and Radanus,[10] whose treatises on perspective are not as common in our schools. Wherefore it should be noted that the investigators of perspective, called "perspectivists," are five in number: the first is Allacen, who has gathered that knowledge into a great book; the second is Vitalio or Vitulio; the third is called Bachon; the fourth Radanus; the fifth investigator of perspective...is said to have been master John of Pisa, who drew together a summa [of perspective] from the books of Allacen and other perspectivists, and this has been named the "*Perspectiva communis*." It can be called "*Perspectiva communis*" because the doctrines commonly maintained [or maintained in common] by the perspectivists have been collected there.[11]

Date of Composition and Intended Audience

Several items of evidence bear on the dating of the *Perspectiva communis*.[12] In the first place, Pecham obviously drew on Bacon's *Opus maius*, the composition of which can be dated with fair precision. Secondly, the *Perspectiva communis* and Witelo's *Perspectiva* contain at least one parallel passage that can be accounted for only on the assumption that one borrowed from the other; moreover, Witelo's *Perspectiva* can be dated within broad limits. Finally, we have Pecham's statements regarding his intended audience and a fair knowledge of those periods of his life during which he would have had the time and motivation to write an optical treatise.

There can be no doubt that Pecham knew Bacon's *Opus maius* when he wrote the *Perspectiva communis*. One of the clearest demonstrations of this fact is Pecham's attack on Bacon's theory of the rainbow: although Pecham does not refer to Bacon by name, there can be no doubt as to the object of his attack, since some of the ideas at issue had not been expressed by any other author.[13]

9. In several manuscripts and two of the printed editions, the *Perspectiva communis* is erroneously attributed to Johannis Pisani or Pysani, apparently a corruption of Johannis Pecham.

10. I have been unable to identify Radanus.

11. The Latin text is quoted by Clemens Baeumker, *Witelo, ein Philosoph und Naturforscher des XIII. Jahrhunderts* (*BGPM*, vol. 3, pt. 2 [Münster, 1908]), p. 185, n. 5.

12. On the dating of the *Perspectiva communis*, see my "Lines of Influence in Thirteenth-Century Optics: Bacon, Witelo, and Pecham," *Speculum*, forthcoming, where certain matters touched upon here are treated in considerably more detail.

13. At one point in his theory of the rainbow, Bacon maintains that the colors of the rainbow are seen, not by emanation of their own species in all directions, but by reflection of incident solar rays from droplets in the

Since the portion of the *Opus maius* dealing with the rainbow was written in the early 1260's, probably about 1263, this date can serve as a *terminus post quem* for the composition of the *Perspectiva communis*.[14]

The relationship between Pecham and Witelo is more obscure. There seems to have been no opportunity for them to meet in person, unless during Pecham's tour of duty at the Papal Curia late in the 1270's, and were it not for the single instance of parallel wording so far discovered, one could conclude that neither was influenced by the other.[15] (A number of historians have claimed that Pecham borrowed extensively from Witelo, but such claims appear to rest entirely on references to Witelo in printed editions of the *Perspectiva communis*; these references were not part of the original text, but were inserted by a sixteenth-century editor.)[16] The passage in question appears in Proposition I.36{39} of the *Perspectiva communis*, where Pecham writes,

...quoniam si alii cuicunque tunice vel humori lesio accidat, salva glaciali, per medicinam recipit curationem et sanatur, ac restituitur visus. Ipsa vero corrupta, corrumpitur visus irrecuperabiliter.

Discussing the same question, Witelo writes, in almost identical terms,

...et si alii cuicunque tunice vel humori accidat lesio, salvo glaciali humore, semper

---

moist cloud to the observer's eye, and that, consequently, even though conditions suitable for the formation of the rainbow exist throughout the moist cloud, the rainbow appears only in those places from which sunlight is reflected to the observer's eye at equal angles (*Opus maius*, pt. 6, chap. 12 [ed. Bridges, vol. 2, pp. 196–97]). These are the ideas that Pecham attacks when he writes, "I fail to grasp that which is maintained by some people, [namely,] that the different colors are produced in the same parts of the cloud but do not appear everywhere, being visible only in those places to which the rays constituting the colors are reflected; for no impressions whatever are seen by means of the rays that generated them, but rather through their own species outside the place of reflection" (Proposition III.20). There are many other indications of the influence of the *Opus maius* on the *Perspectiva communis*; see pp. 26–27, below.

14. On the composition of the *Opus maius*, see Easton, *Roger Bacon*, pp. 110–11, 153, 161–62.

15. Borrowed ideas, in the absence of

similar wording, are difficult to identify, because Pecham and Witelo relied so heavily on the same authors; this is why I have placed such stress on similarities in terminology. Now that I have come across the one instance of parallel wording, it seems likely that others will be discovered. However, despite the fact that I have edited Pecham's treatise and have read extensively in Witelo's, I have come across no others.

16. E.g., A. C. Crombie, *Robert Grosseteste and the Origins of Experimental Science, 1100–1700* (Oxford, 1952), p. 165, takes a reference to Witelo appearing in Proposition II.6 of the 1592 edition of the *Perspectiva communis* as evidence that Pecham based his work on that of Witelo; see also William A. Wallace, *The Scientific Methodology of Theodoric of Freiberg* (Fribourg, 1959), p. 150. The editor responsible for the insertions was Georg Hartmann (1489–1564), who extensively altered the medieval text in preparing the 1542 edition of the *Perspectiva communis*; all later editions then substantially reproduced the Hartmann text. See pp. 57–58, below.

auxilio medicine recipit oculus curationem et sanatur, ac restituitur visus. Ipsa vero corrupta, corrumpitur visus totus sine spe restitutionis.[17]

Alhazen and Roger Bacon present an argument having a resemblance to this, but they do not employ similar terminology.[18] Since it does not appear that Pecham and Witelo were both quoting some third source—I have undertaken quite an exhaustive search of the optical and ophthalmological literature[19]—it can be concluded that one of them had access to the treatise of the other. But which? Before this question can be considered, it will be necessary to examine other evidence for the dating of both Pecham's *Perspectiva communis* and Witelo's *Perspectiva*.

Witelo's work is the easier to delimit in time. In his *Perspectiva*, Witelo made use of William of Moerbeke's translation of Hero of Alexandria's *De speculis*, completed on December 31, 1269.[20] Witelo also dedicated his optical treatise to William of Moerbeke, addressing him in the dedicatory epistle as Papal Confessor, a position William held until April 9, 1278.[21] It is thus apparent that Witelo wrote his *Perspectiva* between January 1, 1270, and April 9, 1278. Further narrowing of this period must be somewhat conjectural. It is possible that the individual named "Witelo" who served as chaplain to the Bohemian king, Ottokar II, and who was sent on a mission to Pope Gregory X in 1274, is identical with the author of the *Perspectiva*; and if that is so, the probability is that Witelo completed the *Perspectiva* while still in Viterbo, before assuming Ottokar's chaplaincy.[22] In any case, it seems likely that Witelo set to work on the

17. Witelo, *Optica*, bk. 3, sec. 4, p. 87.

18. Alhazen's remarks on the same subject are as follows: "...quoniam si contigerit humori glaciali lesio cum salute aliarum tunicarum destruitur visio, et si acciderit residuis tunicis corruptio, remanente ipsarum diaphanitate cum salute glacialis, non corrumpetur visus" (*Opt. thes.*, bk. 1, sec. 16, p. 8). There are conceptual, as well as terminological, differences between Alhazen's argument and that of Pecham and Witelo; see my "Lines of Influence." Bacon wrote: "Nam si ipse laedatur, aliis salvis, destruitur visio, et si ipse sit salvus, et aliis accidat laesio, dummodo maneat eorum diaphaneitas, non destruitur visio..." (*Opus maius*, pt. V.i., dist. 4, chap. 2 [ed. Bridges, vol. 2, p. 27]).

19. I have searched the works of the following authors without discovering any passage that could have served as a source for both Pecham and Witelo: Johannes Mesue, Johannitius, Rhazes, Haly Abbas, Jesu Haly, Albucasis, Canamusali, Avicenna, Alhazen, Averroës, Constantinus Africanus, Beneventus Grassus, Magister Zacharias, Alcoatin, Bartholomew the Englishman, Vincent of Beauvais, and Roger Bacon. See my "Lines of Influence" for additional detail.

20. According to the explicit of the holograph of this treatise in Vat. Ottob. lat. MS 1850, fol. 61v; cf. Martin Grabmann, *Guglielmo di Moerbeke O.P. il traduttore delle opere di Aristotele* (Rome, 1946), p. 162. On the dating of Witelo's *Perspectiva*, see also Aleksander Birkenmajer, "Études sur Witelo, III," *Bulletin international de l'Académie polonaise des sciences et des lettres* (Cracow, 1920), p. 358; and the same author's "Witelo e lo studio di Padova," in *Omaggio dell'Accademia Polacca di scienze e lettere all'Università di Padova* (Cracow, 1922), p. 157.

21. Grabmann, *Guglielmo di Moerbeke*, p. 54.

22. See Clemens Baeumker, "Zur Frage nach Abfassungszeit und Verfasser des irr-

Perspectiva soon after Moerbeke had supplied him with needed translations of Greek mathematical works (he had no official duties at the curia, so far as court documents indicate, and there is no evidence of any other kind of scholarly activity) and that he completed this mammoth project within two to four years; thus the composition of the *Perspectiva* would have taken place between about 1270 and 1273.

Possible dates for Pecham's composition of the *Perspectiva communis* can be determined by considering the audience for which it was written. It has been suggested by Douie that the unrevised version of the *Perspectiva communis* circulated as a *reportatio*, i.e., a set of student notes copied down during Pecham's lectures; this would explain Pecham's remark in the preface of the revised version that the treatise "appeared in public against my intention," and, since such *reportationes* were frequently returned to the author for revision and final publication, it would also explain Pecham's effort "to correct them slightly in order that they may be of benefit to young students."[23] However, Pecham also says, in the same preface, that he wrote his work "at the request of associates," a remark which, in my opinion, casts doubt on the interpretation of the *Perspectiva communis* as a *reportatio*. In any case, the content and format of the *Perspectiva communis* clearly identify it as an elementary textbook. This conclusion is confirmed by Pecham's remark that he has decided to prepare a revision for the benefit of young students. Judged solely on the basis of its audience, then, the *Perspectiva communis* must have been written for the Franciscan friars during Pecham's lectureships at Paris or Oxford, 1269–75, for the clerks of the Papal University during his professorship there, 1277–79, or perhaps for the convent schools of the Franciscan order during Pecham's tenure as Provincial Minister, 1275–79.[24]

These dates for the composition of Witelo's *Perspectiva* and Pecham's *Perspectiva communis* being given, is it possible to determine who borrowed from the other? Witelo wrote his treatise between 1270 and 1278; Pecham

---

tümlich Witelo zugeschriebenen Liber de intelligentiis," in *Miscellanea Francesco Ehrle*, vol. 1 (Rome, 1924), p. 95. "Witelo" was a relatively common thirteenth-century Silesian name, and consequently it is not implausible that a second Witelo should appear in documents of the 1270's; see Maximilian Curtze, "Sur l'orthographe du nom et sur la patrie de Witelo (Vitellion)," *Bullettino di bibliografia e di storia delle scienze matematiche e fisiche*, vol. 4 (1871), p. 70; Baeumker, *Witelo*, p. 199.

23. See the preface, p. 61, below; Douie, *Archbishop Pecham*, p. 12, n. 5. On the

reportatio, see Duns Scotus, *Philosophical Writings*, ed. Wolter, p. xvii; and Rashdall, *Universities*, vol. 1, p. 490.

24. J. L. Peckham thinks that it was "probably...while a lecturer in Paris, Oxford, and Rome, that he had leisure to compose numerous theological, philosophical, and scientific treatises" (John Laimbeer Peckham, *Archbishop Peckham as a Religious Educator* [Scottdale, Pa., 1934], p. 12). On the extensive school system of the English Franciscan order, see Little, *Grey Friars*, pp. 43, 64–66.

probably wrote his between 1269 and 1279. Clearly the borrowing could have occurred in either direction, and a definitive answer appears impossible. Even in the relatively short period of about ten years during which Pecham and Witelo both wrote their treatises, one can imagine any number of means by which the treatise of one might have been communicated to the other. However, two arguments make it appear more likely that Pecham borrowed from Witelo than vice versa. First, it has been argued that Witelo probably composed his *Perspectiva* in the early 1270's, in which event more time would have been available for his treatise to reach Pecham than for Pecham's treatise to reach him. Secondly, it is clear that Witelo wrote his *Perspectiva* in Viterbo, where he was located from early in 1269: not only does he relate that he decided to write a book on optics after observing a waterfall near Viterbo, but it was here also that William of Moerbeke made his translations of Greek mathematical works employed by Witelo in composing his book.[25] Now the Papal Curia was located in Viterbo during most of the 1270's, and it is certain that Witelo was known at court even if he was not officially associated with it. Early in 1277 Pecham arrived at the curia, then still in Viterbo, and he appears to have spent parts of the next two years both in Viterbo and in Rome.[26] It is possible that Witelo was still in Viterbo—we lose track of him in the 1270's—but if not, we can be certain that his *Perspectiva* was called to Pecham's attention; after all, Moerbeke, to whom it had been dedicated, remained with the court until 1278. Thus Pecham's professorship at the Papal University provides a perfectly simple mechanism for the transmission of Witelo's work to Pecham, and we must therefore regard this as the more probable event. Until further evidence appears, we are consequently justified in asserting that the most probable date for Pecham's composition of the *Perspectiva communis* is the period 1277–79.[27]

25. Witelo, *Optica*, bk. 10, sec. 67, p. 462.

26. On the peregrinations of the Papal court during this period, see Augustus Potthast, *Regesta Pontificum Romanorum inde ab anno post Christum natum MCXCVII ad annum MCCCIV*, vol. 2 (Berlin, 1875), pp. 1715–41.

27. Pecham's professorship does not provide an equally good mechanism for the transmission of Pecham's work to Witelo, since it is doubtful that Witelo could have begun his treatise after Pecham's arrival and yet have completed it by April 1278, when Moerbeke gave up the post of Papal Confessor. Furthermore, the quotation that Witelo and Pecham share in common is thoroughly integrated into Witelo's text and does not bear the marks of insertion into a partially completed manuscript.

The conclusion that I have reached is based on innumerable probabilities, and its precariousness must be stressed. It is possible that Witelo wrote his treatise early in the 1270's and that Pecham gained access to it in time to complete his own treatise before his arrival at the curia. On the other hand, it is possible that Witelo borrowed from Pecham: Pecham could have composed the *Perspectiva communis* early in the 1270's (or even in the 1260's), after which it could have been communicated to Witelo in time to permit completion of his treatise by 1278. It is even possible that Pecham and Witelo were both relying on some third source, not yet identified, and that neither knew of the other's treatise.

By modern criteria, a series of lectures on the science of optics appears alien to a theological curriculum, and it may be inquired why, in the thirteenth century, Franciscan friars or clerks at the Papal Curia should have required training in optics. Although the *Perspectiva communis* does not answer this question, it is likely that Pecham considered the science of optics to be valuable for its ability to elucidate theological and moral truths and to aid in Scriptural exegesis. His brother Franciscan, Roger Bacon, had justified the study of mathematics in general by arguing that, "since it has been shown that philosophy cannot be understood unless mathematics is understood, and everybody recognizes that theology cannot be understood unless philosophy is understood, the theologian must know mathematics."[28] Furthermore, Bacon argued, geometrical knowledge is essential to an understanding of the literal sense of the Scriptures (as in the description of Noah's ark or the temple), which in turn is essential to comprehension of the spiritual sense of the Scriptures.[29] Pecham makes similar remarks in the opening lines of his *Tractatus de sphera*, where he writes: "In the present *opusculum* I intend to explain the number, shape, and motion of the principal bodies of the world, and those things that follow therefrom, insofar as is necessary for an understanding of Holy Scripture."[30]

Geometrical optics, according to Bacon, is one of the most useful of all mathematical disciplines for the theologian, because of its remarkable ability to illustrate spiritual truths. In order to demonstrate his point, Bacon presents the following example:

Since the infusion of grace is very clearly illustrated through the multiplication of light, it is in every way expedient that through the corporeal multiplication of light there should be manifested to us the properties of grace in the good, and the rejection of it in the wicked. For in the perfectly good the infusion of grace is compared to light incident directly and perpendicularly, since they do not reflect from them grace nor do they refract it from the straight course which extends along the road of perfection in life. But the infusion of grace in imperfect, though good men is compared to refracted light.... But sinners, who are in mortal sin, reflect and repel from them the grace of God.... But as of bodies from which light is reflected, some are rough,,,,and others are polished,...so sinners living in mortal sin are of two kinds.[31]

28. *Opus maius*, pt. IV (ed. Bridges, vol. 1, p. 175).

29. *Ibid.*, pp. 210–11. Similar ideas were expressed by Bartholomew the Englishman, an earlier Franciscan; see Thomas Plassmann, O.F.M., "Bartholomaeus Anglicus," *Archivum Franciscanum Historicum*, vol. 12 (1919), pp. 98–99, 106–07.

30. The text has been printed in Thorndike, *Sacrobosco*, p. 445.

31. *The "Opus Majus" of Roger Bacon*, trans. R. B. Burke (Philadelphia, 1928), pt. IV, pp. 238–39. See also *Part of the "Opus tertium" of Roger Bacon*, ed. A. G. Little (Aberdeen, 1912), pp. 41–42, on the value of optical marvels in conversion of the infidel. An earlier representative of this genre of literature is Alexander Neckam's *De naturis rerum*.

Bacon continues on, unfolding the parallel between the propagation of light and the infusion of grace into mankind.

In thirteenth-century English and Franciscan circles, the science of optics drew additional justification from the work of Robert Grosseteste, who had been the first lecturer to the Franciscans at Oxford. Not only had Grosseteste dealt with optics in depth, but he had also called attention to the parallel between the radiation of visible light and divine illumination of the intellect; in addition he had argued that light is the first corporeal form in the universe, and by its diffusion from an original point it had generated the extended world. Thus, in order to comprehend the nature and operation of God's creation—an important obligation for any thirteenth-century theologian—the study of optics was a necessity.[32] Similar reasoning could be used to justify all kinds of scientific work.

With the rudimentary scientific knowledge of his audience in mind, Pecham composed an elementary handbook of optical knowledge. In the preface he expressed his purpose in writing the *Perspectiva communis:*

I shall compress into concise summaries the teachings of perspective, which [in existing treatises] are presented with great obscurity, combining natural and mathematical demonstrations according to the type of subject matter, sometimes inferring effects from causes and sometimes causes from effects, and adding some matters that do not belong to perspective, although deduced from its teachings.

It was not Pecham's primary purpose to offer new theories (though occasionally he did), but to present old theories in concise and easily comprehensible form.[33] The most prominent and by far the best work on optics circulating in the second half of the thirteenth century was Alhazen's *Perspectiva*; but this was long and abstruse, and if few scholars possessed the courage to tackle a work of such length, fewer still would have been capable of following the argument in detail. Consequently there was a pressing need for a presentation of Alhazen's principal conclusions without their elaborate demonstrations.

Pecham achieved this objective remarkably well. The *Perspectiva communis* is a compendium of Alhazen's optics; it succeeds in retaining the breadth of Alhazen's achievement and even a measure of its sophistication, while reducing the total quantity of material by 90 percent. Indeed, Pecham sometimes succeeded in shortening one of Alhazen's demonstrations to the advantage of the demonstration, and the *Perspectiva communis* is still the best introduction to Alhazen's *Perspectiva*. But Pecham drew together conclusions from a number of

32. On the importance of optics for Grosseteste, see Crombie, *Grosseteste*, pp. 104–16, 128–31.

33. The same concern for a simple introductory treatment of scientific ideas prompt-ed Pecham to write his astronomical work, *De sphera*, which he justified on the grounds that earlier presentations were difficult, too brief, and false; see Thorndike, *Sacrobosco*, pp. 24, 445.

other sources as well, reconciling them where possible, choosing between them where reconciliation was impossible, and arranging the material in an orderly fashion.

The format of the *Perspectiva communis* is superficially Euclidean, each proposition consisting of an enunciation and a demonstration. Often, however, the "demonstration" does not really demonstrate, but rather explains, exemplifies, or qualifies. Genuine attempts at demonstration are rarely deductive, but consist of an assembling of evidence or authorities.

Revised Version

Unique among the extant manuscripts of the *Perspectiva communis* is MS Digby 218 (referred to here as *D*), which purports to be a revised version of the *Perspectiva communis*. An examination of this manuscript yields the following significant data.

1. The manuscript begins, "A while ago at the request of associates I wrote certain unpolished mathematical essays, which, since I was occupied by other matters, I left uncorrected. These appeared in public against my intention. Consequently, I will endeavor to correct them slightly in order that they may be of benefit to young students."[34] Immediately following this introductory passage is the usual preface to the *Perspectiva communis*.

2. As one proceeds through *D*, the corrections mentioned in the opening statement become obvious. Most of them are in Part I of the *Perspectiva communis*, where six new propositions are inserted, one is deleted, three are moved to new positions (Propositions 14–16 in the other manuscripts become Propositions 29–31 in *D*), and substantive alterations appear in several others. The insertions and alterations are usually intended to clarify an otherwise obscure point or to furnish a missing idea, but occasionally (as in Proposition I.5{7},[35] dealing with pinhole images) the substance of an argument is altered. Part II of *D* includes a preface not found in the other manuscripts and a few other trivial alterations. Part III contains no variations from the other manuscripts that can positively be identified as comprising a revision.

3. A new scribal hand appears in the middle of Proposition II.50, at the top of the verso side of folio 19, the original hand having continued through the bottom of the recto side of the same folio. This is the seventh proposition from the end of Part II.

34. See "Text and Translation," Preface.

35. Braces {} indicate the revised numeration found in *D*; i.e., Proposition 1.5{7} is the fifth proposition of Part I in the unrevised version, but the seventh proposition of Part I in the revised version. No braces are employed within Parts II and III, since the numeration of propositions in these parts has not been altered by revision.

4. Marginal notes, now so faint as to be quite illegible, appear in the lower right-hand margin of folio 19r (the last folio written in the first scribal hand) and continue in the margins of the remaining folios. I am of the opinion that these notes are in a hand more or less contemporary with the two hands responsible for the text of the *Perspectiva communis*. If legible, these notes might explain the change of hand, but unfortunately they are almost completely faded and defy decipherment.

What should one make of these data? In the first place, there appear to be no grounds for refusing to accept the opening statement of *D* at face value and to treat this manuscript as a copy of Pecham's own revision of the *Perspectiva communis*.

Secondly, the significance of the change of scribal hand at the top of folio 19v must be determined. Because the unrevised text seems to resume along with the new hand, it appears that the new scribe was copying from a different, unrevised exemplar. The evidence for this conclusion is the absence of anything that can be identified as a revision after the change of hand. Indeed, strong confirmation is provided by an examination of the proposition numbers in cross-references between various propositions of the *Perspectiva communis*. Because of the insertion, deletion, and rearrangement of propositions in Part I of *D*, only Propositions I.1–I.4 and I.28 retain the same numbers in both the revised and unrevised versions. Therefore, within *D* numerical cross-references to propositions of Part I (other than the five just noted) should be keyed to the revised numeration; any section of *D* in which the reference numbers have not been so adjusted has evidently not been revised. For example, where the unrevised version makes reference to Proposition I.22, we should expect the revised version to cite this proposition by its revised number (i.e., Proposition I.20) or to make allowance for the revised numeration in some other way.

An examination of all such cross-references in the *Perspectiva communis* reveals the following data. Throughout Parts I and II, wherever the unrevised text cites propositions of Part I by number, *D* has (with two exceptions) allowed for the revised numeration of Part I by deleting proposition numbers. For example, in Proposition I.26{24} where the unrevised version reads "*quoniam ex 22 propositione patet*," *D* reads "*quoniam supra patet*"; this is the obvious indication that Proposition I.{24} has been revised. The two exceptions to this rule are Propositions I.83{88}, where *D* cites an earlier proposition by its unrevised number, and II.20, where *D* cites an earlier proposition by what is apparently intended to be its revised number, though off by one (not an uncommon error). This practice of omitting references to proposition numbers is followed in Part I of *D* even when the number of the proposition cited has not been altered by revision. With the single exception noted above, Part II of *D* avoids citing the propositions of Part I by number, but cites by number the propositions of Part II, where revision has not altered the numeration of the propositions. The last cross-reference in Part II to a proposition of Part I is in Proposition II.20. The next cross-reference to a proposition of Part I appears in Proposition III.1; it is by the unrevised number, and all cross-references thereafter are according to the unrevised numeration. Thus the change of hand in Proposition II.50 falls between the last proposition to allow for the revised numeration of Part I and the first proposition that fails to allow for this revised numeration. It is highly probable, then, that the change of hand in Proposition II.50 represents the end of transcription of the revised version in *D*.

Various hypotheses can be formulated to explain why transcription of the revised version ceased at this point of the treatise. It appears most likely that the first scribe, having stopped at the bottom of folio 19r, was unable to continue his work; by the time another scribe took up the task, the revised exemplar from which the manuscript was being copied had disappeared, and he was forced to complete the manuscript from an unrevised exemplar.[36] Alternatively, it is possible that Pecham did not complete his revision beyond this point, although the fact that the first hand ends precisely at the bottom right-hand corner of the page and in the middle of a sentence attests to the termination of the scribe's copying rather than of Pecham's revision.[37] Moreover, by Proposition II.50, Pecham's revisions had degenerated to little more than alteration of the proposition numbers in references to Part I; consequently, unless he had big plans for the revision of Part III, another few minutes of work would have brought the revised version to completion.

Finally, it must be noted that, although no other manuscript containing the same text as *D* has been discovered, *D* has not remained in complete isolation from other manuscripts of the *Perspectiva communis*, for traces of the revised version appear in several other places. For example, Propositions I.{80} and I.{87} of *D*—two of the six propositions added to Part I—are found also in *F* (MS Basel F.IV.30) as Propositions I.77 and I.84 (though misnumbered). These two propositions are the only *major* portions of the revised version found outside *D*, but there are many instances of a phrase or two of *D* appearing also in several manuscripts of the unrevised version. In most cases, it is impossible to

36. Bernhard Bischoff has expressed the opinion that both hands are fourteenth century, probably contemporary, and of English provenance. See p. 12, n. 1 above. From the fact that the first hand terminates at the bottom of the recto side of a folio and the second hand begins on the verso of that same folio, we can be certain that the scribe actually ceased working at this point and that no subsequent parts have been lost. If the first hand had terminated at the bottom of the verso side of a folio, we might have theorized that the latter portion of the manuscript was lost and replaced later by an unrevised substitute.

37. To suppose that Pecham's revision ceased at this point requires the added supposition that he stopped at the bottom of the page and that subsequent copies reproduced his text line-for-line; there is no other way to account for the fact that the revisions end at the bottom right-hand corner of the page in copy *D*—which, as its dating indicates, cannot be the original.

determine with certainty whether the phrase was introduced spuriously into manuscripts of the unrevised version and then borrowed by the copier of either *D* or an ancestor of *D*, whether the phrase in *D* is an authentic revision authored by Pecham and incorporated by some later editor into the text of the unrevised version, or whether it is a portion of both the unrevised and revised versions lost in certain copies of the former. A single example may serve to illustrate the problem. After the first sentence of the demonstration of Proposition I.12{14}, manuscripts *A*, *W*, *F*, and *D* include, but *V*, *B*, *H*, and *L* omit, the following statement: "Furthermore, all colored things are deprived of the customary beauty of their color during a solar eclipse." This statement is relevant to the subject matter of the proposition and consistent with what precedes and follows; yet it can be omitted without leaving a gap in the argument or in the syntax. I have treated this particular passage as a legitimate part of both the revised and unrevised versions, omitted by the tradition giving rise to *V*, *B*, *H*, and *L*; my decision is based on the difficulty of explaining in any other way the existence of the passage in so many manuscripts (some of which are not closely related to each other and not otherwise related to the revised version). So many similar instances appear throughout the text that it has been impossible to supply a discussion of each one. My normal procedure has been to treat extensive variations between *D* and the other manuscripts as legitimate revisions in *D* and variations of only a word or two as the normal errors of transmission, unless the nature of the variation has dictated otherwise. In general I have placed on *D* the burden of proof that its variations from the other manuscripts are authentic revisions. The reader can make his own decision in any particular case by examining the variant readings.

Pecham's Sources

Although his name does not appear in the *Perspectiva communis*, there can be no doubt that Alhazen (Ibn al-Haitham) was Pecham's chief source.[38] Indeed, it is evident that Pecham conceived his work as a compendium of Alhazen's longer and more abstruse *Perspectiva*. Pecham says as much himself when, after discussing the emission of visual rays, he writes, "Whether it goes beyond this, I do not determine, save only by following in the footsteps of the Author [i.e., Alhazen], as I have said before."[39] The only work Pecham cites with any frequency is Alhazen's *Perspectiva*, which he refers to by book and

38. Actually, Proposition I.15 of MS *F* cites Alhazen by name, but no other manuscript agrees with this reading. References to Alhazen by name in the printed editions of the *Perspectiva communis* (e.g. Proposition II.6 of the 1542 and subsequent editions) were inserted by later editors. On the sources used by Pecham in the preparation of his *Tractatus de anima*, see Melani's edition of this work, pp. xli–xlix.

39. Proposition I.46{49}.

chapter or simply as "the *Perspectiva*."[40] Repeatedly Pecham appeals to the authority of "the Author" or "the Physicist," the terms by which he identifies Alhazen;[41] and though occasionally disagreeing with Alhazen, Pecham generally accepts his authority without question. The content and approach of the *Perspectiva communis* are governed largely by the content and approach of Alhazen's *Perspectiva*, and occasionally Pecham quotes Alhazen nearly verbatim.[42] Pecham treats topics in roughly the same order as did Alhazen, often presenting merely Alhazen's conclusion without demonstration or with a much abbreviated demonstration. Pecham's theory of vision, anatomy and physiology of the eye, psychology of perception, and theory of image formation by reflection and refraction derive almost entirely from Alhazen.

Other influences are also apparent. Although Grosseteste's influence on Pecham, Bacon, and Witelo has occasionally been exaggerated,[43] it is clear that several important features of Pecham's thought were derived (ultimately if not immediately) from Grosseteste. Most notably, Pecham expresses his optical theories in terms of the concept of species, developed by Grosseteste from Neoplatonic sources earlier in the century, and admits, with Grosseteste and Bacon, that species issue from the observer's eye as well as from the observed object.[44] Pecham also seems to follow Grosseteste in stressing the importance of mathematical demonstrations in optics and in adopting the threefold division of optics according to the mode of propagation of species or rays.[45] In addition, one can point to parallel passages like the following, the first by Pecham and the second by Grosseteste, as evidence of borrowing:

40. *Perspectiva communis*, Propositions I.1{1}, I.{5}, I.15{30}; II [Preface]; Propositions II.20, II.33, II.50, II.51, II.52, II.53, II.54, II.56, and III.13. Alhazen's *Perspectiva* was printed once as *Opticae thesaurus Alhazeni Arabis libri septem, nunc primum editi a Federico Risnero* (Basel, 1572). However, the title *Opticae thesaurus* was assigned by Risner, and in the Middle Ages the work was known as *De aspectibus* or *Perspectiva*.

41. Propositions I.31{34}, I.43{46}, I.44 {47}, I.46{49}, II.20, II.56, III.2, and III.13. Melani, in his edition of Pecham's *Tractatus de anima* (pp. xxxviii, xliii), identifies Alliandus (to whom Pecham refers) with Alhazen; actually, Alliandus should be identified with Alkindi.

42. See *Perspectiva communis*, Proposition I.62{65}, and Alhazen, *Opt. thes.*, bk. 2, sec. 19, p. 36.

43. E.g., by Crombie, *Grosseteste*, pp. 135–67, 213–32.

44. On Grosseteste's concept of species and its influence on Bacon and Pecham, see David C. Lindberg, "Alhazen's Theory of Vision and Its Reception in the West," *Isis*, vol. 58 (1967), pp. 335–41.

45. On the application of mathematics to optics, see the preface to *Perspectiva communis*; cf. Crombie, *Grosseteste*, pp. 104–16. The threefold division of optics according to the mode of propagation was embodied by Pecham in his division of the *Perspectiva communis* into three books; cf. Grosseteste, *De iride*, in *Phil. Werke*, p. 73. It should be noted, however, that Alhazen and Bacon also discuss the triple mode of propagation; see Alhazen, *Opt. thes.*, bk. 4, sec. 1, p. 102; and *Un Fragment inédit de "L'Opus tertium" de Roger Bacon*, ed. Pierre Duhem (Quaracchi, 1909), p. 90.

...the absolute strength of shorter pyramids is greater [than that of longer pyramids]. Thus mountains are naturally warmer, although they may be cooled accidentally in accordance with their approach to the middle interstice [of the air].[46]

...mountainous places become warmer than valleys, because they receive shorter pyramids and rays. I say that this is so essentially, for accidentally one finds the domination of coldness in many mountainous places either due to the winds blowing higher up or because they reach to the middle interstice of the air.[47]

However, in most cases, including those described above, it is impossible to distinguish Grosseteste's influence from that of Bacon and others, and we are limited to the general claim that Grosseteste's work exercised a pervasive influence on European scientific (and especially optical) thought in the thirteenth century.[48]

Pecham's debt to Roger Bacon similarly eludes precise definition. All scientific writers in the latter half of the thirteenth century (and particularly all English Franciscans writing on optics) repeated a common fund of information, and it is quite impossible to determine precisely how much Pecham learned from Bacon and how much from their common scientific heritage. For example, Pecham would have found in Bacon's optical works precisely the theories contained in Alhazen's *Perspectiva*; therefore Bacon and Alhazen reinforced one another, and, except for an occasional point dealt with by one but not the other, there is no possibility of distinguishing their respective influences on Pecham. All one can say is that in format and manner of expression Pecham is closer to Alhazen and must have relied primarily on the latter in arranging the *Perspectiva communis*.

But by no means is this to be construed as a denial of Bacon's influence. As noted earlier, both Pecham and Bacon were residents of the Franciscan convent in Paris during the very years when Bacon was composing his scientific works, and it is inconceivable that Pecham did not become familiar with them and rely on them when composing his *Perspectiva communis*; as Bacon himself points out, his brothers in the Paris convent knew the content of his writings.[49] Because of the circumstances under which they were written, Bacon's works did not circulate widely during his lifetime, but Pecham might have gained access to them once again during his association with the curia (1277–79) since Bacon had sent several of his works to the Pope about 1267. Moreover, Pecham's familiarity

---

46. Proposition I.19{17}; cf. Proposition II.1.

47. *De natura locorum*, in *Phil. Werke*, p. 66. Translation by Bruce S. Eastwood, "The Geometrical Optics of Robert Grosseteste" (Ph.D. dissertation, University of Wisconsin, 1964), p. 133.

48. It can be demonstrated that Pecham was familiar with Grosseteste's theory of the rainbow (treated by Grosseteste in *De iride*), since he vigorously assails it in Proposition III.19 of the *Perspectiva communis*.

49. See quotation, p. 11, above.

with the content of Bacon's works is demonstrated by his attack on Bacon's theory of the rainbow.[50] More important and equally demonstrative is the fact that Pecham's reconciliation of Alhazen's theory of vision with Grosseteste's conception of species is of the same genre as Bacon's and was doubtless influenced by the *Opus maius* and *De multiplicatione specierum*.[51] Pecham also follows Bacon in his explanation of refraction and in innumerable minor respects.[52]

Yet one is occasionally forced to question how closely Pecham followed Bacon. In Proposition III.11 Pecham treats a case of image formation by refraction not discussed by Alhazen but found in Bacon's *Opus maius*.[53] However, in the proposition Pecham commits a blunder that he could surely have avoided by a careful reading of the corresponding passage in the *Opus maius*.[54] Was Pecham consciously disagreeing with Bacon, or had he not noticed Bacon's discussion? Although no doubt is cast on the fact of Pecham's reliance on Bacon, clearly legitimate doubt remains regarding its precise degree.

Pecham drew sparingly on a wide variety of other sources. He refers by name to Euclid (in connection with the *Elements*), Alkindi, Augustine, Aristotle, a certain Gregory, and Rabbi Moses (Maimonides).[55] In addition he cites a book on anatomy entitled *De elementis*, and Aristotle's *De celo et mundo*.[56] On several occasions Pecham refers to *De speculis*, and the arguments he attributes to it clearly identify it as the medieval Latin version of the *Catoptrica* of Pseudo-Euclid.[57] On one occasion Pecham refers to a work entitled *De visu*, to

---

50. See p. 14, above.

51. For an extensive discussion of this point, see my study, "Alhazen's Theory of Vision," pp. 330–41.

52. On the cause of refraction, see pp. 49–50, below. Cf. my "The Cause of Refraction in Medieval Optics," *British Journal for the History of Science*, vol. 4 (1968–69), pp. 23–38. Another fairly representative example of Pecham's reliance on Bacon is the discussion of the several images appearing in a broken mirror and the double image of the sun when the latter is viewed in a mirror submerged in water; Pecham's juxtaposition of these two topics in the same proposition is strikingly similar to Bacon's treatment of the same phenomena; see *Perspectiva communis*, Proposition II.24; and *Opus maius*, pt. V.iii, dist. 1, chap. 6, (ed. Bridges, vol. 2, pp. 144–46).

53. *Opus maius*, pt. V.iii, dist. 2, chap. 3 (ed. Bridges, vol. 2, p. 151).

54. See the Critical Notes to Part III, n. 23, pp. 267–68.

55. Euclid is cited in Propositions I.5{7}, I.17{15}, I.24{22}, I.39{42}, II.6, and II.23. Alkindi, Augustine, Aristotle, Gregory, and Maimonides are cited, respectively, in the following propositions: I.44{47}, *ibid.*, I.46{49}, I.{25}, and I.{6}; see the notes to these propositions for further discussion of the citations.

56. *De elementis* is cited in Proposition I.31{34}, *De celo* in Proposition III.9. On *De elementis*, see the notes to Proposition I.31{34}.

57. See Propositions II.33, II.50, and II.52. This *De speculis* (or *Catoptrica*) is the work edited by Heiberg from Greek manuscripts (*Euclidis opera omnia*, ed. J. L. Heiberg and H. Menge, vol. 7 [Leipzig, 1895], pp. 286–343) and translated into French from the Heiberg text by Ver Eecke (*Euclide, L'Optique et la Catoptrique*, trans. Paul Ver Eecke [Paris, 1959]). According to C. H.

which he attributes the statement that "no visible thing is seen completely at one time, but rather by the alteration [in time] of the pyramid."[58] This is doubtless a reference to the first proposition of Euclid's *Optica*, drawn from an abridgment of that work circulating in the thirteenth century and used by Bacon.[59] In addition, Pecham's description of a book entitled *De speculis comburentibus* fits Alhazen's work by that title.[60] Finally, as noted above, Pecham may have known and used Witelo's *Perspectiva*.

There were three other purely optical works circulating in the second half of the thirteenth century, any or all of which may have been known by Pecham. The first, Ptolemy's *Optica*, was translated from Arabic to Latin by Eugenius of Palermo in the twelfth century.[61] We know that Pecham's contemporary, Witelo, made use of the *Optica*, since he reproduces Ptolemy's table of refraction,[62] and Bacon also cites the *Optica* frequently. The second work is the *Catoptrica* of Hero of Alexandria, which was translated from Greek to Latin by William of Moerbeke in 1269, and which circulated as Ptolemy's *De speculis*.[63] Finally, the *De speculis comburentibus* of Diocles (second century B.C.) was translated from Arabic to Latin by Gerard of Cremona in the twelfth century and was known to the West as the *De speculis* of Tideus.[64] Besides these there were many medical and ophthalmological works that dealt with the anatomy and physiology of the eye and also with the theory of sight. Among these were Ḥunain ibn Isḥāq's *Ten Treatises on the Eye*,[65] Rhazes' *Liber ad Almansorem* and

Haskins (*Studies in the History of Mediaeval Science* [New York, 1960], p. 179), it was translated from Greek to Latin in the late twelfth or early thirteenth century. This work should not be confused with another Pseudo-Euclidean *De speculis* edited from Latin manuscripts by Björnbo (Björnbo and Vogl, "Drei optische Werke," pp. 97–119); cf. Sebastian Vogl, "Über die (Pseudo-)Euklidische Schrift 'De speculis,'" *Archiv für Geschichte der Naturwissenschaften und der Technik*, vol. 1 (1909), pp. 419–35.

58. Proposition I.38{41}.

59. As with the Pseudo-Euclidean *Catoptrica*, I have used only Ver Eecke's translation of the Heiberg text (references, p. 27, n. 57, above). Euclid's *Optica* has been translated into English by H. E. Burton, "The Optics of Euclid," *Journal of the Optical Society of America*, vol. 35 (1945), pp. 357–72. On Bacon's use of *De visu*, see *Opus maius*, ed. Bridges, vol. 2, p. 1, n. 2. A graduate student of mine, Wilfred Theisen, is now editing the medieval versions of Euclid's *De visu*.

60. See Proposition II.55, below; on *De speculis comburentibus*, see the Critical Notes to Part II, n. 133, p. 265.

61. *L'Optique de Claude Ptolémée, dans la version latine d'après l'arabe de l'émir Eugène de Sicile*, ed. A. Lejeune (Louvain, 1956). On the attribution of this to Ptolemy, see Lejeune's careful argument in the introduction to his edition, pp. 13–26. As Haskins, *Studies*, p. 171, points out, there is no evidence for the date of 1154 frequently assigned to Eugenius's translation. See also the Critical Notes to Part III, n. 25, p. 268.

62. See the Critical Notes to Part III, n.3, p. 266.

63. Hero of Alexandria, *Mechanica et Catoptrica*, ed. L. Nix and W. Schmidt, in *Heronis Alexandrini Opera quae supersunt omnia*, vol. 2, fasc. 1 (Leipzig, 1900), pp. 316–73.

64. Björnbo and Vogl, "Drei optische Werke," pp. 73–94, have edited and analyzed this work.

65. Ḥunain's book was translated into

Liber divisionum, Haly Abbas's *Liber regalis*, Canamusali's *De oculorum curationibus*, Avicenna's *Liber canonis* and *De anima*, Averroës' *Colliget*,[66] Benevenutus Grassus's *De oculis*, Magister Zacharias's *Tractatus de passionibus oculorum*, and Alcoatin's *Liber de oculis*.[67]

Influence

The *Perspectiva communis* was by far the most popular of all medieval treatises on optics, doubtless because of its broad scope and introductory character. One indication of its popularity is the large number of extant manuscript copies. Without going beyond standard bibliographical works, texts or monographs dealing with Pecham and his contemporaries, and easily available catalogues of manuscript collections, I have located sixty-two copies—one from the thirteenth century, twenty-nine from the fourteenth century, twenty-six from the fifteenth century, two from the sixteenth century, one from the seventeenth century, and three for which I have no date.[68] An exhaustive search of manuscript collections would doubtless turn up several more. Nonetheless, sixty-two manuscripts is an exceptionally large number of extant copies of a medieval work on optics, particularly in view of the fact that Pecham's treatise is largely geometrical and thus has no appreciable philosophical, theological, or medical content. No other medieval optical work is extant in nearly as many copies, and we are forced to conclude that the *Perspectiva communis* became the standard elementary optical textbook of the late Middle Ages.[69]

The *Perspectiva communis* retained its popularity long after the advent of printed books. It was printed first about 1482 or 1483, nine times in the sixteenth

---

Latin by Constantinus Africanus. It is available in an English translation from the Arabic in Max Meyerhof, *The Book of the Ten Treatises of the Eye, ascribed to Hunain ibn Ishâq (809–877 A.D.)* (Cairo, 1928).

66. It is not certain precisely when the *Colliget* was translated into Latin—probably in the 1250's or 1290's. The most recent discussion of this problem is in Michael McVaugh, "Arnald of Villanova and Bradwardine's Law," *Isis*, vol. 58 (1967), p. 62.

67. The best sources on the history of medieval ophthalmology are Julius Hirschberg, *Geschichte der Augenheilkunde*, in *Graefe-Saemisch Handbuch der gesamten Augenheilkunde*, ed. Theodor Saemisch, vol. 13 (Leipzig, 1908); and P. Pansier, *Collectio ophtalmologica veterum auctorum*, (7 fascs.; Paris, 1903–33). Pansier includes editions of

a number of Latin ophthalmological texts.

68. See "Manuscripts, Their Sigla, and Printed Editions," below, for a complete list of manuscripts and editions. For the sake of counting, I have (with the exception of Florence, plut. XVII sin. 8) numbered manuscripts dated to either of two centuries among the manuscripts of the earlier century. I do not mean to imply that mine has been a casual or careless search, but only that I have not examined the inaccessible catalogues of several important and many minor manuscript collections.

69. In comparison, I have located nineteen manuscripts of Alhazen's *Perspectiva* and eighteen of Witelo's *Perspectiva*. There is also an abundance of independent evidence of the use of the *Perspectiva communis* in medieval schools; see pp. 30–31, below.

century (including a translation into Italian), and for the eleventh time in 1627.[70] By contrast, Witelo's *Perspectiva* was printed three times in the sixteenth century, Alhazen's only in 1572, and Bacon's not until 1614.[71]

Lectures on the *Perspectiva communis* were included in the curriculum of many universities during the fourteenth through sixteenth centuries. By the 1390's, and continuing at least to the middle of the fifteenth century, the *Perspectiva communis* was the basis of regular lectures at the University of Vienna.[72] In 1390 for the M.A. degree the University of Prague required a student to attend lectures on the *Perspectiva communis*, and Douie claims that it was used as a textbook at Paris as well.[73] The statutes of the University of Leipzig in the fifteenth century repeatedly refer to "*perspectiva communis*," based on Pecham's book, as a topic for lectures; and the editor of the Leipzig (1504) printed edition, Andreas Alexander, explains that he has been appointed by the faculty of arts at Leipzig to lecture on perspective and hence has prepared the book for the use of students.[74] In his *Cursus quatuor mathematicarum artium liberalium* (Alcalá, 1516, 1523, 1526, and 1528), used at the Universities of Paris, Alcalá, and Salamanca, Pedro Cirvelo paraphrases the *Perspectiva communis* in its entirety.[75] Sędziwój

70. Only the first five of these are faithful to the manuscript tradition; see "Manuscripts, Their Sigla, and Printed Editions," below, where the printed editions are listed and discussed. In these eleven editions, I am not including the four editions of Cirvelo's paraphrase, in which large portions of the *Perspectiva communis* are quoted verbatim.

71. Part V of Bacon's *Opus maius* circulated separately as the *Perspectiva*.

72. The Acts of the Faculty of Arts of the University of Vienna reveal that "*perspectiva*" was the subject of lectures annually from 1392 to 1399 (omitting only 1393); and for the years 1395, 1397, and 1399 it is specified that the lectures were on "*perspectiva communis*." The lecturers during those three years were, respectively, Nicholas of Dinkelsbühl, Nicholas Maczen, and Hermann Wallsee. "*Perspectiva communis*" is again mentioned in the Acts of the Faculty of Arts for 1449, requiring at that time twenty-four lectures. See Joseph Aschbach, *Geschichte der Wiener Universität im ersten Jahrhunderte ihres Bestehens* (Vienna, 1865), pp. 92, 143–68, 352; on Nicholas of Dinkelsbühl, see Madre, *Nikolaus von Dinkelsbühl*, p. 10.

73. Rashdall, *Universities*, vol. 1, p. 449,

n. 3; Douie, *Archbishop Pecham*, p. 12. A copy of the *Perspectiva communis* was among the volumes chained in the Great Library of the Sorbonne early in the fourteenth century; see Leopold Delisle, *Le Cabinet des manuscrits de la Bibliothèque Nationale*, vol. 3 (Paris, 1881), p. 90.

74. Helssig, *Die wissenschaftlichen Vorbedingungen*, pp. 17, 21, 37, 46, 56; *Reg. epist.*, vol. 3, p. lx.

75. The third of the four courses is entitled *Breve compendium Perspective communis Ioannis archiepiscopi Cantuariensis de radiis visualibus ac variis modis videndi, ex libris Halacen* [sic], *Alchindi, et aliorum compilatum*. Actually it is as long as Pecham's original. My source on the use of this work at Paris, Alcalá, and Salamanca is William A. Wallace, O.P., "The 'Calculatores' in Early Sixteenth-Century Physics," paper presented before the History of Science Society, Toronto, January 28, 1967. In 1610 the library at Salamanca possessed a printed version of the *Perspectiva communis*; see Guy Beaujouan, *Manuscrits scientifiques médiévaux de l'Université de Salamanque* (Bordeaux, 1962), p. 10.

von Czechel, who lectured on the *Perspectiva communis* at Cracow early in the fifteenth century, points out, in a passage quoted above, that the *Perspectiva communis* was so named because of its common use in the schools; and in 1489 Albert Brudzewski, one of Cracow's most distinguished astronomers, was still lecturing on the *Perspectiva communis*.[76] Finally, at the University of Würzburg, the *Perspectiva communis* was the basis of lectures as late as 1594–95.[77]

But the *Perspectiva communis* served as more than an elementary textbook or source for university lectures. It was the basis, in the late fourteenth century, for several long technical commentaries—the *Questiones super perspectivam* of Henry of Langenstein (d. 1397) and a similar work by Blasius of Parma (written about 1390).[78] Moreover, the *Perspectiva communis* was often cited by authors of other optical or philosophical treatises, such as Duns Scotus (d. 1308) in his *Questiones subtilissime super libros metaphysicorum Aristotelis*, Conrad de Halberstadt (fourteenth century) in his *Liber similitudinum naturalium*, Dominicus de Clivaxo (fl. 1350) in his *Questiones super perspectivam*, Lopez de Corella in his *Secretos de filosophia y medicina* (1539), Francesco Maurolyco (d. 1575) in his *Photismi de lumine et umbra*, Friedrich Risner in his *Opticae libri quatuor* (Kassel, 1606), Giambattista della Porta in his *De refractione* (Naples, 1593), Fabricius of Aquapendente in his *De oculo* (Venice, 1614), Johannes Kepler in his *Ad Vitellionem paralipomena* (Frankfurt, 1604), Ambrosius Rhodius in his *Optica* (Wittenberg, 1611), Willebrord Snell in his marginal annotations to Risner's *Optica*, and G. B. Riccioli in his *Almagestum novum* (Bologna, 1651).[79]

---

76. See pp. 13–14, above. On the use of the *Perspectiva communis* at Cracow, see also Stefan Swieżawski, "La Philosophie à l'Université de Cracovie des origines au XVIᵉ siècle," *Archives d'histoire doctrinale et littéraire du Moyen Age*, vol. 30 (1963), p. 97. On Albert Brudzewski's lectures, see Albertus de Brudzewo, *Commentariolum super theoricas novas planetarum Georgii Purbachii*, ed. L. A. Birkenmajer (Cracow, 1900), p. xxx; Brudzewski also cites the *Perspectiva communis* in his *Commentariolum*, p. 131.

77. Erlangen, Universitätsbibliothek, MS 845, is a student notebook containing the lectures on the *Perspectiva communis* given at Würzburg by Jacob Nivellio.

78. Franco Alessio, "Questioni inedite di ottica di Biagio Pelacani da Parma," *Rivista critica di storia della filosofia*, vol. 16 (1961), pp. 79–110, 188–221; Graziella Federici Vescovini, "Le questioni di 'Perspectiva' di Biagio Pelacani da Parma," *Rinascimento*,

Ser. 2, vol. 1 (1961), pp. 163–243; Lynn Thorndike, *A History of Magic and Experimental Science*, vol. 3 (New York, 1934), pp. 509–10; Graziella Federici Vescovini, *Studi sulla prospettiva medievale* (Turin, 1965), pp. 165–93, 239–67. Henry of Langenstein's *Questiones super perspectivam* was published in Valencia in 1503; I am now preparing a new edition of this treatise.

79. On Scotus, see p. 13, above. On the other authors, see Brian Lawn, *The Salernitan Questions* (Oxford, 1963), pp. 107, 136; Graziella Federici Vescovini, "Les questions de 'perspective' de Dominicus de Clivaxo," *Centaurus*, vol. 10 (1964), pp. 14–28; *The Photismi de lumine of Maurolycus: A Chapter in Late Medieval Optics*, trans. Henry Crew (New York, 1940), pp. 110, 115, 124, 130; Risner, *Optica*, p. 51; Porta, *De refractione optices parte libri novem*, pp. 33, 63; Fabricius, *Tractatus anatomicus triplex quorum primus de oculo...*, *passim*; Johannes Kepler,

Finally, it is evident that Pecham's reputation extended to the artists and engineers, for when Antonio Pollaiuolo decorated the tomb of Pope Sixtus IV (d. 1484) with the Liberal Arts, he characterized *Perspectiva*, the eighth Liberal Art, with phrases drawn from the *Perspectiva communis*.[80] Moreover, Leonardo da Vinci opened his own treatise on light with a quotation from the preface to the *Perspectiva communis*, and Cosimo Bartoli cited Pecham in his *Del modo di misurare le distantie...* (Venice, 1614).[81] This array of evidence illustrates the immense popularity of the *Perspectiva communis* during the later Middle Ages and the Renaissance. It was undoubtedly the most widely used elementary text in optics from the early fourteenth century until the close of the sixteenth century, and as such it is one of the best indices of what was known to the scientific community in general on the subject of optics.

Gesammelte Werke, vol. 2 (München, 1939), pp. 47–48; Rhodius, *Optica*, p. 72; *Risneri Optica cum annotationibus Willebrordi Snelii*, ed. J. A. Vollgraff (Gandavi, 1918), *passim*; and Riccioli, *Almagestum novum*, vol. 1, pt. 2, pp. 643 ff.

80. L. D. Ettlinger, "Pollaiuolo's Tomb of Sixtus IV," *Journal of the Warburg and Courtauld Institutes*, vol. 16 (1953), pp. 258–59.

81. Da Vinci's quotation is reproduced by André Chastel, *Art et humanisme à Florence au temps de Laurent le Magnifique* (Paris, 1959), p. 417. Bartoli, *Del modo di misurare le distantie, le superficie, i corpi, le piante, le provincie, le prospettive, e tutte le altre cose terrene* (Venice, 1614), pp. 4, 30; the first edition of this work was published in 1564. Gezienus Ten Doesschate, *De Derde Commentaar van Lorenzo Ghiberti in Verband met de Middeleeuwsche Optiek* (Utrecht, n.d.), pp. 6–8, demonstrates that Pecham's book was used also by Lorenzo Ghiberti (1378–1455).

Scope and Principal Ideas
of the *Perspectiva communis*

The scope of the *Perspectiva communis* is revealed by the following outline of its contents:

Part I. Vision proper or vision by direct rays

Propositions 1–28 {1–31}: The properties of light and color and their propagation

Propositions 29–46 {32–49}: Anatomy and physiology of the eye and the act of visual perception

Propositions 47–54 {50–57}: Physical requirements for vision

Propositions 55–78 {58–82}: Psychology of vision

Propositions 79–84 {83–89}: Errors of direct vision

Part II. Vision by reflected rays

Propositions 1–18: The properties and law of reflection

Propositions 19–27: Image formation by reflection

Propositions 28–54: Perceptual errors occurring in vision by reflected rays

Proposition 55: Burning mirrors

Proposition 56: The twinkling of stars

Part III. Vision by refracted rays

Propositions 1–3: The propagation of rays through transparent media

Propositions 4–13: Image formation and the perceptual errors occurring in vision by refracted rays

Propositions 14–15: Refraction of rays within the eye

Propositions 16–17: The burning glass and the kindling properties of rays

Propositions 18–22: The rainbow and the Milky Way

Since the *Perspectiva communis* surveys virtually the entire field of optics, it may appear that the title *Perspectiva* (or at least the English cognate *Perspective*) is inappropriate to the contents; for the book deals not only with perspective, but with all medieval questions that could be classified as optical. In fact, however, the title provides a great deal of insight into the character of Pecham's treatise—and, indeed, of medieval optics in general. Pecham's principal objective was to describe how objects appear *to an observer*, whether by direct, reflected, or refracted rays. He explains how a person sees, how he judges size and shape,

33

how errors of vision arise, and where objects seen by reflected or refracted rays appear to be situated. Thus, while Pecham deals with the full range of optical problems, his frame of reference is that of perspective—the appearance of things to an observer. The essential characteristic of medieval optics, distinguishing it from modern optics, is that there is no optical problem without an observer. Medieval optics is a theory of vision.

Theory of Vision

Pecham's theory of vision begins, as Alhazen's had, with an account of the impression made on the eye by light and by color.[1] An observer who looks into a bright light experiences pain, and if he shifts his gaze to a dark place, he will at first find himself incapable of perceiving objects there because of the brightness lingering in his eye. Again, an observer who transfers his gaze from an intensely lighted, bright-colored object to a colored object illuminated by a weaker light will find the two colors intermixed, evidently because the first color does not depart immediately from his eye. From these data Pecham draws the conclusion that "traces of the aforeseen have been left behind in the eye," and consequently the rays must "originate not from the eye but from the luminous body."[2] Thus Pecham contends against the theory of emitted rays; sight results not from visual rays issuing from the eye, but from luminous rays entering the eye.

Pecham resumes his attack on the theory of visual rays toward the middle of Part I, arguing that the emission of visual rays is neither necessary nor sufficient as an explanation of sight:

By assuming that sight occurs through rays issuing from the eye, mathematicians exert themselves unnecessarily. For the manner in which vision occurs is adequately described above [in terms of the intromission of luminous rays], by which [description] all the phenomena of vision can be saved. Therefore it is superfluous to posit such rays.[3]

Rays issuing from the eye and falling on a visible object cannot suffice for vision. If it should be supposed that rays issue from the eye and fall on the visible object as if to seize it, either they return to the eye or they do not. If they do not return, vision is not achieved through them . . . . If they do return, how do they do so? Are they animated? Are all visible objects mirrors... ? Furthermore, if the rays return to the eye with the form of the visible object, they go out in vain, since light itself (or the form of the visible object through the power of light) diffuses itself throughout the whole medium. Therefore the visible object need not be sought out by rays as by messengers.[4]

1. On Alhazen's theory of vision, see my "Alhazen's Theory of Vision," pp. 322–29; Leopold Schnaase, *Die Optik Alhazens* (Stargard, 1889); H. J. J. Winter, "The Optical Researches of Ibn al-Haitham," *Centaurus*, vol. 3 (1954), pp. 190–210; and Vasco Ronchi, *Histoire de la lumière*, trans. J. Taton (Paris, 1956), pp. 33–45.

2. Propositions I.1{1} and I.2{2}.

3. Proposition I.44{47}.

4. Proposition I.45{48}; cf. Proposition I.48{51}.

The argument is brilliant and powerful—though, to assign due credit, borrowed from Alhazen[5]—and appears to have totally discredited the theory of visual rays. But in the very next proposition Pecham makes the shocking statement, very definitely not borrowed from Alhazen and seemingly contradicting all that has gone before, that in fact the eye does have a natural light, which "contributes to vision by its radiance."[6] "For as Aristotle says," Pecham continues, "the eye not merely is the recipient of action but acts itself, just as shining bodies do. Therefore the eye must have a natural light to alter visible species and make them commensurate with the visual power."[7] The evidence Pecham gives for this, besides the authority of Aristotle, is the ability of certain animals to see at night, an ability which could not exist if the eye did not have its own natural light.[8]

A closer examination of Pecham's view reveals that in fact there is no contradiction. The argument of Propositions I.44{47} and I.45{48} is not that visual rays are nonexistent, but that visual rays are neither necessary nor sufficient for explaining sight. In Proposition I.46{49} Pecham simply adds what he sees as a complementary truth, namely, that visual rays, which are neither required for sight nor capable of producing sight by themselves, nevertheless play a contributory role; and that role is to moderate excessively bright lights so that they do not overwhelm the power of sight.[9] In adopting this view, Pecham yields to the authority of Aristotle, Alkindi, and Grosseteste on the existence of visual rays without seriously violating the teachings of Alhazen.[10] As Pecham is careful to point out, "there is some kind of emission of rays, but not of the Platonic type such that rays emitted by the eye are, as it were, immersed in the visible form and then returned to the eye as messengers";[11] visual rays exist, but they perform none of the functions denied to them by Alhazen or by Pecham's own earlier argument.[12] We may feel that Pecham has conceded too much to the visual ray theory, but he is innocent of self-contradiction.

Pecham's concessions to the visual ray theory were closely associated with the doctrine of species.[13] This doctrine, which had been developed by Robert

5. *Opt. thes.*, bk. 1, sec. 23, p. 14; see also my "Alhazen's Theory of Vision," pp. 324–25.

6. Proposition I.46{49}.

7. *Ibid.* The exact reference to Aristotle is *De generatione animalium* 5. 1. 780ª5–15.

8. This argument is based on the premise, explicitly stated by Pecham, that "vision is of the same kind in all animals" (Proposition I.46{49}).

9. Roger Bacon stresses, instead, that the visual rays are necessary to ennoble the species coming from the visible object; see *Opus maius*, pt. V.i, dist. 7, chap. 4 (ed.

Bridges, vol. 2, p. 52).

10. On Aristotle, see *De generatione animalium* 5. 1. 780ª5–15, 780ᵇ34–781ª14. Grosseteste's view appears most clearly in his *De iride*, in *Phil. Werke*, pp. 72–73; cf. Crombie, *Grosseteste*, pp. 117–18. Alkindi's view is expressed in his *De aspectibus* 7, in Björnbo and Vogl, p. 9.

11. Proposition I.46{49}.

12. Roger Bacon makes precisely this point in the *Opus maius*, pt. V.i, dist. 7, chap. 3 (ed. Bridges, vol. 2, pp. 50–51).

13. On species, see my "Alhazen's Theory of Vision," pp. 335–41; Crombie, *Grosseteste*,

Grosseteste from the Neoplatonic concept of emanation, maintained that every natural agent propagates its power from itself to surrounding bodies. Such powers, called "species," are responsible for all efficient causality in the universe. Grosseteste's view was fully assimilated by Roger Bacon and John Pecham and applied to optical problems, for light was but a special case of species—visible species. According to Pecham,

Every natural body, visible or invisible, diffuses its power radiantly into other bodies. The proof of this is by a natural cause, for a natural body acts outside itself through the multiplication of its form. Therefore the nobler it is, the more strongly it acts. And since action in a straight line is easier and stronger for nature, every natural body, whether visible or not, must multiply its species in a continuous straight line; and this is to radiate.[14]

Now it is of crucial importance to note that by the doctrine of species *every natural body*—the eye as well as the visible object—multiplies its species. And from recognition of this fact it was but a short step to assigning some role in sight to the species proceeding from the eye; not only was it plausible that the eye's species should serve some visual function, but ancient authorities had advocated various theories of visual rays that defined the function. For Pecham, the chief restriction on this function was that it must not conflict with Alhazen's rejection of visual rays as the agents of sight;[15] accordingly, Pecham assigned to the eye's own species the relatively minor task of altering or moderating the species of the visible object and making them "commensurate with the visual power."[16] In Pecham's view, as in Alhazen's, luminous rays (i.e., the species of the visible object) remain the principal agents of sight, and visual rays receive almost no further attention in the *Perspectiva communis*.[17]

An intromission theory of sight, such as that advocated by Pecham, necessarily raises anatomical and physiological questions. If sight is something that occurs inside the eye, one would like to know in exact detail what takes place there. Thus questions which were irrelevant or impossible under the emission theory come to the forefront: What is the structure of the eye? What is the

---

pp. 109–10, 144–47; John Henry Bridges, *The Life and Work of Roger Bacon: An Introduction to the Opus Majus* (London, 1914), pp. 94–101; and Sebastian Vogl, "Roger Bacons Lehre von der sinnlichen Spezies und vom Sehvorgange," in *Roger Bacon Essays*, ed. A. G. Little (Oxford, 1914), pp. 205–22.

14. Proposition I.{27}; see also Proposition II.5. On the exact relationship between species and rays, see Proposition I.27{26}.

15. It is true that Alhazen denied the very existence of visual rays, but all he successfully demonstrated is that, if visual rays exist, they are not the agents of vision. See my study, "Alhazen's Theory of Vision," pp. 324–27; Alhazen, *Opt. thes.*, bk. 1, secs. 23–24, pp. 14–15.

16. See p. 35, n. 7, above.

17. Visual rays appear again in Proposition I.48{51}. Alhazen does not speak of "species," but his "forms" are nearly indistinguishable from the Western concept of species except in direction of emanation; see my "Alhazen's Theory of Vision," pp. 332–41.

course of species through it? Which is the sensitive organ of the eye? Of what does the act of vision consist?

Pecham answers the first of these questions with a traditional, but nevertheless quite accurate, description of four tunics (the consolidativa, cornea, uvea, and aranea) and three humors (the albugineous humor, glacial humor, and vitreous humor);[18] his descriptions correspond closely to modern descriptions of the sclera, cornea, uvea, retina, aqueous humor, crystalline lens, and vitreous humor, respectively. Pecham follows Galen, Alhazen, and Bacon in declaring that the sensitive organ is the glacial humor (i.e., crystalline lens). He defends this choice with a concise little argument, which is valid in form but based on a false premise: "The power of sight resides in the glacial humor. Experience teaches this, for if any tunic or humor whatever, save the glacial humor, should be injured, it receives care through medicine and is healed, and sight is restored. However, when the glacial humor itself has been damaged, sight is destroyed irrevocably."[19] Moreover, Pecham contends, the glacial humor is suited to its function as chief organ of sight because it is delicate and sensitive, and "the influence of species can be perceived only by a most subtle body."[20] But precisely how the glacial humor perceives species, Pecham does not say. The function of the other tunics and humors is to enclose, darken, moisten, and protect the glacial humor.

Vision occurs, according to Pecham, as species or rays from the object of sight are received by the sensitive organ the glacial humor. But since rays emanate in all directions from every point on the visible object, every part of the glacial humor receives rays from every point on the object. How, then, is it possible to distinguish different parts of the object from one another? How can an observer, by visual means, gain knowledge of the true spatial relationships of points on an object or objects in the visual field? Pecham poses this problem when he writes, "for if the species of two parts of the visible object were received in the same part of the glacial humor, the parts of the object would not be perceived distinctly by reason of the confusion of forms acting on the same part of the eye."[21]

Following Alhazen in every detail, Pecham solves the problem by recognizing, first, that from every point on the object only one ray falls perpendicularly on the convex spherical surface of the eye and passes into the eye (and eventually into the glacial humor) without refraction,[22] and, second, that unrefracted rays

18. Proposition I.31{34}.

19. Proposition I.36{39}. For a discussion of this argument, see the Critical Notes to Part I, n. 100, p. 250. On Witelo's use of similar wording, see pp. 15–16, above.

20. Proposition I.31{34}.

21. Proposition I.37{40}.

22. All transparent interfaces encountered by the rays, up to and including the front surface of the glacial humor, are considered to be concentric; consequently a ray that is perpendicular to one is perpendicular to all. Pecham refers to the center of curvature of all these surfaces as the "center of the eye."

are stronger than refracted rays.[23] Now since unrefracted rays are stronger, they are obviously the primary agents of vision, and all other rays can be ignored. The problem of vision is thus reduced to the perpendicular and unrefracted rays, one from each point on the object, extending between the object and the center of the observer's eye. These rays constitute a radiant or luminous pyramid, with apex in the observer's eye and base on the visible object. Since the rays of the radiant pyramid (i.e., the perpendicular, unrefracted rays) maintain a fixed order between their origin on the object and their point of convergence at the center of the eye, they do not mingle in the glacial humor (which is anterior to the center of the eye), and there is no possibility of confused vision. Vision, then,

takes place by the arrangement of the species on [the surface of] the glacial humor exactly as [the parts] of the object [are arranged] outside. The possibility of this is obvious, notwithstanding the smallness of the glacial humor, because there are as many parts in the smallest of magnitudes as in the greatest. Species, however, are received without matter. Therefore, regardless of the size of the visible object, its species can be received distinctly and in [proper] order on [the surface of] the glacial humor. Unless this were so, the eye would not see the object distinctly.[24]

Thus a one-to-one correspondence is established between points on the visible object and points on the surface of the glacial humor. The realization of this condition (i.e., the reception by the glacial humor of rays ordered as the points on the object from which they issued) constitutes the act of vision.

Vision is not completed in the glacial humor, however. Rays of the visual pyramid penetrate the various humors and tunics of the eye and reach the glacial humor without refraction. But then, in Pecham's view, before actually converging to a vertex at the center of the eye, they encounter the interface between the glacial humor and the vitreous humor, which is eccentric to all anterior tunics and humors. Here all rays except the axis of the pyramid (i.e., the central ray, which entered the eye through the very center of the cornea and pupil) are refracted away from the center of the eye and hence do not actually converge. This refraction prevents inversion of the visual impression, which would occur if the rays were to intersect and continue onward in inverted order. Once inside the vitreous humor, the rays are no longer bound by the law of transparency (i.e., rectilinear propagation, reflection, and refraction) but pass from this humor into the optic nerve and thence along its tortuous course to the common nerve, where the species from the two eyes are united. The species continue until they reach the "place of interior judgment" in the anterior part of the brain, where the process of vision is "completed."[25]

23. This is a venerable optical principle, stated by Pecham in Proposition I.15{30}; see pp. 49–50, below.

24. Proposition I.37{40}.

25. The argument on the completion of vision is contained in Propositions I.33{36}

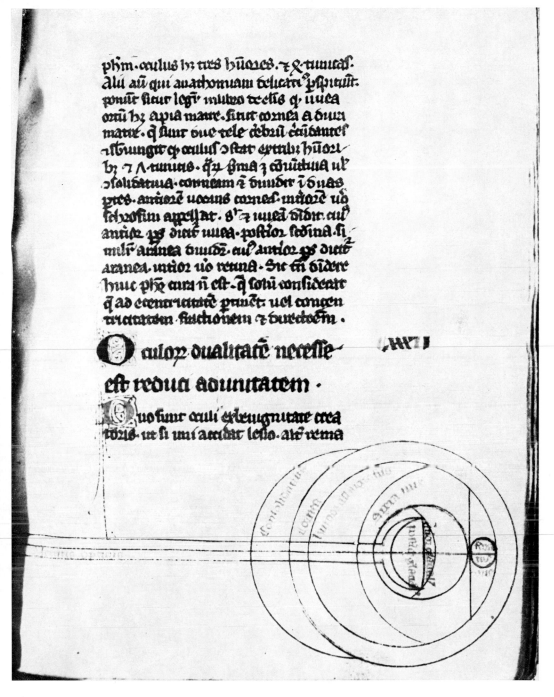

Plate 1. A page from Book I of the *Perspectiva communis*, containing a drawing of the eye. Vatican, MS Vat. lat. 5963, fol. 16r (late 13th or early 14th century).

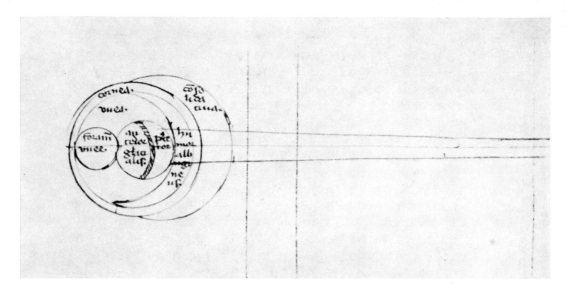

Plate 2a. A drawing of the eye; from Wolfenbüttel, Herzog August Bibliothek, Cod. Guelf. 38.6 Aug. 2°, fol. 212r (early 14th century).

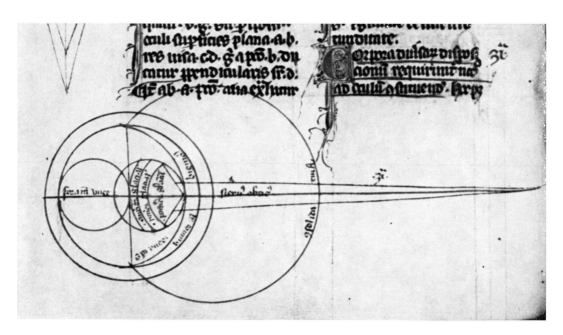

Plate 2b. Part of a page of the *Perspectiva communis* showing a drawing of the eye. Oxford, Bodleian Library, MS Ashmolean 1522, fol. 153v (early 14th century).

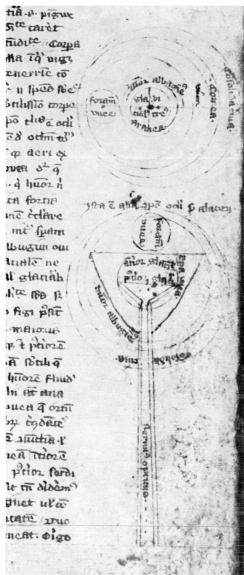

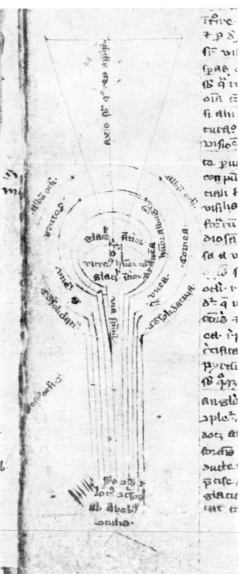

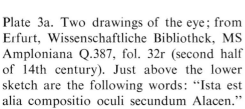

Plate 3a. Two drawings of the eye; from Erfurt, Wissenschaftliche Bibliothek, MS Amploniana Q.387, fol. 32r (second half of 14th century). Just above the lower sketch are the following words: "Ista est alia compositio oculi secundum Alacen."

Plate 3b. Another drawing of the eye from Erfurt, Ampl. Q.387, fol. 32v. This drawing is meant to represent Pecham's own conception of the eye, in contrast to that of Alhazen (see Plate 3a).

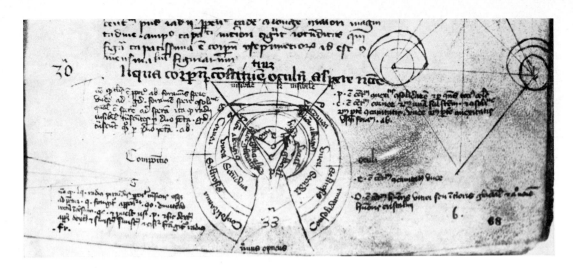

Plate 4a. Part of a page of the *Perspectiva communis*, containing a drawing of the eye. Vatican, MS Vat. lat. 3102, fol. 66r (14th century).

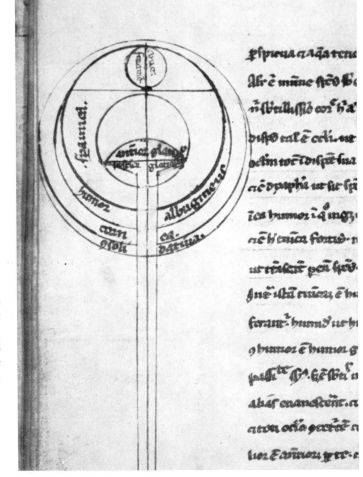

Plate 4b. A drawing of the eye from the *Perspectiva communis*, London, British Museum, MS Add. 17,368, fol. 56v (15th century).

Thus, the process of vision is accomplished through the arrangement of species or rays on the glacial humor; but visual perception requires a final element of verification, which Pecham labels "certification." That is, when the eye views the object as a whole, only the point seen by the central axis of the visual pyramid (which alone passes through the entire eye without refraction) is seen with perfect clarity; hence, if the entire object is to be perceived with maximum clarity—if perception is to be "certified"—the eye must be shifted so that each point of the object is perceived through the central ray.[26]

Nature and Propagation of Light

Pecham's views on the nature of light have been touched upon in connection with the doctrine of visible species: every natural body multiplies its species or form outside itself in all directions, producing visual effects.[27] But for the most part Pecham shows scant interest in the ontology of light and says little about its propagation or multiplication; he wrote nothing remotely comparable to Bacon's *De multiplicatione specierum*. However, we catch a brief glimpse of his views in Proposition II.1, where he explains reflection in terms of the self-diffusive property of species: "...rays of light and color are so constituted as to proceed through a transparent body, and the power of radiating and the onward flow of rays are not brought to an end by the opposition of a dense body of negligible transparency. Since the rays cannot continue in a straight line...the impulse to diffuse produces reflection."[28] Pecham's expression, "the impulse to diffuse"—indeed, his terminology in general—suggests that he would probably accept Bacon's more explicit description of the multiplication of species:

But a species is not body, nor is it moved as a whole from one place to another; but that which is produced [by an object] in the first part of the air is not separated from that part, since form cannot be separated from the matter in which it is unless it should be soul; rather, it produces a likeness to itself in the second part of the air, and so on. Therefore there is no change of place, but a generation multiplied through the different parts of the medium.[29]

Thus species are not corpuscular; they are not pieces of the visible object projected through space. Rather, forms or species are diffused throughout the surrounding media by a process of self-reproduction; and, as Bacon puts it, there

---

and I.40{43}. On the path of species in the optic nerve and the "place of interior judgment," see Proposition I.{7}. An excellent analysis of the whole question of the internal senses is contained in Harry A. Wolfson, "The Internal Senses in Latin, Arabic, and Hebrew Philosophic Texts," *Harvard Theological Review*, vol. 28 (1935), pp. 69–133.

26. On certification, see Propositions I.34{37} and I.38{41}.

27. See pp. 35–36, above.

28. Proposition II.1; cf. Proposition I.{27}.

29. *Opus maius*, pt. V.i, dist. 9, chap. 4 (ed. Bridges, vol. 2, pp. 71–72).

is no "flow from the luminous body, but...a drawing forth out of the potentiality of the matter of the air."[30]

The normal course of species is rectilinear because "action in a straight line is easier and stronger for nature."[31] However, species are reflected when they encounter an opaque surface and refracted when they are obliquely incident on a transparent interface between media of different densities. The fact that species behave according to easily definable geometrical rules—rectilinear propagation, reflection at equal angles, and refraction toward or away from the perpendicular in accordance with the densities of the media—makes it possible to reduce many optical problems to ray geometry, i.e., to a purely geometrical optics in which lines drawn according to these same geometrical rules are used to represent optical phenomena. This does not require the real existence of anything corresponding to rays, but demands only that rays adequately represent the course of light or species. Thus Pecham defines a ray as "nothing but the species of a visible object fashioned into a straight line by extension,"[32] and implies that rays have no real existence:"...it should be known that all the pyramids in a single body of illumination constitute essentially one light," and "an infinite number of reflections must take place from every mirror...nevertheless, the reflections are not thereby actually infinite, since they all form one body of light."[33] Upon this definition of rays, Pecham builds an elaborate geometrical optics, which proceeds almost solely in terms of rays and the geometrical rules governing their behavior, and which pays little attention to the real nature of light.

Although the axiom of the rectilinear propagation of light is central to Pecham's geometrical optics, there are occasions when he appears to doubt its truth, or at least its applicability. Rectilinear propagation is assumed from the beginning of the work, but the principle is not explicitly stated until Proposition I.14{29}, where Pecham writes, "Rays of primary light and color are always propagated in straight lines unless bent by variations in the medium." Pecham introduces no empirical evidence for his statement, but argues that "action in a straight line is easier and stronger for nature."[34] At first glance

30. *Ibid.*, p. 72. In the *Perspectiva communis*, Proposition I.37{40}, quoted earlier, Pecham states that "species...are received without matter," thus agreeing with Bacon on the noncorpuscular character of species.

31. Proposition I.{27}; cf. Propositions I.14{29} and II.3.

32. Proposition I.27{26}.

33. Propositions I.{6} and II.15; cf. Propositions I.{9}, II.18, and III.19.

34. Proposition I.{27}; cf. Proposition II.3. Treatises on geometrical optics normally begin by enunciating and perhaps demon-

strating this central axiom of the rectilinear propagation of light. Pecham's failure to deal with the axiom in thorough fashion can be traced to his close adherence to the Latin version of Alhazen's optics, which omits the first three chapters of Book I of the Arabic text, including an experimental demonstration of the rectilinear propagation of light. For a discussion and German translation of portions of Kamāl al-Dīn's commentary on Alhazen's optics, which reproduces the chapters omitted from the Latin version, see Eilhard Wiedemann, "Zu Ibn al-Haiṭams this rule seems to apply only to primary light, for to secondary or accidental light Pecham attributes the property of "circumfusion";[35] however, Pecham refers elsewhere to the "radiation" of secondary light, a term implying that in his view circumfusion is the resultant of numerous tiny rectilinear paths.

If Pecham's reference to circumfusion creates ambiguity concerning the rectilinear propagation of secondary light, his lengthy discussion of pinhole images at times appears to challenge the rectilinear propagation of primary light.[36] The problem of pinhole images already possessed an ancient history in the thirteenth century and had been treated by Bacon and Witelo among Pecham's immediate predecessors and contemporaries.[37] Pseudo-Aristotle had posed the problem centuries earlier in the *Problemata*: "Why is it that when the sun passes through quadrilaterals, as for instance in wickerwork, it does not produce a figure rectangular in shape but circular?"[38] That is, why does the image conform to the shape of the sun rather than to the shape of the aperture? Is it possible to reconcile this fact and the principle of rectilinear propagation of light?

Pecham applied himself to this puzzle on four different occasions: in his *Tractatus de perspectiva*, in his *Tractatus de sphera*, and in both versions of the *Perspectiva communis*.[39] In the unrevised version, Pecham discusses and rejects

---

Optik," *Archiv für die Geschichte der Naturwissenschaften und der Technik*, vol. 3 (1910–11), pp. 1–53; on the rectilinear propagation of light, see Wiedemann, pp. 24–25, 40–41.

35. Propositions I.14{29} and I.25{23}; cf. Proposition I.{7}, pp. 79–81. "Circumfusion" is the ability of secondary light to "proceed circumferentially," that is, around the circumference of an opaque body or in curved lines.

36. Propositions I.5 and I.{7}, the latter being a revision of the former.

37. On the history of the theory of pinhole images, see David C. Lindberg, "The Theory of Pinhole Images from Antiquity to the Thirteenth Century," *Archive for History of Exact Sciences*, vol. 5 (1968), pp. 154–76; James Waterhouse, "Camera Obscura: History," in *The Encyclopaedia Britannica* (11th ed.; New York, 1910–11), vol. 5, pp. 105–7; Mario Gliozzi, "L'invenzione della camera oscura," *Archeion*, vol. 14 (1932), pp. 221–29; Maximilian Curtze, "Die Dunkelkammer: Eine Untersuchung über die Vorgeschichte derselben," *Himmel und Erde*, vol. 13 (1901), pp. 225–36; Eugène Müntz, "Léonard de Vinci et l'invention de la Chambre noire," *Revue scientifique*, Ser. 4, vol. 10

(1898), pp. 545–47; Guilielmo Libri, *Histoire des sciences mathématiques en Italie*, vol. 4 (Paris, 1841), pp. 303–14; Pierre Duhem, *Le Système du monde* (Paris, 1913–59), vol. 3, pp. 505–17; Joseph Würschmidt, "Zur Geschichte, Theorie und Praxis der Camera obscura," *Zeitschrift für mathematischen und naturwissenschaftlichen Unterricht aller Schulgattungen*, vol. 46 (1915), pp. 466–76.

Alhazen worked out a detailed (and largely correct) analysis of pinhole images, but not in those of his works rendered into Latin. On the theories of Alhazen and his fourteenth-century commentator, Kamāl al-Dīn al-Fārisi, see Eilhard Wiedemann, "Ueber die erste Erwähnung der Dunkelkammer durch Ibn al Haitam," *Jahrbuch für Photographie und Reproduktionstechnik*, vol. 24 (1910), pp. 12–13; Wiedemann, "Über die Camera obscura bei Ibn al Haitam," *Sitzungsberichte der physikalisch-medizinischen Societät in Erlangen*, vol. 46, (1914), pp. 155–69; Joseph Würschmidt, "Zur Theorie der Camera obscura bei *Ibn al Haitam*," *ibid.*, pp. 151–54.

38. *Problemata* 15. 6. 911[b]1, trans. W. S. Hett (London, 1936), vol. 1, p. 333.

39. Pecham's four analyses are discussed

two possible explanations advanced by others before he presents his own view. Under the first explanation, people "assign [the roundness of the image] simply to the roundness of the sun, for since the rays proceed from the sun, the roundness of the rays must result from the roundness of the sun."[40] To support their view, these people cite the fact that "during a solar eclipse the incident rays become crescent-shaped, varying as the portion of the sun cut off by the moon."[41] "But if this cause were sufficient," Pecham argues, "the incident rays would be round both near the aperture and far from the aperture, whereas the contrary is observed."[42]

In the second explanation, people argue that the circularity of the image is explicable in terms of the intersection of rectilinear rays. Pecham, in a lengthy analysis of the various intersecting radiant pyramids passing through the aperture, attempts to demonstrate that, before the rays have progressed far beyond the aperture, the outermost pyramid (which gives shape to the beam as a whole) is round.[43] His demonstration ultimately fails, however, and Pecham concludes that in fact the outermost pyramid formed by the rectilinear propagation of light conforms to the shape of the aperture and therefore could not produce a circular image. "Therefore," he is forced to admit, "it is impossible to attribute the cause of roundness entirely to the manner of radiating [i.e., to the rectilinear propagation of light]."[44] The true explanation of roundness, Pecham decides, is that "the spherical shape is associated with light and is in harmony with all the bodies of the world as being to the highest degree conservative of nature.... Therefore light is naturally moved toward this shape and gradually assumes it when propagated some distance."[45] Pecham has apparently sacrificed the rectilinear propagation of light to a more general law of the natural sphericity or circularity of light.[46]

The revised version of this proposition contains by far the longest and most impressive of Pecham's four analyses of pinhole images. Once again he claims to be presenting the views of others, a device which frequently makes it impossible to determine precisely where his own commitments lie. The first view presented is identical to the final conclusion of the unrevised version: light is round after passing through a triangular aperture because light "is the most

at considerable length in my "Theory of Pinhole Images." The discussion below is a condensation of some of the conclusions reached there.

40. Proposition I.5, p. 67.

41. *Ibid.*

42. *Ibid.*

43. This theory is promising, since it is able to explain why the shape of the image is not the same directly behind the aperture and far behind the aperture.

44. *Ibid.*, p. 73.

45. *Ibid.*, p. 71.

46. Grosseteste discusses the natural sphericity of *lux* in *De luce* (Robert Grosseteste, *On Light*, trans. Clare Riedl [Milwaukee, 1942], p. 10) and in *De lineis* (*Phil. Werke*, p. 64); cf. Crombie, *Grosseteste*, pp. 106–08. Note, however, that the conception expressed by Pecham in Proposition I.5 differs significantly from that of Grosseteste.

excellent of corporeal forms" and therefore "always strives toward the most excellent shape, namely, roundness."[47] However, he notes, against this opinion it is argued that the image would then be circular even during an eclipse, contrary to experience. Moreover, "no matter where in the incident beam the eye is placed, it can see the body of the sun, and sight occurs only in straight lines.... Consequently the beam acquires roundness only insofar as this is caused by radiation in straight lines."[48] It is thus affirmed (whether in Pecham's own view or in his representation of others' views against the first opinion is not quite clear) that light (or sight) proceeds only in straight lines and that the analysis of pinhole images must, therefore, be founded on the principle of rectilinear propagation.

A second view satisfies this condition: "Others claim that roundness is caused by intersection of the [rectilinear] rays and hence in a mathematical manner."[49] The analysis is no longer physical or causal—the tendency of light to assume a spherical shape—but geometrical, based on the fact that the radiation of light can be represented by straight lines; this is to say that rectilinear solar rays, after passing through a noncircular aperture and intersecting one another, *really do* form a circular beam. To elucidate this viewpoint, Pecham again analyzes the radiant pyramids passing through the aperture, but is finally driven to the conclusion that the rays passing through the corners fall outside all round pyramids, so that the incident beam must be angular rather than circular. Thus vanishes the last possibility that a circular image can be formed by rectilinear solar rays passing through a triangular aperture. Pecham's demonstration is geometrically rigorous and his conclusion beyond reproach. "It is clear," he asserts, "that by direct [i.e., rectilinear] radiation the incident rays are noncircular insofar as the aperture is noncircular."[50]

Lest there be any lingering doubt, Pecham introduces an ingenious *reductio ad absurdum*.[51] Imagining an equilateral triangular aperture, he assumes that which is to be disproved, namely, that light passing through this aperture becomes round by direct radiation. If an opaque circular disk is then inscribed within the aperture, three "somewhat irregular triangles" will remain in the corners for light to pass through. Now if it is true that light passing through the entire aperture before insertion of the opaque disk could become round by direct radiation, then light passing now through each of the corners must also become round by the same mechanism. However, if the opaque disk should be removed, radiation passing through the circular region formerly occupied by the disk will also be round; but it is inconceivable "that the small beams

47. Proposition I.{7}, p. 73.
48. *Ibid.*
49. *Ibid.*
50. *Ibid.*, p. 79.

51. The *reductio* is partially implicit, since certain steps have been suppressed. Nevertheless, there is no mistaking the structure of the argument.

passing through the three corners of the aperture outside the periphery of the inscribed circle should, by [direct] radiation, fall on the same circular surface as does the light passing through the interior of the circle inscribed in the aperture."[52] Therefore, light passing through the triangular aperture as a whole —which, after all, is but the sum of the central circular region and the three "somewhat irregular triangles" occupying the corners—cannot become round by direct radiation. But the premise of the whole demonstration was the assumption that radiation incident through the triangular aperture *does* become round by direct radiation; this assumption has therefore led to self-contradiction. Rectilinear rays—by themselves, at least—cannot account for the phenomena of pinhole images.

Thus far in the revised version, Pecham has, with considerable force and clarity, described and then demolished two explanations of pinhole images— apparently the only two contemporary explanations he regarded as viable. However, when he presents his own theory, he becomes vague, and one is able to reconstruct it only by piecing together scattered remarks in the *Perspectiva communis* and the concise summary found in the *Tractatus de sphera*. In the latter work, Pecham distinguishes two components in any incident beam of light—primary rays and secondary rays.[53] Primary rays, which radiate in straight lines from the luminous source, conform to the shape of the aperture; secondary rays, which emanate from the primary rays, pass outside the beam of primary rays and produce a circular image at all times. Now when solar light is incident through a triangular aperture, the primary and secondary images are superimposed, and if the secondary image is sufficiently bright, the composite image appears circular. With this theory in mind, one can understand the significance of several passages in the revised version of the *Perspectiva communis:* for example, where Pecham remarks that "light slightly lacking in roundness can, by the proximity of another light, be judged to have its own natural [i.e., round] shape,"[54] and that "light can also diffuse itself, as though by radiating, outside the [main body of] radiation."[55] Thus Pecham appears to solve the riddle of pinhole images by arguing that one can both accept the phenomenon of circular images by a noncircular aperture and defend the principle of rectilinear propagation if one attributes the circularity of the image to the influence of secondary radiation. It is an ingenious, albeit incorrect, solution.

But the problem of images formed during an eclipse remains. During a solar eclipse, Pecham argues, the primary radiation reveals the eclipse, while the

52. Proposition I.{7}, p. 79.

53. See my "Theory of Pinhole Images" for a fuller analysis. The relevant section from the *Tractatus de sphera* is reproduced in Duhem, *Le Système du monde*, vol. 3, pp. 524–26.

54. Proposition I.{7}, p. 79.

55. *Ibid.* Pecham's reference in Proposition I.{7} to the propagation of light rays through the optic nerves is intended as an illustration of the ability of rays to depart from a rectilinear path.

secondary radiation tends to fill out the circle. However, the eclipse reduces the primary radiation to the point where the secondary radiation (proceeding from the primary radiation) becomes invisible. As Pecham puts it in the *Tractatus de sphera*, "since radiating light is principal and the cause of light diffused accidentally, when the radiating [i.e., primary] light is hindered, secondary light is thereby cut off, so that during an eclipse, the roundness of the [composite] image is not easily discerned."[56] The image therefore is eclipsed so far as sight can perceive. There remains but one difficulty: how is the primary beam now able to conform to the shape of the luminous source rather than to the shape of the aperture? There is no answer, and we must conclude that at this point Pecham's explanation has simply failed.

Perhaps Pecham was aware of some of the deficiencies of his theory. In any case, to the very end he conveys a certain lack of confidence in its adequacy, for he concludes his account of pinhole images in the revised version with the following modest disclaimer: "And I shall not envy anyone treating [the matter] better [than I], but would venerate [him] as a teacher."[57]

Reflection

Rays of light and color are reflected, Pecham explains, because it is their nature to diffuse themselves only through transparent media. When rays of light and color encounter bodies possessing little or no transparency, they are unable to continue in a straight line and so diffuse themselves back through the transparent medium at angles equal to the angles of incidence. When rays of light and color proceeding through air encounter a medium, such as water, with a lower degree of transparency than air, the rays diffuse themselves in two directions: they penetrate the interface and illuminate the water, but they are also reflected at equal angles. Thus Pecham endows rays with an innate property of self-diffusion or self-multiplication that requires expression; if diffusion is obstructed in one direction, it immediately assumes another.[58]

However, there are remarks in the *Perspectiva communis* suggestive of a more mechanistic explanation of reflection. After describing how rays are reflected perpendicularly or obliquely depending on their mode of incidence, Pecham writes, "The same thing is evident in the motion of a body, since a heavy body descending vertically onto a solid body or projected perpendicularly along a line is driven back along the same line; if projected obliquely, it rebounds along a similar line on the other side."[59] However, the claim is not that

56. Duhem, *Le Système du monde*, vol. 3, p. 527.

57. Proposition I.{7}, last sentence.

58. Proposition II.1. On the multiplication of species, see pp. 35–36 and 39–40.

59. Proposition II.6. Pecham borrows this mechanical analogy from Alhazen, who wrote, "Light is reflected along a line having the same slope as the line by which the light approaches the mirror because light is moved

light rays are reflected by virtue of the same causes that operate in the rebound of a heavy body, but only that both are reflected with the same equality of angles; the analogy is intended to elucidate only the geometry of reflection, not the causes of reflection or the nature of the reflected entity.

Pecham presents a miscellaneous collection of information about the process of reflection and the nature of mirrors. Transparency cannot be an essential property of mirrors, he argues, since transparent substances receive rays and thereby reduce the strength of reflection; moreover, mirrors are frequently made of nontransparent substances like iron, steel, and marble. Nevertheless, mirrors may be made of transparent substances, in which case they must be darkened behind or they will not reflect efficaciously. The explanation of this phenomenon is that the lead or black cloth used to darken the back side of the glass prevents transmission of rays, which would otherwise overcome and render powerless the reflected rays. We learn from this same discussion something of the manufacture of mirrors, since Pecham points out that "common glass mirrors are coated with lead," and that "nothing is seen in glass mirrors from which the lead has been scraped."[60]

Reflection occurs from both smooth and rough surfaces, but only rays reflected from smooth surfaces are discerned, since light incident on a rough surface is dispersed and is not received by the eye in regular fashion. Therefore mirrors must be fashioned out of materials "altogether free from sensible pores."[61] Objects seen in mirrors always appear dimmer than they do by direct vision, for two reasons: first, because rays are weakened by bending, and second,

---

very swiftly, and when it falls on a mirror, it is not allowed to penetrate but is denied entrance into that body. And since the original force and nature of motion still remain in it, the light is reflected in the direction from which it came, along a line having the same slope as the original ray. We can see the same thing in natural and accidental motion, for if we allow a heavy spherical body to descend perpendicularly onto a smooth body from a certain height, we will see it reflected along the same perpendicular by which it descended." (*Opt. thes.*, bk. 4, sec. 18, p. 112: "...fiat reflexio lucis secundum lineam eiusdem situs cum linea, per quam accedit ad speculum ipsa lux: est: Quoniam lux motu citissimo movetur: et quando cadit in speculum, non recipitur: sed ei fixio in corpore illo negatur: et cum in ea perseveret adhuc prioris motus vis et natura, reflectitur ad partem, a qua processit, et secundum lineas

eundem situm cum prioribus habentes. Huius autem rei simile in naturalibus motibus videre possumus, et etiam in accidentalibus. Si corpus sphaericum ponderosum ab aliqua altitudine descendere permittamus perpendiculariter super politum corpus: videmus ipsum super perpendicularem reflecti, per quam descenderat.") Alhazen goes on to discuss in similar terms the reflection of a sphere attached to the tip of an arrow, which is shot obliquely at a mirror. For a further analysis of Alhazen's views, see my introduction to the reprint of the Risner edition of Alhazen's and Witelo's works (Johnson Reprint Corporation), forthcoming.

60. Propositions II.7 and II.8. On the early history of mirrors and their construction, see Bruno Schweig, "Mirrors," *Antiquity*, vol. 15 (1941), pp. 257–68.

61. Propositions II.2 and II.10.

because "the color of the mirror is mingled with the reflected light and obscures it."[62]

On the geometry of reflection, Pecham states the law of reflection in full: the angles of incidence and reflection are equal, the incident and reflected rays define a plane perpendicular to the reflecting surface, and the image appears at the intersection of the perpendicular dropped from the object to the reflecting surface and the rectilinear extension, into the mirror, of the reflected ray.[63] Pecham claims that equality of the angles can be "gathered from experience," but he defends it on grounds of symmetry, stating that the ray must be reflected "in the same mode as that in which it would be transmitted [if it were not deflected by a reflecting surface]."[64] The incident and reflected rays define a plane perpendicular to the reflecting surface because "a ray conforms as closely as possible to a rectilinear path," and "if a ray were to forsake that plane, it would be departing doubly from straightness, both by rebound and by deviation."[65]

An elaborate analysis of image formation by reflection dominates Part II of the *Perspectiva communis*. But before proceeding to the geometry of image formation, Pecham finds it expedient to offer a causal account. He argues forcefully that forms or images are not seen in mirrors by virtue of having been impressed in the mirrors. In the first place, objects are seen by reflection in hard mirrors possessing no transparency capable of receiving an impression.[66] Second, if an impression were made in the matter of the mirror, it could be seen from every direction and not just from that direction satisfying the law of reflection. Third, images are often larger than the mirror. Finally, images are located not in the plane of the mirror, but behind it. This final objection suggests an alternative account of reflection: the image is impressed in the matter where it appears to be situated, i.e., behind the mirror at the intersection of the cathetus and the rectilinear extension of the reflected ray.[67] But this cannot be true

62. Propositions II.3 and II.11.

63. Propositions II.6 and II.20. On the third of these principles, see Colin M. Turbayne, "Grosseteste and an Ancient Optical Principle," *Isis*, vol. 50 (1959), pp. 467–72.

64. Proposition II.6.

65. *Ibid.*

66. Note that Pecham considers density and transparency inverse functions of one another; see Propositions II.7, II.19, and III.3.

67. Although Pecham's denial that images are impressions made in mirrors derives from Alhazen's *Perspectiva*, it is possible that the view of impressed images was still a genuine alternative in the thirteenth century. Grosseteste seems to have conceived the rainbow as an impression made in a cloud, which then radiated its species in all directions; and although Pecham does not dispute that aspect of Grosseteste's theory of the rainbow, he is here arguing that *reflection* cannot occur in such a fashion. See *Opt. thes.*, bk. 4, sec. 20, pp. 113–14; *Perspectiva communis*, Propositions II.19 and III.20; on Grosseteste's theory of the rainbow, see my "Roger Bacon's Theory of the Rainbow: Progress or Regress?" *Isis*, vol. 57 (1966), pp. 238–41.

either, since a tower or mountain may appear extended into the earth, which is obviously incapable of receiving such an impression.[68]

The truth, according to Pecham, is that there is no such thing as a real image, for a real image would require an actual impression either in the mirror or at the place where the image appears. By thus denying the reality of images, Pecham is simply maintaining that the rays entering the observer's eye originate not from an image in or behind the mirror, but from the object itself; consequently it is the object rather than the image that an observer perceives. Image formation, therefore, is a quasi-psychological phenomenon—a misapprehension—for an image "is merely the appearance of an object outside its place.... it is the object that is really seen in a mirror, although it is misapprehended in position."[69] Misapprehension occurs because sight is so occupied with the reflected ray, which enters the eye, that it does not perceive the angle between the incident and reflected rays; consequently the incident and reflected rays are "apprehended by the eye as though proceeding without interruption in a straight line."[70]

The second half of Part II is devoted to the geometry of image formation. Pecham applies the law of reflection to determine the location of the image for objects seen in concave and convex mirrors of spherical, cylindrical, or conical figure. He also discusses the conditions under which images are seen and the number of such images, distortions of the image, inversion and reversal, and magnification or diminution of the image. The magnification or diminution is usually expressed in terms of the absolute sizes of object and image rather than in terms of the angles subtended at the observer's eye.[71]

Refraction

Pecham presents no quantitative law of refraction and no numerical data, even though he was familiar with Alhazen's description of apparatus capable of yielding quantitative results, with Grosseteste's quantitative law of refraction, and perhaps with Ptolemy's and Witelo's numerical data.[72] Pecham merely

68. Proposition II.19.

69. *Ibid.*

70. Proposition II.20.

71. See the Critical Notes to Part II, nn. 50 and 125, pp. 257, 265.

72. On Alhazen's quantitative approach to the refraction of light, see Schnaase, *Optik Alhazens*, pp. 13–16, and Winter, "Optical Researches," pp. 201–04; cf. *Opt. thes.*, bk. 7, secs. 10–12, pp. 243–47. On Grosseteste's half-angle law of refraction, see Bruce S. Eastwood, "Grosseteste's 'Quan-

titative' Law of Refraction: A Chapter in the History of Non-Experimental Science," *Journal of the History of Ideas*, vol. 28 (1967), pp. 403–14; cf. Grosseteste, *De iride*, in *Phil. Werke*, pp. 74–75. Ptolemy's table of refraction has been analyzed brilliantly by Albert Lejeune in "Les Tables de réfraction de Ptolémée," *Annales de la Société Scientifique de Bruxelles*, Ser. 1, vol. 60 (1946), pp. 93–101, and in *Recherches sur la catoptrique grecque* (Brussels, 1957), pp. 153–66. Witelo also presents quantitative data, but he has describes the phenomena in qualitative terms: when a ray is obliquely incident on a denser (less transparent) medium, it is refracted toward the perpendicular, and when obliquely incident on a less dense (more transparent) medium, it is refracted away from the perpendicular. The angle of refraction (by which Pecham appears to mean the angle of deviation) varies according to the inclination of the incident ray and the difference in density between the two media.[73]

Pecham's explanation of refraction is based on two premises. The first is that traversal of the first medium must be "commensurate" with traversal of the second; i.e., the strength of the incident ray and the strength of the refracted ray must be comparable or approach equality.[74] This premise, which is not defended by Pecham, appears to have been borrowed from Bacon's account of refraction in *De multiplicatione specierum*.[75] The second premise, gained from both Alhazen and Bacon, is a strange distortion of an idea that is both ancient and plausible. This idea, universally maintained by medieval writers on optics, has already been introduced in Pecham's description of the process of sight: rays entering or emerging from a medium perpendicularly are strongest because they are unrefracted; the fundamental generalization underlying this principle is that bending always weakens, a point that nobody in the thirteenth century would have disputed.[76] But in the context of refraction, Bacon and Pecham twist this idea and propose that rays traversing a medium (quite apart from the event of entrance or emergence) are stronger the closer they approach being perpendicular to the surface of the medium. Thus a ray obliquely incident on a transparent medium gains strength by deviating from rectilinearity and approaching the perpendicular; yet this conclusion violates the starting point of the whole line of thought, namely, that bending weakens.

Combining the two premises, Pecham reasons that a ray passing from a less dense to a more dense medium assumes a position closer to the perpendicular in the denser medium; and the increase in perpendicularity compensates for the weakening effect of greater density. Consequently, the strengths of the incident ray and the refracted ray will be commensurate:

merely reproduced Ptolemy's table of refraction, supplemented by erroneous extrapolation to rays passing from the more dense to the less dense medium; see Witelo, *Optica*, bk. 10, sec. 8, p. 412.

73. Propositions I.15{30}, I.16{31}, and III.3. On the angle of refraction, see the Critical Notes to Part III, n. 3, p. 266.

74. Propositions I.15{30} and III.3. For a more complete account of the cause of refraction, see my article, "The Cause of Refraction."

75. Bk. 2, chap. 3, bound with Bridges's edition of the *Opus maius*, vol. 2, p. 470.

76. Alhazen, *Opt. thes.*, bk. 7, sec. 8, pp. 240–42; Grosseteste, *De lineis*, in *Phil. Werke*, p. 63; Bacon, *Opus maius*, pt. IV, dist. 3, chap. 3, (ed. Bridges, vol. 1, pp. 126–27); Bacon, *De mult. spec.*, bk. 2, chap. 3, and bk. 5, chap. 2 (ed. Bridges, vol. 2, pp. 469–70, 534–35); *Perspectiva communis*, Propositions I.{6} and I.15{30}; see also pp. 37–38, above.

Traversal [of the medium] is strongest...for rays that enter or emerge perpendicularly, and traversal by a nonperpendicular ray is weaker as it diverges from the perpendicular and stronger as it approaches the perpendicular. Therefore a ray meeting a denser and more resistant medium must assume a stronger position, closer to the direct path. Consequently, in order that traversal of the second medium should be commensurate with traversal of the first, the [refracted] ray bends toward the perpendicular erected at the point of incidence on the second medium.[77]

Conversely, a ray obliquely incident on a less dense medium diverges from the perpendicular, thus assuming the path of weakness to compensate for the greater strength associated with a rare (highly transparent) medium.[78] Pecham even makes the more specific claim that "the direction of the ray in the second medium...is proportioned to its direction in the first medium as the resistance of the second medium to the resistance of the first." Since he maintains elsewhere that "greater ability to resist [the propagation of rays] corresponds to greater density," Pecham appears to establish a ratio between directions and densities in the two media.[79]

Pecham's explanation of refraction is not notably original, but is built on the theories of Alhazen and Bacon. Yet Pecham follows neither of them slavishly. He follows Bacon in attempting to fill several gaps in Alhazen's argument while rebuking Bacon for the animistic terms in which that view was expressed.[80] Bacon had written that "the natural power generating the species *desires* [*appetit*] easier traversal and *chooses* [*eligit*] it"; Pecham responds: "...it should not be thought that the ray bends toward the stronger position as by *choice* [*per electionem*], but rather that traversal of the first medium impels [*impellere*] a proportional traversal of the second."[81] It is always a mistake to assume that Pecham (or any other medieval philosopher) follows his sources uncritically; here we have a representative example both of Pecham's reliance on earlier authorities and of his exercise of his own critical powers.

In Part III on refraction, as in Part II on reflection, Pecham devotes a great deal of attention to problems of image formation. He establishes the principle that the image of an object in one medium, when viewed by an observer in another medium, is located at the intersection of the perpendicular dropped

77. Proposition I.15{30}.

78. Proposition I.16{31}.

79. Propositions I.15{30} and III.3. Pecham does not provide metrical definitions that would allow one to set up actual numerical ratios; nor is it clear that he ever actually envisioned the relationship between density and direction in numerical terms.

80. On the relationship between Pecham's explanation of refraction and those of Al-

hazen and Bacon, see my "The Cause of Refraction." On Alhazen's theory see Abdelhamid I. Sabra, "Explanation of Optical Reflection and Refraction: Ibn-al-Haytham, Descartes, Newton," in *Actes du dixième congrès international d'histoire des sciences* (Ithaca, 1962), vol. 1, pp. 551–54.

81. Bacon, *De mult. spec.*, bk. 2, chap. 3, p. 470; *Perspectiva communis*, Proposition I.15{30}.

from the object to the interface separating the two media and the rectilinear extension of the refracted ray.[82] He presents a traditional discussion of objects seen outside their true place and analyzes image formation for plane and spherical interfaces when the object and the eye assume various positions with respect to the center of curvature of the interface.[83]

In discussing refraction, Pecham fails, just as he did in the discussion of reflection, to reconcile his theory of image formation—according to which the image appears at the intersection of the perpendicular dropped from the object and the rectilinear extension of the ray entering the eye—with his general theory of vision—in which the only requirement for clear vision is the orderly arrangement on the surface of the glacial humor of rays from the visible object. The incompatibility of the two theories is apparent particularly in Proposition II.39, where application of the first rule determines that the image of a certain object seen by reflection should be located in or behind the observer's eye. In such a case, Pecham insists, no clear image can be perceived, for "the eye is not designed to receive the forms of things unless they are opposite the face. Therefore things that appear otherwise must be of confused and doubtful appearance."[84] Although from the point of view of modern geometrical optics this is a correct conclusion, how can it be reconciled with Pecham's requirement that for clear perception the rays of an object need only maintain the same order on the glacial humor as the points on the object from which they originated? In the particular instance cited in Proposition II.39, the requirement of order is fully satisfied. Actually Pecham avoids direct encounter with this problem by dealing with image formation one point at a time; consequently he never considers more than a single perpendicular ray incident on the glacial humor at one time, and the issue of the order of rays is not explicitly raised. Indeed, this whole contradiction is unresolvable short of the realization that rays emanating from a single point on the object are brought to a focus within the eye by the refracting power of the glacial humor—a concept that was not to be grasped by anybody in the West for another three hundred years.

82. Proposition III.4. On the history of this principle, see Turbayne, "Ancient Optical Principle," pp. 467–72.

83. Propositions III.6 to III.11.

84. Proposition II.49; see also the Critical Notes to Part II, nn. 90 and 93, pp. 260–61.

Manuscripts, Their Sigla, and Printed Editions

Manuscripts

In preparing this edition, I have used the following eleven manuscripts, selected on the basis of age, legibility, availability, and geographical distribution. The first six manuscripts have been collated in full, and all variations appear in the variant readings given at the foot of the Latin text pages. The other five manuscripts have been referred to, and variants for them given, wherever there have been doubtful readings or where several of the first six manuscripts omit a proposition or a substantial portion of a proposition.

1. V = Vatican, Biblioteca Apostolica Vaticana, Vat. lat. 5963, fols. 1r–68r.
    Date: late 13th century or possibly early 14th century. The earlier date is Lynn Thorndike's; on the possibility of a later date, see p. 12, above.
    Description: Lynn Thorndike, "A John Peckham Manuscript," *Archivum Franciscanum Historicum*, vol. 45 (1952), pp. 451–52.

2. B = Oxford, Bodleian Library, Ashmolean 1522, fols. 148r–175v.
    Date: early 14th century.
    Description: W. H. Black, *A Descriptive, Analytical, and Critical Catalogue of the Manuscripts of Elias Ashmole ... now Deposited in the Bodleian Library* (Oxford, 1845), cols. 1425–30.

3. A = Erfurt, Wissenschaftliche Bibliothek, Amploniana Q.387, fols. 29v–41v.[1]
    Date: second half of 14th century.
    Description: W. Schum, *Beschreibendes Verzeichnis der Amplonianischen Handschriften-Sammlung zu Erfurt* (Berlin, 1887), pp. 648–49.

4. F = Basel, Öffentliche Bibliothek der Universität Basel, F.IV.30, fols. 122r–153v.
    Date: second half of 14th century. This is the opinion of Bernhard Bischoff

---

1. Edward Grant graciously provided a microfilm of this manuscript, as well as of manuscripts 7, 14–15, 27, and 30.

(personal communication, 13 December 1964), based on a photographic reproduction of a single folio.

Description: *Theodoricus Teutonicus de Vriberg De iride et radialibus impressionibus*, ed. Joseph Würschmidt (*BGPM*, vol. 12, pts. 5–6 [Münster, 1914]), p. xiii.

5. *H* = Wolfenbüttel, Herzog August Bibliothek, Guelferbytanus 38.6 Augusteus 2°, fols. 209r–228v.

Date: early 14th century.

Description: O. von Heinemann, *Die Handschriften der Herzoglich Bibliothek zu Wolfenbüttel*, II, vol. 3 (Wolfenbüttel, 1898), pp. 163–64. The old number of this codex is 2458.

6. *D* = Oxford, Bodleian Libary, Digby 218, fols. 1r–23r.

Date: early 14th century. Bernhard Bischoff has confirmed this date for both hands. See p. 23, above.

Description: *Catalogi codicum manuscriptorum Bibliothecae Bodleianae*, vol. 9 (Oxford, 1883), cols. 231–33; *Registrum epistolarum fratris Johannis Peckham archiepiscopi Cantuariensis*, ed. Charles T. Martin, vol. 3 (London, 1885), pp. lxiii–lxiv.

7. *W* = Vienna, Österreichische Nationalbibliothek, 5210, fols. 50r–77r.

Date: 1367.

Description: *Tabulae codicum manu scriptorum praeter graecos et orientales in Bibliotheca Palatina Vindobonensi asservatorum*, vol. 4 (Vienna, 1870), p. 60.

8. *L* = Florence, Biblioteca Medicea Laurenziana, Ashburnham 1467, fols. 1r–26r.

Date: 14th century.

Description: *Catalogue of the Manuscripts at Ashburnham Place. Part the First, comprising a collection formed by Professor Libri* (London, n.d.), no page numbers (see cod. 1467).

9. *O* = Oxford, Bodleian Library, Digby 28, fols. 180r–212r.

Date: 14th century.

Description: *Catalogi codicum...*, vol. 9, cols. 23–25.

10. *P* = Prague, Archivio Capituli Metropolitani, 1272, fols. 21r–32r.

Date: 14th century.

Description: Antonín Podlaha, *Doplňky a opravy k soupisu rukopisů knihovny metropolitní kapitoly pražské* (Prague, 1928), pp. 33–34.

11. *N* = Paris, Bibliothèque Nationale, Fonds Latin 7368, fols. 69r–118v.

Date: 15th century.

Description: *Catalogus codicum manuscriptorum Bibliothecae Regiae*, vol. 4 (Paris, 1744), p. 347.

In addition to those listed above, I have examined and occasionally consulted the following manuscripts of the *Perspectiva communis:*

12.   Cracow, Biblioteka Jagiellońska, 1929, fols. 3r–84v (1430).
13.   Dresden, Sachsische Landesbibliothek, DB.86, fols. 250r–271v (14th century).[2]
14.   Erfurt, Wissenschaftliche Bibliothek, Amploniana F.395, fols. 239r–245r (14th century). First seventy-seven propositions only.
15.   Erfurt, Wissenschaftliche Bibliothek, Amploniana Q.385, fols. 172r–191v (14th century). Omits final proposition.
16.   Florence, Biblioteca Medicea Laurenziana, plut. XVII sin.8, fols. 22r–32r (13th–14th century).[3] Terminates at Proposition III.11.
17.   London, British Museum, Add. MS 8786, fols. 49r–61r (14th century). Slightly abridged.
18.   London, British Museum, Add. MS 17,368, fols. 52r–59v (15th century). First fifty-five propositions only.
19.   Milan, Biblioteca Ambrosiana, G 71 Sup., fols. 49r–60v.[4]
20.   Oxford, Bodleian Library, Bodley 300, fols. 120v–132v (15th century).
21.   Oxford, Bodleian Library, Canonicus Misc. 200, fols. 1r–33r (1409).
22.   Oxford, Bodleian Library, Digby 98, fols. 118r–126r (15th century). Abridged.
23.   Prague, Archivio Capituli Metropolitani, 1284, fols. 65r–81v. (14th century).
24.   Prague, Universitätsbibliothek, 2815, fols. 23r–37v (15th century).
25.   Vatican, Biblioteca Apostolica Vaticana, Ottob. lat. 1850, fols. 65r–75r. Abridged.

2. I am indebted to Marshall Clagett for lending me his microfilm of this codex.

3. The earlier date is Doucet's ("Notulae bibliographicae," p. 309). In view of such an early date, my failure to collate this manuscript must be explained. There were a number of reasons for this: first, I was unable to procure a satisfactory reproduction of it; second, the ink has faded to illegibility in spots; third, the manuscript omits most of Proposition I.5 and the last eleven propositions of Part III; finally, and most significantly, I am doubtful about Doucet's early date. My doubts are shared by Irenaeus Squadrani, O.F.M. ("Tractatus de luce Fr. Bartholomaei de Bononia," *Antonianum*, vol. 7 [1932], p. 209), who assigns this entire codex to the fourteenth century. In sum, I believe this manuscript is early fourteenth century and no better a copy of the *Perspectiva communis* than a number of other manuscripts from the early fourteenth century.

4. The Mediaeval Institute of the University of Notre Dame was kind enough to furnish a reproduction of this manuscript.

26. Vatican, Biblioteca Apostolica Vaticana, Vat. lat. 3102, fols. 64r–84v (14th century).
27. Vienna, Österreichische Nationalbibliothek, 2433, fols. 1r–21r (14th century).
28. Vienna, Österreichische Nationalbibliothek, 3105, fols. 52r–63v (1441).
29. Vienna, Österreichische Nationalbibliothek, 4775, fols. 132r–173r (1455).
30. Vienna, Österreichische Nationalbibliothek, 5274, fols. 3r–52r (1502–03). Corrected by Conrad Noricus.
31. Vienna, Österreichische Nationalbibliothek, 5311, fols. 106r–107r (14th–15th century). Excerpts.
32. Vienna, Österreichische Nationalbibliothek, 5447, fols. 1r–24v (15th century).

I have not examined the following copies of the *Perspectiva communis:*[5]

33. Cambrai, Bibliothèque Municipale, 1330 (14th century).
34. Cracow, Biblioteka Jagiellońska, 552, pp. 151–93 (15th century).
35. Cracow, Biblioteka Jagiellońska, 568, pp. 191–206 (1466).
36. Cracow, Biblioteka Jagiellońska, 640, pp. 429–61 (1419).
37. Cracow, Biblioteka Jagiellońska, 704, fols. 123v–125v (14th century). Terminates at Proposition I.33.
38. Cracow, Biblioteka Jagiellońska, 1840, pp. 257–439 (15th–16th century).
39. Cracow, Biblioteka Jagiellońska, 1844, pp. 1–163 (15th century).
40. Cracow, Bibliotcka Jagiellońska, 1844, pp. 169–261 (15th century).
41. Cracow, Biblioteka Jagiellońska, 1919, pp. 205–75, (14th–15th century).
42. Cracow, Biblioteka Jagiellońska, 1927, pp. 285–358 (1444–45).
43. Cracow, Biblioteka Jagiellońska, 2644, pp. 6–71 (1561). Incomplete.
44. Cracow, Biblioteka Jagiellońska, 2704, fols. 1–50 (1626). Abridged.
45. Florence, Biblioteca Nazionale, Conv. soppr. I.5.25, fols. 1–37 (14th century).
46. Florence, Biblioteca Nazionale, Conv. soppr. I.5.26, fols. 1–29 (15th century).
47. Kues, Bibliothek des St. Nikolaus-Hospitals, 212, fols. 239–250 (15th century).[6]

5. P. Glorieux, *Répertoire*, p. 87, lists an additional copy of the *Perspectiva communis* contained in Assisi cod. 644. However my microfilm of this codex reveals no copy of the *Perspectiva communis*, but a copy of a *Formula confessionum* (fols. 106r–162v), attributed to Pecham in the explicit. My source of information on the eleven Cracow manuscripts is Adam Bednarski, "O krakowskich rękopisach perspektywy arcybiskupa Jana Peckhama," *Archiwum historji i filozofji medycyny oraz historji nauk przyrodniczych*, vol. 12 (1932), pp. 1–14; however, I have corrected Bednarski in several particulars by reference to the printed catalogue.

6. This manuscript was formerly owned

48.   Kues, Bibliothek des St. Nikolaus-Hospitals, 215, fols. 1–24 (14th century).
49.   Leipzig, Universitätsbibliothek, 1461, fols. 125–133 (15th century).
50.   Library of Baldassarre Boncompagni, 363/249, fols. 2–36 (14th century).[7]
51.   Library of Baldassarre Boncompagni, 535, fols. 1–30 (14th century).
52.   London, British Museum, Add. MS 15,108, fols. 150r–179v (1430).
53.   Munich, Bayerische Staatsbibliothek, 25138, fols. 131–175 (15th century).
54.   Oxford, Bodleian Library, Ashmolean 341, fols. 115r–120r (14th century). Abridged.
55.   Paris, Bibliothèque Mazarine, 3472, fols. 1–12 (14th century).
56.   Schlägl (Austria, Premonstratensian Monastery), Stiftsbibliothek, 126 (824.236), fols. 1r–97v (15th century).
57.   Thorn, Gymnasialbibliothek, R.4°.2, fols. 35–68 (14th century).
58.   Valencia, Biblioteca Universitaria de Valencia, 320, fols. 50r–89v (15th century).
59.   Vatican, Biblioteca Apostolica Vaticana, Barberini lat. 357, fols. 109r–122v (1469).
60.   Vatican, Biblioteca Apostolica Vaticana, Regina Suecorum 1235, fols. 32r–62v.
61.   Vatican, Biblioteca Apostolica Vaticana, Regina Suecorum 1253, fols. 34r–61v (14th century).[8]
62.   Vatican, Biblioteca Apostolica Vaticana, Vat. lat. 4082, fols. 1r–21v (15th century).

Printed Editions

The eleven printed editions of the *Perspectiva communis* are as follows:

1.   *Prospectiva communis d. Johannis archiepiscopi Cantuariensis...*, ed. Facius Cardanus. [Milan:] Petrus de Corneno, [1482/83?].
2.   *Perspecti*[v]*a Pisani Carturiensis*, in *Preclarissimum mathematicarum opus in quo continentur... Thome Brauardini arismetica et... geometria hecnon et... Pisani carturiensis perspectiva...*. Valencia, 1503.
3.   *Jo. Archiepiscopi Cantuariensis Perspectiva communis per L. Gauricum Neapolitanum emendata*. Venice: Io. Baptista Sessa, 1504.

---

by Nicholas of Cusa; see J. Marx, *Verzeichnis der Handschriften-Sammlung des Hospitals zu Cues* (Trier, 1905), pp. vi, 203.

7. The first number is from the catalogue of 1892, the second number from the catalogue of 1862; see *Catalogo di manoscritti ora posseduti da D. Baldassarre Boncompagni*, ed. Enrico Narducci (2nd ed.; Rome, 1892),

pp. 216–17. Boncompagni's library has been scattered, and I do not know the present location of this or the next manuscript.

8. I am indebted to Charles J. Ermatinger of the Pius XII Memorial Library at St. Louis University for checking the two Regina codices for me.

4. *Perspettiva Joannis pisani... vulgo communis appellata....* [Leipzig:] Martinus Herbipolensis, 1504.

5. *Jo. archiepiscopi Cantuariensis Perspectiva Communis,* ed. L. Gauricus. [Paris, 1510(?).][9]

6. *Perspectiva communis. Summa cura et diligentia emendata... per Georgium Hartmannum.* Nuremberg: I. Petreius, 1542.

7. *Perspectiva tribus libris succinctis denuo correcta et figuris illustrata, per Pascasium Hamellium.* Paris: Æ Gourbinus, 1556.

8. *Joannis archiepiscopi Cantuariensis. Perspectivae communis libri tres.* Cologne: Arnoldus Birckmannus, 1580.

9. *Johannis archiepiscopi Cantuariensis Perspectivae communis libri tres.* Cologne: Birckmannus, 1592.

10. *I tre libri della perspettiva commune dell'illustrissi...Monsig. Gioanni arcivescovo Cantuariensis, nuovamente tradotti nella lingua Italiana...da Gio. Paolo Galluci Salodiano....* Venice: G. Varisco, 1593.

11. *Johannis archiepiscopi Cantuariensis Perspectiva communis libri tres.* [Cologne(?),] 1627.

These eleven editions fall naturally into two groups. The first five editions contain substantially the same text, and it is clear that the third and fourth are but reprintings, with a few minor alterations, of the first edition; the second and fifth seem to be distinct from the others, though the differences are not of much significance. All five editions in this first group are faithful to the manuscript tradition, differing from the collated text only in a few words here and there and rarely departing from it in substance.[10] The last six editions also form a group containing similar texts, and it is evident that the editions of 1556, 1580, 1592, and 1627 are reprints, and the edition of 1593 a translation, of the 1542 edition. But unlike the first group, the text of this second group departs radically from the manuscript tradition at many points. Apparently Georg Hartmann, editor of the 1542 edition, made many "improvements" in the text, which were then included in subsequent printings. Hartmann's changes were more often linguistic than theoretical, but occasionally his substitutions or expansions were misleading extensions or distortions of Pecham's thought. For example, Proposition I.30 of Hartmann's edition (Proposition I.31{34} of the collated text presented here) departs radically from Pecham's conclusions re-

9. The British Museum *Catalogue of Printed Books* assigns the provenance and date given here. Martin (*Reg. epist.*, vol. 3, p. lx) assigns this edition to Venice, 1505—his information coming, he says, from the British Museum Catalogue.

10. I was in error when I reported, in "The *Perspectiva communis* of John Pecham: Its Influence, Sources, and Content," *Archives internationales d'histoire des sciences,* vol. 18 (1965), p. 39, that only three editions are faithful to the manuscript tradition and that there are ten printed editions.

garding the structure and function of the parts of the eye. Of the vitreous humor, Pecham says only that it is more subtle than the glacial humor; but Hartmann has Pecham saying that "as Galen attests, [the vitreous humor] sustains and nourishes the crystalline lens, and since it is considerably more subtle and like liquefied glass, it is called the vitreous humor."[11] Of the albugineous humor, Pecham writes, "Within the uvea is the albugineous humor which is like the white of an egg. It is transparent, so that species may be conducted through it freely, and damp, to moisten the glacial humor so that the web surrounding it will not be corrupted by dryness."[12] As Hartmann has it, however

This sphere [formed by the crystalline and vitreous humors together] is surrounded by another humor, called the albugineous humor, which some consider the refuse of the crystalline humor. It is like the white of eggs and is fluid and somewhat more subtle [than the crystalline humor]. The function of this humor is to moisten the crystalline humor and keep it from being corrupted by the dryness of the web surrounding it; it moistens the whole eye and defends and protects the crystalline humor from outside circumstances.[13]

It appears that Hartmann's version of this proposition reflects contemporary views of ocular physiology rather than Pecham's. To be sure, this proposition is representative of Hartmann's more radical changes, but it illustrates the lengths to which he would go to improve the text. Considered as a whole, the 1542 edition and the subsequent editions based upon it capture the broad outlines of Pecham's optical theories, but they are untrustworthy in matters of detail.[14]

11. Note that Pecham never mentions Galen by name in the collated text. Hartmann also inserted the names of Alhazen and Witelo into his edition of the *Perspectiva communis*.

12. Proposition I.31{34}.

13. Proposition I.30 of the 1542 edition. Note that Pecham and Hartmann assign opposite functions to the albugineous humor: Pecham has it protecting the web surrounding the glacial humor from dryness, while Hartmann has it protecting the glacial humor from the dryness of the surrounding web.

14. In view of this fact, it is unfortunate that so many studies of Pecham's optics have been based on the 1542 and subsequent editions.

Perspectiva communis

Incipit Perspectiva Fratris Johannis Pecham

[Proemium]

{Scripsi dudum rogatus a sociis quedam mathematice ruditer rudimenta, que tamen aliis occupatus incorrecta reliqui, que etiam contra in-
5 tentionem meam in publicum prodierunt, que idcirco intendo ut potero
perfunctorie corrigere ut prosint iuvenibus studiosis. Igitur} inter physice
considerationis studia lux iocundius afficit meditantes. Inter magnalia ma-
thematicorum certitudo demonstrationis extollit preclarius investigantes.
Perspectiva igitur humanis traditionibus recte prefertur, in cuius area linea
10 radiosa demonstrationum nexibus complicatur, in qua tam physice quam
mathematice gloria reperitur, utriusque floribus adornata. Cuius sententias magnis deductas ambagibus in conclusiva compendia coartabo, mixtis
iuxta modum materie naturalibus et mathematicis demonstrationibus,
nunc effectus ex causis, nunc ex effectibus causas conclusurus, additis
15 etiam non nullis que ibi non habentur, ex illis tamen eliciuntur, prout de
luce tractantem lux omnium dominus dignabitur illustrare. Presens etiam
opusculum in tribus portiunculis partiturum.

1 Incipit…pecham *om. VH* Incipit perspectiva fratris Johannis de pecham Cantuariensis quondam archiepiscopi *B* Incipit perspectiva communis petzani *in
alia manu mg. hab. A* Incipit perspectiva
communis Johannis pysani (*post* pysani
in alia manu add. (pecham)) *F*
6 physice: phylosophie *F*
7 *ante* inter *add. F* et
8 extollit preclarius *tr. F*
9 *post* traditionibus *add. D* huius / prefera-
tur *B* profertur *A*
9–10 linea radiosa *tr. F*
10 complicatur: applicatur *F* / in qua: quia
A / *post* tam *add. A* in

11 foribus *H*
12 *post* sententias *add. D* magis vales / de-
ductis *F* / in conclusiva: inclusis *F*
13 modum: medium *F* / materie *om. A* iter
F / et mathematicis *om. A* / demonstrationibus: de rationibus *A*
14 *post* nunc^2 *scr. et del. D* ?causas / ex^2
om. A / causas *om. FD*
15 etiam *om. V* / qui *H* / illis: ipsis *D*
16 omni *B* / dominus: deus *F* / dignetur F
/ etiam *om. B*
17 in *om. F* / portiunculis: particulis *BF* /
partitur *F* / *post* partiturum *in alia manu
add. V* et continuit

Here Begins the Perspective of Brother John Pecham

[Preface]

{A while ago at the request of associates I wrote certain unpolished mathematical essays, which, since I was occupied by other matters, I left uncorrected. These appeared in public against my intention. Consequently, I will endeavor to correct them slightly in order that they may be of benefit to young students.[1] Now}* among the investigations of physics, light is most pleasing to students of the subject. Among the glories of mathematics it is the certitude of demonstration that most highly exalts the investigators. Therefore, perspective, in which demonstrations are devised through the use of radiant lines and in which glory is found physically as well as mathematically so that perspective is adorned by the flowers of both, is properly preferred to [all the traditional] teachings of mankind. I shall compress into concise summaries the teachings of perspective, which [in existing treatises] are presented with great obscurity, combining natural and mathematical demonstrations according to the type of subject matter, sometimes inferring effects from causes and sometimes causes from effects, and adding some matters that do not belong to perspective, although deduced from its teachings, according as the Master—the light of all men—deems the investigator of light worthy of illumination. Now the present opusculum will be divided into three short sections.

---

* Braces { } are employed to enclose portions of the text contained only in the revised version (MS *D*). See "Editorial Procedures,' above.

Prima Pars

[*Propositio*] *1ª{1ª}. Lucem operari in visum supra se conversum aliquid impressive.*

Hoc probatur per effectum, quoniam visus in videndo luces fortes
5 dolet et patitur. Lucis etiam intense simulacra in oculo remanent post aspectum, et locum minoris luminis faciunt apparere tenebrosum donec ab oculo evacuaverit vestigium maioris luminis. {Talibus experimentis hec veritas declaratur primo capitulo *Perspective*, quod hic probatur ut origo radii declaretur, quoniam non ab oculo sed ab ipso oritur luminoso.}

10 [*Propositio*] *2ª{2ª}. Colorem illuminatum impressive operari in visum.*

Hoc probatur experimentis similibus. Amplius oculus super colorem fortem illuminatum luce forti fixa intentione conversus, si ad colorem debilius illuminatum se deflexerit, inveniet colorem primum secundo ap-parenter permisceri, prius visi vestigiis in oculo derelictis. {Ex hoc patet
15 quod color motus a luce habet suum radium proprium a lucis radio dif-ferentem.}

[*Propositio*] *3ª{3ª}. Quemlibet punctum luminosi vel illuminati obiectum sibi medium totum simul illustrare.*

Hoc probatur per effectum, quoniam quilibet punctus luminosi vel
20 colorati visibilis est in qualibet parte medii sibi obiecti. Sed non videtur nisi imprimendo super visum. Ergo imprimit in omnem partem medii.

---

1 prima pars *om. BH* pars I *V* liber primus
F theoremata *A*
2 1ª *om. H* I *V* prima propositio primi libri *F* (All but *F* number the propositions
in the margin; *H* has no proposition
numbers; subsequent variant readings
for proposition numbers will be omitted.) / *post* lucem *add. F* fortem / operari
in visum: in visum operari *F* / supra se
conversum *om. F* / aliquid *om. F* aliquem *H*

4 hec *F* / effectus *F*
5 lucis *om. A* / intensive *F* / in oculo *om.*
H in visu *F*
6 luminis: lucis *F*
7 evacuaverit... luminis: evacuaverit vestigium minoris luminis *V* evanuerit vestigium maioris luminis *B* vestigium maioris luminis evanescat *F* evanuerit vestigium luminis precedentis *D* / maioris
in alia manu corr. A ex minoris
11 hec *F* / experimentis: per experimenta

Part I

[*Proposition*] *1{1}. Light produces an impression in the eye that is directed toward it.*

This is proved by an effect, for when the eye sees bright lights, it suffers and endures pain. Also, after a glance [at bright lights], images of intense brightness remain in the eye, and they cause a less illuminated place to appear dark until the traces of the brighter light have disappeared from the eye.[2] {This truth, proved here in order to make manifest the origin of the rays—that they originate not from the eye but from the luminous body—is made clear in the first chapter of the *Perspectiva* by observations such as these.}[3]

[*Proposition*] *2{2}. Illuminated color produces an impression in the eye.*

This is proved by observations similar [to the foregoing]. Furthermore, if the eye after being directed with fixed gaze on a bright color illuminated by an intense light[4] is turned aside to a color illuminated more weakly, it will find that the first and second colors appear intermixed because traces of the afore-seen have been left behind in the eye. {From this it is evident that color excited by light has its own rays distinct from the rays of light.}[5]

[*Proposition*] *3{3}. Any point of a luminous or illuminated object simultaneously illuminates the whole medium adjacent to it.*[6]

This is proved by an effect, for any point of a luminous or colored object is visible in any part whatsoever of the adjacent medium. But the point is seen only by making an impression on the eye. Therefore the point makes an impression on every part of the medium. {This will be more clearly evident below,

---

B | similia *B* sensibilibus *F* | oculos *B*
12 intensione *BF* | si *om. D*
13 deflexerit: reflexerit *F* | *post* secundo
   add. B scilicet colori
14 *post* permisceri *in alia manu mg. hab. A*
   quod non posset causam si / prius: pro-
   prius *V* ex prius *D* quod non potest esse
   F / visis *VH* nisi *B*

17 quodlibet *A*
17–18 obiectum sibi medium: medium sibi
   obiectum *F*
18 simul *om. F*
19 *post* effectum *add. F* communem
20 sed: et *F*
21 in *om. V* secundum *F* | *post* medii *add. B*
   sibi obiecti

{Hoc etiam magis patebit inferius, ubi probatur quod quilibet punctus rei vise in speculo replet specie sua totam superficiem speculi.}

[*Propositio*] *4ª*{*4ª*}. *Totum luminosum vel illuminatum pyramidem sui*
25 *luminis in quolibet puncto medii terminare.*
Hoc probatur, quoniam si quilibet punctus luminosi illustrat quem-libet punctum medii, ergo totum luminosum illustrat quemlibet punctum, quod esse non potest nisi luce pyramidaliter in quemlibet punctum cadente, per quam pyramidem videri potest.

30 {[*Propositio*] *5ª*. *In omni puncto medii illuminati pyramides ex pyramidi-bus exoriri.*
{Illud docetur quarto *Perspective* capitulo tertio, ubi docet quod in quolibet puncto sunt acumina duarum pyramidum quarum bases sunt superficies luminosi et superficies cuiuscunque corporis obiecti.}

35 {[*Propositio*] *6ª*. *Pyramides radiosas ab eadem superficie vel diversis pro-cedentes in fortitudine et debilitate effectuali per singula medii puncta differe.*
{Contra quod sciendum est quod licet omnes pyramides in uno lumine contente sint essentialiter lux una, differunt tamen virtualiter, id est effi-caciter, sicut cum lapis proicitur in aquam generatur circuli diversi, qui
40 tamen aquam non dividunt, sic quodammodo non omniphariam. A quo-libet puncto luminosi radius lucis digreditur virtuose et quanto directius tanto fortius; unde pyramides quanto magis oblique oriuntur a superficie luminosa tanto sunt proculdubio debiliores et quanto rectiores tanto sunt fortiores. Et hec est ratio quare tanta est diversitas terre nascentium, omni
45 cessante cultura, ut hic oriatur urtica ibi fere in medietate herba contrarie speciei. Unde quod dicit Rabi Mosse, singulis terre nascentibus in celo stellas singulas respondere, non est necesse, quoniam secundum diversita-tem pyramidum possunt diversa produci germina virtute eiusdem stelle, utpote talium quarto gradu et secundo ac tertio ab sole vel sidere Martiali,
50 concurrente influentia aliarum stellarum calidarum.}

---

24 totum: locum *B*
25 *ante* medii *add*. *D* presentis / medii *in alia manu hab*. *V*
26 hec *F* / probatur: patet *F* / *ante* illustrat *in alia manu mg*. *hab*. *V* illuminat vel / illustrat: illuminat *F*
27 *ante* illustrat *add*. *F* illuminat vel / illu-stret *D* / *post* punctum[2] *in alia manu mg*. *add*. *D* iuxta ergo totum luminosum il-lustrat quemlibet punctum a
28 in...cadente: in quemlibet punctum medii *F*
37 contra *corr*. *ex* ?onda *D*
38 contente *corr*. *ex* cotente *D*
40 *post* non[1] *scr*. *et del*. *D* ?notandum
49 sole *corr*. *ex* eodem sole *D*
50 *ante* aliarum *scr*. *et del*. *D* ab

where it is proved that any point of an object seen in a mirror fills the whole surface of the mirror with its species.}[7]

[*Proposition*] *4{4}. The pyramid of light originating from the whole luminous or illuminated object terminates at any point of the medium.*[8]

This is proved as follows. If any point of a luminous object illuminates any point of the medium, then the whole luminous object illuminates every point [individually]. [But] this can be true only if light falls to the point in the form of a pyramid, under which the object can be seen.

{[*Proposition*] *5. Pyramids proceed from [other] pyramids at every point of an illuminated medium.*

{This is taught in the third chapter of the fourth book of the *Perspectiva*[9] where it is shown that at any point [in a medium] there are vertices of two pyramids, the bases of which are the surface of the luminous object and the surface of any facing body.}

{[*Proposition*] *6. Radiant pyramids proceeding from the same or different surfaces differ in effective strength and weakness at different points in the medium.*[10]

{Although, contrary to this, it should be known that all the pyramids in a single body of illumination constitute essentially one light, nevertheless they differ virtually, i.e., in efficacy. In the same way, when a stone is thrown into water, distinct circles are generated, which nevertheless do not differentiate the water; hence in a sense the water is not of all [different] sorts. Light departs powerfully from any point on a luminous body, and the more nearly perpendicular, the stronger it is; therefore as pyramids proceed more obliquely from the surface of a luminous body, they are without doubt correspondingly weaker, and as they are more nearly perpendicular, they are correspondingly stronger.[11] This is why without cultivation the diversity of earthly plants is so great, so that now a nettle springs up and then, almost in the middle, an herb of a contrary species.[12] Therefore what Rabbi Moses [Maimonides] says—that individual stars in heaven correspond to individual plants on the earth[13]—is unnecessary, since different crops can be produced by the power of the same star according to the diversity of pyramids, i.e., by the star's second, third, or fourth degree[14] from the sun or Mars, with the concurring influence of other bright stars.}

[*Propositio*] 5*ᵃ*. *Incidentias radiosas per angularia foramina transeuntes mediocris magnitudinis in obiectis corporalibus rotundari semperque fieri eo maiores quo remotiores.*

Hoc sequitur ex quarta partim, quoniam radii in quovis puncto medii
55 pyramidaliter terminati non sistunt ibi sed intersecando se procedunt. Igitur quando per foramen incedunt angulare radii, qui in foramine et iuxta se intersecant, vicine se intersecantes in directum producti, cum in tantam distantiam pervenerint quanta est ex alia parte distantia solis dilatentur ad quantitatem solis, quoniam si anguli contra se positi equales
60 et latera ex utraque parte pyramidis equalia sunt, necesse est et bases equales esse, ut patet ex primo Euclidis.

Causam autem rotunditatis incidentie diversi diversimode nisi sunt assignare. Quidam simpliciter solari tribuunt rotunditati ut sicụt radius a sole sic rotunditas a rotunditate, ad hoc argumentum sensibile assumentes
65 quia tempore eclipsis solaris huius incidentie fiunt novaculares secundum portionem quam abscindit luna de sole, propter quod rotunditas videtur esse a rotunditate. Sed si hec causa sufficeret incidentia ista rotunditatem acquireret sic prope foramen sicut longe a foramine, cuius contrarium videmus.

70 Alii subtilius causam attingentes solarem rotunditatem huius incidentie ponunt causam remotam, radiorum autem intersectionem causam propinquam. Per hunc modum accipiatur foramen triangulare *ABC* [Fig. 1], accipiaturque superficies triangula in corpore solido *DEF*, et sit basis pyramidis triangule incidens per dictum foramen, et latera sua lateribus dicti
75 foraminis applicantis, que et terminetur in puncto *G* ultra foramen. Amplius ymaginemur circulum in sole dictum triangulum non penitus circumscribentem sed paulo minorem, et sit *KLM* circumferentiam suam fere illis angulis applicantem. Ab hoc circulo procedunt pyramides rotunde

52 corporalibus *VAHL* corporibus *BWFD*
54 hoc *BWHD* hec *VAF* / quarta partim: penultima partim *in alia manu hab*. D / quovis: quolibet *F*
55 sed *in alia manu hab*. D
56 incidunt *AF* / foramine: foramen *B* / *post* foramine *add*. *F* producti
57 se intersecant *tr*. D / vicine *VWFH* incipiunt dilatari ct nccessc est (erit D) ut radii in foramine *BAD* / se²: sese *F*
58 perveniunt *BA*
59 dilatantur *BA* dilatatur *F* / positi: oppositi *F* / *post* equales *add*. *FD* sunt
60 et¹ *om*. D / pyramidis *om*. B
61 equales esse *tr*. *AF* / (In *V* Proposition 6

intervenes at this point.)
62 nisi sunt *VBA* intuuntur *WF*
62–119 causam...reperire *om*. *HD*
63 simpliciter *om*. *F* / *post* solari *add*. *A* causam / tribuunt *VBL* attribuunt *AWF* / *post* sicut *in alia manu mg. hab*. *V* primus modus assignandi
64 ad: et *F* / assumunt *F*
65 quia: quod *F* / huius *VAL* huiusmodi *BWF* / fiunt: sunt *F*
66 proportionem *V* / luna de sole (de *obs*. A) *BAL* a sole luna *V* linea a sole *F*
67 ista *VAW*; *om*. B ?bene *F* / *post* rotunditatem *add*. B istam
68 acquirerent *B*

[*Proposition*] *5. Incident rays passing through angular apertures of moderate size appear rounded* [*when they fall*] *on facing bodies, and always become greater* [*in breadth*] *with greater distance* [*from the aperture*].[15]

This follows in part from the fourth proposition, for rays that have been terminated in the form of a pyramid at some point in the medium do not stop there but intersect and continue on. Therefore when rays [from the sun] advancing through an angular aperture and intersecting one another in and near the opening have been extended in a straight line to a distance equal to that which separates the sun from the aperture on the other side, they will have spread out to a width equal to that of the sun. This is so because if the vertical angles are equal and the legs of the pyramid on each side [of the aperture] are equal, then it is evident from the first book of Euclid that the bases must be equal.[16]

Various people have endeavored to assign the cause of the roundness of the incident rays in various ways. Some assign it simply to the roundness of the sun, for since the rays proceed from the sun, the roundness of the rays must result from the roundness of the sun. In addition they appeal to sense experience, for during a solar eclipse the incident rays become crescent-shaped, varying as the portion of the sun cut off by the moon; consequently the roundness [of the rays] evidently derives from the roundness [of the sun]. But if this cause were sufficient, the incident rays would be round both near the aperture and far from the aperture, whereas the contrary is observed.[17]

Others more subtly investigating the cause consider the roundness of the sun as a remote cause of such [circular] incidence and the intersection of the rays as the proximate cause. Thus assume triangular aperture *ABC* [Fig. 1] and triangular surface *DEF* in the solid body [i.e., the sun]. Let this triangular surface be the base of a triangular pyramid incident through the aforesaid aperture, let the sides of the pyramid be in contact with the sides of the aperture, and let the pyramid be terminated at point *G* beyond the aperture. Further, let us imagine a circle in the sun not completely circumscribing the aforementioned triangle, but slightly smaller. Let *KLM* be the circumference of this circle, almost passing through the vertices [of the triangle].[18] From this circle, round

---

71 *ante* causam[2] *add. BA* ut

72 triangulare: angulare *B*

73 triangula *VAL* triangularis *BF* / solido *VWL* solis *BA* solari *F*

73–74 basis...triangule *VBL* basis triangulare pyramidis *A* pyramidis basis par basi trianguli *F*

74 incidens *VBWL* incidentis *AF* / et: in *B*

75 applicantis *VAW* applicatis *B* applicans *F*

77 *post* minorem *add. BA* nec tamen circumscriptum a triangulo sed medie quantitatis inter circulum circumscribentem triangulum *et etiam add. B* et circulum circumscriptum ab ipso

quarum nulla potest attingere penitus usque *G*, angustia foraminis impe-
80   diente. Potest tamen aliqua attingere forsitan ad punctum aliquem foramini propinquiorem vel saltem in ipsa superficie foraminis contentum,
verbi gratia sit punctus *H*. Certum est quod angulus pyramidis terminate
in puncto *H* maior est quam angulus pyramidis terminate in *G*, quia brevioris pyramidis. Certum est autem quod radii pyramidis brevioris, ratione
85   maioris anguli quem continent ducti in continuum et directum, secabunt
radios pyramidis longioris; et qui ante intersectionem fuerunt contenti vel
inclusi post intersectionem fiunt includentes. Igitur cum pyramis brevior
sit rotunda sequitur ut post intersectionem dictam incidentiam faciant
rotundam, sicut patet in figure quatenus planities potest figuras solidas
90   declarare. Patet enim quoniam radii pyramidis rotunde *KMH* cadunt in
H et, ibi sese intersecantes, extra triangularem pyramidem sese dilatant.

79 attingere penitus (*in alia manu mg. hab.*
   V) *VFL* pertingere penitus integra *BA* /
   ante G *add. F* ad
79–80 *ante* impediente *add. A* pyramide
80 aliqua *in alia manu del. A* aliquid aliud
   F / attingere *VWFL* pertingere *BA* /
   forsitan *om. B*
82–83 certum...H *om. A*
83 maior est: sit maior *F* / *post* in[2] *add. W*
   puncto / *post* G *add. F* per 21 Euclidis /
   post quia *add. BA* longe
83–84 *post* brevioris[1] *add. B* est
84 pyramidis[2] *om. A*
86 *post* intersectionem *add. B* vel / fuerunt

contenti *VFL; tr.* (*sed secundum verbum*
obs.) *B* fuerint contenti *A*
87 inclusi post: conclusi per *F* / *post* intersectionem *scr. et del. A* ?sunt / fiunt includentes *tr. A* fiunt concludentes *F*
88 *ante* intersectionem *add. F* illam / faciant
   VBWL faciat *A* faciunt *F*
89 sicut: ut *F* / quatenus *VBL* QFG *A*
   quamvis *F* / potest...solidas: figuras
   solidas non potest manifeste *F*
90 quoniam *VBWL* qui *A* quod quoniam
   F / KMH: KLM *F* KNH *B*
91 sese[2] *VBL* se *AWF*

pyramids emanate, none of which can reach *G* [in their entirety] because they are obstructed by the narrowness of the aperture. However, a pyramid can perhaps reach [in its entirety] a point nearer the aperture, or at least a point contained within the aperture, such as point *H*. It is certain that the angle of the pyramid terminated at point *H* is larger than the angle of the pyramid terminated at *G*, since the former pyramid is shorter. Moreover, it is certain

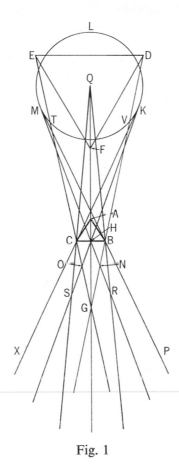

Fig. 1

that, when extended without interruption in a straight line, the rays of the shorter pyramid, by virtue of the greater angle that they contain, intersect those of the longer pyramid. Indeed, those rays that were surrounded or enclosed before intersection come to enclose [the others] after intersection. Therefore, since the shorter pyramid is round, it follows that after intersection its rays make the incident beam round, as is evident in the figure (insofar as plane surfaces are able to represent solid figures). This is clear because the rays of the round pyramid *KMH* fall to *H* and, after intersecting one another there, spread

Amplius si accipiantur radii a sole centraliter egredientes qui sunt fortiores aliis radiando, sicut *QB* et *QC*, ipsi cadunt intra predictam rotundam pyramidem, secantes eam in punctis *R S*. Ergo saltem post illam intersectionem
95 erit pyramis rotunda.

Sed certe hec ymaginatio locum haberet etiam si sol esset magne figure quadrate, in ipso enim esset aliquis triangulus qui posset foramen triangulare directe respicere et circulus triangulum fere circumscribens a quo posset pyramis rotunde procedere. Amplius secundum hoc pyramis rotundi-
100 tatem acquireret subito, scilicet in sectione istarum duarum pyramidum *NO* vel *RS*, quia secundum hoc quicquid esset ultra *NO* vel ad minus *RS* esset rotundum complete, quicquid citra triangulare, cuius contrarium manifeste videmus, quia videmus lumen ipsum paulatim rotunditatem acquirere.

105 Dico igitur istam intersectionem ad rotunditatem posse conferre sed non totam causam ministrare. Sciendum igitur figuram spericam esse luci cognatam et omnibus mundi corporibus esse consonam utpote nature maxime salvativam, que omnes partes suo intimo perfectissime coniungit, unde et stilla in rotunditatem incidit. Ad hanc igitur naturaliter lux move-
110 tur et eam protelata distantia paulatim acquirit. In tempore autem eclipsis fit novaculatio predicta quia impeditur accidentalis et secundaria lucis diffusio in parte illa qua radii solares abscinduntur, deficiente enim principali lumine necesse est secundarium deficere. Amplius si rotunditas esset ex intersectione tunc si sol eclipsaretur in parte orientali deficeret incidentia
115 in parte occidentali et non in eadem parte cum sole. Amplius radii *VX* et *TP* applicant se lateribus foraminis et sequuntur figuram eius, et certum est quod isti omnes alios includunt qui rotunditatem possint radiositate

92 *post* radii *add. F* solares *et scr. et del. A* a QB et QO ipsi cadunt intra predictam pyramidem

93 *ante* radiando *add. F* in / *ante* QB *add. F* sunt / QC: QO *A* / predictam: dictam *B*

94 secantes eam *tr. A* / *post* punctis *add. F* duobus / *ante* ergo *add. F* et / intersectionem: in sectionem *V*

96 *post* certe *add. F* est quod / etiam: et *B*

97 ipsa *B*

98 respicere: inspicere *F* / circumscriberet *F* / *supra* circumscribens *in alia manu hab. V* ret

99 *post* procedere *add. BA* et ita (ibi *B*) rotunditas solis nec (nec *in alia manu corr. A ex* ut) est (*om. B*) causa propinqua nec remota huius rotunditatis / secundum

…pyramis: pyramis secundum hoc *A*

99–100 rotunditatem acquireret *tr. F*

100 in sectione: post intersectionem *F* / istarum: illarum *F* / *post* pyramidum *add. F* in punctis

101 NO vel RS: NO vel PS *B* NORS *A* RS NO *F* / quia *VWFL* et *BA* / quicquid: aliquid *B* / NO^2: ON *F*

102 *ante* rotundum *add. F* totum / rotundum: rotum *V* / completum *B* / *ante* quicquid *add. B* et *et add. F* et similiter / *ante* citra *add. WF* esset

102–3 cuius…manifeste *VL* manifeste huius contrarium *B* manifeste cuius quarum (*scr. et del.* quarum) contrarium *A* cuius contrarium evenire manifeste *F*

103 ipsum *om. F*

105 *ante* dico *add. A* et

outside the triangular pyramid. Furthermore, if we consider rays emanating from the center of the sun, such as QB and QC—these being more strongly radiated than the others—they fall within the aforementioned round pyramid, cutting it at points R and S. Therefore the pyramid will be round at least after that intersection.

But surely the same notion would be appropriate even if the sun were a great square, for in it there would be some triangle that could be aligned with the triangular aperture [as triangle DEF in the round sun] and a circle almost circumscribing that triangle from which a round pyramid could proceed.[19] Furthermore, according to this [reasoning], the pyramid should become round instantaneously at intersection NO or RS of those two pyramids because whatever is beyond NO, or at least beyond RS, is completely round, while that which is before is triangular. [But] the contrary of this clearly appears, for we see that the light acquires roundness gradually.

I maintain, therefore, that intersection can contribute to roundness but cannot serve as the whole cause. It should be recognized, accordingly, that the spherical shape is associated with light and is in harmony with all the bodies of the world as being to the highest degree conservative of nature, all parts of which it joins together most perfectly within itself.[20] This is why a raindrop assumes roundness. Therefore light is naturally moved toward this shape and gradually assumes it when propagated some distance. During an eclipse, however, the aforementioned crescent shape is produced because the accidental and secondary diffusion of light is prevented in the region from which the solar rays are cut off; or when the principal light is removed, the secondary light must cease. Moreover, if roundness resulted from the intersection [of the pyramids at NO or RS], then if the sun were eclipsed on the eastern side, the incident rays would be absent on the western side rather than on the same side as [the eclipsed portion of] the sun.[21] Furthermore, rays VX and TP are in contact with the sides of the aperture and conform to its shape, and it is certain that they encompass all others that could generate roundness by direct radia-

---

106 figuram: luci A / *post* spericam *in alia manu mg. hab.* V figura sperica luci cognata mundi corporibus ?consona nature salvativa / esse luci $VWFL$; *tr.* BA

107 *post* cognatam *add.* F et aque aque (*sic*) / *ante* corporibus *add.* A pyramidalibus / *post* corporibus *add.* B principalibus

108 intimo: vicine F / perfectissime $VBAL$ perfectissimeque WF

109 *post* et *add.* F si / rotunditatem $VBAL$

rotunditate WF / igitur: etiam A / naturaliter lux $VWFL$; *tr.* (*sed primum verbum obs.* A) BA

111 *post* impeditur *add.* B ista

112 *ante* qua *add.* BA in

113 lumine *om.* B / *post* est *add.* F et

114 intersectione: inter B

116 TP: RP B / *ante* lateribus *scr. et del.* V foraminibus

117 possunt F

recta generare. Per modum igitur radiositatis, ut dictum est, impossibile est causam rotunditatis perfecte reperire.

120   {[*Propositio*] *7ª. Incidentias radiosas per angularia foramina transeuntes mediocris magnitudinis in obiectis corporalibus rotundari semperque fieri eo maiores quo remotiores.*

{Hoc sequitur ex quarta partim, quoniam radii in quovis puncto medii pyramidaliter terminati non sistunt ibi sed intersecando se procedunt.
125 Igitur quando per foramen incedunt angulare radii, qui in foramine et iuxta se intersecant, vicine se intersecantes in directum producti, cum in tantam distantiam pervenerint quanta est ex alia parte distantia solis dilatentur ad quantitatem solis, quoniam si anguli contra se positi equales et latera ex utraque parte pyramidis equalia sunt, necesse est et bases equales
130 esse, ut patet ex primo Euclidis. Sed licet per hoc probetur incidentiam ipsam in magna distantia posse equare quo ad magnitudinem superficiei solaris, non tamen per hoc probatur incidentiam huius rotundari, quia impeditur radiatio rotunditatis per improportionem figure foraminis per quod transit. Verbi gratia tempore eclipsis solaris apparet incidentia ra-
135 diosa novaculata secundum quantitatem luminis solaris quod abscindit pars lune interposita inter solem et terram.

{Huius igitur rotunditatis causam alii dicunt esse naturalem, alii mathematicam. Universalem causam assignant huius rotunditatis ipsam proprietatem lucis, quoniam cum lux sit nobilissima formarum corporalium, uni-
140 versaliter tendit ad figuram nobilissimam, scilicet orbicularem, que maxime conveniens est simplici corpori; unde omnes partes mundi simplices rotunditatem habent. Sed contra hoc arguitur quia sic tempore eclipsis non appareret huius incidentia novacularis, sed vinceret radius defectum qui accidit ex interpositione lune per virtutem lucis. Preterea ubicunque pona-
145 tur oculus in incidentia potest videre corpus solis, visio autem non est nisi per lineam rectam. Ergo figura incidentie sequitur modum radiorum huius; cuiuscunque sit figure terminus est linearum radialium. Ergo numquam acquirit rotunditatem nisi quatenus causatur a lineis radiosis.

{Idcirco dicunt alii quod rotunditas causatur per intersectionem radio-
150 rum et per viam mathematicam, ad cuius intelligentiam notandum quod lux solaris dupliciter se diffundit, scilicet directe et radiose, et hec dicitur lux primaria. Item alio modo indirecte in omnem directionem et extra

118 igitur: autem *F*
119 est *om. F*
131 quo ad *corr. ex* quo ad quid *D*
137 *post* causam *in alia manu mg. hab. D* opiniones rotunditatis causam
142 *post* tempore *in alia manu mg. hab. D* contra unam

144 *ante* lucis *in alia manu mg. hab. D* iterum
145 in *in alia manu hab. D*
150 *ante* et *in alia manu mg. hab. D* prima opinio / intelligentiam *corr. ex* incluam *D*
152 directionem *corr. ex* differentiam *D*

tion. Therefore, as already stated, it is impossible to attribute the cause of roundness entirely to the manner of radiating.

{[*Proposition*] 7. *Incident rays passing through angular apertures of moderate size appear rounded* [*when they fall*] *on facing bodies, and always become greater* [*in breadth*] *with greater distance* [*from the aperture*].

{This follows in part from the fourth proposition, for rays that have been terminated in the form of a pyramid at some point in the medium do not stop there but intersect and continue on. Therefore when rays [from the sun] advancing through an angular aperture and intersecting one another in and near the opening have been extended in a straight line to a distance equal to that which separates the sun from the aperture on the other side, they will have spread out to a width equal to that of the sun. This is so because if the vertical angles are equal and the legs of the pyramid on each side [of the aperture] are equal, then it is evident from the first book of Euclid that the bases must be equal.[22] But although it is thus proved that at a great distance the incident beam can be as wide as the solar surface, nevertheless it is not proved that such incident rays are rounded; for the rays are deprived of roundness because roundness does not accord with the shape of the aperture through which they pass. For example, the incident rays appear crescent-shaped during a solar eclipse according to the amount of solar light cut off by the part of the moon interposed between the sun and the earth.

{Therefore some say that the cause of this roundness is natural, others that it is mathematical. [The former] attribute the universal cause of this roundness to a property of light, for since light is the most excellent of corporeal forms,[23] it always strives toward the most excellent shape, namely, roundness. Since this shape is most appropriate for a simple body, all simple parts of the world are round. It is argued in opposition to this view that, if it were true, the incident rays would not appear crescent-shaped during an eclipse, for by the power of light the rays would overcome the defect resulting from the interposition of the moon. Besides, no matter where in the incident beam the eye is placed, it can see the body of the sun, and sight occurs only in straight lines. Therefore, the shape of the incident beam follows from the behavior of such [rectilinear] rays, [so that] whatever its shape, it is the boundary [determined by] radial lines.[24] Consequently the beam acquires roundness only insofar as this is caused by radiation in straight lines.

{Others claim that roundness is caused by intersection of the rays and hence in a mathematical manner. For an understanding of this it should be noted that solar light emanates in two ways: by radiating directly—this is called primary light—and also [by radiating] indirectly in every direction outside the rays. By

radios, sicut sole existente super orizontem domus est plena luce quamvis
nullus eam intret radius solaris; et hec dicitur lux secundaria vel acciden-
155 talis, quia videtur esse per modum alterationis, quo calida et frigida et
similia solent circa se posita alterare. Item sciendum quod duo sunt genera
radiorum solarium, quidam enim sunt diametrales seu verticales a centro
solis per superficiem eiusdem perpendiculariter exeuntes, et isti radii in
directum procedentes numquam concurrunt, ut *AB* et *AC* et *AD* [Fig. 2].
160 Alii sunt radii solares declinantes, hoc est orientes a sole ad angulos in-
equales, ut *BE* et *BF*, et isti radii multiplicant pyramides in medio, ut patet
ex precedentibus, quoniam quilibet punctus solis gignit pyramidem sui
luminis cuius basis est in medio. Item per alium modum a tota superficie
solis visibili procedunt pyramides infinite, terminate singule in singulis
165 punctis aeris obiecti consistentes ex huius radii declinantibus, quarum
tamen quelibet habet axem verticalem et est axis media linea pyramidis.
Et in hoc ultimo genere radiorum querenda precipue est causa rotunditatis
incidentiarum. Verbi gratia sit pyramis *ABC* [Fig. 3]. Certum erit quod
radii *BA* et *CA* conveniunt ad punctum *A* et non sistunt in *A* sed trans-
170 eunt intersecando se, verbi gratia ad puncta *D E*. Et est angulus *DAE*
equalis angulo *BAC* cum sint contraposita. Hiis igitur suppositis, ad causam rotunditatis inveniendam procedunt quidam sic: Detur foramen triangulare equilaterum, id est ysopleurus, qui sit *GHI* [Fig. 4], et sumatur
superficies solis a qua incidunt pyramides per ysopleurum et partes con-
175 trapositas, que fit *KL*. Dicunt igitur quod omni pyramidum transeuntium
per ysopleurum brevior est *KLM*, que scilicet terminatur in medio puncto

means of the latter, when the sun is situated over the horizon, a house is full
of light, even though no solar rays enter it; and this is called secondary or accidental light because it is seen to exist through the mode of alteration, as hot
and cold objects and similar things customarily alter things placed around them.
It should be understood also that there are two kinds of solar rays. Some are
diametrical or vertical, [i.e.,] proceeding from the center of the sun [and emerg-
ing] through its surface perpendicularly; these rays—such as *AB*, *AC*, and *AD*
[Fig. 2]—proceeding in straight lines, never intersect. There are other solar rays
that are inclined, i.e., emerging from the sun obliquely, such as *BE* and *BF*;
these rays produce a multiplicity of pyramids in the medium, as is evident from
the foregoing,[25] because every point of the sun is the origin of a pyramid of
light, the base of which is in the medium. Likewise an infinite number of pyra-

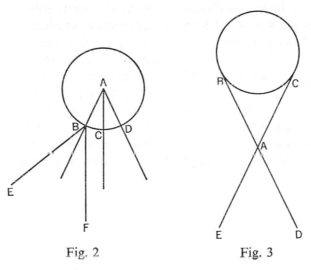

Fig. 2   Fig. 3

mids [with bases on the sun] proceed in a reverse manner from the whole visible
surface of the sun and are individually terminated at distinct points in the adjacent air because of the inclination of the rays. Nevertheless, each of these
pyramids has a vertical axis, which is the middle line of the pyramid. And the
cause of roundness of the incident radiation is to be sought chiefly in this latter
kind of ray. For example, let *ABC* be a pyramid [Fig. 3]. It is certain that rays
BA and *CA* come together at point *A* and do not stop there, but after intersection pass over to points such as *D* and *E*; and angles *DAE* and *BAC* are equal
because they are [vertically] opposite. Therefore, having supposed these things,
some people proceed to assign the cause of roundness as follows. Assume an
equilateral triangular aperture, i.e., an isopleure, *GHI* [Fig. 4]. Let *KL* be the
surface of the sun from which pyramids fall through the aperture and [into]
the region beyond. They say then that *KLM*, which is terminated at the middle
point of the aperture, is shorter than any other pyramid passing through the

foraminis, quoniam axis eius qui est media linea pyramidis est brevissima
cum sit perpendicularis, quod patet ex primo Euclidis. Et si brevissima est
continet maiorem angulum quam alie, et per consequens angulus eius
180   contrapositus erit maior angulis aliarum pyramidum contrapositis; et per
consequens si ducantur linee continentes hos angulos in continuum et
directum per modicum spatium, pyramis contraposita pyramidi *KLM*
omnes alias absorbebit, et habebit incidentiam rotundam qualiter est superficies solis *KL*.

185   {Sed ista responsio nimis ex insufficienta procedit, tria sunt enim genera
pyramidum a superficie solis taliter procedentium; quedam enim applicant
conum suum superficie ysopleuri, et de hiis tenet argumentum predictum
quod absorbentur a breviori pyramide, que est *KLM*. Alie sunt que habent
conos suos inter superficiem ysopleuri et corpus solis, et iste sicut sunt
190   breviores sic sunt obtusiores precedentibus. Tertium genus pyramidum
transit per ysopleurum et habet conos suos ultra superficiem ysopleuri, et
iste sunt ceteris acutiores per regulas supradictas. Igitur ducatur a puncto
K ad angulum *GIH* linea [Fig. 5]. Item ducatur alia linea a puncto *L* ad
angulum *IGH*. Certum est quod ille due linee *KI* et *GL* intersecant se inter
195   superficiem solis et superficiem ysopleuri, puta in puncto *O*, quia ab eadem
basi ad angulos sibi invicem contrapositos ducuntur. Igitur per consequens
habet pyramis maiorem angulum tam intra se contentum quam contra se
positum. Ergo linee continentes hos angulos absorbent, in continuum et

177 qui *corr. ex* que *D*   196 *post* ducuntur *hab. D* intersecant ergo se
188 absorbentur *corr. ex* absorbetur *D*   inter superficiem solis et superficiem
189 *post* ysopleuri *scr. et del. D* et de hiis te-   ysopleuri puta in puncto O
        net argumentum predictum

aperture [and having its vertex in the plane of the aperture]; for its axis, which is the middle line of the pyramid, is shorter than the axis of any other pyramid because it is perpendicular [to the aperture], as is evident from the first book of Euclid.[26] If this is the shortest pyramid, it contains a larger [vertical] angle than the others, and consequently the [vertically] opposite angle will be larger than that of the other pyramids. Therefore if the lines enclosing these angles are extended in a straight line through a small distance, the pyramid [vertically] opposite pyramid *KLM* will swallow up all others, and [its base] is round like the surface of the sun *KL*.

{This answer is insufficient, however, for there are three kinds of pyramids

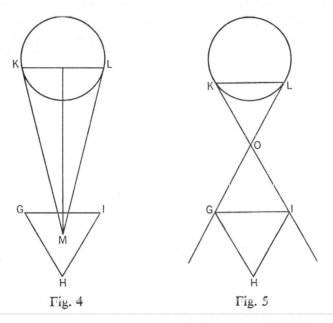

Fig. 4   Fig. 5

proceeding from the surface of the sun in that manner.[27] Some direct their vertices to the surface of the aperture, and the foregoing argument—that they would be swallowed up by the shorter pyramid *KLM*—holds [only] for these. Other pyramids have their vertices between the aperture and the sun, and since these are shorter, they are more obtuse than the aforementioned pyramids. The third kind of pyramid passes through the aperture and has its vertex beyond the plane of the aperture, and these pyramids are more acute than the others, according to the rules mentioned above. Therefore draw a line from point *K* to angle *GIH* [Fig. 5] and another line from point *L* to angle *IGH*. It is certain that lines *KI* and *GL* intersect between the surface of the sun and the plane of the aperture, as at point *O*, because they are drawn from the same base to angles alternately opposite. Consequently the pyramid has a larger angle, both contained within it and placed [vertically] opposite. Therefore, if the lines con-

directum producte, omnium aliarum pyramidum longiorum lineas et incidentias. Sed certum est quod ille linee transeuntes per angulos transeunt
extra omnes pyramides rotundas; ergo necesse est quod incidentia sit angularis et non rotunda. Item si esset foramen circulare faceret incidentiam
rotundam per vim radiationis directe. Ergo videtur quod quantum deest
foramini de rotunditate tantum deest incidentie proportionaliter de rotunditate per viam directe radiationis. Item si in superficie ysopleuri inscri-
batur superficies circuli solidi remanebant tres trianguli partim irregulares
vacui in circuitu circuli. Et si triangulus cum inscripto circulo obiciatur
radio solari lumen transiens per quemlibet triangulorum predictorum,
qui sunt anguli ysopleuri, faciet tandem incidentie sue figuram rotundam
parve rotunditatis. Et si auferatur circulus inscriptus a superficie trianguli
ut libere transeat radius solaris per totum ysopleurum, terminabitur tandem radius sic transiens ad incidentiam maioris rotunditatis, cuius partes
impossibile est esse predictorum trium circulorum portiones. Ergo impossibile est quod per viam radiationis radioli transitantes per tres angulos
ysopleuri extra circumferentiam circuli inscripti concurrant in eadem superficie circulari cum lumine transeunte per concavitatem circuli inscripti
ysopleuro.

{Propter quod videtur non nullis quod rotunditas incidentie causatur
ex utroque ut videlicet per intersectionem habeat dilatationis magnitudinem sed per naturam lucis rotunditatis perfectionem, quia videlicet lux de-
ficiens modice a rotunditate per vicinitatem alterius lucis formam iudicat
connaturalem. Tantus tamen posset esse excessus unius dimensionis super
aliam quod lux radians evanesceret prius inter radios disgregatos quam
rotunditatem acquireret. Quod etiam lux extra radiositatem possit, quasi
radiose, se diffundere patet per simile, quia radius lucis et coloris post-
quam pervenerunt ad humorem glacialem qui est intra centrum oculi procedunt oblique per ramos nervi optici usque ad ipsum nervum opticum,
ubi coniungitur species speciei; et fit una species visibilis ex concursu, et
tamen ille species orientes ab eadem parte rei vise. Sicut impossible est
duas rectas lineas concurrere, ita impossibile esset istas duas species concurrere in eadem parte nervi optici si procederent intra nervos sicut ve-
niunt ad oculum, radiose, sicut hec sequentia declarabunt absque demonstrationis vitio circularis. Et illum processum specierum pro parte extra
rectitudinem facit via spirituum, istum autem facit naturalis convenientia

---

202 *ante* item *in alia manu mg. hab. D* iterum   216 circulari *corr. ex* circuli *D*
205 *ante* item *in alia manu mg. hab. D* iterum   218 *post* propter *in alia manu mg. hab. D*
210 a . . . trianguli *in alia manu hab. D*   hec directe

taining the latter angles are extended rectilinearly, they swallow up the lines and the incident rays of all the longer pyramids. But it is certain that the lines crossing through the corners [of the aperture] pass outside all round pyramids, and consequently the incident rays must be angular rather than round. Besides, if the aperture were circular, it would cause the incident rays to be round by the power of direct radiation; therefore it is clear that by direct radiation the incident rays are noncircular insofar as the aperture is noncircular. Furthermore, if an opaque circular area should be inscribed within the equilateral triangular aperture, three somewhat irregular triangles would remain empty at the periphery of the circle. If this triangle with its inscribed circle should then be placed in the path of solar rays, the light passing through each of the aforementioned triangles, i.e., the corners of the triangular aperture, would [according to the view now being considered] at length form a round incident beam of small diameter. If the inscribed circle were then removed from the surface of the aperture so that solar rays could freely pass through the entire triangular opening, the rays so passing would at length form a round incident beam of larger diameter; and the aforementioned three circles could not possibly be included in this beam. Therefore it is impossible that the small beams passing through the three corners of the aperture outside the periphery of the inscribed circle should, by [direct] radiation, fall on the same circular surface as does the light passing through the interior of the circle inscribed in the aperture.

{On this account it seems to some that roundness of the incident rays has two causes, such that by intersection the rays spread out and by the nature of light they have perfect roundness; for clearly light slightly lacking in roundness can, by the proximity of another light, be judged to have its own natural [i e, round] shape. Yet one dimension [of a noncircular beam] could be so much greater than the other that the radiating light would vanish [by separating] into its individual rays before it could [travel far enough to] acquire roundness.[28] It is evident from a similar case that light can also diffuse itself, as though by radiating, outside the [main body of] radiation; for rays of light and color, after reaching the glacial humor at the center of the eye, proceed obliquely through the branches of the optic nerve to the optic nerve itself where the two species, originating from the same part of the visible object, are joined to produce one visible species by intersection. As it is impossible for two straight lines [proceeding from the same origin] to intersect, so it would be impossible for these two species to converge on the same part of the optic nerve if they were to advance within the nerves in the same manner as that by which they approach the eye, namely, by radiating [directly], as the following considerations, free from the defects of circular demonstration, will prove. But the mode of spirits causes the species to depart partially from a rectilinear path,[29] though it is a natural disposition [of light] and the diffusion of secondary light greatly strengthened by the proximity of [primary] rays that bring this about [in the

235   et lucis secundarie diffusio vicinitate radiorum confortata. Et hec dicta
      sunt sine preiudicio sententie melioris.
          {Ad hoc autem quoniam frequenter circulus huius lucis incidentie est
      debilioris luminis quam sit pars luminis proportionata angulari foramini
      quod transit, et per hoc patet responsio ad obiectum de incidentia tem-
240   pore eclipsis, quoniam lux intensior novaculatur, et tamen ipsa novacula-
      tio luce quadam minori superducitur. Preterea sciendum est quod gloria
      luminis radiosi consistit in radiis verticalibus a centro solis procedentibus,
      de quibus dictum est supra. Et quia tempore eclipsis abscinditur pars
      magna istorum radiorum, alioquin non appareret eclipsis, merito apparet
245   incidentia novaculata, et lumen aliorum radiorum minoratur. Sed per
      omne foramen quantumcunque parvum transit tantum de primo genere
      radiorum quantum de tertio vel secundo, et ideo fortius est lumen extra
      tempus eclipsis et potentius ad figuram huius acquirendam quam tempore
      eclipsis. Quod si queris utrum oculus positus in quacunque parte inciden-
250   tie radiose videat solem ultra ysopleurum, dico quod sic, sicut species
      oblique veniens ad locum iudicii interioris ostendit rem visam. Et ita fit
      visio per radios declinantes dum tamen recte a visibili oriantur. Item ad
      principale est argumentum, quia radius transiens per ysopleurum non
      statim rotundatur sed per spatium; et cum incipit recedere a figura fora-
255   minis primo obtunduntur anguli, et deinde tota figura variatur quasi an-
      gularitas sit magis contraria nature luminis. Et hoc videre poterit qui in
      hiis experiendis voluerit solicitus excubare. Forte posset aliqui videri quod
      ista rotunditas causaretur ex pyramidibus applicantibus conos suos late-
      ribus ysopleuri, quia huius pyramides sunt rotunde utpote a rotunditate
260   solaris superficiei procedentes. Sed illud improbatur ut supra, quia bre-
      viores pyramides absorbent longiores. Preterea tres pyramides rotunde
      non possunt per viam irradiationis convenire in unam pyramidem rotun-
      dam quarum maxime axes differunt et continue disgregantur, omnis enim
      pyramidis unius est axis una.
265   {Nec appareat alicui ridiculosum quod lux ex hiis duabus causis pariter
      rotundetur, quoniam flamma ex particularibus et naturalibus causis ascen-
      dit pyramidaliter, quoniam secundum leges universales mundi ignis habe-
      ret ascendere in forma pyramidi contraria, scilicet secundum dyametros
      mundi, quoniam hec est via brevissima. Sicut grave descendit ad angulum
270   quia movetur ad centrum quod est indivisibile, ita ignis econtra habet
      ascendendo continue dilatari per regulas generales; cum tamen ascensum

237 *post* hoc *in alia manu add. D* est   ergo
239 *ante* quod *hab. D* ?et
241 gloria *corr. ex* similia *D*   252 *ante* item *in alia manu mg. hab. D* iterum
249 *ante* quod *in alia manu mg. hab. D* quo   254 sed *in alia manu hab. D*
251 *ante* veniens *in alia manu mg. hab. D*   257 *ante* videri *scr. et del. D* vi
                                                265 ridiculosum *corr. ex* rudiculosum *D*

case of radiation through an aperture]; and these things are asserted in the absence of any better opinion.

{Since the circle of incident light is often weaker than the light as it passes through the angular aperture because [the former] travels [farther], the reply to the objection concerning incidence during an eclipse is evident; for the stronger light is crescent-shaped, while the circle is filled out by a weaker light. Furthermore, it should be recognized that the splendor of radiant light consists of rays (discussed above) emanating from the center of the sun as vertex. And since many of those rays are cut off during an eclipse—for otherwise the eclipse would not be apparent—the incident rays properly appear crescent-shaped, and the light corresponding to the other rays is diminished. But however small the aperture, as many of the first kind of rays pass through as do those of the third or second kind. Therefore light is stronger and better able to acquire the shape of the latter kind when there is no eclipse than during an eclipse.[30] But if you should ask whether the eye placed anywhere in the incident beam would see the sun beyond the aperture by [direct] radiation, I would answer, yes, just as species obliquely incident on the place of interior judgment exhibit the visible object. Therefore sight is achieved through rays that are inclined [relative to the observer] though nevertheless emanating perpendicularly from the visible object. The case covered by the principal argument is similar, since a ray passing through the aperture is not rounded immediately but within a [certain] distance; and as the rays lose the shape of the aperture, first the corners are blunted and then the shape of the whole is altered as if angularity were quite contrary to the nature of light. This can be seen by anyone who will endeavor to watch very carefully in experiments on these things. Perhaps it could [also] seem that somehow roundness is caused by the pyramids that direct their vertices to the sides of the aperture, for such pyramids are round because they proceeed from the roundness of the solar surface. But this [argument] is rejected [here] just as it was above, since shorter pyramids swallow up longer ones. Furthermore, three round pyramids, the axes of which differ greatly and diverge continuously, cannot collect into a single round pyramid by radiating [directly], since each pyramid has its own axis.

{It should not appear ridiculous to anyone that light should be rounded through the action of two causes, since flame in like manner ascends in the form of a pyramid from both particular and natural causes. For according to general laws of the universe, fire should ascend in the form of an inverted pyramid, i.e., along diameters of the universe, this being the shortest path. Inasmuch as a heavy body descends toward an angle because it is moved toward the center [of the universe], which is a point, just so fire, by performing the contrary [motion] of ascent, must continually expand according to general rules.

---

269 *ante* sicut *hab. D* ?ita

eius videamus contrarium per causas speciales, quia partes interiores ignis magis habent de virtute ignea et ideo velocius se expediunt ascendendo, quod pro tanto est simile, quia nature lucis convenit precipue in circulum
275   dilatari. Nec invidebo melius pertractanti sed ut didascalum venerabor.}

[*Propositio*] *6ª. Omnem punctum luminosi emisperialiter super medium radiare.*

Hoc probatur, quoniam si punctus lucis in dyaphono ponatur orbicu-lariter se diffundit. Cum autem situatur punctus in superficie corporis
280   densi, medietas sibi precluditur spatii, quantum abscindit densitas corpo-ris in quo situatur. Ergo restat sibi diffusio emisperialis, et hoc intelligitur in planis et spericis superficiebus, quoniam in concavis aliter est, ubi con-cavitas prohibet lumen libere ampliari.

{[*Propositio*] *8ª. Omnem punctum luminosi emisperialiter super obiectum*
285   *sibi medium radiare.*

{Hoc probatur, quoniam cum omnia luminosa sint densa, si ymagine-mur punctum lucis poni in perspicuo multiplicabit se in omnem partem equaliter. Ergo speram constituet suo lumine. Sed si sit punctus lucis in superficie luminosi plani vel sperici amittit libertatem sue diffusionis a
290   parte densi et perdit medietatem eius. Ergo restat ut ex se gignat nisi alti-tudine impediatur lumen emisperiale.}

[*Propositio*] *7ª. Radios visibilium impermixte medium illustrare.*

Lumina enim non confundi in medio patet per umbras, que numerantur secundum numerum luminarium. Multe enim candele ad unum opacum
295   tot faciunt umbras quot sunt candele.

{[*Propositio*] *9ª. Radios visibilium unius vel plurium impermixte vel po-tius inconfuse medium illustrare.*

{Istud patet sensibiliter, quoniam si ponatur stilus in medio candelarum tot fiunt umbre quot candele, quod non fieret nisi lumen cuiuslibet a
300   lumine alterius differens remaneret. Hoc patet etiam in luce secundaria, quoniam si lux secundaria solis intret per fenestras sibi vicinas oblique se respicientes, in diversis parietibus unius anguli, si erigatur stilus in con-

274 in *in alia manu hab. D*
275 pertractanti *corr. ex* perstractanti *D*
276 omne *FH*
278 hec *F*
279 punctum *A*
280 sibi *om. B* / quantum *VBHL* quam *AWF*
281 emisperii *F* / hoc intelligitur *BAL*; *tr.* *WF* hoc *VH*
282 in…est: aliter est in concavis *F*
283 prohibet…ampliari: ampliari prohibet

lumen libere *F*
289 *ante* luminosi *scr. et del. D* luas
290–91 altitudine *corr. ex* altunde *D*
292 *post* radios *add. F* diversorum
293 non: in *F* / confundi in medio: medio non diffundi (non *in alia manu alt. ad* radios) *F*
294 ad *om. F*
295 faciunt *in alia manu corr. VH ex* facit / quot: quod *A*

Nevertheless, its ascent appears the opposite [of this] to us from particular causes, for the interior parts of fire have more burning power [than the other parts] and therefore in ascent drive themselves upward more quickly;[31] [this follows] insofar as [the nature of fire] is similar to the nature of light because light is suited to expansion, especially into circular form. And I shall not envy anyone treating [the matter] better [than I], but would venerate [him] as a teacher.}

[*Proposition*] *6. Every point of a luminous body irradiates the medium hemispherically.*[32]

This is proved by the fact that a point of light placed in a transparent medium diffuses itself spherically.[33] However, when the point is situated on the surface of a dense body, it is excluded from half the space insofar as it is cut off by the density of the body on which it is situated. Therefore it can diffuse itself only hemispherically. This is true for plane and spherically convex surfaces,[34] while the situation is different for concave surfaces where the concavity prevents the light from being diffused freely.

{[*Proposition*] *8. Every point of a luminous body irradiates the adjacent medium hemispherically.*

{This is proved by the fact that luminous bodies are dense. For if we should imagine a point of light situated in a transparent medium, it would multiply itself equally in all directions, therefore its light constitutes a sphere. But if the point of light should be on the surface of a flat or spherically convex luminous body, it would lose its freedom to diffuse because of the dense material, and half [the sphere of light] would be cut off. It follows, therefore, that light would proceed hemispherically from such a point unless prevented by some protrusion.}

[*Proposition*] *7. Rays of visible objects illuminate the medium without intermingling.*[35]

That lights are not intermingled in the medium is evident from the shadows, which are as numerous as the lights. For on an opaque surface, a multitude of candles will cast as many shadows as there are candles.

{[*Proposition*] *9. Rays of one or several visible objects illuminate the medium without intermingling, or rather without confusion.*

{This is obvious to sense because if a stylus is placed in the midst [of several candles], it will cast as many shadows as there are candles, [an event] which could not occur unless the light of one candle were to remain distinct from the light of another. The same thing is also evident in the case of secondary light, for if secondary solar light should enter through openings near each other and oblique relative to one another in the two walls of a single corner, and if a stylus should be erected at the intersection of those lights, an observer would

cursu istorum luminum videbit experimentator plures umbras. Hoc etiam ratione colligitur in quibuscunque radiis lucis et coloris, quoniam si pyra-
305 mides luminose ab eodem corpore procedentes miscerentur ita quod confunderentur invicem, quicquid ostenderet una ostenderet alia, cuius oppositum videmus. Licet ergo omnium pyramidum sit lumen unum, habent tamen impressiones distinctas.}

[*Propositio*] *8ª{10ª}. Lucem fortem orientem super visum et medium*
310 *quedam visibilium occultare.*

Hoc patet sensibiliter, hec enim est ratio quare stelle de die non videntur, quoniam lucis solaris vehementia occupat totam capacitatem visus, propter quod etiam omnes minores motus et tactus sunt imperceptibiles propter excessum scilicet maiorum motuum. Unde licet moveant radii
315 stellarum in presentia solis visum, motus tamen non est sensibilis propter excessum fortioris impressionis; quod patet per oppositum, quoniam sole existente in meridie ille qui est in puteo profundo videt stellas perpendiculariter superpositas, quarum radii plus descendunt in profundum quam radii solis oblique super puteum orientes, propter quod earum motus
320 potest esse oculo perceptibilis. Amplius tempore nocturno vehemens ignis in medio aufert intuitionem certificatam eorum que sunt ultra ignem propter eandem rationem.

[*Propositio*] *9ª{11ª}. Lucem fortem super quedam visibilia orientem ipsa oculo abscondere existenti loco lucis temperate.*
325 Hoc patet, quoniam luce forti oriente super corpus sculptum subtilibus incisionibus sculpture non apparent, excessu splendoris visum occupantis impediente. Similiter multa sunt que in tenebris posita lucentia videntur, luci vero exposita disparent vel ad minus non lucent, sicut squame piscium et ignis mediocris, pro supra tacta ratione.

330 [*Propositio*] *10ª{12ª}. Lucem fortem multa visibilia ostendere que debilis occultat.*

Hoc passim ostenditur, quia que in luce modica non apparent ad for-

311 hoc patet: hec enim apparet *F*
313 *post* propter *scr. et del. A* hoc / etiam *VBAL; om. FD* et *H* / omnes ... motus: minores motus omnes *A*
314 *ante* propter *add. A* et insensibiles / scilicet *om. F* / *ante* motuum *scr. et del. A* ma
315 *ante* stellarum *add. A* solares / *post* tamen *add. F* earum / non est *mg. hab. H*

316 fortioris: maioris *F* / quoniam: quia *F*
317 *ante* in[1] *in alia manu mg. hab. F* oriente / ille: iste *F*
318 suppositas *A*
319 super puteum *om. F*
320 potest *in alia manu hab. D* / tempore nocturno *tr. F*
321–22 propter: per *D*
322 eandem rationem: intuitionis causam *F*

see several shadows. This is also grasped by the mind with respect to all rays of light and color, for if luminous pyramids proceeding from the same body should be so mixed as to be mutually confused, what one revealed another would reveal; but we observe the opposite of this. Therefore, although the light of all pyramids is one,[36] nevertheless the pyramids produce distinct impressions.}

[*Proposition*] *8{10}. A strong light that rises over the eye and the medium conceals certain visible objects.*[37]

This is evident to sense, and it explains why stars are not seen during the day, for the intensity of solar light fully engages the capacity for vision. It is also because of the excess of such greater stimuli that all lesser stimuli and tactile sensations are imperceptible. Therefore, although the rays of stars are capable of exciting the visual sense, their action is insensible in the presence of the sun because the impression [of the latter] is stronger. This is evident by [appeal to] the opposite case, for when the sun is at the meridian, a person in a deep pit sees the stars located perpendicularly above him, the rays of which descend to a greater depth than do those of the sun, which fall into the pit obliquely.[38] Consequently the action of those stars is perceptible to the eye. For the same reason an intense fire at night prevents the sure perception of things located beyond it.

[*Proposition*] *9{11}. When the eye is located in a place of moderate brightness, certain visible things, on which a strong light is incident, are concealed from it.*[39]

This is obvious, for when a strong light is incident on a finely carved body, the carvings are not apparent because they have been hidden by the excessive brilliance that fills the sense of sight. Likewise there are many things that appear bright when placed in darkness, but disappear or at least cease to shine when exposed to light—such as the scales of fish and moderately strong fire—for the reason touched on above.

[*Proposition*] *10{12}. An intense light reveals many visible objects that a weak light conceals.*[40]

This is manifest everywhere, since things that do not appear in weak light

---

| *post* rationem *add. F* sequitur alia propositio
323 ipsa *om. B*
324 existente *F* / *ante* loco (*in alia manu A*) *add. AF* in / temperare *D*
325 hoc *om. H* hec *F* / quoniam: quam *H* / luci *A* / orienti *A* / subtilibus: sculptis *D*
326 *ante* excessu *add. F* ex / occupantis *om. F*
327 simili *V*

328 vero *obs. F* / sicut: ut *B* / *ante* squame *scr. et del. D* squame
329 pro: per *F* / tactam rationem *F* / *post* ratione (*in alia manu mg. V*) *add. VWF* id est propter excessum fortioris impressionis
330 que: qui *D* / *post* debilis *add. A* est
332 hec *F* / passim: per sensibile *F* / non: vero *A*

tiorem ducta declarantur. Hec tamen propositio premisse videtur contraria. Si enim lux fortis ostendit, qualiter abscondit? Sed lux fortis abscondit
335   quando proportionem excedit, quia tunc occupat totam capacitatem sensus.

[*Propositio*] *11ᵃ{13ᵃ}. Lucem igneam ex materia flammea radiantem maiorem nocte quam die et de longe quam de prope apparere.*

De die minor apparet claritas quia maiori claritate circumfunditur. De nocte apparet maior quia tenebris iuxta positis in toto suo ambitu libere
340   presentatur. Item de prope minor apparet quando flamma a diffuso lumine discernitur. De longe maior apparet quando pre distantia inter flammam et lumen forte propinquum flamme non distinguitur, sed per modum unius grandis luminaris indivise oculo presentatur.

[*Propositio*] *12ᵃ{14ᵃ}. Colores corporum diversari apud visum secundum*
345   *diversitatem lucium super ipsos orientium.*

Hoc expresse patet in quibusdam coloribus qui in luce mediocri apparent turbidi, in luce forti clari et scintillantes; immo omnino alterius dispositionis in luce solis quam in luce candele. Tempore etiam eclipsis solaris omnes res colorate privantur coloris sui solita venustate. Amplius hoc
350   idem apparet in collo columbe, quod cum unius sit coloris, variis tamen aspectibus varie illustratum sub differenti specie oculo presentatur. Cuius ratio est quoniam efficaciam movendi habet color a luce; et quanto magis movetur a luce tanto efficacius movet. Colores autem debiliores sunt in fortioribus sicut incompletum in completo, et ideo secundum completio-
355   nem lucis est gradus complementi colorum in movendo. In collo tamen columbe aliter quidam esse existimant, diversos scilicet secundum verita-

---

333 *post* videtur *add. F* esse
334 *post* ostendit *add. F* visibilia / *post* qualiter *add. B* et / abscondit¹ *VWHD* absconditur *AL* et absconditur *B* absconditur visibile *F* / *post* sed *add. F* dicendum est quod / abscondit² *in alia manu mg. hab. A*
335 *ante* excedit *add. F* visus / excedit *in alia manu mg. corr. V ex* abscondit / sensus: visus *F* / *post* sensus *in alia manu mg. hab. V* quando scilicet lux fortis dicitur abscondere
336 *post* lucem *in alia manu add. A* fortem / *ante* flammea *scr. et del. H* fa
337 de¹ *om. F*
338 *ante* de¹ *add. F* hec patet / minor apparet *tr. F* / circumfunditur: circumscribitur *B* circumducitur *F*

339 *post* nocte *add. F* autem / *post* apparet *add. F* claritas / *post* iuxta *add. VF* se / in *om. F*
340 *ante* presentatur *add. F* oculo / de... minor: minor de prope de nocte *A* de prope minor de nocte *D* / apparet *om. D* / *post* apparet *add. B* de nocte / quando: quia *F*
340–41 quando...apparet *mg. hab. V* / flamma....quando *om. H*
341 longe *rep. B* / apparet *VBAD*; *om. WF* / quando: quoniam *F* / pre distantia: propter distantiam *F*
342 flamma *D* / unius *om. F*
343 grandus *A*
344 diversificari *D*
345 *post* ipsos *add. A* expresse
346 hec *F* / in¹: de *F*

are revealed when brought into an intense light. However, this proposition seems contrary to the preceding one, for if an intense light reveals, how does it conceal? But an intense light conceals [only] when it exceeds due proportion, since it then fully engages the capacity for sensation.

[*Proposition*] *11{13}. Firelight radiating from burning material appears larger at night than during the day and larger from afar than from nearby.*

The brightness appears smaller during the day [than at night] because it is surrounded by greater brightness. It appears larger at night because, when entirely surrounded by darkness, it is freely exhibited to view. Likewise, it appears smaller from close at hand, since the flame is then discriminated from the diffused light. It appears larger from afar, since the distance makes it impossible to distinguish between the flame and the intense light near the flame, and so they are perceived by the eye undividedly as though a single great light.

[*Proposition*] *12{14}. The colors of bodies appear varied according to the different lights shining on them.*[41]

This is clearly evident in certain colors that appear cloudy in a moderate light, but clear and brilliant in an intense light; in fact, their appearance in sunlight is wholly different from that in candlelight. Furthermore, all colored things are deprived of the customary beauty of their color during a solar eclipse. Moreover, the same thing appears on the neck of a dove, which assumes different appearances when variously viewed and variously illuminated, even though it is of a single color. The explanation of this [phenomenon] is that color is capable of being excited by light; and the more it is excited by light, the more efficaciously it acts [on sight]. However, weaker colors are in stronger colors as the imperfect is in the perfect; therefore the degree of perfection of colors in acting [on sight] corresponds to the [degree of] perfection of the light. Yet some think it otherwise on the neck of a dove, namely, that the different

---

347 *ante* in *add. D* et / *post* forti *add. F* apparent / clarius *F* / immo: ideo *A*
347–48 *ante* dispositionis *scr. et del. H* do / *post* dispositionis *mg. add. A* tam (*alt. A ex* termino)
348–49 tempore...venustate *AWFD; om. VBHL*
349 colorate...coloris: diversificantur in coloribus *F* / sui...venustate *AD; om. F* sui et solita velocitate *W*

350 apparet: patet *F* / unius sit *tr. F* unius *A*
351 illustrata *F* / *post* illustratum *add. D* et / differenti: indifferenti *D*
353 efficacius: magis *F* / *post* movet *add. F* visum
354–55 et...completionem *om. B*
355 coloris *FD* / in[1] *om. A* / tamen: autem *F*
356 estimant *F* / scilicet *om. F*
356–57 veritatem: diversitatem *F*

tem ibi esse colores, sicut et diversas superficies ex diversarum pennarum
pennulis vel pennularum particulis radiantes.

{... In collo tamen columbe aliter quidam esse existimant, diversos
⟨scilicet⟩ secundum diversitatem superficiei ibi esse colores, sicut et diversas superficies ex diversarum pennarum et pennularum particulis radiantes. Sed hoc non est, ut patet experienti.}

[*Propositio*] *13ª. Comprehensio rei vise a visu sequitur proportionaliter
dispositionem lucis orientis super rem visam ac medium et visum.*

Hoc sequitur ex premissis, si enim in fortiori luce color fortius movet
et in minori minus, simpliciter ab ipsa videtur esse movendi efficacia. Et
idem intelligo a parte oculi apprehendendo et medii deferendo.

[*Propositio*] *14ª{29ª}. Radius lucis primarie, similiter et coloris, in rectum semper porrigitur nisi diversitate medii incurvetur se nichilominus accidentaliter diffundendo.*

Dicitur lux primaria que radiose procedit a luminoso, lux secundaria
et accidentalis que est a latere extra radiorum incidentiam, que oblique
et in omnem partem se diffundit. Color etiam radiose multiplicatur, sicut
patet sensibiliter cum radius solis transit per vitream coloratam. Tunc
enim propter lucis efficaciam color sensibiliter radiat super densum sibi
obiectum. Sed quando obviat luci vel colori corpus densum reflectitur ut
a speculo. Quando vero obviat magis vel minus dyaphano recedit a rectitudine, et quasi frangitur vel flectitur in obliquum.

[*Propositio*] *15ª{30ª}. Radius lucis vel coloris ad perpendicularem frangitur occursu medii densioris super quod non est perpendicularis.*

Hoc quamvis in septimo *Perspective* tradatur, hic duxi necessarium
prelibare. Ratio autem generalis fractionis est variatio dyaphoneitatis,
maior enim dyaphoneitas minus resistit luci {quam dyaphoneitas minor
que est in medio densiori}. Quia igitur facilior est transitus per unum

357 esse *om.* F / coloris A / *ante* sicut *add.* V
et *scr. et del.* H et / ex: et A
358 pennulis vel *om.* F / pennularum *om.* F
pennarum A / particulis: partibus F /
post radiantes *add.* F sequitur alia propositio
364 ac: ad F / et: ac A
365 hec F
366 in *om.* A / simpliciter: similiter F
367 *ante* deferendo *add.* F in
369–70 accidentaliter diffundendo *tr.* F
370 *post* diffundendo *mg. hab.* A radii

371 *ante* dicitur *add.* F radius / lux[1] *mg. corr.*
A *ex* dx
372 que[1] *om.* F / *post* latere *add.* F et
373 et *om.* F / *post* diffundit *add.* D {ut supra
tactum est} / sicut: sic H
374 patet: apparet F / solis *BHLD* solaris
VAF / transit...coloratam: transit per
vitrum coloratum A per fenestram vitream coloratam transit F
375 propter: per F
377 magis: maius H / vel: aut D
378 quasi: ?que D / frangitur vel flectitur:

colors really exist there according to the different radiating surfaces formed by the barbs of various feathers or the small parts of barbs.

{... Yet some think it otherwise on the neck of a dove, namely, that different colors exist there according to diversity of the surface, as [there are] different surfaces formed by the small parts of various feathers and barbs. But this is not so, as is evident to an observer.}[42]

[*Proposition*] *13. The visual perception of an object varies in accordance with the disposition of the light incident upon the object, the medium, and the eye.*

This follows from the foregoing, for if color acts [on sight] more strongly when illuminated by a more intense light and more weakly when illuminated by a weaker light, the efficacy of [the color's] action evidently depends solely on the light. And I judge the same situation to obtain with respect to the eye in perceiving and the medium in transmitting.

[*Proposition*] *14{29}. Rays of primary light and color are always propagated in straight lines unless bent by variations in the medium; yet [all the while they are also] diffusing themselves accidentally.*[43]

Light that proceeds as [direct] radiation from a luminous object is called primary; light that passes laterally outside the incident [pyramid of] rays and diffuses itself obliquely and in every direction is called secondary and accidental. Color also is propagated as [direct] radiation, as is manifest to sight when a solar ray traverses colored glass, for then, through the efficacy of light, the color sensibly radiates onto a dense body facing it. But when light or color is opposed by a dense body, it is reflected as from a mirror. When light and color are more or less opposed by a transparent body, they depart from their rectilinear paths and are, as it were, broken or bent sideways.

[*Proposition*] *15{30}. A ray of light or color, when obliquely incident on a denser medium, is refracted toward the perpendicular.*

Although this is taught in the seventh book of the *Perspectiva*,[44] I consider it necessary to examine it here. The universal cause of refraction is variation in transparency, for greater transparency has less resistance to light {than does the lesser transparency of a denser medium}. Therefore, since there is variation in

flectitur vel frangitur *B* refrangitur vel reflectitur *F* frangitur vel reflectitur *D* / flectitur *in alia manu mg. corr. V ex* frangitur

379 perpendiculare *D* perpendicularitatem *B*

380 *ante* occursu *add. F* in

381 hoc: hec *AF* / septimo: VII *B* / *post* perspective *add. F* Alazen / necessario *F*

382 prelibari *F*

384 facilior est *tr. F*

385 medium quam per reliquum, necesse est quod in secundo medio, magis
scilicet distante a luminoso, reperiatur proportionaliter primo in situ, scilicet similis resistentie. Transitus autem perpendiculariter egrediens vel ingrediens fortissimus est, et transitus non perpendicularis tanto est debilior
quanto a perpendiculari remotior et tanto fortior quanto ei propinquior.
390 Quando igitur occurrit medium densius et magis resistens, necessarius est
radio fortior situs et directo propinquior. Unde ut transitus per medium
secundum proportionetur transitui per primum, radius declinat ad perpendicularem erigibilem a puncto casus sui super secundum medium. Unde
patet quod perpendicularis situs fortior est, non tamen per egressum a
395 corpore luminoso, immo per casum perpendicularem super medium. Nec
intelligendum radium ad situm fortiorem declinare quasi per electionem,
immo transitum per medium primum ad sibi proportionalem in secundo
impellere, sicut patet in figura [Fig. 6]. Radius autem a luminoso super
quodcunque medium perpendiculariter cadens omnino non frangitur, quia
400 fortitudo sua nullius dyaphoneitatis obiectu ebetatur, aptius enim movet
omnis radius recte quam oblique. Verbi gratia a corpore luminoso *A* per
aerem super aquam cadit perpendicularis *AG*, nec omnino frangitur; cadit
oblique *AC*, et qui procederet in *B* si esset medium simile, frangitur versus
perpendicularem *DC* et cadit in *E*.

385 medium *om. F* / est *om. B* / secundo
medio *tr. B*
386 scilicet *om. F* / *post* reperiatur *add. F*
magis / primo *om. FD* / in situ: transitus *F* / *post* situ *add* D. {ut est possibile
similiter resistentia qualis erat resistentia primi medii ?econtra (*scr. et del.*
econtra)}
386–87 scilicet...resistentie {*om. D*}
387 perpendicularis *AF*
388 et *om. F* / *ante* tanto *add. F* in
389 quanto...fortior *mg. hab. V*
390 quando: quanto *B* cum *F*/occurrerit *F*/
magis resistens: maioris resistentie *D* /
post necessarius *add. B* vel necessario
390–91 quando...situs *in alia manu mg.*
hab. A
391 et...propinquior *om. A* / directio *F* / ut
om. F
392 proportionaliter *F* / transitu *H* / *post*
primum *add. F* medium / ad *om. H*

392–93 *post* perpendicularem *scr. et del. F*
originale
393 erigibilitatem *B* originalem *F*
394 situs: transitus *F* / tamen: tantum *F*
395 *post* immo *add. F* etiam
396 intelligendi *A* / *post* intelligendum (*in*
alia manu mg. V) *add. VFLD* est / electionem: pellectionem *F*
397 *ante* transitum *scr. et del. F* trasitum /
transit *D* / proportionale *F*
399 perpendiculariter cadens *tr. A*
400 sua *om. H* / obiecto *F* obiectum *A*
401 A: AK *B*
402 cadit[1]: cadat *A* / *ante* perpendicularis
add. F linea / *ante* cadit[2] *add. D* sed que
/ cadit[2]: cadat *A* / *post* cadit[2] *add. F*
etiam
403 oblique AC *tr. A* / AC: AD *F* / qui: sic
F / *post* medium *add. F* sibi / *post* simile
add. F sed / frangeretur *B*

the ease with which media may be traversed, it will necessarily be found that the direction of the ray in the second medium (the one farther from the luminous object) is proportioned to its direction in the first medium as the resistance of the second medium to the resistance of the first.[45] Traversal [of the medium] is strongest, however, for rays that enter or emerge perpendicularly, and traversal by a nonperpendicular ray is weaker as it diverges from the perpendicular and stronger as it approaches the perpendicular.[46] Therefore a ray meeting a denser and more resistant medium must assume a stronger position, closer to the direct path. Consequently, in order that traversal of the second medium should be commensurate with[47] traversal of the first, the [refracted] ray bends toward the perpendicular erected at the point of incidence on the second medium. Wherefore, it is evident that the strongest position is the perpendicular —i.e., perpendicular incidence on the medium, not perpendicular emergence from the luminous body. Also, it should not be thought that the ray bends toward the stronger position as by choice, but rather that traversal of the first medium impels a proportional traversal of the second, as is evident in the figure [Fig. 6].[48] On the other hand, a ray perpendicularly incident on any medium is unrefracted because it is not weakened by the interposition of the transparent body, for every ray is more suited to perpendicular than to oblique motion. For example, perpendicular AG falls from luminous body A through air onto water and is not refracted at all. [Ray] AC, which would proceed to B if the [second] medium were of the same transparency [as the first], falls obliquely and is refracted toward perpendicular DC, falling to E.

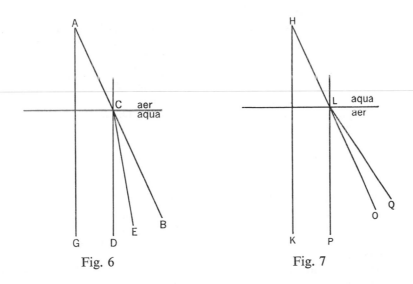

Fig. 6   Fig. 7

405   [*Propositio*] *16ᵃ{31ᵃ}. Radius lucis vel coloris a perpendiculari divertit
cum medium subtilius occurrit.*

Sequitur ex premissa, quia enim medium secundum minus resistit,
minor fortitudo congruit radiis in ipsum a densiori cadentibus. Unde franguntur a perpendiculari. Verbi gratia sit luminosum *H* in aqua existens
410   [Fig. 7], a quo cadat radius *HK* recte et *HL* oblique. Dico quia non procedit directe in *O* nec frangitur versus perpendicularem *PL*, sed ab illa
cadens in *Q*, sicut patet in figura. Et hec est ratio quare res in quibusdam
mediis apparent maiores, in quibusdam minores, ut infra patebit.

[*Propositio*] *17ᵃ{15ᵃ}. In omni puncto medii quo est a luminoso remotior
415   eo in ipso excipitur radius multiplicior.*

Hoc probatur quia quanto punctus plus distat a sole tanto descendit
eius lumen a maiori arcu seu portione solis; et econtra quo propinquior
est soli eo descendit a minori arcu lumen. Igitur in puncto remotiori est
lumen multiplicius, sed ex distantia debilis, quod demonstratur sic. Acci-
420   piantur in corpore sperico luminoso cuius centrum sit *K* duo puncta opposita *A B* [Fig. 8], et diffundatur lumen a puncto *A* per emisperium, ut patet
per sextam supra, cuius emisperii dyameter est linea *CAD*. Certum igitur
est quod a puncto *A* cadit lumen in punctum *D* et non in aliquem propinquiorem corpori luminoso, sicut patet ex 14ᵃ supra. Linea enim *CAD* con-
425   tingens est et inter eam et speram nulla cadit media, sicut patet ex *Geo-*

405 *ante* divertit *add. F* se
407 *ante* sequitur *add. F* hec / enim *obs. D* /
   post medium *add. F* subtilius / *post* secundum *add. F* quod
408 *ante* congruit *scr. et del. F* ?congrui / in
   ipsum *om. F* / *ante* ipsum *scr. et del. H*
   ipsis
410 *ante* a *scr. et del. D* in / cadat *VBHL*
   cadit *AWFD* / *ante* radius *scr. et del. D*
   medius / quia *VAWLD* quod *BFH*
410–11 procedit directe *tr. F*
411 *ante* O *scr. et del. H* B / illa: ista *F*
412 sicut: ut *F*
413 *ante* in *add. F* et
414 quo *om. F* qui *B* / est *om. FH*
415 in *om. AF* / excipitur: recipitur *B* acci-
   pietur *F* / *supra* excipitur *in alia manu*
   hab. *A* ac
416 hec *F* / punctus plus: magis punctus *F*
   punctus *D* / *post* tanto *add. A* etiam *et*
   add. F magis
417 arcu *corr. H ex* actu / econtra: econverso *F* / quo: quanto *F*

418 soli....est² *in alia manu mg. hab. D* /
   post lumen *add. B* eius
419 lumen *om. D* / debilis (*in alia manu alt.*
   A *ad* debilius) *VBALH* debilius *WFD*
419–20 accipiatur *D*
420 sperico luminoso *tr. AF*
421 diffundant *F* / lumen...A *om. B* / A *om. D*
421–22 ut...CAD *om. D*
422 CAD: CDA *B*
422–23 certum...est: certum est igitur *AF*
423 *post* lumen *add. D* radiose / punctum *in*
   alia manu alt. V *ad* puncto / aliquem *om.*
   F aliquam *B*
424 sicut *om. D* ut *F* / patet *om. BD* / ex 14ᵃ
   supra *om. A* {*om. D*} ex 14ᵃ *W* 14 supra
   L ex 14 supra *H* ex 9ᵃ supra *B* / *post*
   supra *add. F* tacta etiam probatur ex
   alio / *ante* linea *add. D* {secundum lineam KD} / CAD: AD *D*
424–25 contingens est *BD*; *tr. F* contingens
   VLH
425 et² *om. H*
425–26 geometria: 15ᵃ geometrie *F*

[*Proposition*] *16{31}. A ray of light or color diverges from the perpendicular when it meets a more subtle medium.*[49]

This follows from the foregoing, for since the second medium is less resistant, less strength is appropriate to rays entering it from a denser medium. Therefore such rays are refracted away from the perpendicular. For example, let there be a luminous point *H* [Fig. 7] situated in water, from which ray *HK* falls perpendicularly and ray *HL* obliquely. I maintain that *HL* does not proceed rectilinearly to *O* and is not refracted toward perpendicular *PL*, but is refracted away from the perpendicular, falling to *Q* as the figure shows. This is why things appear larger in some media and smaller in others, as will be evident below.[50]

[*Proposition*] *17{15}. The beam [of light] received at every point of a medium is more multiplex the farther the point is from the luminous source.*

The proof is that, as the point is farther removed from the sun, the sunlight descends from a larger arc or portion of the sun; conversely, as the point is closer to the sun, the light descends from a smaller arc. Therefore at a more remote point the light is more multiplex, although weak because of the distance. This is demonstrated as follows. Assume two points *A* and *B* [Fig. 8] opposite

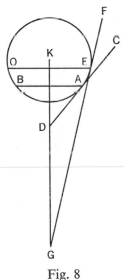

Fig. 8

each other on the spherical luminous body centered at *K*. Let the light from point *A* be diffused in the form of a hemisphere of diameter *CAD*, as shown in Proposition 6, above.[51] Consequently, it is certain that light from point *A* falls to point *D* but to no point nearer the luminous body, as Proposition 14, above, makes clear; for line *CAD* is tangent [to the sphere], and no other line falls between it and the sphere, as is evident from Book 3 of Euclid's *Geometry*.[52]

metria Euclidis 3. Amplius si sumatur punctus supra *A* in corpore luminoso, scilicet *E*, radians per spatium obiectum, et terminus radiationis sit linea contingens *FEG*, certum est quod in linea *KG* primus punctus ad quem pervenit lumen a puncto *E* est *G* et in nullum superiorem, sicut a puncto
430 *A* in punctum *D* et nullum superiorem. Tamen ab omni puncto luminosi mittente radium suum in punctum propinquiorem incidit et radius in punctum remotiorem et non econverso. Unde a toto arcu *EABO* cadit lumen in punctum *G* et non econverso. Lux igitur in puncto recepta tanto multiplicior est quanto a luminoso remotior.

435   [*Propositio*] *18ᵃ{16ᵃ}. In puncto propinquiori fortior est lux unius corporis quam in remotiori.*
Multiplicitas enim luminis in puncto remotiori est ex confluentia radiorum oblique cadentium et per consequens debilium. Lux autem in puncto propinquiori fortitudinem habet ex maiori coniunctione cum suo
440 fonte, que maior est. {Item lux verticalium a centro luminosi directe progreditur secundum rectitudinem linearum, et certum est quod linee a centro egredientes quanto magis a centro distant tanto magis invicem disgregantur. Omnis autem virtus unica fortior est quam divisa. Fortior est igitur lux propinqua quaque remota per se.}

445   [*Propositio*] *19ᵃ{17ᵃ}. Pyramides breviores, quia breviores, partim esse longioribus ab eadem basi procedentibus fortiores, partim debiliores.*
Breviores siquidem quia breviores sunt obtusiores esse necesse est, sicut patet ex primo Euclidis. Sed in obtusioribus radii ad conos se intersecantes quanto angulus conalis est obtusior tanto magis lateribus pyra-
450 midis diversis mutuo appropinquant. Verbi gratia sit pyramis obtusa *ABC* [Fig. 9], et protrahatur latus *AC* in *D* et *BC* in *E*. Igitur cum angulus

426 3 *VHD*; *om.* *F* tertio *B* 15ᵃ *A* tertii *W* tertia *L* / *ante* amplius *add.* *F* sed / supra: infra *D*
427 per (*in alia manu alt. V ad* super): super *FL* / et terminus: est cuius *F*
428 FEG: SEG *D* / certum est *tr.* *B* / certum…KG *om.* *D* / in *om.* *F* / *ante* primus *add.* *F* est
429 est: F *F* / *ante* et *scr. et del.* *A* cum est / superiorem: {viciniorem corpori solari} *D*
429–30 sicut…superiorem *om.* *F*
429–32 sicut….econverso {*om.* *D*}
430 *post* A *scr. et del.* *A* in puncto A / *ante* nullum (*in alia manu V*) *add.* *VAL* in /

tamen: cum *F* / luminosi *BWFH* luminoso *VAL*
431 *ante* mittente *add.* *F* in / *post* punctum *add.* *F* G
431–32 propinquiorem…remotiorem *om.* *F*
432 unde: sed *D* / a: in *B* / EABO *VLH* ABEO *A* EAB *D* EABC *F* ABD *B*
432–33 unde…G *in alia manu mg. hab.* *A*
433 punctum: puncto *A* / G: D *D* / et non econverso *om.* *A* / econverso: {in aliquem punctum superiorem} *D* / igitur *om.* *F* / in²: a *F* / *post* puncto *add.* *F* G et *add.* *D* D
434 multiplicatur *F* / est *om.* *F* / a *om.* *F* / *ante* remotior *add.* *FD* est

Furthermore, if we assume a point such as E on the luminous body above A radiating into the adjacent space, and if the terminus of the radiation is tangent line FEG, it is certain that G is the first point in line KG attained by light from point E and that light reaches no higher point; similarly light from point A is received at point D but at no higher point. However, from every point of the luminous body that sends its ray to a near point [in the medium] a ray is incident also at more remote points, but not vice versa. Therefore light falls to point G from the entire arc $EABO$; [thus every point that illuminates point D also illuminates point G] but not vice versa.[53] Consequently the light received at a point is more multiplex as it is more remote from the luminous body.

[*Proposition*] *18{16}. The light of a single body is stronger at a near point than at a more remote point.*[54]

Indeed, the multiplicity of light at a remote point results from the confluence of rays that fall obliquely and consequently are weak. The light at a nearer point, however, possesses greater strength because of a closer connection with its source. {Moreover, perpendicular rays proceed in straight lines directly from the center of the luminous body, and it is certain that lines emerging from the center become farther separated as their distance from the center increases. But since every united power is stronger than a divided power, it follows that light (of itself) is stronger near [its source] than remote [from it].}

[*Proposition*] *19{17}. Shorter pyramids, because of their shortness, are in some respects stronger and in other respects weaker than pyramids proceeding farther from the same base.*[55]

Indeed, shorter pyramids are necessarily more obtuse because they are shorter, as the first book of Euclid makes clear.[56] But in obtuse pyramids, as the angle of the vertex becomes more obtuse, the rays that intersect to form vertices approach more closely the opposite sides of the pyramid. For example, let ABC [Fig. 9] be an obtuse pyramid, and let side AC be extended to D and

437 enim *om.* D / confluentia: fluentia A
438 autem *om.* B
440 que...est *BAHL*; *om.* F que est maior V que fortitudo maior est D / post fonte *add.* F sequitur alia
445 esse: est H
446 base A / partimque FD
447 breviores[1]: fortiores (*supra* fortiores *in alia manu hab.* breviores) A / *post* siquidem *add.* F pyramides / *ante* esse *mg.*

    hab. A *verba oblita*
447–48 breviores[2]....ad *om.* F
448 ex primo *BWHD* ex prima V primo A
449 conalis *WFD*; *om.* B corporalis *VAH*
449–50 pyramidis diversis *tr.* V pyramidis everse F
450 *ante* mutuo *scr. et del.* F a / appropinquat F / sit: fit A
451 latus *om.* F / igitur cum *tr.* F

ACB sit equalis angulo *ECD*, quia contrapositus est, necesse est tanto reliquos duos esse minores quanto hii duo sunt maiores; et quanto sunt maiores tanto sibi sunt coalterni radii propinquiores, ut *CD* tanto propinquior radio *BC* et econverso quanto maior est angulus *DCE*. Est autem lucis proprietas ut quanto propinquior alteri tanto fiat fortior utraque. Igitur secundum hoc fortiores sunt pyramides breviores naturaliter, nec solum ex causa in 18 assignata. Sed econtra in pyramide longiori lux citra conum est adunata magis quam in breviori, et per hoc excedit breviorem. Simpliciter tamen fortiores sunt breviores. Unde naturaliter montes sunt calidiores, quamvis per accidens infrigidentur in quantum medio interstitio appropinquant.

[*Propositio*] *20ᵃ{18ᵃ}*. *Cuiuslibet pyramidis radiose omnes radios in indivisibili concurrere.*

Si enim conus pyramidis est divisibilis ponatur habere latitudinem. Lineam latitudinis ego dividam per tres partes, quarum prima sit *AB*, secunda *BC*, tertia *CD* [Fig. 10]. Ergo radius cuius terminus est *AB* non

452 ACB: ABC *VBAH* | *post* est[1] *add. D* scilicet ACE et BCD | necesse est *AWF*; *om. VH et tr. BD* | tanto *om. F*

453 *post* esse *add. F* tanto | *post* minores *scr. et del. H* tanto sibi sunt coalterni

454 sibi sunt *tr. B* | coalterni radii *tr. F* | *post* tanto[2] *add. F* est | tanto[2] *rep. H*

455 *ante* radio *add. D* est | *post* et *scr. et del. H* con | et econverso *om. D* | quanto...DCE *om. BD*

456 *ante* alteri *add. F* est radius | fortior utraque: utroque fortior *F*

457 igitur: ideo *F* | hec *D* | fortiores...naturaliter: sunt naturaliter fortiores pyramides breviores *F* | nec: non *FH*

458 in 18 {*om. D*} in 18ᵃ *BA* iam *F* | econtra: econverso *F* | *supra* citra *hab. F* 18

459 est *om. A* | adiuncta *D* | in *om. D* | breviori (*corr. H ex* longiori) *obs. A* longiori *V* | *post* breviori *add. B* vel propinquiori

460 tamen: tantum *A* | fortiores...breviores: breviores sunt fortiores *F* | montes: non *V* modo *H*

461 *ante* quamvis *add. D* naturalibus | infrigidantur *F* | in quantum *om. H et in alia manu hab. V*

461–62 *post* interstitio *add. F* aeris

462 *post* appropinquant *add. F* sequitur alia

463–64 in indivisibili *VWHD* indivisibiliter *AF* indivisibili *B*

465 habere *in alia manu mg. hab. D*

466 ego: ergo *A* | per: in *F* | partes *rep. A*

467 tertia CD *obs. A* | AB: CD *D*

BC to E. Then, since angle *ACB* equals angle *ECD* because they are vertically opposite, these two angles necessarily become larger as the remaining two angles [*ACE* and *BCD*] become smaller; and as the former [two angles] become larger, the alternate rays approach each other. Thus ray *CD* approaches ray *BC*,

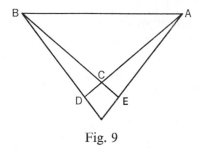

Fig. 9

and vice versa, with the enlargement of angle *DCE*. However, light has the property of gaining strength by approach to another light. Therefore shorter pyramids are stronger by nature and not merely by the cause assigned in Proposition 18. On the other hand, light is more nearly united in a long pyramid than in a shorter one, except at the vertex;[57] and in this respect the longer pyramid exceeds the shorter [in strength]. Nevertheless, the absolute strength of shorter pyramids is greater [than that of longer pyramids]. Thus mountains are naturally warmer, although they may be cooled accidentally in accordance with their approach to the middle interstice [of the air].[58]

[*Proposition*] *20{18}. All rays of every pyramid of radiation converge to a point.*

If the vertex of a pyramid should be divisible, it must have breadth. Let me divide the line of breadth into three parts, the first of which is *AB*, the second *BC*, the third *CD* [Fig. 10]. Therefore the ray terminating on *AB* does not

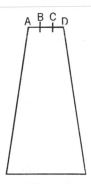

Fig. 10
I have reproduced the figure as it appears in *F, H,* and *D.* In *V, B,* and *A* it is shorter and wider.

concurrit cum radio cuius terminus est *CD*, quod falsum est. Necesse est igitur huius radiorum concursum ultimum fieri in puncto mathematico.

470   *[Propositio] 21ᵃ{19ᵃ}. A luminoso concavo lumen efficacius recipitur in centro.*

Cuius ratio est quoniam ab omni puncto concavi perpendiculares radii, qui sunt ceteris fortiores, confluunt in centro, propter quod virtutes celestium corporum in centro mundi et iuxta ipsum efficacius oriuntur. 475 Hinc ibi conformior dicitur habitatio homini, cuius compositio appropinquat ut est possibile supremi corporis simplicitati.

[Propositio] 22ᵃ{20ᵃ}. Omne luminosum spericum illuminat speram minorem, similiter et chilindrum, plus quam dimidium.

Si enim maior est dyameter luminosi quam sit dyameter opaci, radii 480 cadentes super extrema dyametri opaci non oriuntur a terminis dyametri luminosi *KG* [Fig. 11]. Hoc enim si faceret equidistantes essent et utrobique rectos angulos facerent cum dyametro; et essent per consequens dyametri equales corporum inequalium, quod est impossibile. Oriuntur igitur

468 est¹ *om. D* | CD: AB {quia media est linea BC} *D* | *post* est² *add. F* per diffinitionem

468–69 necesse est igitur: igitur necesse est *F* necesse est *D*

469 huiusmodi *VF* | concursum: occursum *D* | ultimum fieri *tr. D* | *post* mathematico *add. F* id est indivisibili

470 a *om. F* | lumen: luminem *A*

472 perpendiculares *in alia manu corr. D ex* perpendicularis

473 ceteris: ceciter *H* | virtutes: {radii} *D*

474 mundi *BAFD*; *om. VWHL* | *post* mundi *add. D* {quod est terra} | et *om. VF*

475 conformior dicitur *tr. F* | homini: hu-

mane nature *D* | compositio (*in alia manu corr. A ex* complexio) *VAHL* compositio vel complexio *B* complexio *WFD*

476 supremi: nature *F* | simplicis *F*

478 similiter *om. F*

479 enim *om. F* | est: sit *BF* | dyameter²: deameter *D*

480 dyametri¹ *om. D* dyameter *H* | *post* opaci *add. F* CD | a...dyametri²: dyametri a terminis *A*

481 *post* luminosi *add. D* corporis | KG: FG *F* | fecerint *A* fieret *F* facerent *D* | *ante* essent *add. A* erunt

483 igitur: etiam *F*

intersect the ray terminating on *CD*, which is false [according to the definition of a vertex]. Consequently it is necessary that the final intersection of such rays should occur in a mathematical point.

[*Proposition*] *21{19}. Light from a concave luminous body is received most powerfully at the center.*

The reason for this is that, from every point of a concave body, perpendicular rays, which are stronger than others,[59] converge in the center. Therefore the virtues of celestial bodies are incident most powerfully in and near the center of the world. Hence habitation there is said to be very suitable for man, whose constitution approaches as closely as possible the simplicity of the supreme body.

[*Proposition*] *22{20}. A luminous sphere illuminates more than half a smaller sphere or cylinder.*[60]

If the diameter of the luminous body is greater than the diameter of the opaque body, rays incident on the ends of the diameter of the opaque body do

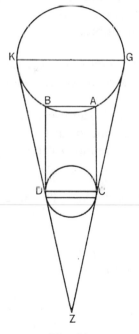

Fig. 11

not originate at the ends of diameter *KG* [Fig. 11] of the luminous body. For if they did, they would be parallel and would form right angles at both ends of the diameter; consequently the diameters of unequal bodies would be equal, which is impossible. Therefore they originate from an arc smaller than a hem-

ab aliquo arcu minori quam sit emisperium, verbi gratia *AB*. Cum igitur
485 a punctis omnibus inter *G* et *A* lumen diffundatur super opacum, si ab *A*
puncto pervenit in *C*, necesse est ab omni puncto superiori provenire ultra
C. Et per consequens quanto opacum propinquius est luminoso tanto
lumen latius perfundetur.

Quod et demonstratur sic. Ut patet supra ex quarta, a superficie lumi-
490 nosi porriguntur pyramides in omnem partem medii obiecti. Cum igitur
minus sit opacum luminoso, et per consequens inter pyramides radiosas
conclusibile, necessario illustratur plus medietate; si enim pyramis latera
sua extremis dyametri *CD* applicaret utrimque angulos rectos constitueret,
sicut patet per 17 tertii Euclidis, et trigonus *CDZ* plus quam duos rectos
495 contineret. Ex hoc patet quod sol illuminat plus quam medietatem lune.

[*Propositio*] *23ª{21ª}*. *Umbrosi luminoso minoris minorem esse umbram,*
sicut equalis equalem et maioris esse maiorem.

Hoc patet ex premissa, quoniam si luminosum maius est quam umbrosum illuminat plus medietate sua, si equale medietatem precise, si minus
500 minus medietate. Et loquor de umbris proiectis in plano, et dico etiam
quantum ad latitudinem umbre.

[*Propositio*] *24ª{22ª}*. *Umbrosum spericum luminoso minus umbram pro-*
icere pyramidalem, equale columpnarem, maius curtam et eversam pyrami-
dem infinitam.

505 Ratio huius propositionis sumitur ex prehabitis, quoniam ex 22 patet
quia umbrosum minus luminoso, ut terra sole, illuminatur plus quam in
medietate. Igitur radii a luminoso cadentes in umbrosum equidistantes

484 arcu *corr. H ex* actu / *ante* AB *add. F* ab arcu / AB *om. A*
485 G et A: A et B *F* A et K *D* / diffunditur *BF*
486 pervenit: provenit *A* / *ante* in *add. F* lumen / superiori provenire *VAHL* superiori pervenire *BD* pervenire superiori *F*
487 quanto opacum *tr. F* / propinquius est *tr. B*
488 lumen latius *tr. B* latius *F* lumine latius *D* / perfundetur: diffundetur *V* diffunditur *F* profundetur *D*
489 et: etiam *BF* / ex quarta *om. D* a quarta *A* / a: ex *F*
490 medii obiecti *tr. V* / *post* obiecti *add. F* vel omnem punctum medii obiecti

491 radiosa *F*
492 conclusive *F* / si: non *A*
493 extriminis *V* / rectos *in alia manu mg. hab. V*
494 sicut: ut *F* / 17ᵃᵐ *F* / tertii Euclidis: *tr. A* tertii Elementorum Euclidis *F* Euclidis *D* / et: ut *F* / CDZ: CFD *A* CDK etiam *F*
494–95 trigonus...contineret *om. D*
495 continet *B* / sol *in alia manu mg. hab. V* / *post* illuminat *add. D* semper longe / *post* lune *add. D* omnium et (et *in alia manu*) stellarum
496 luminosi *VB* / minoris: minori *F*
497 esse *om. F*
498 hec *F* / *post* premissa *scr. et del. H* maioris

isphere, such as *AB*. Thus, since light radiates onto the opaque body from all points between *G* and *A*, and if from point *A* it proceeds to *C*, then from every higher point it must proceed beyond *C*. Consequently the closer the opaque body is to the luminous body, the more widely will the light be spread over [the opaque body].

The same thing is demonstrated as follows. As the fourth proposition (above) makes apparent, pyramids are extended from the surface of a luminous body into every part of the adjacent medium. Therefore, since the opaque body is smaller than the luminous body and consequently capable of being enclosed within the radiant pyramids, it must be more than half-illuminated; for if the sides of the pyramid were to make contact with the ends of diameter *CD*, right angles would be formed at both ends, as Proposition 17 of the third book of Euclid demonstrates,[61] and triangle *CDZ* would contain angles [the sum of which would be] more than two right angles. It is evident, therefore, that the sun illuminates more than half the moon.

[*Proposition*] *23{21}. An umbrageous body smaller than the luminous body casts a shadow smaller than itself, just as an umbrageous body equal to or larger than the luminous body casts a shadow respectively equal to or larger than itself.*[62]

This is apparent from the foregoing, for if the luminous body is larger than the umbrageous body, it illuminates more than half the latter; if equal, precisely half; if smaller, less than half. I speak of the width of the shadow extending behind the umbrageous body as well as of the shadow projected onto a plane.

[*Proposition*] *24{22}. A spherical umbrageous body smaller than the luminous body casts a pyramidal shadow; a body equal to the luminous body, a columnar shadow; a body larger than the luminous body, a shadow in the form of a truncated and infinitely extended pyramid.*

This proposition is explained by reference to the foregoing, for it is evident from Proposition 22 that an umbrageous body smaller than the luminous body (as the earth is smaller than the sun) is more than half-illuminated. Therefore rays falling from the [periphery of the] luminous body onto the [periphery of

498–99 quam umbrosum: umbroso *F*
499 medietatem: medietate *A* / *post* minus
    add. D illuminat
500 minus *rep. F* / in plano *om. H et in alia*
    manu mg. hab. V in planum *F*
502 *post* spericum *add. F* cum / minus:
    maiore *F*
503 pyramidalem: pyramidale *H* / equalem
    F / equale columpnarem *in alia manu mg.*

hab. *A* / maius: magis *F*
505 propositionis *BALD*; *om. VFH* / prelibatis *F* / ex: {supra} *D* / 22 *VHL*; {*om.*
    D} ?12 *B* 23ᵃ *F* 22ᵃ *A*
506 quia: quod *FD* / ut: et *A* / *ante* sole *add.*
    F a / illuminatur: illustratur *F* / quam
    om. A
507 a *corr. B ex* ad

esse non possunt. Tangunt enim circulum non in extremis dyametri sed in extremis corde alicuius minoris corda semicirculi. Igitur anguli recti non
510 erunt in contactu, sicut patet ex 17 tertii Euclidis. Igitur cum radii a maiori magnitudine descendant, necesse est angulos illos esse minores quos constituunt radii ex parte corde predicte a luminoso remotiori. Concurrent igitur necessario ad partem illam, ut docet quarta petitio primi Euclidis.
515 Quod si equalia sibi sunt umbrosum et luminosum radii cadent necessario in extreme dyametri umbrosi et per consequens equidistantes erunt, numquam concurrentes si in infinitum producantur. Si vero maius fuerit umbrosum necesse est umbram esse contrarie dispositionis cum prima istarum trium. Quare erit everse curte pyramidis infinite secundum longi-
520 tudinem, quam figuram *calateidos* appellant. Dico cum sunt umbrosum et luminosum super idem planum.

[*Propositio*] 25ª{23ª}. *Umbram esse lumen diminutum.*
Sicut patet ex 14, quamvis opacum impediat transitum lucis directum et principalem, non tamen secundarium qui circumferencialiter se diffun-
525 dit. In hoc autem differt umbra a tenebra, quia umbra est lux diminuta ubi est privatio lucis primarie et derivatio secundarie. Tenebra vero est si tamen alicubi est ubi nichil est de lumine. Nescio enim si aliquod corporum mundanorum potest omnino lucis transitum impedire, cum nullum penitus natura perspicui sit privatum et ad minus circumfulgentiam im-
530 pedire non potest lucis secundarie.

509 corde alicuius *tr. F* / *ante* corda *hab. B* corde / corda *om. F* / *post* semicirculi *add. D* ultra dyametrum / anguli...non *in alia manu corr. V ex* cum radii a maiori
510 sicut...Euclidis {*om. D*} / 17: 18ª *F* / *ante* Euclidis *add. F* elementorum / igitur cum *tr. F*
510–11 radii a maiori: a maiori radii *V*
511 magnitudine: arcu *F* / descendunt *F* / illos *om. B* suos *A*
512 *ante* quos *add. F* rectis / quos *AWF*; *om. B* quem *VD* ?quae *H* quam *L* / constituerunt *A*
512–13 concurrunt *F*
513 necessario...illam: ad partem illam necessario *F* ad partem illam *D*
513–14 ut...Euclidis {*om. D*}
514 *ante* Euclidis *add. F* elementorum
515 quod: qui *F* / equales *F* / sibi sunt: sunt

scilicet *F* / umbrosum et luminosum: luminosum et umbrosum *D*
515–16 cadunt necessario *B* necessario cadunt *F*
517 *ante* numquam *add. FD* et / producantur *om. V* / maius fuerit *tr. F* magis fuerit *D*
518 esse...dispositionis: contrarie dispositionis *A* contrarie dispositionis esse *F*
519 quare: quarum *F* / erit...pyramidis *VALD* erit vel econtra everse curte pyramidis *B* erunt curte pyramides et econtra *W* curte erunt pyramides et everse *F* erunt everse curte pyramidis (pyramidis *in alia manu corr. ex* pyramides) *H*
520 calateidos *DL* kalateidos *V* caleteidos *B* calaetidos (*supra* calaetidos *in alia manu hab.* they) *A* kalochoides *F* lateidos *H* / *post* dico *add. B* autem *et add. F* tamen / cum: quod *F*

the] umbrageous body cannot be parallel, for they do not touch the circumference [of the umbrageous body] at the ends of a diameter, but at the ends of some chord smaller than the chord of a semicircle. Consequently the angles of contact [between the rays and the chord] are not right angles, as is evident from Proposition 17 of the third book of Euclid.[63] Therefore, since the rays descend from a larger magnitude, the angles formed by the rays on the side of the aforesaid chord more remote from the luminous body must be smaller [than right angles]. The rays must accordingly converge on that side, as the fourth postulate of the first book of Euclid teaches.[64]

If, however, the umbrageous and luminous bodies are equal in size, the rays [issuing from the ends of the diameter of the luminous body] necessarily fall on the ends of the diameter of the umbrageous body, and are consequently parallel, never intersecting even if extended infinitely. However, if the umbrageous body is larger [than the luminous body], the shadow must be of a disposition contrary to that in the first of the three cases. Wherefore it is an infinite truncated pyramid inverted with respect to length, which figure is called *calateidos.*[65] I maintain [the foregoing to be true] when the umbrageous and luminous bodies are over the same plane.[66]

[Proposition] 25{23}. A shadow is diminished light.

As Proposition 14 [above] shows, although an opaque object impedes the direct and principal propagation of light, it does not impede the secondary propagation, which proceeds circumferentially. However, shadows differ from darkness in that shadows are diminished light, [produced] whenever there is a privation of primary light together with a derivation of secondary light. Darkness, however, exists in a place totally deprived of light. I do not know, in fact, if any earthly bodies are capable of altogether impeding the propagation of light, for nothing is totally deprived of transparency and cannot, at any rate, impede the circumfusion of secondary light.[67]

520–21 dico...planum *om. D* / sunt...luminosum: luminosum et umbrosum sunt F

521 *ante* planum *scr. et del. A* spatium / planum *in alia manu corr. V ex* punctum / *post* planum *add. F* id est medium uniforme

523 ex 14 *obs. A* ex 14ᵃ *F* {supra} *D*

525 autem *om. V* / umbra¹ *in alia manu mg. hab. V* / quia: quod *VBA* / est lux *tr. V*

526 *post* ubi *add. F* scilicet / est² *om. A* / derivatio: diminutio *F* / *ante* tenebra *add. F* sed / vero *om. F*

527 tamen (*in alia manu alt. A ad* est): cum *D* / ubi: ibi *B* / lumine: luce *F* / *post* si *add. F* est

527–28 corporum mundanorum *tr. D*

528 *ante* potest *add. F* sit quod / omnino: omnem *F* omnia *H* / lucis transitum *tr. F*

529 perspicui: lucis *F* / circumfulgentiam (*corr. V ex* circumferentiam): circumferentiam *A* circumfluentiam *H*

529–30 impedire...secundarie: lucis secundarie non potest impedire *F*

530 secundare *H*

[*Propositio*] *26ᵃ{24ᵃ}. Quanto sol est propinquior lune tanto eam magis illuminat intensive et extensive.*

Quod intensive patet ex 18. Quod extensive probatur quoniam ex 22 propositione patet quod includitur pyramidibus radiosis a sole proiectis, et quanto soli est propinquior tanto breviori pyramide circumcingitur. Ymaginemur ergo pyramidem aliquam longiorem, cuius latera tangant utrimque in luna puncta *N O* que sunt termini arcus *NO* [Fig. 12]. Amplius latera pyramidis brevioris tangere non possunt extrema arcus *NO*, si enim facerent cum sint ab eadem basi pyramides essent equales; nec possunt tangere extrema arcus maioris quam *NO*, verbi gratia *PQ*, quoniam sic breviorem pyramidem constituere non possent nisi utrimque latera longiorum pyramidum secarent, quod est impossibile cum ab eisdem terminis utrimque procedant, tales enim lineas impossibile est concurrere. Latet tamen lune pars illuminata superior enim est, et videtur portio eius modica donec a sole paulatim elongetur.

{[*Propositio*] *25ᵃ. Lunam cum illuminatur apparenter minus medietate faciem novacularem necessario pretendere.*

{Ad cuius intelligentiam necesse est ymaginari duas superficies, quarum

---

531 luna *F*

531–32 eam...illuminat: eam illuminat ma-gis *B* eam maius eam illuminat *A* magis eam illuminat *FD* / intensive et exten-sive: extensive et intensive *F*

533 patet *in alia manu hab. V* / patet...18 {*om. D*} / 18ᵃ *A* / quod² : et *D* / quoniam *om. F*

533–34 ex 22ᵃ propositione *A* ex 22ᵃ *F* {supra} *D*

534 quod: quoniam corpus lunare *F* / *ante* pyramidibus *add. F* a / radiosis *om. F*

535 soli est *tr. F* soli *D* / circumagitur *A* concluditur *F*

536 ymaginemur: ymagine et nec *H* / tan-

gant *VBWH* tangunt *AFD*

537 utrimque *om. FD* / N O¹ *om. D* / que: qui *B*

537–38 que...NO *om. F*

538–39 si...facerent *om. A*

539 possent *BA*

540 *post* quam *add. F* sit / verbi gratia PQ *om. D* / sic *om. F*

541 possunt *F* / nisi: sed *F* / utraque *F*

541–42 longioris pyramidis *AF*

542 *ante* cum *add. F* quod patet

543 utrumque *F* / procedent *B* procedat *F*

544 tamen: enim *F* / lune pars *tr. A* / *ante* est *add. F* pars / videtur *obs. F* / portio: pars *F* / eius modica *tr. F*

[*Proposition*] *26{24}. The closer the sun is to the moon, the more the former illuminates the latter in intensity and extent.*

That it does so in intensity is evident from Proposition 18. That it does so in extent is proved by Proposition 22, where it is evident that the moon is enclosed by pyramids of radiation extending from the sun; and the nearer the moon is to the sun, the shorter the pyramid by which it is enclosed. Let us imagine, therefore, a long pyramid, the sides of which touch the opposite sides of the moon at points *N* and *O*, the ends of arc *NO* [Fig. 12]. Now the sides of a shorter pyramid cannot touch the ends of arc *NO*, for, if they did, the two

Fig. 12

pyramids would be equal [in length] because they proceed from the same base. Nor can the sides of the shorter pyramid touch the ends of an arc larger than *NO*, such as *PQ*, because in that case, in forming a shorter pyramid, they would intersect both sides of longer pyramids; that is impossible since the pyramids proceed from the same end-points, for it is impossible that such lines should intersect. Nevertheless, part of the moon is concealed because it is illuminated above, and its lower portion is visible only when the moon is slightly elongated from the sun.

{[*Proposition*] *25. When less than half the visible side of the moon is illuminated, its face necessarily appears crescent-shaped.*[68]
{In order to understand this, it is necessary to imagine two surfaces [on the

una est tota illuminata soli directe et facialiter ei opposita, alia vero hu-
550 mano aspectui obiecta. Et iste due superficies aliquando sunt una superficies omnino ut in plenilunio quando idem est quod soli obicitur et quod
oculo representatur, aliquando vero sunt due superficies omnino diverse
ut quando luna coniungitur soli et illuminatur ab ea superius et non inferius. In parte illa que respicit oculum consideratoris, in omni vero alio
555 statu, una superficies pro parte secat aliam, et hoc tripliciter: aliquando
apparet luna illuminata secundum portionem exiguam quantum ad latitudinem portionis, aliquando apparet illuminata secundum quantitatem semicirculi, aliquando vero secundum quantitatem portionis maioris semi-
circulo. In prima istarum apparitionum apparet luna cornubus acuta cava
560 novacule simul, cuius ratio est quoniam si luna haberet in veritate planam
superficiem illuminatam videns unam eius partem posset videre simul
totam. Sed quia habet superficiem in veritate spericam non potest semper
tota pars illuminata videri, quoniam impediente spericitate in tali situ pars
modica directe opponitur oculo consideratoris.
565   {Portio autem visa in novilunio includitur inter duas portiones duorum
circulorum magnorum, quorum unus est super alium inclinatus. Et secant
se mutuo quia uterque transit per polos lune et dividunt speram lune per
equalia; et licet superius probatum sit quod lumen solis illuminat plus
medietate lune et per consequens circulus finiens illuminationem lune fit
570 maior circulo dividente lunam per equalia, non refert tamen quantum ad
propositum, quia excessus unius circuli super alium est insensibilis, propter
quod forte dicit Gregorius super illud lunam incedentem clare, quod sol
illuminat lunam per occultum circulum. Duorum autem circulorum quorum portiones includunt portionem lune visam in novilunio, unus distin-
575 guit partem lune ⟨visam⟩ illuminatam a parte non visa illuminata, alius
vero circulus distinguit partem illuminatam et non illuminatam. Cum igitur
isti duo circuli se intersecant in duobus locis ut dictum est, necesse est ut
hec portio, cum sit acuta in utroque extremo et latior in medio, appareat
bicornis et similis draconi, de quo loquuntur astrologi. In cuius extremi-
580 tatibus sunt eclipses et similes etiam sectori spere, de quo idem loquuntur.
Verbi gratia si ducantur due linee a polo artico ad polum antarticum per
utrumque finem arietis vel alterius signi, apparet igitur hec portio novacularis; et est concavitas novaculationis in superficiei non illuminate, quoniam circulus finis est partis illuminate quomodocunque illuminetur. Et
585 quoniam superficies lune, que sperica est, apparet plana, sicut inferius
declarabitur absque demonstrationis vitio circularis, necesse est ut pars

570 maior *corr. ex* minor *D*   579 astrologi *corr. ex* astrilogi *D*
573–74 quorum *corr. ex* quarum *D*   583 concavitas *corr. ex* concavitatas *D*
576 illuminatam[2] *corr. ex* illuminata *D*

moon], one of which is directly opposite the sun and fully illuminated while the other faces mankind. Sometimes these two surfaces are [in actuality] only a single surface, as during a full moon when the same surface is exposed to the sun and presented to the eye. But sometimes the two surfaces are altogether distinct, as when the moon is in conjunction with the sun and is illuminated above rather than below. However, in every other position [of the sun and moon] one of the surfaces partly overlaps the other in the portion [of the moon] facing the eye of the observer, and this in [any one of] three ways: sometimes the visible illuminated portion of the moon is of scant width, sometimes semicircular, and sometimes greater than a semicircle. In the first case the moon appears horned like the sharp, curved part of a knife;[69] the reason for this [shape] is that if the illuminated surface of the moon were actually a plane, a person seeing part of it would simultaneously see the whole, but since the actual surface is spherical, the entire illuminated sector cannot always be seen because in such a position the sphericity interferes and [only] a small part [of the illuminated portion] is directly opposite the eye of the observer.

{During a new moon, however, the visible portion is contained between segments of two great circles, one of which is inclined relative to the other. They intersect each other because both pass through the poles of the moon and divide the lunar sphere into equal parts; and although it was proved above that the light of the sun illuminates more than half the moon[70] and consequently that the circle enclosing the illuminated part of the moon is larger than the circle dividing the moon in half, nevertheless this is of no significance for the [present] problem because the one circle is insensibly larger than the other, on which account Gregory distinctly says, in passing reference to this lunar occurrence, that the sun illuminates a hidden circle of the moon.[71] However, in the new moon one of the two circles, the segments of which enclose the visible [illuminated] portion of the moon, separates the visible illuminated portion of the moon from the invisible illuminated portion, while the other circle separates the illuminated from the unilluminated part. Consequently, since these two circles intersect in two places (as was said), the [enclosed] portion must appear doubly horned and like the dragon of which the astronomers speak, because it is sharp at both ends and wider in the middle.[72] The eclipsed regions are at the outer edges of this and also resemble a spherical sector, concerning which astronomers say the same thing [as above]. For example, if two lines are drawn from the arctic pole to the antarctic pole through both ends of Aries or some other sign, the [enclosed] portion consequently appears crescent-shaped, and the concavity of the crescent is along the unilluminated surface, because however the moon is illuminated, the boundary of the illuminated region is circular. And because the surface of the moon, which is actually spherical, appears planar (as will be demonstrated below, free from the defects of circular demon-

non illuminata appareat intra concavitatem circuli finientis [?] partem illuminatam.

{Quod si portio lune illuminata visa sit semicircularis non apparet cor-
590 nuta, quia circulus finians partem illuminatam circulus non est inclinatus super circulum continentem superficiem consideratori oppositam, sed secat ipsum ad angulos rectos sperales; et quia directe opponitur oculo consideratoris necesse est quod appareat ei sicut linea recta. Cum autem portio lune visa est maior medietate non potest apparere acuta cornibus, propter
595 evidentem latitudinem superficiei vise, sed apparet gibbosa siquidem finis eius est portio circuli apparenter minoris circulo totalem superficiem continente. Apparet autem minor quia non complet circumferentia circuli illuminate portionis circumferentiam continentis, cum tamen in veritate circuli sint equales.}

600   [*Propositio*] *27ª*{*26ª*}. *Omne corpus visibile radios habere.*
Radius enim nichil aliud est nisi species rei visibilis in directum facta porrectione. Corpora tamen luminosa dicuntur principaliter radiare, quia radiis cetera illustrant, et sol precipue cuius radii sensibiles sunt.

{[*Propositio*] *27ª*. *Omne corpus naturale visibile seu non visibile radiose*
605 *virtutem suam in alia porrigere.*
{Huius probatio est per causam naturalem, quoniam corpus naturale agit per formam suam se extra se multiplicantem. Ergo quanto nobilior tanto est fortior in agendo. Et quia actio in directum est facilior et fortior nature, necesse est ut omne corpus naturale seu visibile seu non visibile
610 suam speciem multiplicet in continuum et directum, et hoc est radiare. Propter quod celum radiat in omni sua parte, non solum secundum stellam, sed etiam si quiesceret nichilominus radiaret.}

[*Propositio*] *28ª*{*28ª*}. *Visionem fieri per lineas radiosas recte super oculum orientes.*
615   Quod patet quoniam nisi species rei visibilis distincte oculum sigillaret oculus partes rei distincte non apprehenderet. Nec posset esse distinctio partialium specierum partes rei representantum nisi per lineas rectas. Ali-

590 *supra* quia *hab. D signum oblitum* / fini-
      ans *corr. ex* finiat *D*
595 gibbosa *corr. ex* gilbosa *D*
596 *post* superficiem *scr. et del. D* concurren-
      te
597 circumferentia *corr. ex* circumferen-
      tiam *D*
601 aliud est *tr. BH*

602 porrectio *D*
602–3 quia radiis: quorum radii *F*
603 sol precipue *tr. A* principaliter sol *F* /
      radii *om. F* / *post* sunt *add. D* pre ceteris
607 multiplicantem *corr. ex* multiplicitatem
      D
613 radiosas: naturales *F*
615 quoniam *om. AD* / distincte *om. B* / si-

stration),[73] the unilluminated region must appear within the concavity of the circle that terminates the illuminated region.

{But if the visible illuminated portion of the moon is semicircular, the moon does not appear horned, for the circle enclosing the illuminated region is not inclined [obliquely] relative to the circle enclosing the surface facing the observer, but cuts it at right spherical angles; and since it is directly opposite the eye of the observer, it must appear to him as a straight line. However, when the visible [illuminated] portion of the moon is more than half [a circle], it cannot appear as a crescent because of the evident width of the surface, but appears gibbous because its boundary is the portion of a circle apparently smaller than the circle containing the entire [lower] surface [of the moon]. It appears smaller because the circumference of the illuminated circle does not fill the circumference of the [aforementioned] containing circle, although the circles are nevertheless actually equal.}[74]

[*Proposition*] *27{26}. Every visible body has rays.*
In fact a ray is nothing but the species of a visible object fashioned into a straight line by extension.[75] Nevertheless, chiefly luminous bodies are said to radiate (and especially the sun, whose rays are sensible) because with their rays they illuminate other things.

{[*Proposition*] *27. Every natural body, visible or invisible, diffuses its power radiantly into other bodies.*[76]
{The proof of this is by a natural cause, for a natural body acts outside itself through the multiplication of its form. Therefore the nobler it is, the more strongly it acts. And since action in a straight line is easier and stronger for nature, every natural body, whether visible or not, must multiply its species in a continuous straight line; and this is to radiate. Because of this, all parts of the sky radiate, and not only the stars, for the sky would radiate even if the stars should be quiescent.}

[*Proposition*] *28{28}. Sight occurs through lines of radiation perpendicularly incident on the eye.*[77]
This is obvious, for unless the species of the visible object were to make a distinct impression on the eye, the eye could not apprehend the parts of the object distinctly; and no distinction could be made among the partial species representing the parts of the object except by perpendicular lines, for otherwise

---

gillarent *F*   617 rectas *obs. A*
616 potest *F* / esse: eum *H*   617–18 aliter: alias radii *F*

ter enim invicem confunderentur et rem confuse oculo representarent. Amplius abscissis lineis rectis inter visibile et visum, visio cessat. Ergo oppo-
620 situm oppositi est causa.

[*Propositio*] *29ᵃ. Oculus quantitati capiende non congrueret si rotundus non esset.*

Propter multa enim citius capienda, necessaria est oculo rotunditas propter facilitatem motus et revolutionis. Amplius si pars illa per quam
625 immutatur non esset sperica, non videret uno aspectu nisi sibi equale. Quod patet quoniam visus est per lineas rectas super visum orientes perpendiculariter, quarum concursus est in centro oculi, ut docebitur infra. Si enim esset superficiei plane, non venirent super eum perpendiculares nisi a superficie sibi equali. Verbi gratia sit per impossibile oculi super-
630 ficies plana *AB*, res visa *CD* [Fig. 13]. Igitur a puncto *B* ducatur perpendicularis super *D*. Item ab *A* puncto alia extrahatur perpendicularis que cadet in *C*. Cum *AB* et *CD* sint equidistantes (hoc supponatur quia inde inconveniens non sequitur), erit linea *AC* perpendiculariter extracta per ypothesim equalis linee *BD*, et per consequens linea *BA* equalis *DC*. Hoc
635 est res visa visus latitudinem non potest excedere. Quod si est falsum, sequitur ut oculus non sit figure plane sed sperice magis, in cuius centrum possunt radii perpendiculariter cadere a longe maiori magnitudine. Amplius capacitati interiori convenit rotunditas, quoniam figura capacissima est ysoperimetrorum, id est figurarum commensurabilium.

618 enim invicem *om. F* / confunduntur *B* / presentarent *F*
619 abscisis...rectis: lineis rectis abscisis *F* / visio *om. F*
621 quantitate *F*
623 *ante* propter *add. F* est causa / necessario *A*
624 *ante* propter *add. F* et / illa: prima *F*
624–25 per...immutatur: immutatur per quam *F*
626 quoniam: quia *F*
627 docebitur infra *tr. F*
628 enim: non *A* / *post* enim *add. F* oculi / perpendiculariter *AF*
629–30 oculi superficies *tr. F*
631 super *om. F* / D: BD *F* / ab A puncto: a puncto A *F* ex a puncto A *D* / alia extrahatur: extrahatur alia linea *F* alia ab suprahatur *H*
632 cadat *F* / *ante* cum *add.* BA ergo *et add.*

F et si sic *et add. D* igitur / cum: tunc *F* / sunt *F* / hoc: quod *D* / quia: quoniam *F* / inde *om. F*
633 erit: sit *F* / perpendicularis *F*
634 yposim *H* / BD: BCD *B* / *post* BA *scr. et del. A* latitudine non potest excedere / *ante* equalis² *add.* AF est / *post* equalis² *add. F* linee / DC: CD *F* / *post* DC *add.* BAWF sicut patet ex (ex *om. W*) 33ᵃ et 34ᵃ (23 et 34 *A*) primi Euclidis (primi elementorum Euclidis *F*) et / hoc...visa VHL ita est res visa AF ita res visa BW et ita visus *D*
635 *ante* latitudinem *add. D* hanc / latitudine *H* / non...excedere: excedere non potest *F* / est falsum *tr. A* falsum *H*
636 sequitur...non: non sequitur ut oculus *F* / magis *om. D* / cuius *om. A* / centro AF
637 perpendiculares *D* / maiore *F*

the species would mingle together and would exhibit the object to sight con-
fusedly. Besides, when perpendicular lines between the visible object and the
eye have been intercepted, vision ceases. Accordingly, the opposite effect requires the opposite cause.

[*Proposition*] *29. The eye would be unsuited for the perception of size if it
were not round.*[78]
Because of the many things that must be quickly perceived, the eye must
be round so that it can easily move and turn. Furthermore, if the part through
which the eye is acted upon were not spherical, the eye could see at a single
glance only things equal [in size] to itself. This is evident because vision occurs
through straight lines incident perpendicularly on the eye and intersecting at
its center, as will be taught below.[79] If the eye had a flat surface, only perpendiculars from a surface of equal size could reach it. For example, although impossible, let the eye have a plane surface *AB* [Fig. 13], and let *CD* be the visible

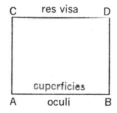

Fig. 13
The figure is found exactly as above only in *F* and *D*. *V*, *H*, and *B* omit the figure; *A*
and *W* extend the visible object *CD* to a length greater than the surface of the eye *AB*
and represent the entire eye rather than just its surface.

object. Then drop a perpendicular from *B* to *D*. Likewise, draw another perpendicular from point *A* to point *C*. Since *AB* and *CD* are parallel (this may
be assumed since no absurdity follows from it), line *AC*, drawn perpendicularly
by hypothesis, will be equal to line *BD*; consequently line *BA* will equal line
DC. That is, the thing seen cannot exceed the breadth of the eye. However,
since this is false,[80] it follows that the eye is not flat but more nearly spherical,
and into its center rays can fall perpendicularly from a magnitude far greater
[than the eye]. Moreover, roundness accords with interior capaciousness, because [the sphere] is the most capacious of all isoperimetric (i.e., commensur-
able) figures.

638 capacitati interiori: maiore capacitati *F*   est anterioris glacialis / *ante* figura *scr.*
    capacitati *D* / *post* rotunditas *add. F* que   *et del.* D spera / figura *om. F*

640   {[*Propositio*] *32ᵃ*. *Oculus quantitati capiende non congrueret si rotundus non esset.*

{Patet quod, propter magna et multa corpora celeriter capienda, multum confert rotunditas oculi, propter quam potest celeriter revolvi. Preterea si pars oculi anterior, per quam fit visio, esset plana numquam
645   videret oculus uno aspectu perfecte nisi sibi equale. Quod patet quoniam visus est per lineas rectas super visum perpendiculariter orientes, ut patet ex proxima precedente. Si autem esset superficiei plane....}

[*Propositio*] *30ᵃ{33ᵃ}*. *Aliqua corporum oculum constituentium a spere necesse est deficere complemento.*
650   Verbi gratia consolidativa, pinguedo scilicet alba, que circumdat oculum, si totum circumdaret, oculus nichil videret, quia ipsa dyaphoneitate caret. Similiter uvea habet foramen in anteriori parte, similiter et glacialis deficit a rotunditate.

[*Propositio*] *31ᵃ{34ᵃ}*. *Corpora diversarum dispositionum requiruntur ne-*
655   *cessario ad oculum construendum.*

Hoc patet quoniam pars illa in qua viget vis visiva est tenera et passibilis multum, quoniam perspicua et aquea tenerrime compositionis. Aliter enim non congrueret subtilitati spirituum visibilium a cerebro venientium; aliter etiam species subesse immateriali et depurato minime reciperet. Nec
660   percipi posset tactus earum nisi subtilissimo corpore. Hic autem humor faciliter corrumperetur nisi aliis fortioribus circumdaretur. Hinc dispositio talis est oculi ut sit tunica extima que dicitur consolidativa, fortis et pinguis ad retinendum oculum totum in dispositione sua. Intra quam est tunica que dicitur cornea quia cornu est similis que fortis est quia aeri
665   exponitur, et est dyaphona ut sit speciebus pervia.

Intra istam est tunica que dicitur uvea, que nigra est ad uve similitu-

642 corpora *corr. ex* corpus *D*
648 oculum *rep. A*
649 complemento *om. A*
650 consolidativa...scilicet: consolidativa
    scilicet pinguedo *A* consolidativa pin-
    guedo videlicet *F* consolidativa piguedo
    (*sic*) scilicet *D* / alba: albugo *F*
650–51 *post* oculum *add. D* anterius
651 nichil: non *F* / ipsa *om. D* ista *F* / *post*
    dyaphoneitate *add. D* exterius
652 caret *VWHL* careret *BAFD* / *post* parte
    add. F sua / similiter² et *tr. F*
653 definit *H* / deficit a rotunditate: {rotun-
    ditatem perfectam deficit ergo oculus a

rotunditate completa} *D*
654 *ante* dispositionum *add. F* specierum vel
655 construendum *VHLD* constituendum
    BAF
656 hec *F* / quoniam: quia *D* / illa *om. F* /
    vis *om. B* virtus *FD*
656–57 passibilis multum *tr. F* passiva mul-
    tum *B*
657 quoniam: quia *F* / *post* quoniam *add.*
    D est
658 enim *om. F*
659 etiam: enim *AF* / reciperentur *F*
660 posset...earum: posset actus earum *D*
    tactus earum posset *F* / *post* nisi *add.*

{[*Proposition*] *32. The eye would be unsuited to the perception of size if it were not round.*

{It is evident, because of the numerous large bodies that must be quickly perceived, that roundness of the eye is of great benefit, making it possible for the eye to be revolved swiftly. Moreover, if the front part of the eye, through which vision takes place, were flat, the eye could see at a single glance only things equal to itself. This is evident because vision occurs by straight lines incident perpendicularly on the eye, as is evident from the preceding proposition. If the eye had a flat surface....}[81]

[*Proposition*] *30{33}. Some of the bodies constituting the eye must depart from complete sphericity.*[82]

For instance, if the consolidativa (i.e., the white fat) that surrounds the eye were to surround it entirely, the eye would see nothing because the consolidativa lacks transparency. The uvea, too, has an opening in front, and the glacial humor also departs from sphericity.

[*Proposition*] *31{34}. Bodies of various dispositions are required for the constitution of the eye.*[83]

This is evident, for the part in which the power of sight resides is very delicate and sensitive because it is transparent and watery and of the most delicate composition. If this were not so, it would be unsuited to the subtlety of the visual spirits coming from the brain; yet neither would the species in any way admit of being subject to the immaterial and purified. Furthermore, the influence of species can be perceived only by a most subtle body. This humor, however, would be easily corrupted if it were not surrounded by other stronger ones. Hence the eye is so disposed that there is an outermost tunic called the consolidativa,[84] strong and thick so as to maintain the entire eye in its proper arrangement. Within the consolidativa is a tunic called the cornea because it is like horn. The cornea is hard, [as it must be] because of its exposure to the air, and transparent in order to be pervious to species.

Within the cornea is the tunic called the uvea. The uvea is black like a

---

B in

661 faciliter *om. F* facilitate *A | post* fortioribus *add. F* ipsum conservantibus | *ante* circumdaretur *scr. et del. F* circumdatur

662 extima *VHLD* extrema *BAF*

663 totum *om. F* | sua *om. V | post* sua *add. F* in qua est

664 quia *om. A* | cornu est similis: est similis

cornu (cornu *in alia manu*) *A* | que[2]: quia *F* | quia: et *F* | aerea *F*

665 exponitur *om. F* | pervia: provisa *A*

666 istam: quam tunc *F* | dicitur uvea *tr. BAD* | que[2]: quia *F*

666–67 nigra...similitudinem: ad similitudinem uve nigra *F*

dinem ut obscuretur in ea humor in quo viget visus, qui humor nisi obscuraretur aliquantulum species visibiles in eo non apparerent. Et est hec
tunica fortis ne resudet ex ea humor in ea contentus, habens in anteriori
670 sua parte foramen circulare ut transeant per eam species, cuius dyameter
est circiter quantitatem lateris quadrati intra speram uveam descriptibilis.

Intra istam tunicam est humor albugineus similis albumini ovi, dya-
phonus ut per eum species libere ferantur, humidus ut humectet humorem
glacialem ne tela eum circumdans siccitate corrumpatur.

675 Intimus humor est humor glacialis glaciei similis, humidus ut sit a luce
passibilis—non solum perspicuitate sed passibilitate sensus—sed est subtilis ut faciliter moveatur. Et est aliquantulum spissus ut species in eo figi
possint; alias evanescerent. Et hic humor dividitur in duos, habet enim
anteriorem partem maioris spere portionem et toti oculo concentricam et
680 equidistantem anteriori parti visus; habet et posteriorem que vitrea dicitur
que subtilior est anteriori parte. Et hec due circumdantur tela quadem
subtili que aranea appellatur, similis tele aranee, cuius tele officium est
humorem illum fluidum continere. Et ita secundum istum Physicum oculus habet tres humores et 4 tunicas.

667 qui: quia *FD* / nisi: si *B*
667–68 obscuraretur: obscuretur *A*
668 *post* visibiles *scr. et del. F* nu / in eo *om.*
  F
669 resudat *F* / ex ea humor: humor ex ea *F*
  / in ea contentus: contentus in ea *F*
670 sua parte *tr. AF* / eam: ipsum *F* / *post*
  cuius *add. FD* foraminis
671 circa *F* / *ante* quantitatem *add. A* ad /
  lateris *om. F* / infra *F* / *post* speram *scr.
  et del. F* uvea
672 simili *F* / albumini *VHLD* albugini
  BAWF
673 eum *WFH* eam *VBALD* / humectet
  humorem: humore est *A*
674 glacialem: in glaciabilem *F* / *post* tela
  add. F aranea / eum *W* ea *VH* eam
  BAFLD / corrumpat *A*
675 humor[1]: humorum *VH* / est *om. F* /

humor[2] *om. F et in alia manu mg. hab.*
  D / *ante* glaciei *add. F* est etiam / glaciei
  in alia manu corr. A ex glaciali
676 sed: et *F*
677 faciliter moveatur: species faciliter et
  subtiliter moveantur *F*
679 *post* maioris *in alia manu mg. hab V*
  minoris / *post* spere *scr. et del. F* fortiorem
680 equidistantie *H* / *ante* anteriori *add. F*
  ab / parte *F* / et *VBHL* etiam *AFD* /
  post posteriorem *add. D* partem
681 que…est: et est subtilior *F*
682 subtiliori *F* / appellatur: nunccupatur *A*
  dicitur *F* / *ante* similis *add. F* et est /
  officium est *tr. F*
683 humorem illum *tr. A* / ita: ista *V* sic *F* /
  istum ?physicum *VBHD*; *tr. A* istum
  modum *F*

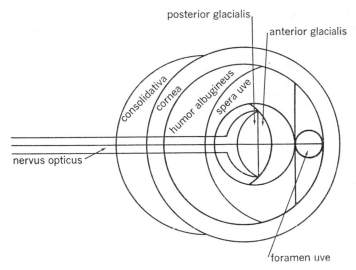

posterior glacialis

anterior glacialis

consolidativa

cornea

humor albugineus

spera uve

nervus opticus

foramen uve

Fig. 14

This figure reproduces the schematic drawing of the eye that appears in Vat. lat. 5963, fol. 16r (see Plate 1). The only change I have made is to correct the nomenclature slightly by reference to similar drawings appearing in other manuscripts of the *Perspectiva communis*; cf. the Critical Notes to Part I, n. 83, pp. 247–49.

grape to darken the humor in which [the power of] sight resides, for unless that humor is darkened, the visible species will not appear in it. This is a strong tunic to prevent the enclosed humor from exuding, and, so that species may pass through, it has a circular aperture in front,[85] the diameter of which is about the size of the side of the square that can be inscribed within the sphere of the uvea.

Within the uvea is the albugineous humor,[86] which is like the white of an egg. It is transparent, so that species may be conducted through it freely, and damp, to moisten the glacial humor so that the web surrounding it will not be corrupted by dryness.

The glacial humor,[87] which is like glass, is the innermost humor. It is moist in order to be sensitive to light—by virtue not only of transparency but also of the passibility of sense—and it is subtle so that it might be easily stimulated [by species]. It is also somewhat dense to permit the retention of species within it, for they would otherwise die away.[88] This humor is divided into two parts: it has an anterior part[89] that is a portion of a larger sphere, and this part is concentric with the whole eye and parallel to the front of the eye; and it has a posterior part called the vitreous, more subtle than the anterior part. These two parts are surrounded by a certain fine web like a spider web, called the aranea;[90] the function of the aranea is to contain this moist humor. And so, according to the Physicist,[91] the eye has three humors and four tunics.

685   Alii autem qui anathomiam delicatius perspiciunt ponunt, sicut legitur
in libro *De elementis*, quod uvea ortum habet a pia matre sicut cornea a
dura matre que sunt due tele cerebrum circumdantes, et subiungit quod
oculus constat ex tribus humoribus et 7 tunicis, quarum prima est coniunctiva vel consolidativa. Corneam etiam dividit in duas partes, anteriorem
690 vocans corneam interiorem vero schrosim appellat. Similiter et uveam
dividit cuius anterior pars dicitur uvea, posterior secundina. Similiter aranea dividitur, cuius anterior pars dicitur aranea, interior vero retina. Sic
tamen dividere huic physice cura non est, que solum considerat que ad
ecentricitatem pertinent vel concentricitatem fractionem et directionem.

695   [*Propositio*] *32ᵃ{35ᵃ}. Oculorum dualitatem necesse est reduci ad unita-
tem.*
     Duo sunt oculi ex benignitate creatoris ut si uni accidat lesio alter
remaneat. Origo autem eorum hec est, quoniam ab anteriori parte cerebri
oriuntur duo nervi concavi directi ad anteriorem partem faciei, qui primo
700 coniunguntur et fiunt unus nervus, qui inde ramificatur in duos ad duo
foramina concava sub fronte, in quibus dilatantur. Et creatio oculorum
fit super ipsorum nervorum extremitates. Species igitur visibilium per
utrumque recipitur, quod si iste species non unirentur res una due appareret, sicut etiam patet si digito supposito ipsi oculo oculus unus a suo situ

685 alie *F* | autem *om. B* | qui *om. A* que *F*
     | ponunt: dicunt *F*
686 in *om. A* | elementionibus *F* | ortum
     habet *tr. F* | *ante* sicut *scr. et del. F* sic |
     sicut: et sic *D*
687 quod *om. B*
688–89 coniunctiva vel consolidativa: con-
     solidativa vel coniunctiva *F*
690 vocantes *F* | vero *om. F et mg. hab. D* |
     appellat *om. F*
691 dicitur *om. A* | *post* posterior *scr. et del.*
     F C | secundina: retentiva *F*
691–92 similiter...retina *om. F* | aranea *om.*
     A
692 *ante* dividitur *scr. et del. B* dicitur
693 dividere...physice: divideremus huic
     physice (divideremus *in alia manu alt. ex*
     dividere) *A* dividere physice *F* | cura non

est: non est cura *A* | que²: quedam *F*
694 pertinentia *F* | *ante* fractionem *add. F*
     vel | fractionem *om. A* | et *om. A* vel *F*
695 reducere *AF*
697 ex: de *F*
698 remaneat: maneat *F* | origo *obs. F* | an-
     teriori: interiori *VH*
699 que *F*
700 coniungutur *V* | inde: quidem *D* | ra-
     mificantur *FD* | *post* duos *add. A* nervos
     | ad: a *V* in *F*
702 super: sub *A* | ipsorum *om. D* | *ante* ner-
     vorum *scr. et del. F* oculorum
703 species *om. A* | re *F* | *post* res *add. F*
     visa | due: die *H*
703–4 apparerent *BF* apparet *H*
704 si: a *B* | oculus unus *tr. BF* unus *D* | suo
     situ *tr. D*

Others who investigate anatomy more attentively, however, consider (as it is observed in the book *De elementis*)[92] that the uvea takes its origin from the pia mater and the cornea from the dura mater—the pia mater and dura mater being two webs that surround the cerebrum. This book adds that the eye is composed of three humors and seven tunics,[93] the first of which is the conjunctiva or consolidativa; and it divides the cornea into two parts, calling the anterior part the cornea and the interior part the schrosim. It divides the uvea similarly, calling the anterior part the uvea and the posterior the secundina.[94] Likewise the aranea is divided, the anterior part being termed the aranea and the interior part the retina. Thus to divide the eye, however, is not the concern of physics, which considers only what pertains to eccentricity or concentricity, refraction, and direction [of the rays].

[*Proposition*] *32{35}. The duality of the eyes must be reduced to unity.*[95]
The benevolence of the Creator has provided that there should be two eyes so that if an injury befalls one, the other remains. However, their source is as

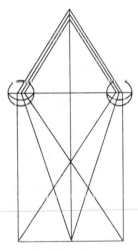

Fig. 15
This figure is not called for by the text, but it appears in most early manuscripts. Among the manuscripts collated for this edition, it is omitted by *W*, *F*, and *D*.

follows. Two hollow nerves originate in the anterior part of the cerebrum and are directed toward the face. At first these are joined and form a single nerve, but then they branch into two [nerves] at the two hollow openings beneath the forehead; here they are spread apart, and on the ends of these nerves the eyes are formed. Accordingly, the species of visible things are received by both eyes so that, if the species were not united, one thing would appear as two. This is evident also when a finger is placed under the eye and one eye is elevated

705 elevaretur; res una due videretur quoniam species per duos oculos recepte in communi nervo non coniunguntur. Necesse est igitur species in communi nervo coniungi et ibi uniri.

[*Propositio*] *33ª{36ª}. Sperarum oculum constituentium necesse est aliquas esse mutuo ecentricas.*

710 Hoc patet quoniam cum species rei visibilis pyramidaliter super oculum oriatur, cuius pyramidis conus ymaginabilis est in centro oculi, si nulla esset dyaphoneitatis diversitas radii in centro illo concurrentes, ulterius procedentes, se in centro secarent, et dextra apparerent sinistra et sinistra dextra. Hinc ingeniavit natura ut anterior glacialis idem centrum
715 habeat cum cornea et cum humore albugineo ne species per ipsas transeuntes frangantur antequam pertingant ad vim sensitivam que in glaciali viget. Deinde occurrente sibi interiori glaciali que est eis ecentrica sive humore vitreo que subtilior est quam anterior glacialis, disgregantur radii et franguntur a perpendiculari. Et hinc per viam spirituum defertur species
720 usque ad locum iudicii interioris.

[*Propositio*] *34ª{37ª}. Omnium tunicarum et humorum centra una continet linea.*

Hoc probatur per effectum quoniam aliter non posset lux omnes tunicas et humores regulariter introire, nec aliquis posset radius non fractus rema-
725 nere. Et per consequens certificatio non posset esse per deportationem oculi super visibile ab extremo ad extremum, quod est falsum.

[*Propositio*] *35ª{38ª}. Omnium radiorum super visum orientium unum solum necesse est transire non fractum.*

Cuius ratio est quoniam super speras ecentricas impossibile est plures
730 una linea esse perpendiculares. Pyramis igitur radiosa sub qua res videtur

705 elevatur *H* elevetur *D* / re *F* / *post* una *add. F* visa illic / due: die *H* / videtur *HD* / *post* quoniam *add. D* tunc
706 nervo: numero *H* / non *om. F* / coniungunt *A* / species *om. A*
709 mutuo *in alia manu hab. V*
710 hec *F* / cum *om. A*
711 si *om. B*
712 dyaphoneitas *A* dyaphaneita *VH* / diversitas: variatio *F* / centro illo *tr. D* centro uno *F*
713 se...secarent: in centro secarent se *F* si in centro secarent *H*
713–14 et sinistra *om. F* sinistra *H*

714 glacialis *om. F*
715 habet *A* / *ante* humore *scr. et del. H* ho / species *om. F*
716 franguntur *F* / antequam: numquam *B* / pertingat *A* attingant *F* / sensitivam: visivam *F* / *post* que *add. A* tamen
717 occurrente: concurrentes *F* / ecentrica: concentrica *D* / sive: sui *F*
718 *ante* humore *add. F* in / que: qui *D* / radii *om. F*
719 via *F* / deferuntur *F* defertur *in alia manu corr. V ex* defertus
720 *ante* interioris *add. B* superioris vel
721 et...centra: centra et humorum *A*

from its [customary] position: one thing [then] looks like two because the species received through the two eyes are not joined in the common nerve.[96] Therefore [if vision is to be single,] species must be brought together in the common nerve and united there.

[*Proposition*] *33{36}. It is necessary for some of the spheres constituting the eye to be mutually eccentric.*[97]

This is evident as follows. Since the species of the visible object is incident on the eye in the form of a pyramid, the vertex of which is to be imagined at the center of the eye, the rays converging at that center would intersect and proceed beyond if there were no change in transparency; and right would appear left and left right. Hence nature has arranged for the anterior glacial humor to have the same center as the cornea and albugineous humor so that species traversing them should not be refracted before they reach the sensitive power residing in the glacial humor. Then upon meeting the interior glacial humor, which is eccentric to [the cornea and albugineous humor], or the vitreous humor, which is more subtle than the anterior glacial humor, the rays are separated and refracted away from the perpendicular.[98] From there the species is carried to the place of interior judgment by the way of spirits.

[*Proposition*] *34{37}. The centers of all the tunics and humors are contained on one line.*[99]

This is proved by an effect, for otherwise light could not enter all the tunics and humors in a regular manner, nor could any ray remain unrefracted. Consequently there could be no certification by the conveyance of the eye over the visible object from one end to the other, and that is false.

[*Proposition*] *35{38}. It is necessary for only one of all the rays incident on the eye to pass through unrefracted.*

The explanation of this is that it is impossible for more than one line to be perpendicular to [each of several] eccentric spheres. Therefore with the excep-

---

721–22 continet linea *tr. F*
723 hec *F* | *ante* omnes *add. D* per
724 intrare *F* | *ante* radius *scr. et del. H* p
724–25 remanere: manere *F*
725 esse: fieri *F* | *ante* per *add. A* et
726 *ante* ad *add. A* usque | est: patet *F*

729 ratio *in alia manu mg. hab. D* | ecentricas...plures: plures ecentricas sola *D*
730 una...esse: esse una linea (*post* linea *scr. et del.* esse) *A* lineas quam unam esse *F* una linea est *D* | perpendicularis *D*

tota frangitur in ingressu interioris glacialis, excepta linea illa que transit per omnia centra, que axis appellatur.

[*Propositio*] *36ᵃ{39ᵃ}. Visum vigere in glaciali humore.*

Hoc experimento docetur, quoniam si alii cuicunque tunice vel humori
735   lesio accidat, salva glaciali, per medicinam recipit curationem et sanatur, ac restituitur visus. Ipsa vero corrupta, corrumpitur visus irrecuperabiliter.

[*Propositio*] *37ᵃ{40ᵃ}. Visionem fieri per hoc, quod in glaciali est ordinatio speciei sicut exterius rei.*

Huius possibilitas patet, non obstante parvitate glacialis, quoniam tot
740   sunt partes minime sicut maxime magnitudinis. Species autem sine materia recipiuntur. Ergo quantumcunque sit visibile quod videtur, species eius distincte et ordinate recipi potest in glaciali humore, quod nisi fieret oculus rem distincte non videret. Si enim species duarum partium rei visibilis in eadem parte glacialis recipiantur, partes rei distincte non cognoscerentur
745   pre confusione formarum moventium oculum in eadem parte.

[*Propositio*] *38ᵃ{41ᵃ}. Rei visibilis comprehensio fit per pyramidem radiosam, apprehensionis certificatio per axem super visibile transportatam.*

Pyramis enim radiosa a visibili oculo impressa rem oculo representat, sed certificatio fit de visibili per rotationem oculi super rem que basis est
750   pyramidis. Licet enim tota pyramis sit perpendicularis super centrum oculi, id est anterioris glacialis, non tamen super totum oculum. Unde sola perpendicularis illa que axis dicitur, que non frangitur, rem efficaciter representat, et alii etiam radii quo ei sunt propinquiores eo fortiores et potentiores in representando. Ad hoc igitur oculus rotatur ut res que simul

---

732 axis appellatur *tr. F* / *post* axis *add. F* et sic patet propositio sequitur alia

733 glaciali humore *tr. F*

734 hec *F* / docetur: patet *A* / quoniam: quod *B* / alii cuique *A* alicui *F* / tunice: tumor *A*

735 salvo *F* / medinam *H* / recipit curationem *tr. F* recipit *B* / sanatur: salvatur *F*

736 *post* vero *add. F* glaciali / corrumpitur: corrumpet *F*

737 *post* glaciali *add. F* humore / est ordinatio *tr. D*

738 sicut: ut *V* (*supra* ut *in alia manu hab. V* sicut) / exterioris *B*

739 parvitate glacialis *tr. F* parvitate glaciali *B* / quoniam: quod *F*

740 *post* sicut *add. D* et / autem: enim *BF*

741 recipiuntur *obs. A* recipitur *F* / ergo quantumcunque *tr. F*

742 et ordinate *om. F* / possunt *F* / *post* humore *add. F* et ordinate et

743 rem...videret: distincte non videret rem *F*

744 eandem partem *F* / cognoscentur *F*

745 pre confusione: propter confusionem *BF* / *post* parte *add. F* sequitur alia

746 rei visibilis *om. F*

748 *ante* oculo[1] *add. F* in / impressa *corr. V* *ex* repremessa

749 *ante* per *add. D* fit / rotationem: girationem *D* / *ante* oculi *add. A* id est / *post* rem *add. F* visam

749–50 basis est pyramidis: pyramidis est basis *F*

tion of the line passing through all the centers, called the axis, the entire pyramid of radiation under which an object is seen is refracted upon entrance into the interior glacial humor.

[*Proposition*] *36{39}. The power of sight resides in the glacial humor.*[100]
Experience teaches this, for if any tunic or humor whatever, save the glacial humor, should be injured, it receives care through medicine and is healed, and sight is restored. However, when the glacial humor itself has been damaged, sight is destroyed irrevocably.

[*Proposition*] *37{40}. Vision takes place by the arrangement of the species on* [*the surface of*] *the glacial humor exactly as* [*the parts*] *of the object* [*are arranged*] *outside.*[101]
The possibility of this is obvious, notwithstanding the smallness of the glacial humor, because there are as many parts in the smallest of magnitudes as in the greatest. Species, however, are received without matter. Therefore, regardless of the size of the visible object, its species can be received distinctly and in [proper] order on [the surface of] the glacial humor. Unless this were so, the eye would not see the object distinctly; for if the species of two parts of the visible object were received in the same part of the glacial humor, the parts of the object would not be perceived distinctly by reason of the confusion of forms acting on the same part of the eye.

[*Proposition*] *38{41}. Visible objects are perceived by means of the pyramid of radiation; perception is certified by the axis* [*of the pyramid*] *being conveyed over the visible object.*[102]
To be sure, the pyramid of radiation, impressed on the eye by the visible object, manifests the object to the eye; but the visible object is certified by a turning of the eye [all about] over the object, the latter being the base of the pyramid. For although the whole pyramid is perpendicular to the center of the eye, i.e., the anterior glacial humor, it is not perpendicular to the whole eye. Therefore only that perpendicular called the axis, which is not refracted, manifests the object efficaciously, and other rays are correspondingly stronger and better able to manifest [the object] as they are closer to the axis. Therefore the

750 sit perpendicularis *tr. F*
751 id est: scilicet *F* / anterioris glacialis *tr.*
    F / super *om. A*
752 perpendicularis *om. B* / illa: linea *F* /
    que² non frangitur *om. F*

753 etiam *om. D* / ei: eo *F* / sunt *om. B*
754 *ante* in *add. F* et / igitur...rotatur: rota-
    tur igitur oculus *F* / que simul *tr. A* que
    simul est *F*

755 sub pyramide ea presentatur per hanc perpendicularem successive oriens
efficaciter discernatur. Et de hac certificatione dicit auctor libri *De visu*
quia nullum visibile simul totum videtur, sed pro immutatione pyramidis.
Dicunt communiter loquentes quia omne quod videtur videtur sub angulo
vel forma triangulari.

760   [*Propositio*] *39ᵃ{42ᵃ}. Non sub quocunque angulo rem videri.*
Nec enim est visio sub angulorum acutissimo, id est angulo contingentie, quia ille angulus, sicut probat Euclides, est indivisibilis. Angulus
autem sub quo videtur per axem dividitur per quem visio completur. Amplius determinata est anguli magnitudo sub quo potest esse visio quoniam
765 dyameter foraminis uvee, sicut docet anathomia, est quasi dyameter quadrati descriptibilis intra speram uveam. Ergo si ab extremis huius foraminis
linee in centrum ducantur constituent super eum angulum rectum. Hoc
patet quoniam ab angulis quadrati ducte linee secant se ortogonaliter.
Igitur si in centro uvee esset visio videretur sub angulo recto precise si
770 dyameter foraminis esset latus quadrati precise. Nunc autem centrum
oculi, quod est anterioris glacialis, interius est quam centrum uvee quia
uvea est minor quam cornea, et secat corneam quia foramen eius cornee
applicatur. Igitur maximus angulus sub quo est visio radiosa est minor
recto nisi foramen uvee sit paulo maior quantitate predicta. Nec loquor hic
775 de visione per radios extra pyramidem radiosam super oculum orientes de
quibus infra habebitur.

[*Propositio*] *40ᵃ{43ᵃ}. Visum fieri sub curta pyramide et angulo inchoato.*
Ex predictis hoc patet, quoniam radii pyramidis omnes uno excepto

755 ea: illa *BF* ei *D* / presentatur: representatur *AD* / *post* presentatur *add. F* oculo
/ orientem *F* / *post* oriens *add. A* est
756 discernitur *F* / libri: verbi *A* in libro *FD*
757 quia: quod *F* / simul…videtur: totum
simul videtur *F* / pro: per *AF* / immuta-
tionem *AF*
758 *post* dicunt *add. F* et / communiter: contra *H* / quia: quod *AF* / omne: esse *H* /
videtur sub angulo: sub angulo videtur
(videtur *in alia manu mg.*) *V* sub angulo
H videtur angulo triangulari *F*
759 vel: in *B* / trianguli *A* trianguli videtur *F*
et angulari *H*
761 nec: non *H* hec probatur non *F* / enim
om. A / angulorum (*in alia manu corr. D
ex* angulo): angulo *BF* / *ante* angulo *add.
F* sub

761–62 contingentie *om. A*
762 ille: iste *F* / Euclidis *A* / indivisibilis
corr. H ex indivisibiles
763 sub quo: per quem *F* / *post* quem *scr. et
del. D* d
764 determinata: declarata *A* / esse: fieri *F*
765 docet *corr. H ex* donec / dyameter²:
latus *F*
765–66 quadrati descriptibilis: descripti quadrati *F*
766 intra: inter *A* / *post* uveam *scr. et del. D*
sunt / ergo *mg. hab. D* / extremitate *F*
767 linee *om. V* / *post* centrum *add. D* oculi /
ducuntur *F* / constitueret *A* constituunt
F / hoc (*in alia manu corr. V ex* habet):
ista *F* quoniam hoc *D*
768 quoniam *om. D*
769 videbitur *B* videtur *AH* / recte *VA*

eye is turned about so that the object, which is perceived under the pyramid all at once, is discerned efficaciously by appearing along this perpendicular successively. The author of the book *De visu* says, concerning this certification, that no visible thing is seen completely at one time, but rather by the alteration [in time] of the pyramid.[103] [But] in common parlance it is said that every visible object is seen under an angle or triangular figure.

[*Proposition*] *39{42}. It is not under every angle that objects are seen.*

Indeed, there is no vision under the most acute of angles, i.e., an angle of tangency, because that angle, as Euclid proves, is indivisible;[104] whereas the angle under which [an object] is seen is divided by the axis through which vision is completed. Furthermore, the magnitude of the angle under which vision can occur is limited because the diameter of the opening in the uvea is nearly equal to the diameter [i.e., side] of the square inscribed within the sphere of the uvea, as anatomy teaches. Therefore if lines are drawn from the extremities of this opening to the center [of the sphere of the uvea], they form a right angle there.[105] This is obvious, for lines drawn from the angles of a square intersect perpendicularly. Consequently, if the power of sight were located at the center of the uvea and the diameter of the opening were precisely the side of the [aforementioned] square, [an object] would be perceived under precisely a right angle. But, on the contrary, the center of the eye (i.e., the anterior glacial humor) is behind the center of the uvea because the uvea is smaller than the cornea; and the uvea intersects the cornea since its opening is in contact with the cornea. Therefore the largest angle under which vision by [direct] radiation occurs is smaller than a right angle unless the aperture of the uvea should be slightly larger than the aforementioned size.[106] I do not speak here concerning vision by rays falling on the eye outside the pyramid of radiation, which will be considered below.[107]

[*Proposition*] *40{43}. Sight takes place under a broken pyramid and an incomplete angle.*

This is evident from the aforesaid, for all rays of the pyramid except one

---

770 *ante* foraminis *add. A* a / nunc: ipsum *F*
771 oculi *om. B* / quod: qui *D*
772 *ante* minor *scr. et del. D* quam / eius: est
    H
773 est[1] *om. A* fit *F*
774 foramine *B* / sit: est *F* / paulo *om. D* /
    maior: maius *D* minus *F* / nec: uvee *A*
    / hic *om. F*

775 visione: divisione *A* / per radios: radii
    D / orientis *H*
776 *post* habebitur *add. F* sequitur alia
777 curta: ?recta *B* / *post* inchoato *add. F* a
    glaciali humore
778 ex...patet: hec patet ex predictis *F* /
    hoc *corr. V ex* hic / uno excepto *tr. F*

occurrente interiori glaciali franguntur, ut dictum est, a perpendiculari,
nec ulterius in conum constringuntur. Quamvis igitur radii ad angulum
inclinentur non tamen angulariter applicantur nisi ymaginarie tantum.
Immo cum pervenit species ad humorem vitreum, id est interiorem glacialem, secundum legem spirituum magis procedit quam secundum legem
dyaphoneitatis; incurvatur enim secundum viam spirituum usque ad nervum {communem}.

[*Propositio*] *41ᵃ{44ᵃ}. Declinatio radiorum angularis iuvat ad comprehensionem quantitatis.*

Hoc patet quia per dispositionem speciei in glaciali habetur cognitio
rei. Quia igitur quanto radii ad acutiorem angulum declinant tanto amplius species adunatur et constringitur, necesse est ut per consequens nisi
aliud impediat rei quantitas ex hoc minor videatur in oculo. Sed hoc ad
cognitionem quantitatis non sufficit, ut infra patebit non circulo demonstrando.

[*Propositio*] *42ᵃ{45ᵃ}. Per radios qui oblique super oculum oriuntur visio
vigoratur et ampliatur.*

Vigoratur inquam quoniam, licet per solos perpendiculariter orientes
fiat visio certificata et distincta principaliter, tamen certum est quod licet
punctus in visibili signatus videatur per radium suum oculum perpendiculariter tangentem, nichilominus ut patet ex predictis occupat totam pupillam. Dominatur autem motus perpendicularis et iste cooperatur. Amplius
extra pyramidem radiosam aliqua videntur cuius pyramidis angulus minoris latitudinis est quam se habeant res que uno aspectu videri possunt.
Radii ergo illorum super oculum venientes aliquo modo tangunt et movent oculum per radios in ingressu oculi fractos et ad centrum declinan-

779 occurrente: concurrente *B*
780 conum: communi *B* / constringentum *B*
   restringuntur (*in alia manu mg. alt. V ex*
   constringuntur) *VF* constringunt *A* / *an-*
   te quamvis *add. F* id est concurrunt /
   angulos *F*
781 *post* tamen *add. D* invicem / applicantur *in alia manu mg. hab. A* / tantum:
   solum *B*
782 pervenerint *F* / *ante* vitreum *scr. et del. F*
   vit / vitrum *A* / id est: et *B* / interiorem
   AWFD anteriorem *VBH*
782–83 glaciem *D*
783 spirituum...legem *om. A*
784 incurvantur *F* inclinatur *B* / viam: le-

gem *F*
785 {communem} *om. VBAH* obticum *F*
788 hec *F* / quia *VWHD* quoniam *BAF* /
   congnitio *D*
789 quanto: quando *A*
789–90 amplius: magis *F*
790 adunatur *VWHD* adunantur *BAF* /
   constringuntur *BF* / ut *om. FD*
791 aliud: ad *B* / *post* impediat *add. F* ut / rei
   quantitas *tr. F* / in oculo *om. D*
792 cognitionem quantitatis *tr. F* / infra
   patebit *tr. F* infra *A* / non²: in *AF*
792–93 *ante* demonstrando *add. A* patet
794 super...oriuntur: oriuntur super oculos
   A

are refracted away from the perpendicular when they meet the interior glacial humor, as has been stated,[108] and they are not drawn together into a vertex beyond. Therefore, although the rays may be inclined toward an angle, they do not form an angle except in the imagination.[109] On the contrary, when the species has reached the vitreous humor, i.e., the interior glacial humor,[110] it proceeds more according to the law of spirits than according to the law of transparency; indeed it is curved according to the mode of spirits all the way to the {common} nerve.[111]

[Proposition] *41{44}. The angular declination of rays assists in the comprehension of size.*[112]

This is evident, for knowledge of a thing is obtained by the arrangement of its species on [the surface of] the glacial humor. Consequently, as the rays decline toward a more acute angle, the species is accordingly more united and drawn together; therefore, the size of an object, barring any impediments, must seem smaller to the eye. But this does not [wholly] suffice for knowledge of size, as will be evident below by noncircular demonstration.[113]

[Proposition] *42{45}. Sight is strengthened and amplified by rays that are obliquely incident on the eye.*[114]

I say that sight is strengthened because, although certified and distinct vision is achieved principally through single [rays] perpendicularly incident [on the eye, and] although a point on the visible object is seen clearly through its own ray touching the eye perpendicularly, nevertheless it is certain, as is evident from the foregoing, that it [i.e., the point] fills the whole pupil. Yet the perpendicular motion predominates and the oblique cooperates. Furthermore, objects subtending an angle [at the eye] narrower[115] than that of [the largest] objects visible at a single glance can be seen outside the pyramid of radiation. Therefore rays falling from those objects onto the eye touch it in some way and stimulate it; [the eye is thus stimulated] by means of rays refracted upon entrance into the eye and bent toward the center, so that such objects are weakly

---

795 et ampliatur *in alia manu mg. hab. A*
796 *post* solos *add. WF* radios
797 tamen…est: certum tamen est *F* / quod *om. F*
798 visibiliter *A* visibilis *F* visibili *in alia manu mg. corr. V ex* visibi / *post* oculum *add. V* suum
799 *post* occupat *add. D* {specie sua}
799–800 *post* pupillam *add. F* quia quilibet

punctus visibilis multos ?mittit radios super oculum non perpendiculariter
800 autem: enim *F* / iste: alius *D* / *post* iste *add. F* obliquus
801–2 minoris: maioris *W*
802 *ante* se *scr. et del. F* se / se habeant: si haberent *B*
803 illorum: istorum *F*
804 oculum: oculos *A* / oculi *om. A*

805 tes, ut talia ab oculo debiliter advertantur. Illa autem que sunt oculo
facialiter obiecta efficacius representantur quia tam recte quam reflexe
apprehenduntur. Quare autem punctus presentatus per diversos radios in
uno loco appareat tangetur in tractatu de radiis fractis.

[*Propositio*] *43ᵃ{46ᵃ}. Operationem visibilis in visum esse dolorosam.*
810 　{Idem siquidem immittitur in sensum et in contrarium. Nichilominus}
hoc probatur {sic}, quoniam operatio visibilis in visum est unius generis.
Cum ergo operatio fortiorum lucium in visum sit lesiva sensibiliter et dolo-
rosa, sequitur omnes lucium operationes tales esse, quamvis non perpen-
datur. Et hoc est argumentum Physici de qualitate visus, et sequi neces-
815 sario videtur, quoniam nullum est visibile tantum oculo delectabile quod
non continuatione inspectionis ipsum efficiat fatigatum, cuius fatigationis
causa esse videtur precedens inspectio. Hoc quidem sapit iste Physicus,
quamvis aliud dicant phylosophi naturalia tractantes, quoniam sensibile
est perfectio sensus, igitur in actu sentiendi non est aliquid tristitiam indu-
820 cens nisi sit immoderatum. Nec videtur cogere ratio si excellens sensibile
inducit dolorem ergo mediocre, motus enim vehemens gravat, motus mediocris delectat et iuvat. Restringitur igitur quod hic dicitur ad visionis
cuiuscunque prolongationem, non ad quamcunque brevem inspectionem.

[*Propositio*] *44ᵃ{47ᵃ}. Mathematicos ponentes visum fieri per radios ab*
825 *oculo micantes superflue conari.*
　Visus enim sufficienter fit per modum prescriptum, per quem salvari
possunt omnia circa visum apparentia. Ergo superfluum est ponere sic
radios. Hoc dico auctoris *Perspective* vestigia sequendo, quamquam aliud
doceat Alkindius *De aspectibus*, aliud Platonici senserint, aliud phylo-
830 sophi sapere videantur in multis locis, aliter Augustinus qui innuere
videtur quod virtus anime aliquid in lumine oculi operetur aliter quam

805 ut: et *F* / advertuntur *F* / illa: ista *F*
806 facialiter: faciliter *HD* / *post* obiecta
　　add. D facilius et / efficacius *corr. A ex*
　　faciliter / quia *om. A* / reflexe: refracte *F*
807 diversos radios *tr. FD*
808 tangitur *A*
811 hec *F* / *ante* visum *add. F* ipsum
812 operatio…lucium: fortiorum luminum
　　operatio *F*
813 omnium *A*
813–14 perpendiculariter *F*
814 et¹: etiam *F* / *ante* de *add. AD* capitulo
　　et *add. B* ?causa
814–15 necessario videtur *tr. F*

815 quoniam: quod *B* / tantum oculo: oculo
　　tam *F*
816 continue *A*
817 causa *om. A* / esse videtur *tr. F* / quidem:
　　autem *A* / sapit…physicus: sapit iste
　　?phylosophus *FD* iste physicus sapit *B*
818 aliud…phylosophi: phylosophi aliud
　　dicant *A* alia dicunt phylosophi *F*
819 perfectius *A* ?perspectivum *F* / sensus
　　om. A / actu: actibus *F*
820 sit *om. D* / videntur *H* / cogere: tangere
　　F
821 inducat *D* / motus enim: quia motus *D*
　　/ motus² *om. F*

perceived by the eye. Those objects, however, that are placed directly in front of the eye are exhibited more efficaciously because they are apprehended by both rectilinear and bent rays. However, why a point perceived by various rays should appear in a single place will be touched upon in the treatise on refracted rays.[116]

[Proposition] *43{46}. The action of the visible object on the eye is painful.*

{[This is true] since the same thing is introduced into sense and into its contrary.[117] Nevertheless,} it is proved as follows. Because the action of the visible object on the eye is of a single kind and the action of bright lights on the eye is sensibly painful and injurious, it follows that all actions of light are painful and injurious, even if they do not seem to be. This is the argument of the Physicist on the properties of sight,[118] and it is seen to follow necessarily, since there is no visible object so delightful to the eye that, when continuously observed, it does not cause fatigue, the cause of which is clearly the preceding observation [of the object]. Now the Physicist construes it this way, but philosophers who treat natural things say otherwise, [insisting that,] since the sensible object is the perfection of sense, nothing induces pain in the act of perception unless it is excessive [in its action]. But the argument that, if a superior sensible body induces pain, an ordinary one must do so also, is not compelling, for a violent action distresses while a moderate action delights and pleases. Therefore what has been said here is limited to all prolonged observation and does not apply to every brief glance.

[Proposition] *44{47}. By assuming that sight occurs through rays issuing from the eye, mathematicians exert themselves unnecessarily.*

For the manner in which vision occurs is adequately described above, by which [description] all the phenomena of vision can be saved. Therefore it is superfluous to posit such rays. I say this following in the footsteps of the author of the *Perspectiva*.[119] Nevertheless, Alkindi teaches differently [in the treatise] *De aspectibus*,[120] the Platonists have judged otherwise,[121] and philosophers are seen in many places to understand differently. Augustine, who declares that the power of the soul has an effect on the light of the eye in a manner different

---

821–22 mediocres *A*

822 et iuvat *om. D* | *post* ad *scr. et del. F* visionem

823 cuiuscunque: cuiuslibet *F* | *post* non *add. F* autem / quemcunque *D*

824 *ante* ponentes *scr. et del. D* radios

825 superfluo *D*

828 *post* radios *add. D* egredientes / quam-

quam: quemadmodum *A* quamvis *F* / aliud *om. A* alia *F*

829 Alkindius *in alia manu hab. D* Alkandius *A* Alchindus *F* / *ante* aliud[1] *add. F* et / senserunt *VHF* / phylosophi: physici *A*

830 sapere: sentire *A* / videtur: videntur *BH*

831 virtus *om. D* / aliquid *om. F* / sit *om. A*

adhuc sit investigatum, {vel quod radii ab oculo micantes virtute anime vegetentur}.

[*Propositio*] *45ª{48ª}*. *Radios quoscunque ab oculo micantes et orientes super visibile ad visionem impossibile est sufficere.*

835 Quod si ponantur radii ab oculo exire super rem visibilem quasi contingendam, aut redeunt ad oculum aut non. Si non redeunt visio per eos non fit, cum anima a corpore non exeat. Si redeunt, qualiter? Numquid animati sunt? Numquid omnia visibilia specula sunt radios reflectendo? Amplius si redeunt cum forma rei visibilis ad oculum frustra exeunt, quo-

840 niam lux ipsa vel forma visibilis virtute lucis in totum medium se diffundit. Ergo non est necesse ut radiis quasi nuntiis requiratur. Amplius quomodo aliqua virtus oculi usque ad sidera protendetur etiam si corpus totum in spiritus resolveretur?

[*Propositio*] *46ª{49ª}*. *Lumen oculi naturale radiositate sua visui conferre.*

845 Oculus enim, ut dicit Aristoteles, non solum patitur, sed agit quemadmodum splendida. Lumen igitur naturale necessarium est oculo ad alterandum species visibiles et efficiendum proportionatas virtuti visive, quoniam ex luce solari diffunduntur sed ex lumine oculi connaturali oculo contemperantur. Hinc dixit Aristoteles quod cum motus ad exterius fortis

850 est fit visio. Cum motus ad interius fortis est, sicut patet in radio solis, obruit visum, nec patitur se proportionari visui. Sic ergo patet quoniam aliquo modo fit emissio radiorum, sed non modo Platonico, ut radii ab oculo emissi quasi in forma visibili immergantur et intincti revertantur oculo nuntiantes. Aliquid tamen operantur radii in visu modo predicto,

855 quod etiam patet quoniam visus in omnibus animalibus est unius rationis cum igitur quedam animalia per lumen oculorum suorum sufficiant coloribus virtutem multiplicativam dare ut ab eis nocte videri possint, sequitur

832 investigant *A* / *post* investigatum *add. F* sequitur alia
835 ponatur *D* / quasi *om. F*
835–36 continendam *F*
836 redeunt[1,2]: rediunt *F*
837 exiat *F* / redeant *D* rediunt *F* / qualiter *om. F*
838 animati....numquid *om. A* / specula sunt *tr. D* / reflectendo (*in alia manu corr. V ex* flectendo) *VBL* inflectendo *A* flectendo *H* reflectentes *FD*
839 rediunt *F* / cum: tunc *F* / exeunt: exit *F*
841 non est necesse: necesse non est (*ante* non *scr. et del.* est) *B* / radius *BF* species

radiis *D* / nuntius *F* / requiratur: utatur *A* / quomodo: quoniam *A*
842 usque *om. FH* / protendetur: protenderetur *F* protenditur *A* / etiam: et *D* / *ante* in *scr. et del. H* re
843 spiritus: species *F* ?specie *B* / resolveretur *in alia manu corr. V ex* resolvetur
844 conferre *in alia manu corr. D ex* ferre
846 *post* splendida *add. F* corpora / oculi *D*
847 virtute *VA*
848 diffunditur *D* / oculi *om. F*
849 dicit *BF* / *ante* motus *add. F* lucis / ad: ab *B* / exterius: interius *A*
850 *ante* motus *add. F* vero / motus: maius

from any that has hitherto been investigated {or that rays issuing from the eye are animated by the power of the soul}, also teaches otherwise.

[*Proposition*] *45{48}. Rays issuing from the eye and falling on a visible object cannot suffice for vision.*[122]

If it should be supposed that rays issue from the eye and fall on the visible object as if to seize it, either they return to the eye or they do not. If they do not return, vision is not achieved through them, since soul does not issue from body. If they do return, how do they do so? Are they animated? Are all visible objects mirrors by [virtue of the property of] reflecting rays? Furthermore, if the rays return to the eye with the form of the visible object, they go out in vain, since light itself (or the form of the visible object through the power of light) diffuses itself throughout the whole medium. Therefore the visible object need not be sought out by rays as by messengers. Moreover, how would any power of the eye be extended all the way to the stars, even if the whole body were transformed into spirit?

[*Proposition*] *46{49}. The natural light of the eye contributes to vision by its radiance.*[123]

For as Aristotle says, the eye not merely is the recipient of action but acts itself, just as shining bodies do.[124] Therefore the eye must have a natural light to alter visible species and make them commensurate with the visual power, for the species are emitted by the light of the sun but moderated with respect to the eye by mixing with the natural light of the eye.[125] This is why Aristotle said that sight occurs when the outward action [of the eye] is strong,[126] [for] when the action entering the eye is strong, as with a solar ray, it overpowers sight; nor, of itself, can this inward action be made commensurate with sight. It is evident, therefore, that there is some kind of emission of rays, but not of the Platonic type such that rays emitted by the eye are, as it were, immersed in the visible form and then returned to the eye as messengers. But rays [emitted by the eye] do have some effect on sight in the manner described above. This is evident as follows. Since vision is of the same kind in all animals, and certain animals are able to bestow a multiplicative power on colors by the light of their eyes so as to see them at night, it follows that the light of the eye has some

---

A / in: de *F*

851 patitur: poterit *F* / proportionare *F* / quoniam: quod *F*

853 quasi…visibili: in forma quasi invisibili *F* / immergantur: intingantur *FD*

854 tamen *om. A* sed *D* / operantur: cooperantur *A* / visum *FD* / modo predicto

tr. VH

855 patet *in alia manu mg. hab. V* / *post* rationis *add. A* ut patet

856 cum: quoniam *A*

856–57 *ante* coloribus *scr. et del. D* colobus

857 videri *corr. D ex* videre / possunt *A*

ut lumen oculi aliquid in lumine operetur. Et an aliquid ulterius faciat non diffinio nisi huius Auctoris, ut dictum est, vestigia sequendo.

860   *[Propositio] 47ª{50ª}. Sine luce nichil videri.*

Color enim sine luce non potest efficaciter radiare, quoniam primum in omni genere est causa omnium posteriorum. Prima autem radiositas est lucis, et ideo omnis alia ab ipsa causatur. Color igitur ad minus efficaciter radiare non potest nisi luci admixtus.

865   *[Propositio] 48ª{51ª}. Visum nichil comprehendere nisi proportionali distantia presentatum.*

Distantia siquidem vel remotio visibilis requiritur ad visionem, si enim res visibilis oculo supponatur luce non perfunditur, et per consequens movere non potest visum. Quod si ipsum visum sit luminosum, dico, ut in 870 46 tactum est, quoniam visibile viso, per lumen oculo contemperatum, fit oculo proportionatum. Unde et quidam senes melius vident in maiori distantia quam in minori, quoniam lumen oculorum suorum, quod est multum sed non clarum, in disgrediendo serenatur, et serenatum speciei rei visibilis superfunditur ut efficacius moveat. Alii etiam sunt qui habent 875 lumen modicum et non serenum, et illi appropinquissimo vident. Alii habent lumen multum et clarum, et illi a remotiori vident. Super omnes autem alios qui oculos profundos habent, ceteris paribus, a remotiori vident, quoniam radii luminares ab oculo micantes non ita disperguntur sicut ab oculis prominentibus, et adunati fortius super visibile porriguntur.

880   *[Propositio] 49ª{52ª}. Sola videri recte facialiter obiecta.*

Hoc patet ex prehabitis, visus enim fit principaliter per pyramidem

---

858 aliquid¹ *om. H* / in....aliquid² *om. D* / in lumine *om. F* / operatur *F* / aliquid ulterius *tr. F*
859 diffinit *A* / nisi huius: nichilominus *F* ut huius *A*
861 luce *in alia manu hab. A* / efficaciter radiare *tr. A*
862 omnium *om. BF* / radiositas est *tr. F* visio est *D*
863 omnia *F* / alia: visio *D* / causantur *F*
864 luce *F* / *post* admixtus *add. F* sequitur alia
865–66 distantia *om. A*
867 vel: et *F*
868 oculo *corr. D ex* oculatur / supponatur: super ponatur *D* / *post* consequens *add.*

A videre
869 movere non potest: non potest movere (*ante* movere *scr. et del. A* ipsum) *BA* / visum² *om. F*
869–70 in 46: ex 46ª *A* in 46ª *F* in 48 *H* {etiam supra} *D*
870 viso *VBHL; om. D* visui *AF*
870–71 contemperatum fit oculo *om. H et in alia manu mg. hab. V* fit oculo *D*
871 et *om. B* etiam *D* / vident *om. F*
872 *post* minori *add. F* vident
873 in disgrediendo (*corr. V ex* in disgrediento): disgrediendo *B* ingrediente *AH* disgregatur et *F* / *ante* serenatur *scr. et del. H* cerenatur / serenatur: servatur *A* / serenatum: servatum *A*

effect on [external] light. Whether it goes beyond this, I do not determine, save only by following in the footsteps of the Author,[127] as I have said before.

[*Proposition*] *47{50}. Nothing can be seen without light.*[128]

For without light, color cannot radiate efficaciously, because the first member of every genus is the cause of all [members] that follow. However, the first radiance is that of light; therefore every other radiance is caused by the radiance of light. Consequently color cannot radiate—efficaciously at least—unless mixed with light.

[*Proposition*] *48{51}. The eye perceives nothing that is not exhibited at an appropriate distance.*[129]

Sight requires distance or remoteness of the visible object, for if the visible object is set directly before the eye, it is not bathed in light and consequently cannot stimulate sight. But if sight itself is luminous, I say (as Proposition 46 concluded) that [the species of] the visible object, moderated with respect to the eye by mixing with the light [of the eye], is made commensurate with [the capacity of] the eye. Wherefore some old people see better at a great than at a small distance because the light of their eyes, which is intense but unclear, is clarified by propagation; and when it has been clarified, it is transmitted to the species of the visible object so that the latter may act more efficaciously. There are others who have a weak and unclear light; they see [best] when very close [to the object]. Others have a clear and intense light, and they see [best] from a distance. However, those people who have deep-set eyes, other things being equal, see [better] from a distance than do any of the others, because luminous rays issuing from their eyes are not dispersed as much as rays from prominent eyes, and, having maintained their unity, they are directed more strongly onto the visible object.[130]

[*Proposition*] *49{52}. Only things opposite the face are seen by means of straight lines.*[131]

This is evident from that which has been said,[132] for vision takes place

874 moveatur *V* / etiam: in *H*
875 modicum *in alia manu hab. A* / *ante* non *add. F* clarum et illi melius vident a prope alii etiam sunt qui habent lumen modicum et / illi *om. D* isti *F* illo *H* / appropinquissime *F*
876 multum *in alia manu hab. A*
877 autem alios *tr. V* / *post* alios *add. F* illi / oculos...habent: oculos habent pro-

fundos *B* habent visum profundum et oculos profundos *F* / paribus: prohibet *H*
878 micantes: procedentes *F*
879 oculis: oculo *B* / preeminentibus *F* / adunati: adiuncti *D*
880 facialiter: faciliter *B*
881 hec *F* / prehabitis: predictis *B* / enim *om. A* / fit principaliter *tr. A*

radiosam a basi opposita super visum perpendiculariter orientem. Fit etiam visus per radios extra pyramidem super oculum orientes. Sed super oculum oriri non possunt nisi qui in superficie oculi non cadunt sed ex
885 adverso eius oculo se representant. Et dico videri recte quoniam reflexive in speculis aliqua aliter videntur, ut infra videbitur.

[*Propositio*] *50ᵃ{53ᵃ}*. *Nichil videri nisi proportionaliter quantum.*
Cuius ratio est quoniam ut patet supra, visus fit per pyramidem radiosam cuius basis est res visa. Ergo necesse est quod videtur esse quantum
890 et proportionaliter quantum, non igitur diminutum quoniam tale non sufficeret oculum dolorose et efficaciter imprimere, ut dicit 43 propositio. Et corpus excellentis magnitudinis uno aspectu videri non potest, ut patet ex 39.

[*Propositio*] *51ᵃ{54ᵃ}*. *Visum non fieri nisi per medium dyaphonum.*
895 Cuius ratio est quia species non multiplicantur nisi per corpora dyaphona, quorum subtilitas congruit formis multiplicandis, ut sine materia, id est materialibus conditionibus, ut est possibile oculo imprimantur. Quia tamen omne corpus est susceptivum influentie celestis, certum est nullum corpus omnino carere perspicuitate, cum sit communis superiori et infe-
900 riori corpori. Hinc est quod nulla densitas prohibet omnino transitum virtutum et specierum, quamvis nos lateat. Hinc linces videre dicuntur per medium parietem.

[*Propositio*] *52ᵃ{55ᵃ}*. *Omne visibile necesse est medium in densitate transcendere.*
905 Cuius ratio est quia nichil potest esse coloratum aut luminosum nisi densum. Amplius nec glacialem movere posset si in perspicuitate eam excelleret. Amplius sine luce nichil videtur; quod si illud quod videtur per-

882 radiosam *AWFD* radicatam *VBH* / base *F* / perpendiculariter: proportionaliter *F*
883 etiam visus *tr. F* / oculum *om. H* / sed: et *B*
884 oculi non cadunt *in alia manu mg. hab. D*
885–86 reflexive in speculis: in speculis reflexive *F*
886 aliqua aliter *tr. B* aliqualiter *F* / ut…videbitur *om. F*
887 proportionabiliter *F*
888 est *om. V* / patet supra *tr. F* / visio *F*
890 *ante* diminutum *add. F* esse
891 oculo *BF* in oculum *D* / doloroso *B* / ut

rep. H / ut…propositio {*om. D*} / dicit *om. F* / *ante* 43 *add. H* in / 43: 43ᵃ *F* / et: etiam *F*
892 excellentis: excessive *D* / posset *F*
892–93 ut…39 *om. F*
893 ex 39: {supra} *D*
895 quia: quod *D* / multiplicatur *F*
896 ut: nec *F*
897 id est: et *F* / *ante* materialibus *add. VF* sine / ut: nec *F* / *ante* oculo *add. F* quod
898 tamen: cum *FD* / *post* celestis *add. F* que est immaterialis / est *in alia manu mg. hab. V*
900 densitum *B*

principally through a radiant pyramid perpendicularly incident on the eye from a base opposite [the eye], but also through rays incident on the eye outside the pyramid. However, [rays] can fall onto the eye only [from] those objects that are not located on the surface of the eye but manifest themselves to the eye from a position of opposition. And I say [here] that they are seen by means of direct lines, because they are seen otherwise by reflection in mirrors, as will be evident below.[133]

[*Proposition*] *50{53}. Nothing is seen unless it is of appropriate size.*[134]

The explanation of this, as presented above,[135] is that vision occurs through a radiant pyramid, the base of which is the visible object. Therefore, [to be seen, an object] must have [not only] size, but sufficient size. It must not be minute because such a thing would not suffice to impress the eye painfully and powerfully, as Proposition 43 maintains [it must]; and a body of great size cannot be seen at a single glance, as Proposition 39 makes clear.

[*Proposition*] *51{54}. Sight occurs only through a transparent medium.*[136]

The explanation of this is that species are multiplied only through transparent bodies, the subtlety of which is suited to the multiplication of forms, so that they may be impressed on the eye as far as possible without matter, i.e., without material conditions. Nevertheless, because every body is susceptible to celestial influence, it is certain that no body lacks transparency altogether, since it is common to [every] superior and inferior body. Therefore no density completely prohibits the propagation of powers and species, although that propagation may be imperceptible to us. Hence lynxes are said to see through walls.[137]

[*Proposition*] *52{55}. Every visible object must have a greater density than the medium.*[138]

The reason for this is that nothing can be colored or luminous unless it is dense; moreover, an object could not affect the glacial humor if it were to exceed that humor in transparency. Furthermore, nothing is seen without light; but if that which is seen were transparent like air, light could not be retained

901 *post* hinc *add. F* etiam / linces: luces *D* / dicuntur *om. AD*
902 medium parietum: parietis medium *A* / *post* parietem *add. D* affirmantur
903 medium in densitate: in densitate medium *F*

905 quia: quod *H* / esse: omne *A* / aut: vel *A* et *F*
906 nec glacialem: glacialem non *F* / si *om. H* / *post* si *add. F* res visa / eam: eque *D*
906–7 excelleret: transcenderet *B*
907 videtur[1]: videre *D* / quod[1]: quia *F*

spicuum esset sicut aer, lux in eo figi non posset, sine cuius immixtione
nulla species potest radiare, ut patet ex 47, movent enim simul lux et color.

910   [*Propositio*] *53ᵃ{56ᵃ}*. *Omnia que videntur tempore comprehendi.*
Immutatio enim sensibilis non fit nisi in tempore, sicut docent illusiones
sensuum in veloci quorundam transportatione. Amplius discretionem rei
non nisi in tempore fieri patet quoniam in corpore circumagitato punctus
videtur circulus. Amplius celum velocissime movetur, nec tamen perpen-
915 ditur nisi in tempore perceptibili. Amplius quamvis secundum quosdam
immutatio fieri possit instantanee, hoc tamen ab illa phylosophia est extraneum, ut infra non circulo demonstrabitur. Certificatio tamen de visibili non fit nisi in tempore transportatione axis radialis super rem visam,
ut patet supra 38.

920   [*Propositio*] *54ᵃ{57ᵃ}*. *Visionem non lucide fieri sine congrua sanitate
oculi.*
Hoc idcirco dicitur quia error visus aliquando est a causa exteriori, per
egressum a proportione in aliqua conditionum ad visum necessariarum,
ut distantia vel oppositione vel huius; aliquando ex causa interiori, sicut
925 vel pro oculi debilitate et paucitate spirituum vel infectione oculi ab extraneo humore vel alia lesione.

[*Propositio*] *55ᵃ{58ᵃ}*. *Varias et multas esse intentiones visibiles, et
quasdam primo quasdam secundario comprehendi.*
Siquidem 22 sunt intentiones visu comprehensibiles: lux et color, re-
930 motio vel distantia, situs, corporeitas, figura, magnitudo, continuatio, dis-
cretio vel separatio, numerus, motus, quies, asperitas, lenitas, dyaphoneitas, spissitudo, umbra, obscuritas, pulcritudo, turpitudo, similitudo, et
diversitas. Hee sunt principales intentiones, et alie secundarie que sub hiis
continentur, sicut ordinatio sub situ collocatur, et scriptura et sculptura
935 sub figura et ordinatione, rectitudo et curvitas sub figura, amplius mul-

908 commixtione *F* mixtione *D*
909 irradiare *A* / ut…47 {*om. D*} / 47: 47ᵃ
    F / movent…simul: quia simul movent
    F
910 *ante* tempore *add. F* in
912 discretionem rei *tr. F*
913 *ante* patet *add. F* quod / circumgirato *AF*
914 *post* celum *scr. et del. B* mo
914–15 perpenditur: percipitur *F*
915 quamvis…quosdam: secundum quos-
    dam quamvis *F*
916 fieri possit *tr. F* fieri posset *A* / illa: ista

    AHD / phylosophia: physica *A*
916–17 est extraneum *tr. F*
917 non: in *BF* / circulo: tertio *B* / tamen:
    tantum *A* ?cum *D*
918 transportationis *F* in spectatione *A*
919 *post* supra *add. F* ex / 38 {*om. D*} 38ᵃ *AF*
922 hec *F* / idcirco dicitur: igitur demonstra-
    tur *F* / quia: quod *HD*
923 egressum: recessum *F* / *post* a *add. F*
    debita / aliqua considerationum *A* ali-
    quam conditionum *F* / necessaria *A* ne-
    cessariam *WF* necessariorum *D*

in it, and without the admixture of light no species can radiate. This is clear from Proposition 47, for light and color act together.

[*Proposition*] *53{56}. All things that are seen require time for their perception.*[139]

[This is so] because change becomes sensible only in a period of time, as we are taught by illusions of the senses in the swift movement of things. Furthermore, it is evident that an object can be discerned only in a period of time, since a point on a rotating body appears as a circle. Besides, the sky is moved very swiftly, yet its motion is grasped only in a perceptible time. Moreover, although according to some people change can occur instantaneously, this is foreign to accepted philosophy, as will be shown below by noncircular demonstration.[140] Nevertheless, certification of a visible object is achieved only in a period of time by the passage of the axis of the [pyramid of] radiation over it, as Proposition 38 makes clear.

[*Proposition*] *54{57}. Soundness of the eye is required for clear vision.*

This is asserted because sight sometimes errs through an external cause when some condition necessary for vision, such as distance or opposition or something of this kind, departs from [due] proportion. Sometimes it errs through an internal cause, such as weakness of the eye and paucity of [its] spirits, or an infection of the eye by a foreign humor, or some other injury.

[*Proposition*] *55{58}. The visible intentions are numerous and varied, and some are apprehended primarily and some secondarily.*[141]

Indeed there are twenty-two intentions capable of being grasped by sight: light, color, remoteness or distance, position, corporeity, shape, size, continuity, distinction or separation, number, motion, rest, roughness, smoothness, transparency, density, shadow, darkness, beauty, ugliness, similarity, and diversity. These are the principal intentions, and other secondary intentions are contained under these, as arrangement is subordinate to position, writing and carving to shape and arrangement, straightness and curvature to shape, multi-

---

924 oppositio *F* / huiusmodi *FD*
925 pro *om. F* ab *A* per *D* / debilitatem *D* / paucitatem *D* / infactione *H*
925–26 extraneo *obs. A*
927 visibiles *om. F* / et *om. F*
928 *ante* primo *add. F* primas / *ante* quasdam *add. AD* et
929 *post* sunt *scr. et del. V* due / intentiones *om. F* / *post* intentiones *add. A* visibiles

930 *post* figura *add. A* et
932 obscuritas pulcritudo *tr. A*
933 et *om. F*
934 continentur: ordinantur *F* / *post* sub *add. A* suo / et² *om. B* vel *F*
935 *post* figura *scr. et del. V* vel / et¹ *om. V* / *ante* rectitudo *add. A* et / rectitudo: certitudo *H*

titudo et paucitas sub numero, et equalitas et augmentum sub similitudine et diversitate, et alacritas et risus et huius que comprehenduntur ex figura faciei, et sic de aliis multis. Principaliter siquidem movent visum lux et color suis speciebus oculum sigillantes et ex consequenti alias prenomi-
940 natas visui representantes, quem sub eisdem qualificant.

[*Propositio*] *56ᵃ{59ᵃ}. Non omnes intentiones visibiles comprehendi sensu spoliato.*

Dico sensum spoliatum solum sensum quoniam quedam comprehenduntur non solo sensu sed cooperante virtute distinctiva et argumentatione,
945 quasi imperceptibiliter immixta, quedam etiam adminiculo scientie acquisite. Verbi gratia cum apprehenduntur duo individua esse similia, ipsa similitudo neutra est formarum, nec comprehenditur solo sensu sed collatione unius ad alterum. Similiter etiam colorum differentia et aliarum rerum. Amplius scriptura non comprehenditur solo sensu sed per distinc
950 tionem partium eius, quam facit vis distinctiva mediante visiva. Similiter res assuete cum videntur, quod statim vise cognoscuntur, non est nisi ex relatione speciei recepte ad habitum memorie, et hoc quasi per ratiocinationem.

[*Propositio*] *57ᵃ{60ᵃ}. In distinctione visibilium rationem imperceptibi
955 liter operari.*

Nullum enim visibile cognoscitur sine distinctione intentionum visibilium vel sine collatione aut relatione ad universalia cognitorum prius a sensibilibus abstracta, que fieri non possunt absque ratiocinatione. Sed tempore non indiget perceptibili vis distinctiva in hiis communiter com
960 prehensis, quia arguit per aspectum ad sibi notissima, nec arguit per comparationem et ordinationem propositionum, vis enim distinctiva nata est arguere sine difficultate, que etiam aptitudo naturaliter exeritur. Unde

936 et² *om. F* / augmentatio *B*
937 et² *om. F* / huiusmodi *F* / ex: sub *F*
938 siquidem: si quid *D*
939 ex *om. V* / consequenti *mg. hab. H*
939–40 prenominatas *om. F*
940 *post* visui *scr. et del. A* presentatus / quem *VD* que *BAFH* quam *L* / sub… qualificant: sunt eiusdem qualitatis *F*
941 non omnes *om. F* / *ante* sensu *add. F* solo
943 quoniam: quem *H*
944 solum *H* / argumentiva *F*
945 quasi: animi *B* / *ante* imperceptibiliter *add. F* insensibiliter et / etiam: autem *F*

/ *ante* adminiculo *add. B* et
945–46 acquisito *A*
946 cum *om. A* / apprehenduntur: comprehenduntur *AF*
947 nec: ut *A* / apprehenditur *B*
947–48 collatione *corr. D ex* collocatione
948 alteram *HD* / etiam: et *FD* / *post* et *add. D* etiam
949 non *om. B* / apprehenditur *F*
950 quam: quas *F*
951 *post* assuete *add. F* stare / quod *om. F* / statim *om. F* / vise: in se *A* visu *F* visui *B*
952 recepte: accepte *B* / hoc *om. H*
955 operari (*ante* operari *in alia manu hab. V*

tude and paucity to number, equality and increase to likeness and diversity, joy and laughter and such things that are apprehended from the shape of the face [to shape], and similarly of many others. Indeed it is chiefly light and color that act on vision, impressing the eye with their species and consequently representing to sight the other intentions named above, which invest sight with the qualities [of the visible object] through light and color.

[*Proposition*] 56{59}. *Not all the visible intentions are apprehended by naked sense.*[142]

I call sense alone "naked sense" because some things are apprehended not by sense alone but by the cooperation of argumentation and the discriminative faculty, intermingled almost imperceptibly; and some things are apprehended also with the aid of acquired knowledge. For example, when two individuals are perceived to be similar, this is not a similitude of forms; nor is [the similarity] perceived by sense alone, but rather by comparison of one [individual] to the other. The same is true for differences of colors and other things. Moreover, writing is not grasped by sense alone, but as the discriminative faculty distinguishes its parts through the mediation of the power of sight. Similarly, when familiar things are seen, although they are recognized immediately, it is only by relation of the species received to the disposition of the memory, and this [is accomplished] as though by reasoning.

[*Proposition*] 57{60}. *Reason operates imperceptibly in the distinction of visible objects.*

For no visible object is recognized without a distinction of the visible intentions or without a comparison or relation to the universals of known things previously abstracted from sensible things; and this cannot occur without reasoning. But the discriminative faculty does not need [to linger] a perceptible time over commonly grasped things because it instructs itself regarding well-known objects at a glance, and not by a comparison and the ordering of propositions; for the discriminative faculty was designed to inform without difficulty, an aptitude that is naturally operative. This is why there are children

---

argumentari) *VWFH* argumentari (*supra* argumentari *in alia manu hab. A* operari) *BALD*

956 visibile: visibilium *F*

957 collatione: cognitione *F* / aut: vel *BF*

958 sensibilibus *VAWF* sensibus *BHD* / *ante* abstracta *scr. et del. H* asi

959–60 comprehensis: apprehensis *F*

960 *post* arguit[1] *scr. et del. A* ?ut / *post* per[1] *scr. et del. A* ad / *post* ad *add. F* speciem / nec: ?valet *F*

961 propositionis *F*

962 exoritur *B* exigitur *AF*

etiam in pueris apparet qui magis pulcra minus pulcris solent preponere,
non nisi ratione naturali facta eorum comparatione.

965   [*Propositio*] *58ª{61ª}. Lucem et colorem comprehendi sensu spoliato.*
Per hoc enim tantum apprehenditur quia ultimum sentiens hiis tingitur.

[*Propositio*] *59ª{62ª}. Inter lucem et colorem simul oculum moventes
solam discernere virtutem distinctivam.*
Tangunt siquidem pupillam et movent secundum eandem partem. Igi-
970   tur in sensu confuse recipiuntur, et ita per sensum distingui nequeunt.
Igitur non distinguntur nisi per experientiam de luce et colore habitam et
scientiam acquisitam.

[*Propositio*] *60ª{63ª}. Quiditatem lucis et coloris solo sensu minime comprehendi.*
975   Hic dicitur quiditas coloris species coloris, que non discernitur nisi
per relationes ad formas consuetas. Similiter lucis quiditas, quod scilicet
sit lux solis vel lune vel ignis, ex scientia dinoscitur, non ex sensu, cum
tamen color in quantum color et lux in quantum lux sensu spoliato capiantur.

980   [*Propositio*] *61ª{64ª}. Nullam intentionem visibilem preter lucem et colorem solo sensu comprehendi.*
Hoc patet quoniam quiditas coloris, inter omnes differentias, immediatissima est colori, sic et quiditas lucis luci. Si igitur quiditates non solo
sensu capiuntur, multo fortius nec alie quecunque intentiones visibiles,
985   sed per distinctionem, argumentationem, et scientiam, ex quo patet quod
solum lux et color et non quiditas lucis vel coloris sunt proprium obiectum
visus.

963 *post* pueris *add. F* magis / que *D* / pulcra: pulchre *F*
964 eorum: est *H*
966 comprehenditur *A* / quia...tingitur:
   quia ultimum sentiens hiis tangitur *D*
   hiis sensus distinguitur puta luce et colore et sic patet propositio *F*
967 oculum moventes: moventes sensum *F*
968 *ante* discernere *scr. et del. H* d
969 *post* siquidem *add. F* lux et color / movens *D*
970 confuse *om. F* / recipiuntur: reperiuntur
   F / distingivi *A*
971 distinguitur *A*

972 *ante* scientiam *add. F* per / *post* acquisitam *add. F* sequitur alia *et add. B* igitur
   non distinguntur nisi per experientiam
   de luce et colore habitam et
973 solo sensu *tr. BAD*
975 hec *F* / dicitur: patet quoniam *F* / *ante*
   species *add. F* dicitur / coloris[2] *om. A*
976 *ante* consuetas *add. H* speciales / *post*
   consuetas *add. F* id est ad alias species
   coloris / quod: quid *A* / scilicet: si *F*
977 sit: fit *A* / vel[1] *om. B* et *VA* / cum *om. F*
978–79 capiantur *VWHD* capiatur *BA* capiuntur *F*
982 hec *F* / *post* omnes *add. F* intentiones vel

who customarily prefer the more beautiful to the less beautiful merely through a comparison made by natural reason.

[*Proposition*] *58{61}. Light and color are apprehended by naked sense.*[143]
For they are apprehended only because they tinge the ultimate sense.

[*Proposition*] *59{62}. Only the discriminative faculty discerns between light and color acting on the eye simultaneously.*[144]
Since light and color touch the pupil and act on the same part, they are received in the sense commingled and cannot be distinguished by the sense. Therefore they can be distinguished only by previous experience of light and color and by acquired knowledge.

[*Proposition*] *60{63}. The essence of light or color is not perceived by sense alone.*[145]
The species of color, here called the essence of color, is discerned only by relation to familiar forms. Similarly, the essence of light, whether it be the light of the sun or of the moon or of fire, is discerned by knowledge and not by sense, although color is grasped as color and light as light by sense alone.

[*Proposition*] *61{64}. No visible intention except light and color is perceived by sense alone.*[146]
This is evident because the essence of color, of all the differentiae, is most immediate to color and similarly the essence of light to light. Therefore, if the essences [of light and color] (much less all the other visible intentions) are grasped not by sense alone but by differentiation, argumentation, and knowledge, it is evident that only light and color (and not the essences of light and color) are the proper objects of sight.[147]

982–83 immediatissima est *tr. F*
983 *ante* quiditates *add. F* iste
984 capiantur *F* / quecunque *om. A* / intensiones *D*
985 scientiarum *F*

986 solum *om. H* / lucis *om. AH* / vel: et *F* / coloris: coloreitas *A* / sunt...obiectum: sunt primum obiectum *A* proprium obiectum sunt sensus *F*

[*Propositio*] *62ᵃ{65ᵃ}. Colorem in eo quod color prius comprehendi sua quiditate.*

990 Hoc ex premissis patet, quoniam color in eo quod color ex sola tinctione capitur, quiditas autem eius non nisi per scientiam et argumentationem. Hoc etiam experimento patet, quoniam coloratum in luce, sub obscura positum, coloratum esse cernitur, et tamen coloris quiditas ignoratur.

995 [*Propositio*] *63ᵃ{66ᵃ}. Sola distantia mediocris est visui certificabilis, et hoc per corpora interiacentia continuata et ordinata.*

Distantia siquidem visibilis visu non comprehenditur, sed ratiocinatione colligitur, docente hac phylosophia sic. Si enim clausis palpebris res non videtur que videtur apertis, sequitur et consequenter colligitur ut illud
1000 quod videtur non sit visui adherens; et hoc est in anima quietum sine necessitate argumentationis iterande in qualibet visione. Dico igitur quod comprehensio quantitatis distantie accipitur a quantitate corporum interiacentium. Verbi gratia nubes in terra plana videntur celo coniuncte; in terra montuosa videntur terre propinque quia alicubi montium altitu-
1005 dinem non excedunt. Certificatio igitur distantie nubium causatur a comprehensione corporis interiacentis; quod si corpora interiacentia ordinata non sunt sed confusa, certificare non poterit apprehensio quantitatem. Amplius si non sit distantia mediocris non pertinget visus ad plenam distinctionem corporum remotiorum interiacentium propter debilitatem
1010 speciei visibilis ex distantia, sicut docetur supra 18 propositione.

[*Propositio*] *64ᵃ{67ᵃ}. Certificari quantitatem distantie per resolutionem interiacentis spatii ad magnitudinem mensure scientialiter note.*

Si enim corpora interiacentia sunt secundum totum et partem equaliter incerta, numquam ex ipsis certificabitur incerta distantia. Ergo necesse est
1015 in ea aliquid certum reperire, cuius quantitatis notitia per experimentum sit nota, ad quod totum spatium resolvatur, sicut ad pedem vel quantita-

---

988 colorem: color *B*
990 hec *F* / quod color *om. A*
990–91 *ante* tinctione *in alia manu mg. hab.*
    V ?ipsa / tinctione: intentione *F* / *post*
    tinctione *add. D* pupille
991 et: vel *A*
992 hec *F* / experimento patet *tr. D*
993 obscuro *A*
995 est visui *tr. F* / *post* est *scr. et del. D* i
996 hoc *om. A*
998 docente *om. A* / phylosophia: scientia *D*
999 videtur apertis *tr. F* / consequens *B*

1000 *ante* non *add. A* quod / non sit visui:
    visui non sit *F* / in anima quietum:
    manifestum *F*
1003 *ante* celo *scr. et del. D* in
1004 terre *om. F*
1005 excedunt: extendunt *D*
1006 quod…interiacentia *om. A*
1007 sint *D* / certificari *F* / quantitatum *F*
1008 si: sic *A* / non pertinget *om. A*
1009 remotorum *F* / debilitationem *V*
1010 docetur…propositione: docetur supra
    18ᵃ *B* docetur supra 18ᵃ propositione

[*Proposition*] *62{65}. Color, in that which is colored, is perceived [as color] before its essence is grasped.*[148]

This is evident from the foregoing, since color, in that which is colored, is perceived [as color] solely through the tinging [of the ultimate sense], but the essence of color [is perceived] only through knowledge and argumentation. This is evident also from experience, since an object that is colored in light [still] appears colored when placed in the shade, even though the essence of color is ignored.

[*Proposition*] *63{66}. Only moderate distances are certifiable to sight, and those by means of continuous and ordered intervening bodies.*[149]

Indeed the distance [from the observer] to the visible object is not perceived by sight, but is determined by reasoning, as this philosophy teaches.[150] For if an object that is visible when the eyes are open is not visible when they are closed, it follows and is rightly concluded that the object is not immediately adjacent to the eye; and this is evident[151] for all [instances of] vision without it being necessary to repeat the argument. Therefore I say that perception of the magnitude of a distance derives from the magnitude of the intervening bodies. For example, clouds over flat land seem to be attached to the sky; over mountainous land they seem to be near the earth because they nowhere exceed the height of the mountains. Therefore certification of the distance [from the observer] to the clouds derives from perception of the intervening bodies; however, if the intervening bodies are not well-ordered but confused, the understanding will be incapable of certifying the magnitude. Moreover, if the distance is immoderate, sight does not achieve full differentiation of the more remote intervening bodies because the visible species are weak on account of the distance, as is taught above in Proposition 18.

[*Proposition*] *64{67}. The magnitude of a distance is certified by the resolution of the intervening space into magnitudes of exactly known measure.*[152]

For if the intervening bodies are equally uncertain according to whole and part, the uncertain distance will never be certified by reference to them. Therefore within that distance something certain must be discovered, the magnitude of which may be known by experience and in terms of which the whole space

---

A supra ex 40ª docetur *F* docetur {supra} *D*
1012 ad *om. A*
1013 totum et partem: partem et totum *F*
1014 incerta[1]: iuncta *B* / est *om. B*

1015 eo *D* / *post* ea *add. F* distantia / experientiam *F*
1016 sit: fit *D*
1016–17 *ante* quantitatem *add. FD* ad

tem corporis mensurantis vel aliquid quod sit promptum ymaginationi mensoris.

[*Propositio*] *65ª{68ª}. Distantiam orizontis maiorem apparere quam alte-*
1020   *rius cuiuscunque partis emisperii {quod supereminet orizonti}.*

Hoc patet ex 63, si enim ex corporum quantitate distantia dinoscitur, ubi maior magnitudo interiacere videtur necesse est ut etiam maior distantia videatur. Sed inter orizontem et videntem interiacere videtur tota latitudo terre, inter videntem et cenith, nichil. Ergo incomparabiliter plus
1025   distare videtur orizon quam alia pars celi quecunque.

[*Propositio*] *66ª{69ª}. Orizontem apparere terre coherentem.*
Huius ratio est quia non comprehenditur aliquo modo spatium inter ultimam partem terre visibilem et ipsum celum.

[*Propositio*] *67ª{70ª}. Longitudinem radiorum a visu comprehendi.*
1030   Quod patet per experimentum in speculis, ubi creditur res esse in extremitate linearum radialium, quas totas estimat porrigi in continuum et directum, et secundum illas iudicat partem que visum movet. Unde species movens oculum non solum ostendit oculo ipsum obiectum sed medium radium, cuius ipsa species est extremum, in quo tamen radio figi non po-
1035   test aspectus quia totus ipse radius similitudo est alterius. Ex hac tamen propositione radiorum egredientium fortissimum posset sumi argumentum.

[*Propositio*] *68ª{71ª}. Situm oppositionis rei vise distinctione compre-*
hendi.
Intentio siquidem situs tria includit: oppositionem rei diametralem,
1040   et positionem respectu oculi secundum rectitudinem et obliquitatem, et ordinem partium rei invicem. Primus igitur modus distinctione dinoscitur,

1017 aliquid *om. D* / ymaginationi: ad yma-
      ginationem *F*
1018 mensuris *F*
1019–20 *ante* alterius *add. D* alicuius
1020 cuiuscunque…emisperii: partis emi-
      sperii cuiuscunque *BA* cuiuslibet partis
      emisperii *F* partis emisperii *D*
1021 hec *F* / ex 63 {*om. D*} ex 83 *H* / quan-
      titate…dinoscitur *corr. ex* distantia
      quantitate dinoscitur *VBFH* distantia
      quantitate demonstratur *A* distantia
      quantitate disnoscitur (*sic*) *D*
1022 ut etiam *tr. F* ut *B*

1023 videatur: oriatur *A*
1024 latitudo terre *tr. A* / *ante* inter *add. F*
      sed / nichil: vel *A* / plus *om. A*
1025 celi: circuli *A*
1027 huius: cuius *F*
1028 celum: circulum *A* / *post* celum *add. F*
      sequitur alia
1030 *ante* ubi *scr. et del. F* ubi / ubi *in alia*
      manu hab. A ut cum *D* / creditur res
      esse: res esse creditur (creditur *in alia*
      manu) *A* res creditur esse *F* dicitur res
      esse *D*
1031 totas *corr. H ex* totat / estimant *B*

can be resolved, such as the foot or the length of a measuring body or something that comes readily to the imagination of the measurer.

[*Proposition*] *65{68}. The horizon appears farther away than any other part of the hemisphere {that rises above the horizon}.*

This is evident from Proposition 63, for if distance is gathered from the size of [the intervening] bodies, then the distance must appear greater where greater magnitude is seen to intervene. But between the horizon and the observer, the whole breadth of the earth is seen to intervene; between the observer and the zenith, nothing. Therefore the horizon appears incomparably farther away than any other part of the sky.

[*Proposition*] *66{69}. The horizon appears attached to the earth.*

The reason for this is that the space between the sky and the farthest visible part of the earth cannot be perceived by any means.

[*Proposition*] *67{70}. The lengths of rays can be perceived by sight.*[153]

This is evident from experience with mirrors, wherein the object is believed to be at the end of radial lines, which are all judged to be extended continuously and rectilinearly and through which one examines the part [of the object] that acts on sight. For this reason the species acting on the eye exhibits to the eye not only the object but also the ray serving as intermediary, the end of which is the species itself; [this is true] even though sight cannot be fixed on the ray because the entire ray is the likeness of something else.[154] Nevertheless, a very strong argument for the emission of rays [from the eye] can be drawn from this proposition.[155]

[*Proposition*] *68{71}. Through a distinction a visible object is perceived to be opposite [the observer].*[156]

Indeed the intention of position includes three things: diametrical opposition of an object, straightness or obliquity of position relative to the eye, and the order of the parts of an object with respect to each other. The first mode [of the three] is discerned through a distinction, for an object is considered to

existimat *D*
1032 illas: istas *F*
1033 ostendit *om. A* / ipsum *om. F*
1034–35 *ante* potest *scr. et del. F* possunt
1035 hoc *H* / tamen *om. F*
1036 propositione: proportione *A*

1037–38 comprehendi: apprehendi *F*
1040 *post* positionem *add. D* {natura 3 situs rei vise}
1041 invicem *om. F* / distinctione *om. H et in alia manu mg. hab. V* diffinitione; ?distinctive *A*

res enim per hoc opposita facialiter esse perpenditur quia forma eius super visum perpendiculariter oritur, quod esse non posset nisi opponeretur. Amplius cum opponitur videtur, cum non opponitur latet.

1045   [*Propositio*] *69ᵃ{72ᵃ}. Situm obliquitatis comprehendi ex comprehensione diversitatis distantie extremorum rei visibilis.*

Cum enim certificatur distantia secundum quo docetur in 63 propositione, necesse est ut si extrema inequaliter distare reperiantur, ut res oblique aspiciens oculum iudicetur.

1050   [*Propositio*] *70ᵃ{73ᵃ}. Tertiam situs differentiam ex ordine speciei in oculo comprehendi.*

Sic enim cognoscitur ordo partium rei distincte, ut patet ex 37, et sic ordinatio partium dinoscitur.

   [*Propositio*] *71ᵃ{74ᵃ}. Figuram rei visibilis comprehendi ex duabus ulti-*
1055 *mis situs differentiis.*

Verbi gratia, ex maiori distantia medii quam extremorum apprehenditur concavitas et econverso convexitas, et omnes figure incisionis comprehenduntur ex comprehensione ordinis partium rei visibilis.

   [*Propositio*] *72ᵃ{75ᵃ}. Figuram rei multum distantis minime certificari.*
1060   Cuius ratio est quia nec distantia certificari potest, et per consequens nec situs nec figura.

   [*Propositio*] *73ᵃ{76ᵃ}. Quantitatem anguli sub quo res videtur minime sufficere quantitati rei visibilis capiende.*

Quod patet quoniam si in circulo producantur se secantes dyametri
1065 ortogonaliter ponaturque una dyameter obiecta oculo fere facialiter, reliqua vero per consequens oculum oblique valde respiciens sub longe minori angulo oculo apparebit, sicut patet in figura [Fig. 16]. Nec tanto minor quanto angulus est angulo minor, sic enim non appareret circulus sed oblonge figure globus, quod falsum est.

1042 esse *om. F* / perpenditur: apprehenditur *F*
1044 latet *om. A*
1047–48 in 63 propositione *corr. ex* in 63ᵃ propositione *W* in 62 propositione (*corr. B ex* 61) *VBA* in 61 propositione *F* in 82 propositione *H* {supra} *D*
1048 ut¹ *om. D* / ut² *om. F*
1049 aspiciens: respiciens *D* reaspiciens *B*

1050 tertiam: certam *F*
1052 *post* patet (*in alia manu mg. V*) *add.* *VAH*{*D*} supra / ex 37 {*om. D*} ex 37ᵃ *AF*
1054 comprehendi *in alia manu hab. A*
1054–55 ultimis...differentiis: differentiis ?situs ?ultimis *A*
1056 maiore *F*
1057 omnis *B*

be opposite the face when its form is perpendicularly incident on the eye, and that could not be if the object were not in opposition. Furthermore, when an object is in opposition, it is seen, but when not in opposition, it is concealed.

[*Proposition*] *69{72}. Obliquity of position is ascertained when the distances to the extremes of an object are perceived to be different.*[157]
When distance is certified (in the manner taught in Proposition 63), then, if the extremes are discovered to be unequally distant, the object must be deemed oblique relative to the eye.

[*Proposition*] *70{73}. The third difference of position is perceived from the order of species in the eye.*[158]
For in this manner the order of the parts of an object is distinguished, as is evident from Proposition 37; and thus the arrangement of parts is discerned.

[*Proposition*] *71{74}. The shape of a visible object is perceived from the second and third differences of position.*[159]
For example, concavity is perceived when the distance to the middle is greater than that to the extremes, and convexity vice versa. And any shape that may be fashioned is grasped by perception of the order of the parts of the visible object.

[*Proposition*] *72{75}. The shape of a very remote object cannot be certified at all.*[160]
The reason for this is that distance cannot be certified and consequently neither can position or shape.

[*Proposition*] *73{76}. The size of the angle under which an object is seen does not suffice for apprehension of its size.*[161]
This is obvious, for if diameters of a circle are drawn intersecting perpendicularly and one of them is placed opposite and almost facing the eye, so that the other is very oblique relative to the eye, the latter will appear under a much smaller angle [than the former], as is evident in the figure [Fig. 16]. But this diameter will not appear smaller in the same proportion as the angle is smaller, for if so, a circle would appear not round but oblong, and that is not the case.

1057–58 comprehunduntur (*sic*) V
1058 *post* rei *add.* F visibilis
1063 quantitati *in alia manu hab.* A
1064 si *om.* A / secantes: intersecantes F
1065 *ante* ortogonaliter *in alia manu add.* A non / ponaturque: ponatur quia D / una *om.* F

1066 oblique: relique A / *ante* valde *scr. et del.* D valde / *post* minori *add.* A scilicet A
1067 *ante* tanto *in alia manu add.* F tamen
1068 est angulo *om.* H / apparet BAF apparent H

1070   [*Propositio*] *74ª{77ª}. Comprehensionem quantitatis ex comprehensione procedere pyramidis radiose et basis comparatione ad quantitatem anguli et longitudinem distantie.*

Sola igitur cognitio quantitatis anguli ad quantitatem non sufficit discernendam, confert tamen ad hoc, sicut patet supra ex 41 propositione.
1075   Angulus quidem comprehenditur ex dispositione forme in oculo, sed quia etiam ipsi radii ab oculo capiuntur, ut docuit 67 propositio, non est certitudo notitie quantitatis nisi referendo angulum equalem cum inequali longitudine radiorum ad basim inequalem, quia in anima quietum est lineas ab angulo procedentes tanto amplius ab invicem distare quanto
1080   remotius protenduntur, et per consequens tanto maiorem basim continere. Quod autem virtus apprehensiva quantitatis ad longitudinem distantie respiciat nec solum ad angulum experimento probatur, quoniam si monoculus aspiciat aliquem parietem magnum et quantitatem eius certificet deinde oculo suo manum anteponat, ipsa manus videbitur sub eodem
1085   angulo vel sub maiori quam paries visus est, nec tamen tanta ei apparebit quantus paries apparet quia minus distat.

[*Propositio*] *75ª{78ª}. Certificatio quantitatis fit completive per motum axis.*

Apprehensio enim per ipsum certior est, et ideo defertur super basim
1090   et super spatium et intra angulum sub quo res videtur, sicut patere potest ex 38.

1071 procedere...comparatione *om. A /*
       comparatione: temperatione *F*
1073 *ante* sola *in alia manu add. A* dinoscitur
       / ante cognitio *scr. et del. D* confusio
1074 supra *om. BF /* ex 41 propositione *{om.*
       D} et corr. ex ex 40ª propositione *B*
       ex 48 propositione *V* ex 42 propositione *A* ex 41ª (*in alia manu mg. corr. F*
       ex ex 40ª) *F* ex 4 propositione (*post* 4
       hab. spatium) *H*
1075 quidem *om. A*
1076 etiam ipsi *tr. V /* docuit 67 propositio:
       docuit 67ª propositio *F* docuit 69 propositio *B* docuit sed 7 propositio *H*
       {supra patet} D
1077 *post* cum *add. F* angulo
1078 longitudine: et longitudinem *FD /*
       in...quietum *in alia manu alt. F ad* ut

       alibi demonstratum
1079 *ante* amplius *scr. et del. H* a
1082 respicit *BA*
1084 *ante* manum *scr. et del. D* manum */*
       post manum *add. VH* suam */* anteponat: opponente *F*
1084–85 eodem angulo *tr. F*
1085 quam: quo *F /* ei apparebit *tr. F*
1088 axis *mg. hab. H*
1089 certior *in alia manu corr. V ex verbo*
       oblito
1090 supra *AF / post* angulum *add. A* sensibilem
1090–91 sicut...38 *{om. FD} et corr. ex*
       sicut patet ex 37 (38ª *W*) *BW* sicut
       patere ex 39 *V* sicut patere potest ex
       37 (3 *H* 39ª *L*) *AHL*

Fig. 16

D omits this figure; all other manuscripts fail to draw the diameters mutually perpendicular.

[*Proposition*] *74{77}. Perception of the size [of an object] derives from perception of the radiant pyramid and comparison of the base to the length and to the
size of the angle.*[162]

Therefore knowledge of the size of the angle is not alone sufficient for
discerning the size [of the object], but contributes to it, as is evident above in
Proposition 41. Indeed the angle is apprehended from the disposition of the
form in the eye; but because the rays themselves are also perceived by the eye,
as Proposition 67 showed, certain knowledge of size can be obtained only by
a comparison of equal angles having rays of unequal length to unequal bases,
for it is manifest that lines proceeding from an angle diverge in proportion to
their extension and consequently contain a proportionately large base. However, as experience proves, the faculty that apprehends size considers the magnitude of the distance [from the observer] and not only the angle. For if a one-
eyed man looks at a large wall and, after certifying its size, places his hand
before his eye, the hand will appear under an angle equal to or larger than that
under which the wall is seen; nevertheless, the hand will appear to him smaller
than the wall because it is less distant.

[*Proposition*] *75{78}. Certification of size is achieved completely by motion
of the axis [of the radiant pyramid].*

For apprehension is more certain through the axis [than through any other
ray], and therefore the axis is conveyed over the base and over the space and
within the angle under which the object is seen, as is evident from Proposition 38.

[*Propositio*] *76ª{79ª}. Nulla quantitas rei immoderate distantis est oculo certificabilis.*

1095 Re enim multum distante axis que suo motu certificat visum in parva parte rei visibilis translatus nullum facit angulum sensibilem in centro visus, quoniam ut supra patet res multum distantes sub acutioribus videntur angulis, et ideo translatio axis intra acutum angulum modica non est visui perceptibilis nec satis efficacis apprehensionis. Amplius nec certificatur quantitas spatii interiacentis, ut docet propositio 63.

1100 {[*Propositio*] *80ª. De corpore sperico plus quantitative videri duobus quam uno oculo.*

{Hoc patet quoniam si dyameter spere vel chilindri sit equalis distantie duorum oculorum invicem, sequitur ex predictis ut ⟨non⟩ videatur nisi duobus oculis medietas spere. Sed unus oculus non potest medietatem 1105 attingere, quia sic radios suos applicaret extremis dyametri spere, et triangulus sub quo res videtur haberet duos angulos rectos et amplius angulum conalem.}

[*Propositio*] *77ª{81ª}. Distinctionem visibilium ex distinctione colligi radiantium formarum.*

1110 Quando enim species oculum moventes sunt diverse, res diversas necesse est apparere nisi distantia earum ab oculo diversitatem abscondat. Et per oppositum intellige qualiter continuitas apprehenditur, que est octava intentio. Et ex hoc intellige qualiter apprehenditur numerus, qui est 10 intentio.

1115 [*Propositio*] *78ª{82ª}. Motus comprehenditur ex diversificatione situs rei mote ad aliud immotum vel ad visum ipsum.*

Quamdiu enim eundem habet situm ad aliud immotum, et ipsum immobile videtur. Et quia visus nichil videt nisi sub forma prescripta, percipitur motus cum apud centrum visus immoti variatur angulus declinatio-
1120 nis sensibiliter.

1092 *ante* est *add. F* ab oculo
1094 axix (*sic*) *H* / qui *B* / parva *om. A*
1095 translata *D* / nullum: multum *F* / *ante*
      sensibilem *scr. et del. F* visibilem
1096 quoniam *om. A* / sub *om. H* ab *F*
1097 acutum *in alia manu corr. V ex* acuta
1098 *ante* visui *scr. et del. H* motui / nec²:
      non *B*
1099 ut…63 {*om. D*} / propositio 63 *corr.*
      ex propositio 63ª *W* propositio 62 (*in*

      alia manu alt. A ad propositio 63) *VBA*
      62 propositio *F* propositio 82 *H*
1100–1107 de….conalem (This proposition
      appears only in *D* and *F*, and I regard
      it as a genuine revision. In *D* it appears
      as a continuation of the previous prop-
      osition, but I have treated it as a
      separate proposition both because it
      appears separately in *F* and because its
      subject matter distinguishes it from

[*Proposition*] *76{79}. No quantity of an exceedingly remote object can be certified by the eye.*

For if the object is at a great distance, transferral of the axis, which by its motion certifies sight, over a small part of the visible object makes no sensible angle at the center of the eye because (as was shown above)[163] very remote objects are seen under very acute angles. Therefore a slight translation of the axis within an acute angle is imperceptible to sight and insufficient to be effectively apprehended. Furthermore, the magnitude of the intervening space cannot be certified, as Proposition 63 teaches.

{[*Proposition*] *80. A larger portion of a spherical body is seen by two eyes than by one eye.*[164]

{This is obvious, for if the diameter of a sphere or cylinder is of the same length as the distance between the two eyes, it follows from the aforesaid that two eyes are required for vision of half the sphere.[165] But a single eye cannot see half, because, if it could, its rays would touch the ends of the diameter of the sphere, and the triangle under which the thing is seen would have two right angles in addition to the angle at the vertex.}

[*Proposition*] *77{81}. Differentiation of visible things derives from differentiation of the radiating forms.*[166]

For when the species acting on the eye are different, different things must appear unless their distance from the eye conceals their diversity. By the converse, it is understood how continuity (the eighth intention)[167] is apprehended; and from this it is understood how number (the tenth intention) is apprehended.

[*Proposition*] *78{82}. Motion is perceived through variation in the position of the moved object relative to an immobile object or to the eye itself.*[168]

Indeed, as long as the object maintains the same position relative to an immobile object, it appears immobile itself. And because the eye sees an object only under a prescribed form, motion is perceived when the angle of declination at the center of a motionless eye is varied sensibly.

Proposition I.{79}.)
1101 quam *F* quaqua *D*
1102 quoniam *F*; *om. D*
1103 sequitur *F* sequntur *D* / nisi *D* vise *F*
1105 extremis dyametri *F* extremus dyameter *D* / *post* et *add. F* sic
1110–11 necesse *in alia manu hab. A*
1111 eorum *D*
1112 apprehenditur: comprehenditur *D*
1112–13 octava *corr. ex* nona (*in alia manu*

mg. *F*) *VBFA* nova *HD*
1113 et: etiam *B* / apprehenditur numerus *tr. F* comprehenditur numerus *A* / que *F*
1114 10ª *BF*
1116 ad² *om. B* / visum ipsum *tr. A*
1117 immotum: motum *F*
1118 prescripta: scripta *V* predicta *F*
1119–20 declinationis *in alia manu corr. A ex* ?declinans

[*Propositio*] *79ª{83ª}. Omne visibile ad utrumque oculum in maiori parte consimiliter situari.*

Quod patet quoniam quando utroque oculo inspicitur, utriusque pupilla ad rem dirigitur, et axes duorum oculorum in eodem puncto rei vise 1125 figuntur, qui opponitur centro utriusque, et uno moto alter consimiliter movetur. Alii autem radii singulorum oculorum habent in maiori parte situm consimilem respectu axium, et ideo res apparet in maiori parte una et eodem modo disposita utrique oculo quoniam, sicut supra patet, certificatio de re visibili est per axes.

1130 [*Propositio*] *80ª{84ª}. Ex variato sensibiliter situ visibilis respectu duorum axium ipsum duo apparere.*

Si enim visibile ad unum axem sit dextrum ad alium sinistrum, sensibili diversitate apparet unum duo. Verbi gratia si figantur axes oculorum *F G* [Fig. 17] in puncto *H* diligenti contuitione, apparebit *K* duo, similiter 1135 et *H*, quia utrumque est uni axi dextrum et alteri sinistrum. Amplius si ex eadem parte respiciant axes, sed ex magna declinatione ad partem unam, sit sensibilis variatio anguli quem constituit radius sub quo videtur res tante declinationis cum utroque axe; apparet similiter unum duo. Verbi gratia *M* punctus ex eadem parte respicit axem utrumque *AC* et *BC* [Fig. 1140 18]. Tamen propter magnam variationem anguli *MAC* et *MBC* fit diversificatio situs in oculo, et apparet unum duo. Aliis etiam modis apparet unum duo, sicut supra ostensum est.

1123 quoniam: quia *F* / oculo *om. A*
1124 axes: maxime *A*
1125 alter: alius *F* / *post* alter *add. A* et
1127 situm *VWFD* situs *B* sicut *AH* / res *mg. corr. V ex verbo oblito* / apparent *BF* / uno *F*
1128 disposite *F* / utroque *F* utriusque *D*
1132 *post* dextrum *add. F* et / alium: aliud *FD* / *ante* sinistrum *scr. et del. D* ad
1132–33 sensibile *A*
1133 figuntur *F*

1134 continuatione *A* intuitione *F*
1136 sed: si *B* / magna: maxima *F*
1137 sit: fit *F* / anguli *om. A* / constitutum *A* constuit *D* / *ante* radius *scr. et del. F* angulus
1138 apparet similiter *tr. FD* apparet *A*
1139 AC: AB *F*
1141–42 unum....unum *om. H* / aliis...duo *in alia manu mg. hab. V*
1142 ostensum est: est ostensum in 33ª propositione *F*

[*Proposition*] *79{83}. Every visible object is situated similarly, for the most part, with respect to each of the eyes.*[169]

This is evident because, when an object is considered by each eye, the pupil of the eye is directed toward the object, and the axes of the two eyes are fixed on the same point in the object, opposite the center of the eye; and when one eye is moved, the other is moved similarly. Moreover, other rays have nearly similar positions relative to the axes of their respective eyes; and therefore the object usually appears single and disposed in the same manner relative to each eye because, as was shown above,[170] certification of the visible object is achieved by means of the axes.

[*Proposition*] *80{84}. An object appears double when it has a sensibly different position relative to the two axes.*[171]

If the visible object is to the right of one axis and to the left of the other, the object appears double because of the sensible difference. For example, if the axes of the eyes *F* and *G* [Fig. 17] are fixed on point *H* with a steady gaze,

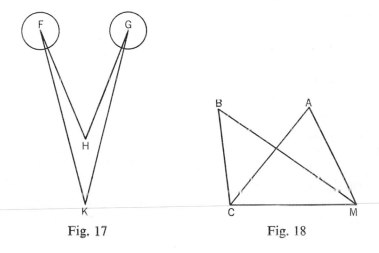

Fig. 17   Fig. 18

K will appear double—and similarly *H* [will appear double when the gaze is fixed on *K*]—because each is to the right of one axis and to the left of the other. Furthermore, if a point is on the same side of both axes but has a large declination with respect to one, there is a sensible variation between the angles formed by the axes and the rays under which the object is seen; as before, the single object appears double. For example, point *M* [Fig. 18] is on the same side of both axis *AC* and axis *BC*. Nevertheless, because of the great difference between angles *MAC* and *MBC*, there is diversity of position in the eye, and one object is seen as two. An object can appear double in other ways also, as was shown above.[172]

[*Propositio*] *81ª*{*85ª*}. *In apprehensione visibilium, iuxta sensum scientiam et rationem vel sillogismum varie errari.*

1145   Verbi gratia in luce et colore, qui sensu comprehenditur, erratur ex distantia. Multi enim minuti colores videntur ex distantia unus color, similiter et in luce debili unus color videtur alius esse. Quod si dixeris sensum non decipi circa proprium obiectum, scito proprium obiectum esse colorem tantum et lucem, non autem aliquam speciem lucis et coloris que solo
1150   sensu minime capiuntur, ut supra visum est. Similiter et secundum scientiam et rationem accidit deceptio, unde mota aliquando videntur quiescentia et econverso.

[*Propositio*] *82ª*{*86ª*}. *Stellas in orizonte maiores apparere quam in aliqua celi parte.*

1155   Hoc probatur quia patet ex 65 propositione quod magis distare videntur cum sunt in orizonte et quia ex equali angulo ad maiorem distantiam relato res maior esse iudicatur, ut patet ex 74. Cum in orizonte sub eodem angulo presentetur oculo sub quo alibi in celo et sub maiori spatio videatur presentari, concluditur in orizonte rem apparere maiorem. Tamen si
1160   secundum veritatem distantia esset maior, angulus esset minor, et res videretur minor; non autem sic est. Immo angulus equalis ad apparenter maius spatium collatus rem iudicat esse maiorem. Ad hoc est interpositio vaporum, de qua tangetur infra.

{[*Propositio*] *87ª*. *Solem et stellas in orizonte apparenter magis aquiloni*
1165   *esse vicinas quam in alia celi parte.*

{Cuius ratio sumitur ex predictis. Ducatur enim linea a loco solis vel stelle orientis usque ad locum eiusdem occidentis vel ab orizonte recedentis. Item ducatur alia linea equidistans eidem transiens per oculos consideratoris ad partes predictas. Verbi gratia sit prima linea *AB*, secunda
1170   linea *CD* [Fig. 19]. Certum est ex predictis quod extrema istarum duarum

1144 vel: et *A*

1145 que *A* / comprehenduntur *BF* / *ante* erratur *scr. et del. H* r

1146 *ante* minuti *add. BA* in / minuti: inimici *D* mixti *B*

1147 debiliter *V* / videt *D* / *ante* alius *scr. et del. D* esse / *post* alius *add. F* color

1149 *post* et[1] *scr. et del. V* non *et add. H* non

1150 visum: ostensum *F* / et *om. F*

1153 in...apparere: in oriente maiores apparere (apparere *om. A*) *BA* apparere maiores in oriente *F* / aliqua: alia *F*

1154 celi parte *tr. F*

1155 quia patet *om. A* quod patet *HD* / 65 *W* 62 (*supra* 62 *in alia manu hab. V* 63) *VBFD* 62ª *A* 82 *H* / *post* quod *add. F* stelle

1156 orizonte: oriente *BA* / quia *om. B* / *post* quia *scr. et del. A* cum

1157 74 *corr. ex* 73 *VBAFH* 3 *D*

1158 celo: circulo *A*

1158–59 videtur *F*

1160 maior...esset[2] *in alia manu mg. hab. D et om. F*

1160–61 et...minor *om. B*

1161 ad *om. F* / apparenter *obs. A* apparen-

[*Proposition*] *81{85}. Along with sense, knowledge and reason (or syllogism) err in various ways in the perception of visible objects.*[173]

For example, in the case of light and color, which are perceived by sense, sense errs because of distance, for many small colors appear from a distance to be one color. Similarly, in a weak light one color appears to be another. But if you should say that sense is not deceived about its proper object, [I reply that] by agreement the proper object [of sight] is merely color and light and not some [particular] species of light or color, which is not apprehended by sense alone as was seen above.[174] Deception occurs similarly according to knowledge and reason; wherefore moving objects sometimes appear to be at rest and vice versa.

[*Proposition*] *82{86}. Stars appear larger on the horizon than in any other part of the sky.*[175]

This is proved because, as is evident from Proposition 65, they appear more distant when they are on the horizon and because an object is judged larger by the correlation of an equal angle with a greater distance, as Proposition 74 shows. Since an object on the horizon is perceived by the eye under the same angle as [that under which it would be perceived] elsewhere in the sky and since it appears to be at a greater distance, the object is judged larger when on the horizon. However, if the distance were really greater, the angle would be smaller, and the object would appear smaller;[176] but that is not the case. On the contrary, because of the equal angle correlated with the apparently greater space, the object is judged larger. The interposition of vapors, which will be touched on below, works to the same end.[177]

{[*Proposition*] *87. The sun and stars appear to be nearer the north when on the horizon than when in any other part of the sky.*[178]

{The explanation of this is gathered from the aforesaid. Let a line be drawn from the point where the sun or a star rises to the place where it sets or withdraws from the horizon. Likewise, let another line be drawn parallel to [and north of] the first, passing through the eyes of the observer toward the aforesaid regions. For instance, let the first line be *AB* and the second line *CD* [Fig. 19]. It is certain from the foregoing that the ends of these two lines appear closer

---

tis *F*
1162 collocatus *F*
1163 tangitur *A* / *post* infra *in alia manu mg.*
　　hab. *A* in 3ª parte
1164 apparenter *D* apparentes *F* (This prop-

osition appears in *F* as well as *D*.)
1165 vicinas *D* viciniores *F* / quam *F* quaque
　　D
1167 orizonte *D* oriente *F*
1169 secunda *F* secundam *D*

linearum minus apparent distare quam media earundem, quia media istarum linearum quasi in prospectum sunt, et deprehenditur superficialiter
spatium interiacens. Sed extrema linearum multo magis distant et sub acutiori angulo videntur, nec ita deprehenditur spatium interiacens extremis
1175   sicut medio. Apparent igitur extrema viciniora aquiloni, quia minus apparent distare a linea aquilonari predicta.}

[*Propositio*] *83ᵃ{88ᵃ}. Corpora sperica in distantia apparere plana.*
Cum enim spericitas vel etiam concavitas discerni non possit nisi ex
comprehensa inequali distantia partium rei vise, necesse est in huius per-
1180   ceptione visum deficere pre immoderatione distantie, sicut patet ex 72. Si
igitur nulla pars rei vise plus altera distare videatur, necesse est unius
dispositionis apparere totam superficiem rei vise.

[*Propositio*] *84ᵃ{89ᵃ}. Quadratas magnitudines in distantia apparere
oblongas.*
1185   Cuius ratio est quoniam excessus radiorum cadentium in latera quadrati oblique respicientia oculum non est proportionalis proportione sensibili ad radios cadentes in latus quadrati directe oculum respiciens per
comparationem ad totam distantiam, id est visus non sufficit discernere
obliquitatem lateris quod oblique videtur et sub radiis longioribus et
1190   minori angulo. Et ideo tale latus apparet minus. Quod si angulus quadrati
recte opponitur visui, apparebit quadratum rotundum visu, angulum pre
distantia minime discernentem.

Explicit Prima Pars

1173 interiacens *D* inter limites *F*
1174 extremis *D* extremi *F* / medio *D* medii
      F
1177 *post* corpora *scr. et del. D* predicta
1178 vel: et *A* / etiam *om. B* / posset *B*
1179 comprehensione *F* comprehensu *A* /
      inequalis *F* / partium *om. F*
1180 immoderamine *B* moderamine *D* /
      72 *corr. ex* 73 *VBAFHD*
1181 altera: alia *F* / videtur *B*

1186 proportionalis: proportionaliter *A* pro-
      portionabilis *F*
1187 respiciens *BAW* respicientis *VD* respi-
      cientes *FH*
1188 id est *obs. F* et *B*
1192 discernente *H*
1193 explicit...pars: *om. FH et mg. hab. D*
      explicit pars prima *V* explicit libri
      primus *B*

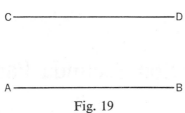

Fig. 19

D and F, the only manuscripts containing Proposition I.{87}, to which this figure pertains, do not include the figure. D, however, includes no figures beyond Figure 13. The text clearly calls for a figure but does not give enough information to permit its reconstruction beyond the two lines AB and CD; however, cf. Figure 43.

together than their middles, because their middles are almost in the eye [of the observer], and the intervening space is perceived superficially.[179] But the ends of the lines are much farther [from the observer] and appear under a more acute angle, and the space between the ends is not perceived in the same way as is that between the middles. Therefore the ends [of the line connecting the rising and setting of the sun or star] appear nearer the north because they appear less distant from the aforementioned northern line.}

[*Proposition*] *83{88}. Spherical bodies appear flat from a distance.*
Since convexity[180] and concavity can be discerned only when the parts of the visible object are perceived to be unequally distant, sight must fail in the perception of sphericity when the distance is immoderately great, as is evident from Proposition 72. Therefore if no part of the visible object appears farther away than any other, its entire surface must appear to be of the same disposition.

[*Proposition*] *84{89}. Square figures appear oblong from a distance.*
The reason for this is that the excess of the rays falling on the sides of the square obliquely situated relative to the eye over the rays falling on the sides of the square directly facing the eye is not sufficiently large in comparison to the whole distance [for the lengths] to form a sensible ratio; i.e., sight does not suffice to discern the obliquity of the side that is seen obliquely and under longer rays and a smaller angle.[181] Therefore such a side appears smaller [than others]. But if a corner of the square is directly opposite the eye, the square will appear rounded, the angle being completely undiscerned because of the distance.

Here Ends Part I

Incipit Secunda Pars

[Proemium]

{Circa scientiam de speculis tripliciter consideratio exercetur: primo in cognoscendo naturam et differentias speculorum et modum et locum reflexionum, secundo in experiendo locum ymaginum, tertio in quirendo differentias errorum specularium et differentias speculorum.

{Istius tripliciter considerationis prima traditur in quarto, secundo in quinto, tertia in sexto.}

[*Propositio*] *1ᵃ. Luces primas et secundarias puras et coloribus immixtas a densorum corporum superficiebus reverberari.*

Hoc per experimentum patet in speculis ferreis et huius aliis. Amplius propter reflexionem radiorum a superficie terre est calor intensior prope terram quam in medio aeris interstitio, et in vallibus ad quas utrimque montium densitas radios reflectit. Cuius ratio est quoniam radius lucis et coloris per dyaphonum natus est incedere et quoniam occurrente corpore denso parum dyaphonorum virtus radiationis et influentia radiosi terminata non est. Quia in directum transire non potest in reflexionem ducitur diffusionis impulsu, non solum occurrentibus corporibus opacis et terrestribus verum etiam perspicuis minori genere perspicuitatis, cuiusmodi est aqua et vitrum. Unde radius solis quoad sui nobiliorem puritatem reflectitur ab aqua, et tamen secundum aliquid sui aquam ingreditur aquam illustrans. Unde et in aqua existens quis videre posset solem et lunam.

1 incipit...pars *in alia manu mg. hab.* (*et post* pars *add.* de speculis) *V* incipit libri secundus de speculis *B* incipit secunda *in alia manu mg. hab. A* secunda pars huius libri *mg. hab. H* incipit liber secundus *F* incipit secunda *D*

3 exercetur *corr. ex* excercetur *D*

9 et²: que *B*

10 a densorum: a tersorum *F* adversorum *D*

11 *post* hoc *add. B* patet / per *om. FD* / experimento *F* / huius: huiusmodi *F*

12 calor: color *D*

13 utrimque: utrumque *BA*

14 reflectit: inflectit *A* / est *om. D*

16 dyaphono *BAF* / radiosi: radiosa *FD*

16–17 terminata: nata *H*

17 *ante* quia *add. B* et / *post* potest *scr. et*

Here Begins Part II

[Preface]

{The investigation of mirrors is threefold: first, understanding the nature of and differences between mirrors and the manner and place of reflection; second, locating images; third, investigating the differences between [various] errors of reflection and the differences between mirrors.

{The first part of this threefold investigation is consigned to the fourth, the second part to the fifth, and the third part to the sixth [book of Alhazen].}

[*Proposition*] *1. Primary and pure secondary light and unmixed colors rebound from the surfaces of dense bodies.*[1]

This is evident from experience with mirrors of iron and other materials. Moreover, because rays are reflected from the surface of the earth, heat is more intense near the earth than in the middle interstice of the air[2] and [is also intense] in valleys to which rays are reflected by the density of the mountains on both sides. The reason for this is that rays of light and color are so constituted as to proceed through a transparent body, and the power of radiating and the onward flow of rays are not brought to an end by the opposition of a dense body of negligible transparency. Since the rays cannot continue in a straight line—when opposed not only by opaque and terrestrial bodies, but also by transparent bodies having a weaker kind of transparency, such as water and glass—the impulse to diffuse produces reflection.[3] Therefore, as to its nobler purity, a solar ray is reflected from water; nevertheless, some part of it enters and illuminates water. Therefore a person situated in water would be able to see the sun and moon.

---

del. A in reflexionem non potest
18 impulsum *AD* / corporibus *om. B*
19 perspicuis: perspicuitatem *A*
20 *post* unde *add. FD* etiam / quoad: usque

ad *D* / nobiliorem *om. D*
21 aquam[1]: aqua *A* / aquam[2] *BWHD*
aqua *VAF*
22 solem: aquam *B*

[*Propositio*] *2ª*. *Reflexiones solas a regularibus superficiebus factas ab oculo sentiri.*

25   Dico superficies regulares illas que sunt dispositionis uniformis in omnibus partibus suis, verbi gratia planas, concavas, convexas, et huius. Irregulares autem sunt superficies corporum asperorum, in quas cadens lux dispergitur et distrahitur, ne regulariter super oculum oriri possit. A superficiebus autem regularibus eodem modo reflectitur ordinate quo in ipsis
30   recipitur secundum pyramides radiosas. Et ideo quia visus non fit sine pyramidibus radiosis, per tales et non alias superficies contingit speculari, sicut enim radii illi si essent in directum porrecti ostenderent oculo illud cuius sunt, sic et reflexi ostendunt, sed alio modo, essentiale enim est radiis corpora declarare quorum sunt similitudines.

35   [*Propositio*] *3ª*. *Luces reflexas similiter et colores debiliores esse directe radiantibus.*

Cuius causam prebet non solum elongatio a fonte, immo magis debilitatio ex obliquatione. Rectitudo siquidem lucis cognata processui, sed etiam omni operi nature, dirigit et expedit naturam, omnis enim motus
40   tanto est fortior quanto est rectior, et per consequens rectitudine sublata necesse est latescere ex parte vigorem. Hec etiam est ratio quare lumen solis transiens per vitreas coloratas colorem ipsum facit sensibiliter radiare et tingere opacum sibi obiectum, propter fortitudinem scilicet radii quasi directe radiantis. Non autem hoc potest radius a solido reflexus, fortitudo
45   enim lucis necessaria est colori non solum movendo ipsum sed etiam movendo cum ipso medium, in quo excedit radii fortitudo vitrum penetrantis quamvis aliquantulum frangatur.

[*Propositio*] *4ª*. *Reflexiones factas a superficiebus fortiter coloratis nichil aut tenuiter visum movere.*

50   Cuius ratio est quia, ut proximo patuit, lux directa fortior est quam reflexa, similiter et color. Quod si illa superficies sit regularis et multum polita, res in ea videri poterunt, sed non prout sunt, immo colore speculi vestite.

25 dicas *A* / irregulares *H*
26 plana *D* / et huius *om. F*
27 autem *om. B* / sunt *om. F* / corpora *A* / qua *A*
28 oriri possit *tr. F*
29 autem *om. A* / irregularibus *A*
30 et ideo: non *B*
31 *ante* per *add. F* ideo / *ante* alias *add. F* per

32 porrecti: portensi *F*
33 sic et: sicut *A*
34 corpus *B*
35 *post* colores *scr. et del. A* ?et
38 cognato *B* / *post* cognata *add. F* non solum ministrat
39 *ante* omni *add. A* in / operi: operationi *D* / *ante* dirigit *scr. et del. H* dio / *post* dirigit *add. F* namque

[*Proposition*] *2. Only reflection from regular surfaces is discerned by the eye.*[4]

I call those surfaces regular that are of uniform disposition in all their parts, as plane, concave, convex, and so forth. The surfaces of rough bodies are irregular, and light incident upon them is dispersed and scattered so that it cannot fall on the eye in a regular fashion. However, light is reflected from regular surfaces in the form of radiant pyramids in the same order as that in which it is received. Therefore, since sight occurs only through radiant pyramids, observation [by reflection] occurs only through such [regular] surfaces and not through others; for just as the rays, if extended in straight lines, would exhibit to the eye the object to which they belong, so they exhibit it when they have been reflected, although in a different way,[5] for it is essential to rays to manifest the bodies of which they are the likenesses.

[*Proposition*] *3. Reflected light or color is weaker than that which is radiated directly.*[6]

This is caused not only by the separation [of the light or color] from its source, but also (and more significantly) by the weakness that results from bending. Since straightness is naturally associated with the propagation of light (as well as with every other action of nature), it arranges and orders nature, for every action is strong in proportion to its straightness; consequently, when straightness is lacking, strength must be decreased. That is why light from the sun passing through colored glass causes the color [of the glass] to radiate sensibly and to bathe facing opaque bodies in color, i.e., because rays are strong when they radiate nearly in a straight line. However, a ray reflected from a dense body cannot cause the glass to radiate sensibly, since the light must be strong enough to excite not only the color itself, but also the medium along with it; the strength of the [solar] ray penetrating the glass exceeds this [requirement] even though it is slightly refracted.

[*Proposition*] *4. Reflections from strongly colored surfaces affect vision slightly or not at all.*[7]

As shown in the preceding proposition, the reason for this is that direct light and color are stronger than reflected light and color. However, if the [reflecting] surface is regular and highly polished, objects will be visible in it, not as they really are but vested with the color of the mirror.

---

41 est[1] *VWF; om.* H erit *BAD* | est ratio *tr. A* est B ratio *D*

42 *ante* vitreas *add. F* fenestras

43 tangere *F* | scilicet *om. F*

44 hoc potest *tr. BF*

45 necesse *A* | etiam: in *D*

46 excedit: procedit *F*

49 aut: autem *H*

50 quia *om. F*

51 colores *B* | *post* illa *scr. et del. H* srf

52 rei *D* | immo: uno *F* nimio *D*

[*Propositio*] *5ª*. *Luces et colores a speculis reflexos res quarum sunt*
species oculo ostendere.

Quod patet quoniam species genita a re visibili essentiali habet rem
ostendere cuius est similitudo, quoniam in se esse fixum non habens necessario ducit in alterum cuius est. Quamvis igitur reflectatur manet sibi
essentia sua, et ideo rem ostendit, in situ tamen alio, cuius ratio infra
patebit.

[*Propositio*] *6ª*. *Angulos incidentie et reflexionis equales esse, radiumque*
incidentem et reflexum in eadem superficie esse cum linea erigibili a puncto
reflexionis.

Dicitur angulus incidentie quem constituit radius cadens super speculum cum superficie speculi vel ex una parte vel ex alia cum linea ymaginabiliter erigibili puncto reflexionis; angulus reflexionis quem cum eisdem
constituit radius reflexus. Equalitas autem angulorum experimento colligitur et ratione utcunque probatur, quoniam si radius incidens transire
posset in profundum speculi cum linea perpendiculari super punctum reflexionis in profundum ducta constitueret angulum equalem angulo incidentie, quia anguli contra se positi sunt equales secundum Euclidem. Ergo
eodem modo resilit quo transiret. Ergo necesse est ad equalem angulum
reverberari, unde si perpendiculariter cadit in speculum in se reflectitur,
si oblique cadit oblique et reflectitur in partem aliam; sicut et in motu
corporali patet, quoniam aliquod ponderosum descendens motu recto in
solidum corpus vel proiectum lineariter si recte proicitur per eandem lineam reverberatur, si oblique per consimilem sicut resilit in oppositam
partem.

Amplius perpendicularis radius fortior est aliis, non solum propter con-
ditionem radii absolutam, sed propter modum oriendi super rem obiectam,
sicut patet ex declaratione 15 propositionis prime partis. Fortitudo igitur

54 reflexi *F*
56 genita *obs. A* / genita a re *om. F* / visibilis *F* / essentiale *VH* essentialem *B* essentialiter *F* / *post* essentiale *scr. et del.*
   H a
56–57 rem ostendere *tr. A*
57 *post* cuius *add. B* ratio / quoniam: quoniam enim *A* qui enim *B* quod enim *F* /
   ante esse *add. F* est / esse…habens:
   fixum esse non habens (esse *in alia ma-*
   nu) *A* esse fixum non habent *B* esse non
   habens fixum *F*
57–58 necesse *A*
58 igitur *obs. A* / *post* manet *add. F* tamen

59 *post* rem *scr. et del. H* d / tamen: cum *D*
61 reflexiones *H*
64 incidentie *om. A* / constituit: ostendit *A*
   / super *mg. hab. B*
65–66 ymaginat *D*
66 erigibilia *D* eligibili *B* / *ante* puncto
   add. BF a / angulus reflexionis *mg. hab.*
   D / eisdem: esset *B*
67 radius *BWD* angulus *VAFH* / equalitas:
   qualitas *D* / *ante* experimento *add. A* ex
68 utcunque: utrumque *BAD* utrimque
   uterque *F*
70 constituent *H*
70–71 incidenti *B*

[*Proposition*] *5. Light and color reflected from mirrors manifest to the eye the objects of which they are the species.*[8]

This is evident, because a species produced by a visible object has the essential property of manifesting the object of which it is the likeness; for since the species has no permanent being in itself, it necessarily reveals the object of which it is the species. Therefore, even though it is reflected, it maintains its essence and thereby reveals the object—albeit in another position, the reason for which will be evident below.[9]

[*Proposition*] *6. The angles of incidence and reflection are equal, and the incident and reflected rays are in the same plane as the line erected [perpendicularly] at the point of reflection.*[10]

The angle formed by the incident ray and either the surface of the mirror (on one side) or the imaginary line erected [perpendicularly] at the point of reflection (on the other side) is called the angle of incidence; the angle formed by these [i.e., the surface of the mirror and the imaginary perpendicular] and the reflected ray is called the angle of reflection. Equality of the angles is gathered from experience and proved by reason in any of several ways; for if an incident ray could advance into the depth of a mirror, it would form (with the perpendicular extended into the depth [of the mirror] at the point of reflection) an angle equal to the angle of incidence because, according to Euclid, vertical angles are equal.[11] Therefore the ray recoils in the same mode as that in which it would be transmitted [if it were not deflected by a reflecting surface], and consequently it must rebound at an equal angle [to the angle of incidence]. Accordingly, if it is incident on the mirror perpendicularly, it is reflected back on itself; if it is incident obliquely, it is reflected obliquely toward the other side. The same thing is evident in the motion of a body, since a heavy body descending vertically onto a solid body or projected perpendicularly along a line is driven back along the same line; if projected obliquely, it rebounds along a similar line on the other side.[12]

Furthermore, the perpendicular ray is stronger than [all] others, not only because of the absolute nature of the ray but also because of the mode of incidence on the object, as the exposition of Proposition 15, Part I, makes clear.

---

73 cadet *A*

74 si...reflectitur *om. A* / oblique² *om. F* / et¹ *om. F* / et²: etiam *VH* / in² *om. H*

75 corporali *obs. A* / *post* ponderosum *add. F* densum / *ante* motu *add. F* in

76 vel: id est *F* / lineariter: linealiter *BFD*

77 sicut *obs. F* situm *B*

80 modum *om. B*

81 patet...15: ex declaratione 15 *F* ex declaratione patet 15 *B* patet in declaratione 12 *A* {patet} *D* / propositionis *om. FD* / *post* partis *add. F* patet

radii cadentis est secundum quantitatem anguli quem radius constituit in cadendo, sed fortitudo radii in reflectendo est secundum fortitudinem radii in cadendo. Ergo modus reflexionis sequitur modum incidentie.

85   Amplius illas tres lineas esse in eadem superficie patet, quia radius incessui rectitudinis ut est possibile se conformat, quoniam innata est luci rectitudo. Quod si superficiem illam egrederetur dupliciter a rectitudine deficeret, et resiliendo et divertendo.

[*Propositio*] *7ª. Dyaphoneitatem speculi essentiam non intrare, ei tamen*
90   *per accidens alicubi conferre.*

    Si enim res in speculo ostenduntur per radios reflexos, ut iam patet, igitur perspicuitas, per quam species in profundum ingreditur speculi, impedit non expedit visionem, quoniam reflexio est a denso quia densum est, propter quod specula consueta vitrea sunt plumbo subducta. Quod si, ut
95 quidam fabulantur, dyaphoneitas esset essentialis speculo, non fierent specula de ferro et calibe, a dyaphoneitate remotissimis, nec etiam de marmore polito, cuius tamen contrarium videmus. In ferro autem et huius propter intensionem nigredinis non est efficax speculatio. In quibusdam tamen lapidibus debilis coloris multo clarior est speculatio quam in vitro.

100   [*Propositio*] *8ª. In speculis vitreis plumbo abraso nichil apparere.*

    Cuius ratio est quoniam, licet a vitri superficie fiat aliqua reflexio, tamen quando vitrum ex alia parte non obumbratur transit per ipsam lux directa, que reflexam vincit fortitudine sua, sicut patet ex 3ª premissarum huius partis. Quod si apponatur pannus obscurus et niger vel huius aliquid tunc
105 poterit videri, quia tunc nichil directe transit per vitrum, quod sit magne in radiando efficacie.

[*Propositio*] *9ª. Superficies regulariter speculares septiformes esse.*

    Est enim speculum planum, est spericum tam concavum quam convexum, est pyramidale tam intra quam extra politum, est etiam columpna-

82 *post* quantitatem *in alia manu mg. add.* V radii / quem: quoniam *D*

84 modus *obs. A*

85 eadem superficie *tr. F* / quia: quod *H*

86 incessui: intensive *F* / ut *om. A* / *ante* se *add. F* luci / innata *mg. hab. D*

87 quod: quia *F*

88 et[1] *om. F* / *ante* divertendo *scr. et del. A* reflectendo

89 non: nam *A* / *ante* ei *add. A* non / ei: et *F*

90 alicubi: aliquid *A*

92 in *om. F* / profundum ingreditur *tr. F*

93 *ante* non *add. F* et / non expedit *om. A* / quia…est[2] *om. F* / est[2] *om. B*

94 sunt plumbo *tr. F* sunt plumba *B*

95 *ante* speculo *scr. et del. H* i / *post* speculo *scr. et del. A* vero / non *om. A* / fierunt *A*

96 *ante* de[1] *scr. et del. H* et / et: vel *A* / *ante* calibe *scr. et del. H* calide / remotissima *A*

97 huius: huiusmodi *F*

98 intentionem *A*

99 tamen *om. B* / *post* speculatio *add. F* ut

Therefore the strength of the incident ray varies with the size of the angle of incidence, and the strength of the reflected ray varies with the strength of the incident ray; consequently the mode of reflection follows the mode of incidence.

It is evident also that the three lines [i.e., the incident ray, the reflected ray, and the perpendicular] are in the same plane, because a ray conforms as closely as possible to a rectilinear path, since straightness is natural to light. However, if a ray were to forsake that plane, it would be departing doubly from straightness, both by rebound and by deviation.

[*Proposition*] *7. Transparency is not essential to mirrors, but may be conferred on them as an accident.*

For if (as is now evident) an object is exhibited in a mirror by reflected rays, transparency, through which a species proceeds into the depth of the mirror, obstructs rather than aids sight, since reflection occurs at a dense body because of its density. Therefore common glass mirrors are coated with lead. But if, as some say, transparency were essential to mirrors, mirrors would not be made of iron and steel—so far removed from transparency—nor of polished marble; but the contrary is true. Yet observation [of objects by reflection] is not efficacious in iron and such materials because of the intensity of their blackness. Nevertheless, observation [by reflection] is clearer in certain stones of weak color than in glass.

[*Proposition*] *8. Nothing is seen in glass mirrors from which the lead has been scraped.*

The reason for this is that, although some reflection can occur from a glass surface, direct light passes through when the glass is not shaded on the other side, and its strength overcomes the reflected light, as Proposition 3 of this part makes clear. But if a dark, black cloth or something of that kind is applied [behind the mirror], the reflected light can be seen because nothing is transmitted directly through the glass, which is then of great efficacy in radiating.

[*Proposition*] *9. Regular reflecting surfaces are of seven types.*[13]

Indeed, mirrors are plane, spherically concave or convex, pyramidal and polished either inside or outside, or columnar and polished either inside or out-

in adamante
101 quoniam: quod *D* / fiet *B* fiat *corr. H ex* fiet
102 quando: quoniam *A*
103 ex 3ª: quanta *D* / premissarum *om. F* premissorum *B*

104 huius aliquid *tr. VB* huiusmodi aliquid *F*
105 transit per vitrum: per vitrum transit *F*
106 in...efficacie: efficacie in radiando *F*
107 regulariter *in alia manu corr. V ex* regulares
109 etiam: in *D*

110 re politum intra et extra. Et in hiis septem differentiis, plano scilicet, sperico concavo et convexo, pyramidali interiori et exteriori, similiter columpnari interiori et exteriori, sunt per singula diversa apparitionum genera, ut patebit. Quedam autem sunt superficies irregulares que quamquam sint polite, scilicet partim plane partim convexe vel concave; in eis
115 tamen facies apparent distorte propter irregularem reflexionem a superficiei diversitate.

[*Propositio*] *10ª. Materia speculi est lenitas intensa, forma vero perfecta politura.*

Hic dicitur lenitas magna partium continuitas carens poris sensibilibus
120 omnino, unde lignum et huius corpora non possunt esse specula. Politura vero intelligitur omnis asperitas amotio. Si igitur sit corpus lene multum et intense politum erit speculum essentialiter. Ad hoc tamen ut speculum lucide visibilia representet exigitur ut non sit coloratum colore sensibili. Requiritur etiam ut nec pulvere nec anhelitu nec humore sit respersum,
125 et hoc est quod dicunt oportet speculum esse tersum.

[*Propositio*] *11ª. Res in speculis apparere universaliter debilius quam directe.*

Cuius ratio est quoniam, ut patet ex 3ª, forme reflexe debiliores sunt, et ideo debilius representant, et ideo debiliter movent propter quod homo
130 vix sue forme recordatur. Amplius color speculi immiscetur luci reflexe et obfuscat eam, propter quod facies apparet tincta. Latent etiam faciei macule propter debilitatem reflexionis.

[*Propositio*] *12ª. In quolibet puncto speculi, obiecto luminoso, duas lucis terminari pyramides, unam incidentem et aliam resilientem.*

135 Prima pars huius patet ex 4 prime partis. Et quoniam lux reflectitur a polito sequitur secunda pars propositionis, ut etiam pyramis inde a quolibet puncto reflectatur.

110 intra: intus *B* / et^2 *om. A*
111 interiori…similiter: intra et extra *F*
112 *ante* interiori *add. B* et
113 quidam *A* / autem *om. B* / sunt *om. D* sub *H* / *ante* irregulares *scr. et del. H verba oblita* / que *om. D*
113–14 quamquam: quamvis *A*
114 convexe vel concave: concave et convexe *B* / in eis: ne hiis *D*
115 apparet *H* / regularem *H*
117 *post* materia *add. A* autem / lenitas: levitas *D* / vero *om. F*

119 lenitas: levitas *D* / partium *om. A* / continuitas (*in alia manu corr. V ex* concavitas concavitas (*sic*)): concavitas *BH*
120 omnino *om. A* / huiusmodi *F*
121 vero *om. B* / asperitatis *VBAF* / sit corpus *tr. B* / lene: leve *HD*
122 et *om. F* / *ante* tamen *scr. et del. F* autem
124 nec^1: non *F* / nec^2 *om. H* / nec^3 humore *om. D*
125 dicitur *F*
127 est…patet *om. H* / quoniam *in alia manu hab. V* / 3ª: 3 huius partis *F* 3 *D*

side. As will be evident, individual things vary in appearance according to the following seven different types [of mirrors]: plane, spherically concave and convex, pyramidal inside and outside, and columnar inside and outside. However, some surfaces are irregular, i.e., partly plane and partly convex or concave; even though such surfaces are polished, figures appear distorted in them because of irregular reflection resulting from variations in the surface.

[*Proposition*] *10. The matter of mirrors is intense smoothness, the form perfect polishing.*[14]

By "smoothness" is meant great continuity of parts altogether free from sensible pores; therefore wood and such bodies cannot be mirrors. By "polishing" we understand the removal of all roughness. Consequently, if a body is very smooth and highly polished, it is essentially a mirror. However, so that the mirror may represent visible things clearly, it must not be sensibly colored. It is required also that it should not be covered with dust, breath, or moisture, and for this reason they say that a mirror must be wiped clean.

[*Proposition*] *11. Objects always appear dimmer in mirrors than by direct vision.*[15]

As Proposition 3 shows, the explanation of this is that reflected forms are weaker and therefore represent [the object] more weakly. Consequently they act [on sight] weakly, for which reason a man remembers his own appearance with difficulty.[16] Furthermore, the color of the mirror is mingled with the reflected light and obscures it, and as a result the face appears tinted. Moreover, blemishes of the face remain hidden because of the weakness of reflection.

[*Proposition*] *12. When a luminous object is present, two pyramids of light are terminated at every point of a mirror, one incident and the other reflected.*[17]

The first part of this is evident from Proposition 4 of Part I. And since light is reflected from a polished surface, the second part of the proposition follows, for thus [it follows that] a pyramid is also reflected from every point.

---

129 debilius...ideo *om.* H / *ante* homo *scr. et del.* A facies

130 *post* forme *add.* FD in speculo apparente (apparentis D) / *post* amplius *add.* A si / et *om.* D

131 obfuscat: obscurat F / eam *obs.* A / *post* facies *scr. et del.* D facit / appareret A / tincta latent: quandoque tincta latente F

132 macula F macule *corr.* D *ex* macules / reflexionis *om.* D

134 et BWFD; *om.* VAH

135 4 {*om.* D} 4ᵃ AF / prime partis: huius partis B {prima parte} D / lux reflectitur *tr.* F

137 puncto *om.* VA

[*Propositio*] *13ª. A quolibet puncto luminosi in quemlibet punctum speculi obiecti radium incidere.*

140   Hoc sequitur ex 3ª prime partis.

[*Propositio*] *14ª. A quolibet puncto luminosi porrigi pyramidem totam obiecti speculi superficiem occupantem.*

Hoc sequitur ex sexta prime partis.

[*Propositio*] *15ª. A superficie speculi infinitas fieri completas reflexiones*
145 *forme visibilis.*

Hoc patet ex prehabitis. Verbi gratia sit res visa plana et speculum planum. Tota species rei vise non solum recipitur in tota superficie speculi sed etiam in qualibet parte eius, et quamvis partes a quibus potest fieri reflexio sint finite, per diversam tamen compositionem cum aliis partibus
150 sunt infinite. Cum igitur secundum modum incidentie sit reflexio, oportet infinitas fieri reflexiones a quolibet speculo, secundum enim pyramidem aliam et aliam fit visio in quolibet puncto alio et alio. Nec tamen propter hoc sunt infinita actu, quia hec omnia sunt unum corpus lucis. Reflexiones autem complete sunt que rem totam ostendunt.

155   [*Propositio*] *16ª. Radium super speculum perpendiculariter orientem in se reflecti.*

Hoc sequitur ex sexta partis huius, quoniam si per aliam lineam reflecteretur per minorem angulum resiliret, et non essent equales anguli incidentie et reflexionis.

160   [*Propositio*] *17ª. Lucem reflexam per agregationem fieri fortiorem luce incidente.*

Omnis siquidem virtus unita plus infinita et similiter radii cum disperguntur debilitantur et cum adunantur fortificantur et ad aliquem effectum magis sufficiunt radii reflexi adunati quam directi dispersi. Hinc enim est
165 quod in speculis concavis spericis ad solem positis ignis accenditur, si enim

138 a *om. VH* / *ante* punctum *add. VH* et
140 hoc *obs. A* / 3ª...partis: {prima parte} *D*
142 superfaciem *D*
143 hec *F* / sexta...partis: 6 prime partis *B* {prima parte} *D*
144 a: in *FD*
146 hec *F* / sit (*in alia manu mg. corr. V ex* si): *om. B* si *H*
147 species: superficies *D* / tota²: sola *D* / speculi *om. A*

148 et *om. D*
149 per...tamen: tamen per diversam *A* / compositionem: comparationem *AF*
149–50 finite...sunt *om. D*
150 incidentie *obs. A* / sit: fit *F*
152 nec: non *F* / tamen *om. D*
154 complete sunt *tr. A* complete *D* / *post* ostendunt *in alia manu add. V* orientem
157 hec *VFH* / sexta: 6 *B* septima *D* / partis huius *tr. F* / aliam lineam *tr. F*
157–58 reflectentur *H*

[*Proposition*] *13. A ray from every point of a luminous body is incident on every point of a facing mirror.*[18]

This follows from Proposition 3 of Part I.

[*Proposition*] *14. A pyramid is extended from every point of a luminous body to occupy the whole surface of a facing mirror.*[19]

This follows from Proposition 6 of Part I.

[*Proposition*] *15. From the surface of a mirror there are an infinite number of complete reflections of the form of the visible object.*

This is evident from the foregoing.[20] For instance, let there be a flat object and a plane mirror. The whole species of the visible object is received not only by the whole surface of the mirror but by every part of it; and although the parts from which reflection can occur are finite in number, nevertheless they are infinite by various combinations with other parts.[21] Therefore, since reflection occurs according to the mode of incidence, an infinite number of reflections must take place from every mirror, for there is a different pyramid corresponding to each point [of the mirror] through which sight occurs. But nevertheless, the reflections are not thereby actually infinite, since they all form one body of light. Now complete reflections are those that present the entire object.

[*Proposition*] *16. A ray perpendicularly incident on a mirror is reflected back on itself.*[22]

This follows from Proposition 6 of this part, since, if the ray were reflected along any other line, it would recoil through an angle smaller [than the angle of incidence], and the angles of incidence and reflection would not be equal.

[*Proposition*] *17. By aggregation reflected light becomes stronger than* [*directly*] *incident light.*[23]

[This follows] because every united power is stronger[24] and because rays are weakened when dispersed and strengthened when brought together and because reflected rays that have been brought together suffice better for the production of any effect than do direct rays that have been dispersed. That is why fire can be kindled in spherical concave mirrors facing the sun; for if the mirror

---

161 incidentie *B*
162 *ante* omnis *scr. et del. A* debilitantur et cum adunatur fortificantur / *ante* infinita *add. B* est / infinita: non unica est *F*
162–63 dispergantur *A*

163 adiuvantur *D*
164 adunari *H* / dispersi *obs. A* / enim *om. F*
165 concavis *om. A* / *ante* accenditur *scr. et del. H* as

directe radiis solis opponatur radios omnes partim super unum punctum partim super lineam incidere, necesse est omnes enim ab eodem circulo reflexi cadunt in punctum unum; quia talium equales sunt anguli incidentie, erunt ergo etiam reflexionis. Quod igitur lux directa ignem non generat
170 ex hoc provenit quod radii solis concurrere non possunt nisi fracti aut reflexi.

[*Propositio*] *18ª. Lucem speculo incidere et reflecti per lineas naturales.*
Linea siquidem radiosa naturalis est nec salvatur radii essentia nisi in latitudine aliqua. Et quia apparitio in speculis mutatur secundum diversi-
175 tatem figure, planum est quod a puncto mathematico non fit reflexio, quia illius nulla est secundum superficies diversificatio.

[*Propositio*] *19ª. Formas in speculis apparentes per impressionem in speculis factam minime videri.*
Credunt enim homines non nulli quod res in speculis appareant per
180 ydola que speculis imprimantur, et res quasi in ydolis apparere, ydola tamen ipsa primo videri. Et iste error geminatur, quidam enim dicunt ydolum imprimi ipsi speculo et ibi esse ac visum movere, quod multipliciter falsum esse ostenditur, quoniam in speculis ferreis et adamantinis videntur res in quibus nulla est perspicuitas receptiva impressionis. Amplius
185 si res imprimeretur speculo diffunderet se undique a speculo, et posset res videri in omni parte respectu speculi, quod falsum est, non enim videtur res nisi oculo existente in eadem superficie cum puncto viso et cum puncto reflexionis, equalibus existentibus angulis incidentie et reflexionis. Amplius quantitas ydoli numquam excederet quantitatem speculi, quod fal-
190 sum est. Amplius si ydolum imprimeretur speculo appareret in speculo et non ultra speculum, quod falsum est, apparent enim ydola in concursu ymaginario radii cum catheto. Amplius perspicuitas nichil facit ad essentiam speculi per se, ut supra docuit 7ª propositio huius partis.

166 radiis solis *tr. F* / opponitur *F* / *post* opponatur *add. D* ratur
166–67 unum...super *om. D*
167 lineam: aliud *F* / incidere *BAWF* incedere *VD* recedere *H* / omnes enim *om. A* / enim: esse *B*
168 cadant *A* / in *om. B* super *F* / punctum *om. B* / equales sunt *tr. B*
169 *ante* erunt *scr. et del. A* ergo / erunt ergo *tr. B*
170 hoc *om. H* / non possunt *om. D*
172 *ante* speculo *add. A* in / et *om. B*
173 essentialiter *F*

174 speculo *F* / mutatur: unitatur *D*
175 *post* figure *add. F* obiecte / reflexus *A*
176 illius nulla *tr. F* / secundum *om. A* / superficies diversificatio *tr. A* superficiem diversificatio *F*
178 factam *om. D*
180 imprimuntur *VFH* / in *om. D* ex *B*
181 geminatur: generatur *FD* / dicunt: habent *B*
182 ydola *F* ydoli *H* / *post* imprimi *scr. et del. V* in / ipsi speculo *tr. V* / ac: et *F*
183 ostendunt *B* ostendit *H* / ferreis *in alia manu mg. hab. H*

directly faces solar rays, all those rays converge partially on a point and partially on a line.[25] [This follows] because all rays reflected from the same circle must converge on one point, since equal angles of incidence [for all rays incident on one circle] lead to equal angles of reflection. Therefore direct light does not generate fire, because solar rays cannot converge unless refracted or reflected.

[*Proposition*] *18. Light is incident on and reflected from a mirror along natural lines.*[26]

[This is so] because a radiant line is natural, and the essence of a ray cannot be preserved except in some width. And since the appearance [of an object] in a mirror varies with the shape of the mirror, it is clear that reflection does not occur from a mathematical point since a mathematical point has no diversity of surface.

[*Proposition*] *19. Forms appearing in mirrors are not seen by means of impressions made in the mirrors.*[27]

Some people believe that objects appear in mirrors by means of images that are impressed in the mirrors and that the objects appear, as it were, in the images, even though the images themselves are seen first. This error has been compounded, for some say that the image is impressed into the mirror itself and exists there and acts on sight.[28] This is shown to be false in various ways, for objects are seen in iron and adamantine mirrors in which there is no transparency capable of receiving the impression. Besides, if a thing were impressed into the mirror, it would diffuse itself from the mirror in all directions and could be seen [in the mirror] from every direction relative to the mirror. [But] this is false, since the object is seen only if the eye is located in the same plane as the visible point and the point of reflection and if the angles of incidence and reflection are equal. Furthermore, [if the image were impressed into the mirror,] its size would never exceed the size of the mirror, which is false. Moreover, if an image were impressed into the mirror, it would appear there and not beyond, which is false, for the image appears at the imaginary intersection of the ray and the perpendicular. In addition, transparency of itself is not essential to mirrors, as was taught above in Proposition 7 of this part.

184 res *in alia manu mg. hab. V* / est *om. B*
186 respectu *om. H*
187 visio *H* / puncto[2] *mg. hab. D*
188 *ante* angulis *scr. et del. D* oculis
189 ydole *F* ydoli *corr. D ex* ydolis / excedent *H* / quantitatem speculi *tr. H*
190 *ante* speculo *add. B* in / appareret *om. F*

apparet *D* apparent *H* / in speculo *om. F*
191 apparet *H* / ydola *mg. hab. B*
192 ymaginarie *A* / *post* ad *scr. et del. D* ad
193 ut…docuit: ut supra ?doctum est *A* {patet ut supra} *D* / 7ª…partis {*om. D*} / 7ª propositio (*in alia manu H*) *VHW*; *tr. B* 7ª propositione *A* 7 propositio *F*

Idcirco dicunt alii ydolum non imprimi speculo sed ubi apparet, in concursu radii cum catheto scilicet ultra speculum ubi apparet ydolum, quod
falsum est quoniam in aqua turris apparet esse in terra tantum quantum
est in aere. Et si ponatur mons eneus in loco apparitionis ita limpide
apparet ac si ponatur ibi aer vel aqua. Ergo nichil ibi imprimitur.

Quid est igitur ydolum? Dico sola apparitio rei extra locum suum.
Verbi gratia aliquando oculus ut supra patuit de uno iudicat duo esse,
quia res apparet non solum in loco suo sed extra locum suum. Ita est in
proposito quo ad hoc quia res in speculo secundum veritatem videtur sed
in situ erratur et aliquando in numero, ut infra videbitur.

[*Propositio*] *20ᵃ. In speculis planis et aliis in maiori parte ymagines apparere in concursu radii cum catheto.*

Cathetus est linea perpendicularis ducta a re visa super superficiem
speculi, seu plani seu sperici. In concursu enim radii ymaginabili, sub quo
res videtur, cum perpendiculari ducta a re perpendiculariter super superficiem speculi apparet esse illud quod in speculo videtur. Cuius ratio colligi
potest ex 67 propositione prime partis, ipsa siquidem longitudo radiorum
oculo presentatur. Sed quia pars radii reflexa movet visum immediate et
in illam visus intendit, illa etiam mediante per se apprehendit partem radii
incidentem in speculum ita quod totus radius presentatur oculo quasi
procedens in continuum et directum; reflexionem enim oculus advertere
non potest, qui nichil apprehendit nisi partem radii qui visum qualificat.
Necesse est igitur rem que in speculo videtur, si supra speculum est, sub
eodem apparere in concursu ymaginabili radii cum catheto.

Verbi gratia sit speculum *ABG,* sit res visa *CK,* oculus videns *D*

---

194 non *scr. et del. V* | *ante* speculo *add. A* in
    | ubi *om. F*
195 ubi: nichil *A* | ydolum *om. A*
196 quoniam: ut *A* | aqua *in alia manu corr.*
    H ex qua | in terra *in alia manu mg. hab.*
    V | tantum quantum *mg. corr. D ex* tam-
    quam
197 *post* eneus *add. B* vel igneus
198 apparet: appareret *B* | poneretur *B* |
    ibi¹ *om. B* | ergo nichil: nichil igitur *A*
    | ibi² *om. BAD*
199 est igitur *tr. F* est *H* | dicitur *A* | extra:
    ultra *B* | *post* locum *scr. et del. D* locum
    | suum: situm *D*
200 de...duo: duo de uno iudicat *B* | iudi-
    cat *in alia manu mg. corr. V ex* indicat |
    post duo *scr. et del. H* locum suum ita
    est in proposito

201 *post* suo *scr. et del. A* esse
202 hoc *in alia manu mg. hab. D* | quia
    VBWHL; om. A quod (*in alia manu mg.
    hab. D) FD* | secundum...videtur *VAH
    DL* videtur secundum veritatem *B*
    secundum veritatem ista modo non
    videtur *F*
202–3 sed...erratur: quia erratur in situ *F*
203 videbitur: patebit *B* | *post* videbitur *add.
    F ex* ista sequitur corpore quod res in
    speculo comprehenditur tantum ex for-
    ma lucis et coloris a corpore colorato il-
    luminoso a speculo procedente ad ocu-
    lum
207 seu¹ *om. F* | ymaginabilis *BFH* | sub:
    super *B*
208 perpendiculariter *om. D*

Therefore other people maintain that   ot into the
the mirror but [into the matter] at the p   ars, i.e., at
the intersection of the ray with the perpe   r. [But] this
is false, since a tower [seen] in water ap   the earth as
it [actually] extends into the air. And i   nd of bronze
is located at the place of its image, [it appears as
transparent as if air or water were lo   [it is evident
that] nothing is impressed there.

What then is an image? I say that   ace of an object
outside its place. For example, some   thing to be two,
as was evident above,[29] because the   in its true place
but also outside it. So in the present case, it is   is really seen in a
mirror, although it is misapprehended in position and sometimes in number,
as will be seen below.[30]

[*Proposition*] 20. *In plane mirrors, and for the most part in others, the images appear at the intersection of the ray and the cathetus.*[31]

The cathetus is the line dropped perpendicularly from the visible object to the surface of the mirror, whether plane or spherical. Indeed, that which is seen in a mirror appears to be located at the imaginary intersection of the ray under which the object is seen and the perpendicular dropped from the object to the surface of the mirror. This can be explained by reference to Proposition 67 of Part I, since [by that proposition] the lengths of rays are perceived by the eye. But because the reflected part of the ray acts directly on sight and sight occupies itself with that part, through its mediation the part of the ray incident on the mirror is so perceived that the whole ray is apprehended by the eye as though proceeding without interruption in a straight line; for reflection cannot be discerned by the eye, which perceives nothing except the part of the ray that [actually] conveys the qualities [of the visible object] to sight. Therefore an object seen in a mirror, if above the mirror, must appear beneath it at the imaginary intersection of the ray and the cathetus.

For example, let *ABG* [Fig. 20] be the mirror, *CK* the visible object, and *D*

209 *post* speculi *add.* B sub quo
209–10 colligi potest *tr.* A
210 67 *corr. ex* 66 *VB* 6ª *A* 88 *H* 66ª vel 72 *F*
    {lxxi} *D* / siquidam *F*
211 quia *om.* F / et *rep.* D
211–12 reflexa…radii *om.* A
212 intendit: tendit *B* / etiam: enim *F* / me-
    diante *VWFD* in mediate *B* medietate *H*
213 incidentis *F* / speculum *BFLD* specula-

tionem *VAWH* / *post* speculum *scr. et*
del. D quando / ita quod: itaque *F* /
quasi: quod *A*
214 enim: eius *A* / advertere: ad necesse *H*
215 nichil: vel *H* / qui²: que *BF*
216 si: que *F*
217 eodem: eo *BD* speculo *F*
218 speculum ABG *tr.* *F* / CK *VW* KC
    BAFH C D

[Fig. 20]. Cadant igitur radii *KA* et *CB* a re visa, que reflectantur ad ocu-
220 lum per radios *AD* et *BD*. Igitur *KA* videtur continuari *AD* et *CB* videtur
continuari *BD*; igitur *KA* et *CB* apparent porrigi in profundum speculi
sub eisdem angulis sub quibus reflectuntur, quoniam anguli contra se positi
sunt equales. Et cadit *DA* in *E*, *DB* vero in *F*. Amplius in perpendiculari
predicta, id est in catheto, res eodem modo apparet quo in situ proprio.
225 Dico in speculis planis quare rectius est ibi apparere. Et hec est ratio
Auctoris libro 5 capitulo 2.

    [*Propositio*] *21ª. Altitudines in speculis suppositis eversas apparere.*
    Hoc patet ex proxima, hoc tamen refert quia in speculis planis res visa
tantum apparet in profundo quantum desuper eminet, quod demonstra-
230 tur. Cadat enim cathetus a puncto viso *C* [Fig. 21], et sit *CEF*, sitque
radius sub quo *C* videtur *BGF*, radius cadens a re visa *CG*. Certum est
igitur in trigonis *CEG* et *FEG* quia latera *EG* et *GC* sunt equalia lateribus
GE et *GF*, sicut patet ex proxima, et angulus *CGE* equalis est angulo *EGF*,
quoniam anguli contra se positi sunt equales et anguli incidentie equales
235 sunt angulis reflexionis. Ergo basis *CE* equalis est basi *EF*. Res igitur
tantum apparet ultra speculum vel sub ipso quantum est supra. Quod si
oculus videat se ipsum idem accidet, quamvis perpendiculariter radius

219 cadunt *F* / KA (*in alia manu hab. V*)
    VBAW; *om. D* CB *F* K *H* / et *om. D* /
    que: quod *D* qui *B* / *ante* ad *add. H* ad
    oculos
220 radios AD et: medium *D* / KA...et *om.*
    D / KA *BW* KCA *VAH* CA *F* / vide-
    tur[1]...AD[2] *om. B* / CB (*in alia manu*
    mg. hab. D) *WBD* KCB *VAH* KB *F*
220–21 CB...CB *in alia manu mg. hab. D*
221 BD *om. B* BA *F* / igitur...porrigi *om. B*
    / KA *AW*; *om. D* KCA *VH* CA *F* /
    CB *AWD* KCB *VH* KB *F* / apparet *D*
222 eisdem angulis: eodem angulo (*post*
    eodem *scr. et del. D* g) *D* / quibus re-
    flectuntur: quo reflectitur *D* / anguli *om.*
    D / anguli...se: se contra anguli *H*
223 DA in E *om. D* AD in E *F* DQ in E *H* /
    DB (*in alia manu mg. corr. V ex* AB): B
    F BD *H* / vero *obs. A* et *om. D* non *H* /
    in F: infra *H* / *post* F *add. F* que est
    terminus perpendicularis / amplius: qui
    est *D* / in[3] *obs. D* et *om. H* / perpendi-
    cularis *D*

224 predicta...catheto: predicta scilicet in
    catheto (in *om. B*) *BF* scilicet in catheto
    predicta *A* predicte catheti ergo in ca-
    theto (ergo in catheto *mg. hab.*) *D* / in
    om. H / eodem...apparet: apparet eo-
    dem modo *A* eodem modo apparent *F*
    / *post* proprio *hab. B* et
225 quare: quia *B* queritur *H* / rectus *A* /
    ibi apparere: apparentia ibi *F*
225–26 ratio auctoris *tr. V*
226 5: quinto *F* 2 *H* / 2: 5 *A* secundo *F*
227 iltitudines *B*
228 hoc[1]: hec *F* / *post* ex *add. F* 20ª huius
    sive / hoc[2] *om. H* / quia *VWH* quod
    BAFD
229 quantum: quam *D*
230 cadit *FD* / cathetas *H* / C et *obs. A* /
    et...CEF *om. B*
232 CEG: CGEG *A* / et[1] *om. D* / et EFG
    om. H / quia: quod *F* / EG: GC *F* GE
    BD / GC: GE *F*
233 GE: GC *A* EG *F* / angulus: angulis *B* /
    CGE: EGC *F* / equalis est *tr. F* equalis

the eye of the observer. Rays *KA* and *CB* fall from the visible object and are reflected to the eye along rays *AD* and *BD*. Consequently *KA* appears to be the [direct] continuation of *AD*, and *CB* of *BD*; it follows that *KA* and *CB* seem to be directed behind the mirror under the same angles at which they are reflected because vertical angles are equal, and *DA* falls to *E* and *DB* to *F*. Furthermore, the object appears on the aforementioned perpendicular, i.e., the cathetus, exactly as in its true location. I say "in plane mirrors" because the appearance [of images] is more faithful there [than in curved mirrors]. And this is the explanation of the Author in Book 5, Chapter 2.[32]

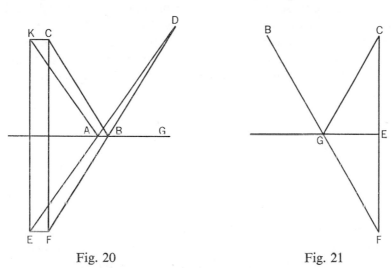

Fig. 20   Fig. 21

[*Proposition*] *21. Altitudes appear inverted in mirrors placed beneath them.*[33]

This is evident from the previous proposition; nevertheless it is relevant [here], since in plane mirrors the visible object appears to extend as far below the mirror as it actually projects above. This is demonstrated as follows. Let the cathetus *CEF* [Fig. 21] fall from the visible point *C*, let *BGF* be the ray under which *C* is seen, and let *CG* be the ray falling from the visible object. It is certain, then, that sides *EG* and *GC* are equal to sides *GE* and *GF* in triangles *CEG* and *FEG*, as the previous proposition shows, and that angle *CGE* is equal to angle *EGF* because vertical angles are equal and angles of incidence are equal to angles of reflection. Therefore base *CE* is equal to base *EF*; consequently the object appears as far beyond or below the mirror as it actually is above. The same thing would occur if the eye should look at itself, even though the ray would [then] be incident perpendicularly, because (as has been said)[34] the

---

V | EGF *obs. A* GF *B*   refex / equalis est *tr. F*
234–35 equales² sunt *tr. AF* equalis sunt *D*   236 quantum: quam *AF* | *post* supra *add.*
235 anguli *H* | *ante* reflexionis *scr. et del. H*   *F* se

oriatur, quoniam ut dictum est radius ipse comprehenditur. Amplius perpendicularis radius non est secundum esse naturale sed ymaginarium.
240   Declinat ergo secundum veritatem et procedit ita demonstratio ut supra.
In aliis tamen speculis aliter est ut patebit infra.

[*Propositio*] *22ª. In speculis planis facialiter obiectis facies apparere preposteratas et sinistra dextris permutatim opposita.*

Huius propositionis prima pars patet ex premissa, ex eodem enim se-
245   quitur ut superius appareat inferius, ex quo sequitur ut anterius appareat
posterius. Amplius secunda pars sequitur quoniam in speculo eadem res
apparet sibi opposita, res autem opposite habent dextra sinistris opposita
permutatim. Quare autem res opposita appareat ex hoc est quia pars radii
movens oculum dirigitur in oppositum, et propter hoc totus radius velud
250   in partem illam quasi porrectus accipitur, et per consequens res in extremo
eius videtur.

[*Propositio*] *23ª. In speculis planis unam solam ymaginem apparere.*

Sit enim res visa *A* in speculo *BEG* [Fig. 22], et sit oculus *F*, sitque
visio per radium incidentem *AE* et radium reflexum *EF*. Dico quod punc-
255   tus *A* non potest reflecti super punctum *F* ab alio puncto speculi quam
ab *E*, quod si potest detur punctus in quem cadat radius *AC*. Igitur reflexio erit ad equalem angulum; cum igitur angulus incidentie *C* sit maior
angulo incidentie *E*, quia est extrinsecus ad angulum *E* in triangulo *AEC*,
erit angulus reflexionis ei coniunctus maior angulo reflexionis *E*. Ergo im-
260   possibile est concurrere radios *CK* et *EF* super punctum unum ex parte

238 quoniam: quando *B* / ipse *om. F*
239 esse naturale: essentiale *A*
240 ergo *om. H* / ita *om. F* / *post* supra *add.*
    F ostensum est
242–43 preposteratas *VBWD* preposteras *F*
    prepostaras *A* prepostatas *H*
243 oppositio *B*
244 huiusmodi *H* / enim *om. B*
247 opposita: opponi *VH* / autem: enim *A*
248 quare: queritur *H* / quia: quod *FD*
249 diregatur *H*
250 quasi: qua *B*
250–51 in² …eius: eius quasi extremo *A* in
    extremo eius esse *F* in extremo esse eius
    D

251 videbitur *B*
253 A *om. H* / BEG: BGE *VH* BCG *A*
254 et: vel *A*
255 F: S *H*
256 E: C *H* / quod: quia *VH* / potest: prout
    H / *ante* punctus *scr. et del. H* p
256–57 reflexus *A*
257 *post* erit *add. V* G
258 incidentie *om. D* / extrinsecus *in alia*
    manu alt. V ad intrinsecus
259 reflexionis: reflexus *B*
259–60 impossibile: possibile *F*
260 CK: CF *D* / punctum unum *tr. F* punc-
    tum unde *H* / *post* parte *scr. et del. V* ex
    parte

ray itself is perceived. Moreover the ray is not [exactly] perpendicular in its natural state of being but only in the imagination. Therefore in truth it inclines, and the demonstration proceeds as above. The case is different for other [than plane] mirrors, however, as will be evident below.[35]

[*Proposition*] 22. *In plane mirrors directly opposite, figures appear turned around, and right appears opposite left and vice versa.*[36]

The first part of this proposition is evident from the foregoing; for it follows that the higher appears lower, from which it follows that the front appears at the rear. Furthermore, the second part follows because an object appears opposite itself in a mirror, and the object and image have right opposite left and vice versa. But the reason why the image should, on this account, appear opposite is that the part of the ray acting on the eye is directed to the opposite side, and therefore the entire ray is received as though extended in that direction. Consequently the object appears at its extremity.

[*Proposition*] 23. *Only one image [of a single object] appears in a plane mirror.* Let *A* [Fig. 22] be an object visible in mirror *BEG*, let *F* be the eye, and

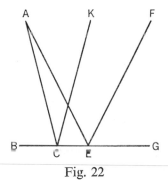

Fig. 22

let sight occur by means of incident ray *AE* and reflected ray *EF*. I say that point *A* cannot be reflected to point *F* by any point on the mirror other than *E*; if it could, let that point be the one onto which ray *AC* falls. Then since reflection [of this latter ray] will be at an angle equal [to its angle of incidence] and since the angle of incidence [at] *C* is greater than the angle of incidence [at] *E* because the former is the angle exterior to *E* in triangle *AEC*, the angle of reflection associated with *C* will be greater than the angle of reflection [at] *E*.[37] Therefore it is impossible for rays *CK* and *EF* to intersect at a point on the

K et *F*, angulus enim *BEF* cum angulo *GEF* valet duos rectos; ergo angulus *BEF* cum angulo *GCK*, qui est maior angulo *GEF*, valet plus quam duos rectos. Ergo ex alia parte concurrent linee *FE* et *KC* et non ex ista, per quartam petitionem primi Euclidis. Amplius si alius est punctus reflexionis

265 quam *E*, non in longitudine speculi sicut ponitur sed in latitudine, ergo erit ducere perpendicularem ab oculo equidistantem perpendiculari erigibili ab alio puncto, et ita ab uno puncto plures erunt perpendiculares ducibiles, quod est impossibile. Et currit demonstratio de reflexione respectu unius oculi.

270   [*Propositio*] *24ᵃ*. *In speculo fracto mutato situ partium diversas ymagines apparere.*

Hoc patet per experimentum, quod si partes speculi fracti ad eundem situm coaptentur ad quem ante fractionem non plures apparebunt ymagines in fracto quam non fracto. Plurificatio enim apparitionum non est

275 propter fractionem sed propter situs partium mutationem, in speculo enim concavo integro plures apparent ymagines ut infra patebit. Sed quia, ut docuit 12 et 15 propositio, a qualibet parte speculi fit reflexio sed in partes diversas ex mutatione situs partium fractarum, fieri potest ut sit reflexio ad eandem partem et per consequens simul diversas ymagines apparere et

280 non plures sed unam pretendere. Amplius ex consimili causa accidit quando speculum ponitur in aqua ex eodem luminoso plures apparere ymagines. Fit enim reflexio a superficie aque. Cum lumen radiosum intrat in aque profundum necesse est ergo ut occurrente speculo inde reflectatur, et iuxta diversitatem situs et superficiei speculi necesse est aliud eiusdem

285 luminosi ydolum apparere. Et sic credo cum sole non stellam aliquam

261 K et *om*. D / *post* F *in alia manu add*. A cum / angulus enim *tr*. A (*post* enim *scr. et del*. enim) / cum angulo: cum E *in alia manu* A / GEF *om*. A / *post* rectos *in alia manu mg. add*. A et angulus ?KEC rem...(*verba oblita*) plus

261–62 duos...valet *om*. F / ergo...rectos *om*. A

261–64 angulus¹....Euclidis *om*. D

262–63 plus....concurrent *om*. H

263 linee: plane H / *ante* FE *add*. B et / istam B / per *corr*. A *ex* parte

265 E: ED F / *post* non *add*. A ergo / longitudinem D / *post* latitudine *add*. A ergo esset ducere perpendicularem ab oculo equidistantem perpendiculari erigibili sicut ?positio sed in latitudine (*scr. et del*. sed in latitudine)

266–67 *post* erigibili *in alia manu mg. hab*. A in ?latitudine

267 *post* puncto² *add*. F et ita ab uno / erunt *om*. A / perpendiculares *om*. D

268 respectu *om*. F

269 oculi *WFD; obs*. A circuli *VBHL*

273 situm: locum F / *post* situm *add*. H caput / *post* quem *add*. FD erant / ante: an H

274 *post* quam *add*. AD in / apparitionum: fractionum F

275 situ B / enim *om*. V

276 sed: debet H

276–77 ut²...propositio {*om*. D}

277 12: 13ᵃ BF / et 15 propositio: et 12 propositio H propositio et 15 (15ᵃ B) BA propositio huius et 14ᵃ F

277–78 sed...diversas: cum igitur diversa-

side of the mirror toward K and F, for angle BEF and angle GEF have a sum equal to two right angles; therefore angle BEF and angle GCK (which is larger than angle GEF) have a sum larger than two right angles. Consequently lines FE and KC intersect beyond the mirror and not on the near side, by the fourth postulate of the first book of Euclid.[38] Furthermore, if the point of reflection is other than E, [by virtue of a shift of the point] not lengthwise (as assumed) but in breadth,[39] it would be possible to drop a perpendicular from the eye [to this new point of reflection] parallel to the perpendicular erected at the other point; thus there would be more than one perpendicular leading from a single point [to a plane surface], which is impossible. And this demonstration concerning reflection holds for one eye.[40]

[*Proposition*] *24. When the parts of a broken mirror have been shifted from their positions, several images appear.*[41]

Experience makes this evident, because if the parts of a broken mirror are fitted together in the same positions they occupied before breaking, the images will be no more numerous in the broken than in an unbroken mirror. Indeed multiplication of images is not the result of breaking but of alteration of the positions of the parts, for several images appear in an unbroken concave mirror, as will be evident below.[42] But since, as Propositions 12 and 15 have taught, reflection occurs at every point of a mirror and, [if the mirror is broken,] in various directions through alteration of the positions of the broken parts, it is possible for the reflected rays to converge at the same place so that the various images appear simultaneously, manifesting not several things but one. Furthermore, it is for a similar reason that several images of one luminous body appear when a mirror is placed in water, for reflection occurs at the surface of the water, [and] since light rays proceed into the depth of the water, they must [also] be reflected when they encounter the mirror; because of the diversity of the position and surface of the mirror [relative to the water surface] another image of the same luminous body must appear. Therefore I do not believe, as it seems

rum partium F
278 partium fracturam: per fracturam F
279 et per consequens: sequitur F
280 sed...pretendere: pretendere sed unam solam F
280–81 quando: quod in D
281 speculum *om.* H | aqua: ea qua B
282 fit: sit B | intret D | in *om.* F
283 ut *om.* F
284 *ante* necesse *scr. et del.* H i | est *om.* D

285 *post* apparere *add.* A sicut multis videtur | sic *om.* A | *post* cum *add.* F predicto experimento speculi positi in aqua cum | non: in D | *ante* stellam *add.* D predicto experimento speculi ita positi in aque ut
285–86 et...apparere *in alia manu mg. hab.* V | aliquam apparere *tr.* F aliam apparere A

apparere, sicut multis videtur et mihi aliquando eronee videbatur, sed ipsi soli ex diversitate superficierum aque et speculi diversa ydola generari. Ydola tamen hoc modo plura non habet nisi valde luminosum, quia lumen aquam ingrediens debile est et reflexum iterum a speculo debilius, 290 ut vix possit nisi sit fortissimum originaliter impressionem sensibilem generare.

[*Propositio*] *25ᵃ. In speculo plano duobus oculis unam apparere ymaginem.*

Cuius ratio est quoniam licet a diversis punctis fiat reflexio ad utrum-295 que oculum, tamen superficies reflexionis secant se in catheto, et terminatur aspectus utriusque oculi ad idem, sicut patet aptando demonstrationem 20 propositionis utrique oculo.

[*Propositio*] *26ᵃ. In omni superficie reflexionis quatuor precipue puncta contineri, et quod extra illam est minime videri.*

300 Hii quatuor puncti sunt centrum visus, punctus apprehensus, terminus axis, id est perpendicularis ducte a centro visus in speculum, et punctus reflexionis. Nec videtur quod extra istam superficiem est, sicut patet ex 23 propositione.

[*Propositio*] *27ᵃ. In speculis planis invenire punctum reflexionis.*

305 Sit enim *A* [Fig. 23] punctus visus, *B* centrum visus, speculum *DGH*, et ducatur cathetus *AH* et producatur ultra speculum quantum est *A* super speculum, usque in *Z*, et ducatur recta *BZ* per punctum speculi *G*. Dico quod *G* est punctus reflexionis. Ducatur enim radius *AG*; angulus enim

286 videtur *om. A* / et: ut *D* / *ante* eronee *add. F* licet
287 *ante* generari *scr. et del. F* ?generaliter
287–88 generari ydola *om. H*
288 plura: planeta *B* / nisi: non *H* / *ante* valde *scr. et del. F* vade
289 debile: debilire *H* / est *in alia manu mg. hab. V* / *ante* reflexum *scr. et del. H* h / a...debilius: debilius a speculo *A* de speculo debilius *H*
290 *post* impressionem *scr. et del. D* secundum debilem *et add. H* sensibili ?g (*scr. et del.* g) / sensibilem *mg. hab. D*
292 in *om. B*
294 quoniam: quia *F* / a diversis: adversis *D* adversas *H*
295 *ante* secant *scr. et del. H* s

295–96 terminantur *D*
297 20: tertie *F* xxi *D* / *ante* utrique *add. F* vel 20ᵐᵉ huius / oculo: ?conclusionem *B*
298 reflexionis *in alia manu mg. hab. D*
299 illa *BAD*
300 hii: hec *F* / quatuor puncti *tr. VH* / terminus *om. A*
302 istam: ipsam *F* / *ante* sicut *add. B* situm / 23: 23ᵃ *BA* 14ᵃ vel 23ᵃ *F* 24 *D*
303 *post* propositione *add. F* huius
304 *ante* punctum *scr. et del. H* p
306 A: id est *H*
306–7 super speculum *om. F*
307 *post* recta *add. F* *BF* linea
308 *post* radius *add. F* vel linea recta AH usque ad punctum G erit / AG *om. F* / angulus enim *tr. F* angulus *A*

to many and as it has sometimes erroneously seemed to me, that a star appears along with the sun; rather, separate images of the sun are produced because of the difference [in position] between the surface of the water and that of the mirror. However, only a very strong light produces several images in this way, since light is weakened by entering the water and becomes still weaker after reflection from the mirror; consequently it can scarcely generate a sensible impression unless it was originally very strong.

[*Proposition*] *25. The image seen in a plane mirror by two eyes is single.*[43]

The explanation of this is that, although the points at which reflection [from one object] takes place are different for each eye, nevertheless the planes of reflection[44] intersect in the cathetus, and the sight of both eyes is terminated at the same thing, as can be seen by applying the demonstration of Proposition 20 to each eye.

[*Proposition*] *26. There are four principal points in every plane of reflection, and what is outside that plane cannot be seen.*[45]

These four points are the center of the eye, the point perceived, the end of the axis (i.e., of the perpendicular [to all the tunics of the eye] dropped from the center of the eye to the mirror),[46] and the point of reflection. And what is outside that surface is not seen, as is evident from Proposition 23.

[*Proposition*] *27. To find the point of reflection in a plane mirror.*[47]

Let *A* [Fig. 23] be the visible point, *B* the center of the eye, and *DGH* the mirror. Let cathetus *AH* be drawn and extended to *Z*, as far behind the mirror as *A* is in front of it, and let straight line *BZ* be drawn through point *G* of the mirror. I say that *G* is the point of reflection. Thus draw ray *AG*; now angle

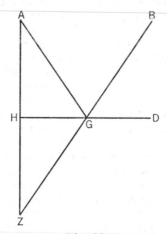

Fig. 23

ZGH equalis est angulo *DGB* quia ei contra positus. Item etiam equalis
310 est angulo *HGA* quia equales sunt trianguli *HZG HGA*, ut supra patet.
Ergo equales sunt anguli *HGA* et *DGB*; ergo a puncto *G* est reflexio et
non ab alio. Contingit tamen unum apparere duo in speculo plano propter
elongationem visibilis ab axe, sicut etiam in visibili directo supra ostensum
est accidere.

315   [*Propositio*] *28ᵃ*. *In speculis planis figure et quantitatis veritatem apparere.*

Sit enim speculum planum *FLR* [Fig. 24] cui superemineat longitudo
ZH, et ducantur radii *ZL* et *HR* reflexi ad oculum *E*, ducantur et catheti
a puncto *Z* et *H*, *ZS* et *HK*. Quoniam igitur catheti equidistantes sunt erit
320 ymago in terminis cathetorum eiusdem quantitatis cuius *ZH*. Ergo quantitas eadem apparet que directe. Figura etiam eadem quoniam quelibet
pars tantum apparet sub speculo quantum est supra speculum, ut ex prehabitis patet. Necesse est igitur partes invicem eundem ordinem retinere
quem secundum veritatem habent. Contingit tamen rem in speculis planis
325 apparere minorem quam sit ex eisdem causis ex quibus in visu directo,
scilicet ex distantia. Hoc igitur verum est quod minimus error accidit in
hiis speculis, in situ tantum et in hiis que sunt omni speculo communia,
sicut supra patet in 3ᵃ propositione huius partis et 4 et aliis non nullis.

309 est *om. F* / contra positus: oppositus *F*
    contraponitur *D* / *post* contra *in alia*
    manu mg. add. V est / *post* positus *in*
    alia manu add. A est / etiam *om. F*
310 est angulo *om. F* / HGA¹: GHA *F* HAG
    D BGA *H* / trianguli: anguli *B* / *ante*
    HGA² *add. B* et
311 et DGB *om. H* / ergo a puncto *om. A* /
    G: BG *H* / est reflexio: igitur esse ?re-
    flexionis *A*
311–13 et²....etiam *om. A*
312 contingit: ut *H*
313 *ante* sicut *scr. et del. D* sicut / visibili:
    invisibili *B* / *ante* supra *add. F* ut
314 accidere: accidit 79 prime partis *F*
317 sit: dicunt *H* / enim *om. B* / planum
    FLR cui *om. A* / FLR *VBW* FLK *F*
    FLX *H* FH *D* / superemineat *F*
318 et¹ *om. F* / ducantur¹: ducatur *H* / *post*
    ZL *scr. et del. A* ZHZG / HR *VW*; *om.*
    A HK *F* HI *BHD* / E *om. A* / ducantur²
    om. F / *post* catheti *scr. et del. D* et

318–19 HR...et² *om. A*
319 punctis *F* / Z et H *om. F* / ZS: et ZF *B*
    ZL *F* / HK: KH *B*
320 *post* terminis *add. A* et / *post* cuius *add.*
    BF est / ZH: Z et H *F*
321 *ante* etiam *add. D* est
321–22 que....apparet *om. H*
322 sub speculo *om. F*
322–23 ex prehabitis: prehabitum *F*
323 patet: est *F* / *post* eundem *scr. et del. A*
    speculum / *post* ordinem *scr. et del. H* or
323–24 ordinem....rem *om. A*
324 tamen: tantum *H* / rem...planis: in spe-
    culis planis rem *BF*
325 ex quibus *om. B* / *ante* in *add. F* fit
326 est *om. A* / quod: quoniam *B*
327 *post* speculis (*in alia manu mg. V*) *add.*
    VF scilicet / hiis² *om. A* / omnium *A*
328 supra patet *rep. A* / patuit *V* / 3ᵃ: 13ᵃ *F*
    / propositione...partis *om. F* / partis *om.*
    A / 4 *corr. ex* 4ᵃ *D* 41 *VAH* 14 *B* 14ᵃ *F*

ZGH and angle *DGB* are equal because they are [vertically] opposite each other. Likewise angles *ZGH* and *HGA* are equal because triangles *HZG* and *HGA* are equal, as was shown above.[48] Consequently angles *HGA* and *DGB* are equal, and reflection takes place at point *G* and no other. Nevertheless one object can appear as two in a plane mirror because of the elongation of the visible object from the axis, as was shown above to happen with an object visible directly.[49]

[*Proposition*] 28. *In plane mirrors, the true shapes and sizes [of objects] appear.*[50]

Let *FLR* [Fig. 24] be a plane mirror, above which is situated length *ZH*; draw rays *ZL* and *HR* reflected to the eye *E*, and draw perpendiculars *ZS* and *HK* from points *Z* and *H*. Since the perpendiculars are parallel, the image at

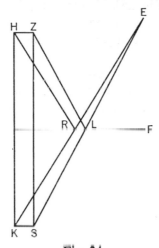

Fig. 24

their [lower] extremities will be of the same size as *ZH*. Thus the size appears the same as [when seen] directly. The shape also [appears] the same because any part appears as far below the mirror as it is above the mirror, as was shown previously.[51] Therefore the parts [of an object] must retain the same relative order as they have in reality. Nevertheless, in plane mirrors a body appears smaller than its true size for the same reason as [that which operates] in direct vision, namely, distance.[52] It is true, therefore, that a slight error does occur in plane mirrors, but merely in position and in those things that are common to all mirrors, as shown above in Propositions 3 and 4 of this part and in others.

[*Propositio*] *29ª. In speculis spericis extra politis omnes accidunt errores*
330 *qui in planis.*

Communes quidem sunt cause errandi, tum quia lux debilitatur ex
reflexione, tum quia res apparet extra locum suum et sibi ipsi opposita
ut supra visum est. Accidunt etiam plures errores quam in planis ut patebit.

[*Propositio*] *30ª. In speculis spericis exterioribus apparet ymago in con-*
335 *cursu radii cum catheto, id est linea ducta in centrum spere.*

Hoc probari potest per experimentum et ex causis naturalibus, ut supra
patet in speculis planis. In hoc tamen est diversitas, quia in planis ut supra
visum est res semper apparet sub speculo quantum est supra; hic autem
ymago aliquando apparet in ipsa speculi superficie, aliquando intra, ali-
340 quando extra. Verbi gratia sit punctus visus *E*, oculus *G*, punctus reflexionis
N, centrum spere *D* [Fig. 25]. Planum est quia locus ymaginis est *K*. Quod
si ponatur visibile in *B* apparebit ymago in *O*. Quod si adhuc ponatur
visibile propinquius spere apparebit visibile extra speram, ut patebit pertractanti.

345 Punctum autem reflexionis est facile invenire in hiis maxime cum equaliter distant oculus et res visa a spera. Alias in inveniendo puncto est
maior prolixitas quam difficultas vel utilitas, sicut patet inspicienti capitu-

331 quidem: enim *F*
332 tum *om. H* / *post* res *add. H* tamen / ipsi
om. B
333 ut[1] *om. D* / *post* errores *add. F* in spericis / quam in planis *om. B* / ut patebit
om. D
335 *ante* linea *add. B* in / spere *om. B*
336 et *om. B*
336–37 naturalibus...speculis *om. A*
337 quia: quod *D*
338 semper: tantum *B* / *post* speculo *add. F*
tantum / hic *obs. A*
339 ymago aliquando *tr. F* / intra: in recta *B*

340 sit: ut *H*
341 N: M *A* / quia: quod *BF* / K: H *D* /
quod: ?or *H*
342 *ante* in[1] *add. F* extra speram / B: H *F* /
O: E *B* / *post* adhuc *scr. et del. H* ?patet
/ *post* ponatur *add. B* adhuc
343 *post* visibile[1] *add. F* in F / propinquens
H / patet *BF*
343–44 pertractanti *corr. A ex* pertanctanti
345 facile *WFD* faciliter *VBAH*
346 oculo *H* / a *om. H* / in *om. BAFH* /
punctum *AF*

[*Proposition*] *29. All errors that occur in plane mirrors occur [also] in convex spherical mirrors.*[53]

Indeed the causes of error are common [to both kinds of mirrors]: sometimes that light is weakened by reflection and sometimes that the object appears outside its true place and opposite itself, as was seen above.[54] But more errors occur [in convex spherical mirrors] than in plane mirrors, as will be evident [below].[55]

[*Proposition*] *30. In convex spherical mirrors the image appears at the intersection of the ray and the cathetus, i.e., the line dropped [from the object] to the center of the sphere.*[56]

This can be proved by experience and [can be shown to result] from natural causes, as it was for plane mirrors above.[57] Nevertheless plane mirrors and convex spherical mirrors differ in that an object always appears as far below a plane mirror as it actually is above it, whereas in a convex spherical mirror the image appears sometimes on the surface of the mirror, sometimes inside the mirror, and sometimes outside it.[58] For example, let *E* [Fig. 25] be the visible point, *G* the eye, *N* the point of reflection, and *D* the center of the sphere. It is

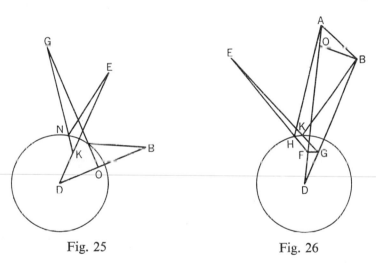

Fig. 25   Fig. 26

clear that the image is located at *K*. However if the visible object should be placed at *B*, the image would appear at *O*; if the visible object should be placed still closer to the sphere, the image would appear outside the sphere, as will be evident by careful investigation.[59]

The point of reflection is easy to find in these [mirrors] when the eye and the visible object are at exactly equal distances from the sphere.[60] Otherwise the length [of time required] to find the point is greater than the difficulty or utility, as can be seen by examining the section [in Alhazen's *Perspectiva*] on images.[61]

lum de ymagine. Ex hoc etiam apparet quod ymago in hiis speculis est propinquior speculo quam res visa, quod contra est in planis ut supra
350   patuit.

[*Propositio*] *31ᵃ. In speculis spericis exterioribus partes rei sicut sunt ordinatas apparere.*

Verbi gratia sit res visa *AB*, centrum speculi *D*, oculus *E* [Fig. 26]. Planum est quod radius *EH* concurrit cum perpendiculari in puncto *F* et
355   radius *EK* in puncto *G*. Erit ergo ymago *GF* minor quidem re visa; tamen partes inconfuse apparent et ordinate. Quod si res visa ponatur in eodem situ cum dyametro sicut *OB*, idem iudicium apparebit, sicut patet ductis lineis ad *OB* sicut *AB*.

[*Propositio*] *32ᵃ. In speculis spericis recta in maiori parte curva apparere.*
360   Hoc intellige de curvitate non ad centrum speculi inflexa sed a speculo aversa. Verbi gratia sit res visa *ABC* [Fig. 27], oculus *D*, qui non sit in

348–49 est propinquior *tr. F*
349 *ante* propinquior *scr. et del. A* prolixior / contra: econtra *B* / planis: spericis *B*
354 est *om. H* / EH: est *H* / cum *in alia manu hab. A* / F *AWF* EF *VBHD*
355 radius *om. F* / EK: CK *B* EH *D* / quidem *om. A*
356 si *om. A*

357 sicut¹ *om. A* / OB: AB *B* DB *A*
358 OB: DB *A* / *ante* AB *add. F* ad
359 *post* recta *add. H* et
360 hoc...curvitate *om. F* / inflexi *D* / sed a speculo *om. A*
361 *ante* aversa *add. H* a / aversa: eversa *VA* / verbi gratia *om. F*

From that section also it is apparent that the image in convex spherical mirrors is nearer the mirror than is the visible object, [a relationship] which is in contrast to [that for] plane mirrors as shown above.[62]

[*Proposition*] *31. In convex spherical mirrors the parts of an object appear ordered as they actually are.*[63]

For example, let the visible object be *AB* [Fig. 26], the center of the mirror *D*, and the eye *E*. It is clear that ray *EH* intersects the perpendicular [from *A*] at point *F* and that ray *EK* [intersects the perpendicular from *B*] at point *G*. Therefore the image *GF* will indeed be smaller than the visible object; nevertheless, the parts [of the object] appear distinct and in order.[64] But if the visible object were placed in the same location, with its diameter [aligned] like *OB*, the same judgment would hold, as is evident because the lines have been drawn to *OB* exactly as to *AB*.[65]

[*Proposition*] *32. Straight things usually appear curved in convex spherical mirrors.*[66]

This curving is to be understood not as a bending in toward the center of the mirror but as a turning away from the mirror.[67] For example, let *ABC* [Fig. 27] be the visible object and *D* the eye, which is not in the same plane as

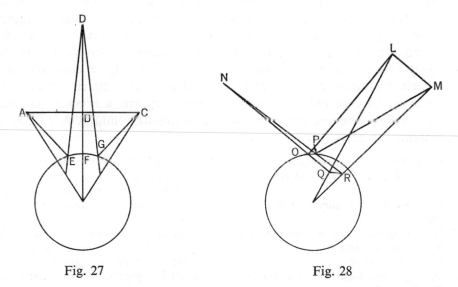

Fig. 27   Fig. 28

Fig. 27. The manuscripts err unanimously in drawing this figure, confusing incident rays *AE* and *CG* with the perpendiculars to the surface of the mirror. I have not drawn the image of *ABC* or indicated the location of the image of point *B*, since these do not appear in the manuscripts, and it is not certain that Pecham was capable of establishing their exact location.

eadem superficie cum re visa, et reflectatur ad oculum per *DE, DF, DG.*
Apparet igitur res curva, quod ad sensum demonstrari non potest in plano
sed in solida figura faciliter apparebit experimentatori. Cuius ratio est
365 quoniam in omnibus speculis figura ymaginis sequitur modum superficiei
reverberantis, fit enim a superficie reflexio secundum modum superficiei.
Sed quia res visa apparet, oportet ut et curvitas rei non appareat in reflexione ad speculum sed in aversione a speculo. Et hoc est intelligendum
quando visus non est in eadem superficie cum linea visa et centro spere.
370 Ex causa etiam simili apparet quod in superficiebus irregularibus sicut in
speculis quibusdam valliculosis facies apparent monstruose. In predictis
tamen speculis aliquando recta apparent recta, si videlicet linea visa et
centrum spere sunt in eadem superficie cum ipso visu. Verbi gratia sit res
visa *LM* [Fig. 28], oculus *N*, puncta reflexionis *O P*; planum est quod
375 ydolum erit linea recta *QR.*

[*Propositio*] *33ª. In speculis spericis ymagines in maiori parte minores
esse rebus visis.*

Huius ratio a duobus sumitur. Primo quoniam ut supra visum est concursus radiorum cum catheto propinquior est oculo quam in planis. Radii
380 autem ab eodem puncto procedentes quanto magis protenduntur tanto
habent extrema magis distantia, et econtra quanto minus protenduntur
minus distant extrema. Ergo sicut demonstratum est in planis equalem
esse ymaginem rei vise, sequitur in spericis minorem esse. Secundo dico
quod a maiori superficie fit reflexio in planis quam in spericis, sicut probat
385 auctor libri *De speculis.* Cuius causa est quoniam radii a convexis reflexi
magis disgregantur quam a planis propter declinationem circuli a quo est
reflexio. Ut ergo radii ad visum concurrant oportet a breviori superficie
fieri reflexionem, et per consequens rem apparere minorem. Et hec est
intentio auctoris libri *De speculis.*

362 *post* eadem *scr. et del. V* parte / *post* ad
    scr. et del. D *?*de / DG *in alia manu corr.*
    V ex AG
363 igitur *om.* H / *ante* curva *scr. et del.* A
    *?*curs
364 faciliter apparebit *tr.* B / apparet *F* /
    *?*experimentationem A
365 quoniam: quod D
366 reverberantis...superficiei *om.* AD / fit
    BFHL sit *VW*
367 sed *om.* F / visa: versa *VB* visa vel versa
    F / ut et *tr.* B ut F
368 in *om.* AD
369–373 spere....spere *om.* A
370 quod: quoniam D

371 villiculosis F / monstrouose H
372 aliquando recta *tr.* F / apparent recta
    corr. ex apparent non recta *VBWFHL*;
    om. D / videlicet: scilicet F / linea *om.*
    VH
373 in...superficie: superficie in eadem H /
    ipso visu: viso ipso B / sit: dit H
374 LM: locum H LE *?*quondam D / N:
    enim H / puncti D / *ante* quod *add.* B
    enim / *post* quod (*in alia manu mg. V*)
    add. VA enim
375 erit: esset H / QR *om.* B
378 huiusmodi H / *post* huius *add.* A ergo
379 est *om.* A / *post* oculo *add.* F in speculis
    spericis

the visible object [and the center of the mirror]; and let the object be reflected to the eye through [rays] *DE, DF*, and *DG*. Consequently the object appears curved, [a fact] which cannot be demonstrated to the mind in a plane but will easily appear to the investigator in a solid figure. The explanation of this is that, for all mirrors, the shape of the image follows the shape of the reflecting surface, for reflection takes place at the surface according to its shape. And since the visible object appears, it is necessary also that curvature of the object should appear not as a bending back toward the mirror but as a turning away from it; and this is applicable when the eye is not in the same plane as the visible line and the center of the sphere.[68] It is through action of the same cause that faces appear monstrous in irregular surfaces such as certain mirrors full of shallow depressions. Nevertheless in the aforesaid mirrors straight things sometimes appear straight,[69] namely, if the visible line and the center of the sphere are in the same plane as the eye. For example, let *LM* [Fig. 28] be the visible object, *N* the eye, and *O* and *P* the points of reflection; it is clear that the image will be straight line *QR*.

[*Proposition*] 33. *In convex spherical mirrors the images are usually smaller than the visible objects.*[70]

The explanation of this is twofold. First, as was seen above, the intersection of the rays with the perpendicular is closer to the eye than it is in plane mirrors.[71] However, as the length of rays proceeding from the same point is greater, so also is the separation between their ends; and conversely, as the rays are shorter, the separation between their ends is smaller. Therefore from the same demonstration that showed the image and visible object to be of equal size in plane mirrors, it follows that the image is smaller than the visible object in convex spherical mirrors. Second, I maintain that reflection occurs from a larger surface area in plane than in convex spherical mirrors, as the author of the book *De speculis* proves.[72] The reason for this is that rays reflected from convex surfaces are more widely dispersed than those reflected from plane surfaces because of the declination of the circle from which reflection occurs. Therefore, in order that the rays may impinge on the eye, reflection must take place from a smaller surface, and consequently the object appears smaller. This is the theory of the author of the book *De speculis*.

---

380 quanto: quando *H*
380–81 tanto...protenduntur *om. A*
381 habent...magis: magis habebunt extrema *F*
382 *ante* minus *add. F* tanto / distant: differant *H* / demonstratum est: demonstratur *A*
383 secundo: ?decundo *H*
387 reflexio *in alia manu mg. hab. V* circuli *H* / *ante* ut *scr. et del. V* circuli
388–91 minorem...apparere *om. A*
389 *ante* auctoris *scr. et del. D* et

390   Que intelligenda sunt in maiori parte quoniam in aliquo situ contingit
rem apparere in hiis speculis eiusdem quantitatis cuius est, in aliquo
maioris, sicut probatur in 6 *Perspective*, cum videlicet ymago non equidistat rei vise, cum etiam facit angulum acutum cum radio cuius casus est
propinquior centro, tunc enim potest ymago esse equalis vel maior. Et
395   hoc latuit auctorem libri *De speculis*. Propter siquidem situm obliquum
rei respectu speculi contingit unum radium respectu alterius breviari, ut
ex obliquo incessu possit ymago rem excedere vel ei equari.

[*Propositio*] *34ª. In speculis convexis quo minora sunt eo in eis minores
ymagines apparere.*
400   Cuius ratio plana est quoniam quanto spera minor tanto concursus
cum catheto centro propinquior, et locus ymaginis angustior quo brevior
ei semidyameter obviare dinoscitur.

[*Propositio*] *35ª. In speculis columpnaribus extra politis iidem accidunt
errores qui in planis et spericis.*
405   Hic est sermo de columpna rotunda que in longitudine convenit cum
planis, in rotunditate cum spericis, et ideo utrorumque errores participat.

[*Propositio*] *36ª. In speculis columpnaribus tripliciter fieri reflexionem.*
Potest enim fieri reflexio a longitudine columpne vel a transverso vel
a situ medio inter utrumque obliquo. Cum autem fit reflexio a longitudine
410   accidit sicut in planis, cum scilicet linea visa est equidistans linee longitu-
dinis columpne, et tunc est locus ymaginis concursus radii cum perpendiculari ducta super columpne longitudinem. Et tunc apparet res sicut in
planis, hoc excepto, quod quia reflexio fit a linea naturali oportet rem
curvam apparere, sicut supra de speculis convexis visum est. Quod si fiat
415   reflexio a transverso columpne, ut fiat reflexio a linea circulari equidistanti
basibus columpne, erit locus ymaginis superficiem circuli reflexionis; et

390 sunt: est *F* / contingit: convenit *H*
391 *ante* in² *add. F* et
392 in *om. B* / 6ª *A* / non *om. F*
392–93 equidistet *A*
393 etiam: que *H*
394 ymago esse *tr. F*
395 latet *A* / *ante* siquidem *add. BF* hoc /
    situm: sicut *BAH*
396 *post* speculi *add. F* situm / contingit:
    communiter *A* convenit *H* / *post* alterius
    scr. et del. D a / ut: igitur *A*
397 *post* obliquo *add. B* rei in / incessu: re-
    cessu *B* in sensu *H* / *ante* excedere *scr.*

et del. H e
398 que *A*
400 plana est *tr. FD*
401 *ante* cum *add. F* radii / cum: in *D* / cen-
    tro *om. V*
402 ei *rep. F* / semidyameter: se in dyametro
    B
403 iidem: hiidem *D*
404 *ante* spericis *scr. et del. H* se
405 longitudinem *H* / convenit *om. A*
407 reflexionem *VWHL* reflexiones *BAFD*
409 obliqui *H* obiluquo *D* / fit *om. A* sit *H*
410 *ante* accidit *add. B* columpne / *ante* linea

These things are to be understood as the more usual case, since in convex spherical mirrors there are positions in which the object appears according to its true size and other positions in which it appears larger, as is proved in Book 6 of the *Perspectiva*,[73] namely, when the image is not parallel to the visible object and forms an acute angle with a ray falling very close to the center [of the mirror]; for then the image can be equal to or larger than [the object]. This was unknown to the author of the book *De speculis*. Indeed, since the object is oriented obliquely with respect to the mirror, one ray is shorter than the other; thus, because of the oblique approach [of its rays], the image can be equal to or larger than the object.[74]

[*Proposition*] *34. The smaller a convex [spherical] mirror is, the smaller is the image that appears in it.*

The reason for this is clear, since, as a sphere becomes smaller, the intersection [of a ray] with the perpendicular is closer to the center, and the place occupied by the image is narrower because it is seen to be met by a shorter radius.

[*Proposition*] *35. The same errors occur in convex columnar mirrors as in plane and spherical mirrors.*[75]

This discussion concerns round columns, which conform to planes in longitude and to spheres in roundness; therefore they participate in the errors of both.

[*Proposition*] *36. There are three modes of reflection in [convex] columnar mirrors.*[76]

Reflection can occur from the longitude of the column, from a transverse section, or from an oblique section intermediate between the other two.[77] When reflection occurs from the longitude as in plane mirrors, i.e., when the visible line is parallel to the axis of the column, the image is located at the intersection of the ray with the perpendicular dropped [from the object] to the axis of the column; and the object appears exactly as in plane mirrors, with the exception that, since reflection occurs from a natural line, the object must appear curved, as was seen above in connection with convex [spherical] mirrors.[78] But if reflection takes place from a transverse section of the column, i.e., from a circular line parallel to the base of the column, the image is located in the plane of the circle of reflection;[79] and the appearance is somewhat similar to that in [convex]

scr. et del. A ?linea / linea: line (alt. ex linee) H / linee: line H
411 concursus radii tr. A
413 fit: sit H / naturaliter V

414 visum est tr. B
415 a linea: aliqua a (a in alia manu) A
416 erunt H / superficiem corr. ex centrum VBAFHD / ante circuli add. H enim

apparitio similatur quodammodo ei quod in spericis est predictum, ut
locus ymaginis aliquando appareat infra circulum, aliquando extra, aliquando in ipso circulo. Res tamen minor apparet quam in spericis. Cum
420   vero medio modo fit reflexio accidit etiam varie de quantitate in quantum
sectio columpne magis accedit ad latitudinem vel longitudinem columpne.
Et potest esse locus ymaginis similiter vel ultra vel citra speculum vel in
ipso speculo.

[*Propositio*] *37ᵃ. In pyramidalibus extra politis multiplicari reflexiones*
425   *sicut in columpnaribus.*
Hoc patet quia potest fieri reflexio a longitudine pyramidis vel a latitudine vel medio modo, et secundum hoc diversificantur apparitiones sicut
in columpnaribus, et predicto modo etiam diversificatur locus ymaginis et
figura rei apparentis. Hoc tamen differt quoniam in hiis res apparet pyra-
430   midata eadem ratione qua columpnaris in columpna. Unius rei tamen ab
uno puncto super unum locum fit reflexio sicut in columpnaribus et aliis
exterius politis.

[*Propositio*] *38ᵃ. In speculo pyramidali quo locus reflexionis est cono*
propinquior eo ymago minor.
435   Hoc patet ex hiis que supra habita sunt de speculis spericis convexis
propositione 34.

[*Propositio*] *39ᵃ. In speculis concavis spericis quoniam possibile est ra-*
dium perpendiculari non concurrere necesse est aliter quam in premissis
locum ymaginis apparere.
440   Verbi gratia esto speculum concavum *FPY* [Fig. 29] cuius centrum sit
D, et ducatur dyameter *DA*, et sit oculus *A*, ducaturque alia dyameter
istam orthogonaliter secans que sit *YF*, ducaturque *AE* equidistans, signen-
turque puncta in *YF* dyametro *M*, *T*, *K*, *Q*. Planum est igitur quod *AE*
non concurrit cum perpendiculari. *M* reflectitur a puncto *N* et concurrit
445   cum perpendiculari extra speculum in puncto *L*. *T* reflectitur ab *E* et non

417 similatur: assimilatur *AF* / quodammo-
    do ei *tr. F* / ei *obs. D* / quod: que *D* /
    in…est: est in spericis *D* / predictum
    om. D / ut: ubi *A*
418 appareat *om. A* / *post* extra *add. A* cir-
    culum
419 *post* ipso *scr. et del. A* et
420 *ante* medio *scr. et del. H* n / etiam varie
    tr. F varie *AD*
421 magis accedit *tr. A* magis accidit *D* / la-
    titudinem: altitudinem *H*

422 ymaginis similiter: magis situs *B* / vel¹
    om. B
426 *post* a¹ *scr. et del. H* r / longitudinem *H*
427 *ante* diversificantur *add. H* diversitatem
427–28 apparitiones…diversificatur *om. A*
428 in *om. D* / predicto modo *tr. BFD* /
    etiam *om. AF*
429–30 pyramita (*sic*) *B* pyramidato *H*
430 unius: cuius *D*
431 locum: punctum *F* / *ante* aliis *add. F* in
432 exterius: extra *BA*

spherical mirrors, as described above,[80] so that the image can be located within the circle, outside it, or on it. Nevertheless the object appears smaller than in [convex] spherical mirrors. Furthermore, when reflection occurs in the intermediate fashion, the size [of the image] varies as the section approaches more closely the latitude or longitude of the column; and again the image can be located outside, inside, or on [the surface of] the mirror.[81]

[Proposition] 37. Reflections are multiplied in convex pyramidal mirrors just as in columnar mirrors.[82]

This is evident, since reflection can occur from the longitude of the pyramid, from its latitude, or in an intermediate mode, and the images are correspondingly diverse, just as in columnar mirrors. The location and shape of the images vary in the same way.[83] However, pyramidal mirrors differ in that the object appears pyramidal in them for the same reason as that for which it appears columnar in a column. Nevertheless reflection of one object from one point to one place occurs as in columnar and other convex mirrors.

[Proposition] 38. In pyramidal mirrors the image becomes smaller as the place of reflection approaches the vertex.

This is apparent from what was said about convex spherical mirrors above in Proposition 34.

[Proposition] 39. Since it is possible for a ray not to intersect the perpendicular in concave spherical mirrors, the location of the image must be different from the foregoing.[84]

For example, let FPY [Fig. 29] be a concave mirror with its center at D. Draw diameter DA and let A be the eye. Draw another diameter YF intersecting the first one perpendicularly, draw AE parallel to it, and mark points M, T, K, and Q on diameter YF; it is clear, then, that AE does not intersect the perpendicular [YF].[85] M is reflected from point N, and [the extension of the ray incident on the eye] intersects the perpendicular outside the mirror at point L. T is reflected from E and does not intersect the perpendicular.[86] K is

433 speculis pyramidalibus A

434 ante ymago add. B est

435 post hoc add. H autem / post supra scr. et del. D hoc ?prima / habita mg. hab. D

436 34: 30ᵃ vel 24ᵃ huius F et 6 D / supra 34 hab. B 20

438 perpendiculari non concurrere: non concurrere perpendiculari B perpendicularem non concurrere F

441 ducaturque: ducatur B

443 MTKQ: in TKQ H / igitur om. A

444–45 M…perpendiculari VBAWL; om. FHD

445 post L scr. et del. A M et add. V et / T: G BA / ante reflectitur add. F et / reflectatur FHD / E corr. A ex ?EO / non scr. et del. A

concurrit cum perpendiculari. *K* reflectitur a puncto *C* et concurrit cum perpendiculari in puncto *S*. *Q* vero reflectitur a puncto *G* et concurrit in puncto *O*. Quod si sumatur in dyametro *DA* punctus *Z* et ipse reflecti poterit a puncto *E*, et non concurrit *AE* radius cum perpendiculari *ZD*
450 nisi in ipso oculo.

Igitur locus ymaginis puncti *M* est ultra speculum in *L*, locus ymaginis *K* retro oculum in *S*, locus ymaginis *Q* retro speculum in *O*, locus *Z* in ipso oculo, locus ymaginis *T* in ipso speculo. Quoniam enim *T* est divisibilis punctus, secundum superiorem sui partem haberet apparere ultra
455 speculum, secundum inferiorem vero infra. Quia autem forma una est necesse est ut appareat in medio loco, scilicet in ipso speculo in puncto *E*. In hiis autem diversitatibus apparitionum nusquam apprehenditur veritas ymaginis nisi cum eius locus fuerit ultra speculum aut inter visum et speculum. Unde que apparent in ipso oculo vel retro caput non apparent
460 cum certificatione rei visibilis, quoniam visus non est natus acquirere formas nisi facialiter obiectas.

[*Propositio*] *40ᵃ*. *Res existentes in centro speculi concavi non videntur.*

Reflexione videri non potest quoniam radii ab ea perpendiculariter cadunt super superficiem speculi. Redeunt ergo in se ipsos et ita ad nullum
465 punctum declinant extra centrum. Cum igitur oculus sit extra centrum non videbit id quod in centro est.

446 reflectatur *F* / *C om. B* / cum² *om. A*
446–48 *C....O om. D*
447 S (*in alia manu corr. A ex* B): C *B* / reflectatur *F*
448 Z *om. B* / *ante* E *scr. et del. A signum oblitum* /
449 concurrit: currit *B* / ZD nisi: Z dum *H*
451 puncti...ymaginis *om. D* / M: O *F* / speculum in: spatium M *B*
452 S *corr. ex* C *VAFHD* T *B* / Q *om. B* / Z: S *B*
453 *post* ipso *add. D* loco / *ante* locus *add. A* igitur / ymaginis *om. B* / *post* ymaginis *scr. et del. H* E / T¹: S *D* speculo: oculo *V* / enim *om. D* / T²: S *D* / *post* est *scr. et del. D* in
454 sui partem *tr. B* / *post* haberet *scr. et del. A* ultra
455 autem *obs. A* aut *D*

456 est *om. D* / ipso: medio *A* / E *VW*; *obs. A C BFHD*
457 numquam *A*
458 eius locus *tr. A* / ultra: intra *A* / inter: intra *B*
458–59 aut...speculum *om. A*
459 apparent¹: apparet *HD* / oculo: speculo *HD* / apparent²: appareant *D* / *post* apparent² *add. F* in ipso
461 nisi: natura *H* / facialiter obiectas *tr. FH*
462 existens *D* / concavum *D* / non *om. D* nunc *B* / videtur *D*
463 reflexionem *D* / quoniam: quod *B* / ab ea *om. A*
464 cadent *A*
465 declinat *A* / sit: fit *D*
466 id: illud *F* ad *A* / in...est: est in centro *V* intentus est *A*

reflected from point C and intersects the perpendicular at point S.[87] Q is reflected from point G and intersects [the perpendicular] at point O. However, if we consider point Z on diameter DA, it also can be reflected from point E, and ray AE intersects perpendicular ZD only in the eye itself.[88]

Therefore the image of point M is located beyond the mirror at L, the image of K behind the eye at S,[89] the image of Q behind the mirror at O,[90] [the image of] Z in the eye itself,[91] and the image of T in the mirror. Since T is a divisible point,[92] it should appear beyond the mirror according to its higher part, but within the mirror according to its lower part.[93] However, since

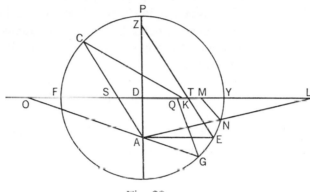

Fig. 29

form is one, it must appear in the intermediate place, namely, on the mirror itself at point E. Nevertheless, in these various appearances, the truth of the image is not perceived except when the image is located beyond the mirror or between the eye and the mirror.[94] Thus those images that appear in the eye itself or behind the head do not have their appearance certified as does an object [directly] visible, because it is not natural for sight to perceive forms unless they are opposite the face.

[*Proposition*] 40. *Objects located at the center of a concave mirror are not seen.*

[Such an object] cannot be seen by reflection, since its rays fall perpendicularly on the surface of the mirror. Consequently they return on themselves and so turn aside to no point outside the center; and since the eye is outside the center, it cannot see that which is in the center.

[*Propositio*] *41ᵃ*. *Oculus existens in centro speculi concavi sperici videt se tantum.*

Hoc sequitur ex premissa indirecte quoniam cum res extra centrum 470 posita radios habeat super superficiem speculi cadentes oblique. Sequitur etiam ut radii ad partem oppositam reflectantur et non in ipsum centrum, equales enim sunt anguli incidentie et reflexionis.

[*Propositio*] *42ᵃ*. *Oculus existens in semidyametro speculi concavi sperici nichil videt eorum que in illa semidyametro continentur.*

475 Sit enim dyameter *ABC* [Fig. 30], et sit oculus in parte dyametri *BC* in puncto *D*. Dico igitur quoniam impossibile est aliquem punctum linee *BC* redire in *D*. Quod si potest, cadat linea *CF*. Planum est quod reflectetur ad equalem angulum, et erit linea reflexa per consequens corda equalis portionis sicut est *EF*, quod esse non potest ex parte illa. Ergo necesse est 480 ut in partem aliam reflectatur.

[*Propositio*] *43ᵃ*. *Quilibet punctus dyametri speculi concavi qualibet producte potest esse locus ymaginis.*

Verbi gratia sit circulus *AMG* [Fig. 31], sitque dyameter *AG*, centrum sit *D*, sumaturque alia dyameter *ME*, sitque oculus *E*. Palam quoniam *L*

467–72 videt....reflexionis *om. A* (This is replaced by the text of Proposition 42, which I refer to below as *A'*.)
469 hec *F*
470 habeat: hanc *H* / super *om. H* supra *F*
471 in *om. D*
472 enim sunt *tr. F* sunt *D*
473 sperici *in alia manu hab. V*
474–80 nichil....reflectatur (This material appears twice in *A*. It erroneously replaces the text of Proposition 41, and it appears again in the lower margin of fol. 38r. I provide variant readings for both appearances, denoting the former as *A'* and the latter as *A*.)

474 semidyametro *VA'FHD* dyametro *BA*
475 dyametri: dyametro *A'*
476 igitur *in alia manu mg. hab. V* / quoniam *VBAA'H* quod *FD*
477 D: B *A'* / potest: punctus *A'* / CF *VBA* super F *F* EF *A'D* F *H* / quod² *om. B*
477–78 reflectitur *F*
479 *post* parte *add. A* E
480 parte *H*
481 qualibet: quantumlibet *F*
482 potest esse *tr. B*
483 *post* AG *add. D* et
483–84 AG...dyameter *om. B*
484 D: GD *H* DG *D* / sumatur *A* / *post* palam *add. F* est

[*Proposition*] *41. An eye located at the center of a concave spherical mirror sees only itself.*[95]

This follows indirectly from the foregoing, since rays from an object located outside the center fall obliquely onto the surface of the mirror. It follows that the rays are reflected to the opposite side and not into the center, for the angles of incidence and reflection are equal.

[*Proposition*] *42. An eye situated on the radius of a concave spherical mirror sees [by reflection] nothing situated on that radius.*[96]

Let *ABC* [Fig. 30] be the diameter, and let the eye be at point *D* on side *BC* of the diameter. I say that it is impossible for [a ray from] any point on line *BC* to return [by reflection] to *D*. But if it could, [let the point be *C* and] let [its ray] fall [onto the mirror] along line *CF*. It is clear that it will be reflected at an angle equal [to the angle of incidence], and consequently the reflected line will be a chord of equal length, such as *EF*, which cannot be on the same side [of the diameter as *D*]. Therefore it must be reflected to the other side.

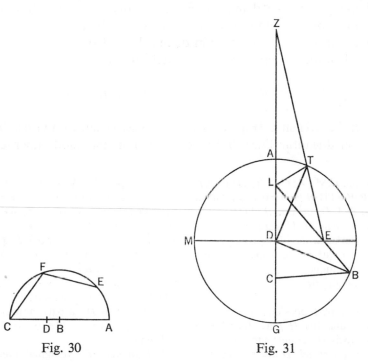

Fig. 30   Fig. 31

[*Proposition*] *43. The image can be located at any point on the diameter of a concave mirror, however far that diameter may be extended.*[97]

For example, let *AMG* [Fig. 31] be a circle, *AG* its diameter, and *D* its center. Let another diameter, *ME*, be taken, and let *E* be the eye. Clearly *L* is

485   videtur in *Z* si anguli *DTL* et *DTE* sunt equales. Similiter et punctus *C* reflectitur a *B* ad *E* et videtur in *L*. Et ita secundum diversam situationem rei visibilis potest videri in parte dyametri quantumcunque producte, dum tamen proportionaliter quantitati speculi.

     [*Propositio*] *44ª*. *Punctum visum in speculo concavo sperico a pluribus*
490   *locis speculi reflexum possibile est unicam habere ymaginem.*

     Quamvis enim a pluribus locis fiat reflexio simul, non tamen propter hoc necesse est diversas apparere ymagines, quoniam omnes radii visuales talis speculationis in eodem puncto concurrunt cum catheto; et hoc intelligitur centro visus et re visa existente in eadem dyametro, tunc enim possi-
495   bile est ut a quolibet puncto circuli fiat reflexio unica tamen existente ymagine. Verbi gratia sit speculum *ABZG* [Fig. 32], et sit dyameter *AZ* in qua sit *H* res visa et *E* centrum visus. Dico quod reflexio est a puncto *G*, quoniam triangulus *HGD* est equalis triangulo *DGE*, ut patet ex lateribus et angulis qui sunt super *D* et erit locus ymaginis punctus *E*. Similiter fit
500   reflexio a puncto *B* eadem ratione et idem locus ymaginis. Immo fit a pari reflexio a toto circulo qui per lineam *BG* intelligitur, et tamen unica est ymago scilicet *E*. Dico circulum quem, dyametro *AZ* ymaginabiliter immota, describet *G* punctus orbiculariter motus.

     [*Propositio*] *45ª*. *Re visibili et visu extra speram existentibus in diversis*
505   *dyametris, ab uno solo puncto fit reflexio.*

     Verbi gratia sit *C* [Fig. 33] punctus visus, *H* centrum visus, *D* centrum spere, et ducantur linee *HD* et *CD*. Planum est quod superficies *HDC*

485 *ante* in *add.* H M / Z: G et *B* / DTL *corr.*
    ex DTB *V* BTD *B* DCL (C *in alia manu*
    A) AFH de L *D* / et[1] *om. B* / DTE: DCE
    (C *in alia manu A) AFHD* / sint *F*
486 E: D *F* / et[1] *om. B*
487 quantumcunque *in alia manu mg. corr.*
    V ex quantumque
488 proportionetur *BF*
489 a *om. H*
490 possibile est *tr. F* possibile *A*
491 quamvis: quantus *H* / a...fiat: fiat a
    pluribus locis *D* / simul: sunt *H*
492 *post* hoc *scr. et del. D* autem / necesse
    mg. hab. D / est *om. D* / diversas appa-
    rere *tr. A* / *post* quoniam *scr. et del. D*
    tantum / omnes *mg. hab. D*
493 speculationis: speculi rationis *D*
494 enim: eius *D*
495 est *om. D* / tamen *om. F* causa *B*

496 ymaginis *B* / ABZG: ABXG *B* / et sit
    dyameter: et dyameter sit *V* et dyameter
    B sit dyameter *AF* / AZ: AE *B*
497 E: C *D D B* / est *om. V*
498 *ante* quoniam *scr. et del.* H q / est equa-
    lis *tr. A* / triangulo *om. F* / DGE: DEG
    AF DBGE *B*
499 erit: est *F* / *post* E *scr. et del.* H s
500 B *in alia manu mg. hab. V* / immo: uno
    D / fit: sit *D* / a pari: appari *D*
500–501 puncto....reflexio *om. H*
501 unica: una *F*
502 dyameter *BF* / ymaginabiliter *om. A*
503 discriberet *A* / *ante* orbiculariter *scr. et*
    del. H o
504 re (*in alia manu mg. corr. A ex* de): de
    D / *ante* speram *scr. et del.* H s / diversis
    om. D
505 fit: fieri *B*

seen at *Z* if angle *DTL* equals angle *DTE*. Similarly point *C* is reflected from *B* to *E* and is seen at *L*.[98] Therefore according to the various positions of the visible object, the image can be seen in [any] part of the diameter, extended however far, so long as it is not out of all proportion to the size of the mirror.

[*Proposition*] *44. It is possible for a visible point, reflected from several [different] points in a spherical concave mirror, to have a single image.*[99]

Although reflection occurs at several places at the same time, it is not therefore necessary for different images to appear, since all the visual rays in such observation intersect the cathetus at the same point; this is true when the center of the eye and the visible object are situated on the same diameter, for then it is possible for a single image to exist even though reflection occurs from any point on the [great] circle [whose plane is perpendicular to that diameter]. For example, let *ABZG* [Fig. 32] be a mirror and *AZ* the diameter on which the visible object *H* and the center of the eye *E* are located. I say that reflection

Fig. 32

occurs at point *G* because triangle *HGD* equals triangle *DGE*, as is evident from [the equality of] the sides and angles that are above *D*; [therefore] the image is located at point *E*. Reflection occurs at point *B* for the same reason, and the image is located in the same place. Indeed reflection occurs in like manner from the whole circle represented by line *BG*; nevertheless there is but a single image, namely, at *E*. By "the circle" I mean that which is described if point *G* is moved circularly while diameter *AZ* is regarded as stationary.[100]

[*Proposition*] *45. When the visible object and the eye are located outside the sphere on separate diameters, reflection occurs at one point only.*[101]

For example, let *C* [Fig. 33] be the visible object, *H* the center of the eye, *D* the center of the sphere, and draw lines *HD* and *CD*. It is clear that plane

506 H...visus² *om.* F   507 HD: HG *F* / HDC: HCD *V* HD *B*

secat speram speculi concavi in circulo *EBAG*. Ergo *C* non reflectitur ad
H nisi ab aliquo puncto huius circuli, sicut patet supra ex propositione 26.
510 Et certum est quod non fit reflexio ab arcu *GB* quoniam linea ducta ab *H*
cadit super eum exterius non interius. Reflectetur ergo ab arcu *QA* in
cuius extremis terminantur *CD HD*. In hoc autem arcu unus solus est
punctus a quo possit fieri reflexio, scilicet *Z*, qui est terminus linee *LD*
dividentis angulum *HDC* per equalia, et ducantur linee *CZ HZ*. Sequitur
515 etiam ut triangulus *DCZ* sit equalis triangulo *HDZ* si *HD* et *CD* sunt
equales, et per consequens angulus *HZD* equalis erit angulo *DZC*.

Quod si *HD* sit minor quam *CD* vel econverso, re visa et oculo inequaliter distantibus, nichil refert, ducta enim contingente *KF* vel etiam
linea secante circulum et istas lineas ad equalitatem, idem sequitur. Nec
520 potest ab aliquo puncto arcus *QA* fieri reflexio. Quod si potest, sit *O*,
et ducantur linee *HO* et *CO*. Planum est quod *ZC* minor est quam *CO*
cum sit propinquior centro. Amplius *HO* minor est quam sit *HZ* eadem
ratione. Sumaturque linea *ODM* dividens angulum *HOC* per equalia; ergo
cum *HZL* et *CZL* sint trianguli similes eadem erit proportio *CZ* ad *HZ*
525 que est *CL* ad *LH*. Erit etiam proportio *CO* ad *HO* sicut *CM* ad *MH*,

508 speculi: circuli *A* / concavam *B* / in circulo *om. A* / *ante* circulo *scr. et del. V*
speculo / EBAG: CBAG *B* EGBH *F*
509 nisi *om. A* / puncti *D* / patet supra *tr. F*
patet scilicet *A* / 26 *corr. ex* 18 *VBAD*
18ª *H* 18 huius *F*
510 et *om. FD* / certum: centrum *H* / arcu
om. D
511 reflecteretur *V* / ab arcu *om. F* / QA (*in
alia manu corr. A ex* QL): QH *F*
511–12 non....extremis *mg. hab. H*
512 extremis *VBWF*; *om. A* exterius *HD* /
terminatur *D* / CD: CE *B*
513 possit...reflexio: fieri reflexio possit *B*
514 CZ HZ: CZ et HZ *A* CHZ *HD*
515 etiam: et *H* / *post* ut *add. H* D / DCZ
VW CDX *B* CDZ (*post* CDZ *in alia
manu add. A* ?ZHD sint equales) *AFHD*
/ HDZ: HDX *B* / HD *WF*; *om. A* AD
VBHD
515–16 sit...DZC *om. A*
516 per *om. H* / HZD: HCD *B* HZO *F* /
equalis erit *tr. F* / DZC: DZCE *B*

517 si: super *A* / quam *om. F* / *post* oculo
add. V etiam
518 KF *om. H* HZ *D* / etiam: et *H*
519 linea *om. B* / *ante* ad *add. V* et / *ante*
idem *add. A* et
520 aliquo: alio *VH* / *post* puncto *add. A*
AH / QA *om. HD* / *ante* fieri *add. FHD*
alia / O: C *B*
521 et[1] *om. B* / linee *om. B* / ZC...est[2]: Z
minor est *VB* est minor *A* minor est *HD*
522 *ante* centro *scr. et del.* D ?certo / HZ:
HOZ *B*
523 sumaturque: sumatur est *A* / ODM:
CDM *B* / HOC (*in alia manu corr. A ex*
H): HCT *F* hoc *H*
524 cum *VBWF*; *om. HD* et *obs. A* / *ante*
HZL *add. A* non / HZL: HZS *B* / CZL:
ZL *F* / sint: sunt (*alt. D ex* sint) *BHD* /
erit: et *A* / *post* proportio *add. HD* hic
cum semper C pro C / CZ *om. HD* /
HZ: HC *F*
525 qui *A* / LH: HL *B* / CM ad MH: DM
ad YH *F*

HDC cuts the sphere of the concave mirror along circle *EBAG*. Therefore *C* is reflected to *H* only by some point on this circle, as is evident from Proposition 26, above.[102] It is certain that reflection does not occur from arc *GB* because the line dropped from *H* falls on its exterior rather than on its interior. Therefore it will be reflected from arc *QA*, at the extremities of which *CD* and *HD* are terminated. Nevertheless there is only one point on this arc from which reflection can occur, namely, *Z*, which is the end of line *LD*, which divides angle *HDC* into equal parts; draw lines *CZ* and *HZ*. It follows, then, if *HD* and *CD* are equal, that triangle *DCZ* is equal to triangle *HDZ*; consequently angles *HZD* and *DZC* are equal.

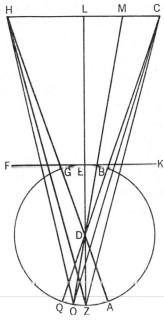

Fig. 33

But if *HD* were smaller than *CD*, or vice versa, so that the object of vision and the eye were unequally distant [from the sphere], it would make no difference, for if tangent *KF* is drawn (or else a line cutting through the circle and reducing those lines [*HD* and *CD*] to equality), the same thing follows. And reflection can occur at no other point [than *Z*] of arc *QA*; for if it could, let that point be *O* and draw lines *HO* and *CO*. It is clear that *ZC* is smaller than *CO* since [the latter] is nearer the center, and *HO* is smaller than *HZ* for the same reason. Assume line *ODM* dividing angle *HOC* into equal parts;[103] then since *HZL* and *CZL* are similar triangles, the proportion of *CZ* to *HZ* will be the same as that of *CL* to *HL*. Also the proportion of *CO* to *HO* will

quod est impossibile, ergo illud ex quo hoc sequitur, scilicet a puncto *O* fieri reflexionem. Hee tamen demonstrationes current cum duo puncta rei, scilicet visibilis et centri visus, sunt extra speram et supra contingentem ductam a termino linee dividentis angulum dyametrorum per equalia.

530   [*Propositio*] *46ª. Possibile est idem in speculo concavo duas habere ymagines.*

Intellige quod ad hoc ut res duas habeat ymagines duo requiruntur. Primum est ut sit reflexio a pluribus partibus speculi super oculum. Secundum est ut locus ymaginis sit alius et alius secundum diversitatem reflexio-
535 num; alius inquam et alius sensibili distantia. Et iuxta hoc secundum diversitatem situs ad speculum potest res habere duas ymagines vel tres vel 4 et non plures. Verbi gratia sint due dyametri speculi se orthogonaliter secantes, *BDQ ADG* [Fig. 34]. Ducatur iterum tertia dyameter *EDZ* que dividat angulum *BDG* per equalia, et a puncto *E* termino dyametri medie
540 ducantur due perpendiculares super duas dyametros primas, scilicet *EC* et *EH*. Erit ergo triangulus *ECD* equalis triangulo *EHD*. Quod si oculus ponatur in *H* et visibile in *C* reflectetur forma *C* a puncto *E* ad *H*, et erit locus ymaginis in *E* quoniam *EH* equidistat *CD*. Amplius *C* reflecti potest a puncto *Z* quoniam trianguli *CDZ* et *HDZ* sunt equales, sicut faciliter
545 probari potest, cum *DZ* sit communis et anguli contra se positi equales. Angulus etiam *QDA* dividitur per equalia. In hoc autem situ non potest fieri reflexio a pluribus partibus speculi, sicut patet repetendo demonstrationem precedentis propositionis. Locus autem secunde ymaginis est *F*.

526 hoc sequitur *tr. B* sequitur *F* / O *AW* C *VBHD* CH *F*
527 fieri *om. B* / tamen: mihi *A*
528 scilicet *om. D* / centrum *A*
532 ut: quod *F* / duas habeat *tr. F* duas habeant *B*
533 oculum *in alia manu corr. A ex* oculi
534 ut: quod *F*
534–35 reflexionis *F*
535 et[2] *om. D* / *ante* iuxta *scr. et del. H* ?ius
536 ad speculum: et speculi *F* / habere duas *tr. A* / vel[1]: et *A*
537 se orthogonaliter *tr. B*
538 BDQ: BDA *D* DHQ *B* / dyametri *B*

539 dividit *D* / dyameter *D*
540 *ante* super *add. B* quia
541 et *om. A* / EH: H *F* / erit: esset *A* / ergo *om. D* / EHD: EDH *V*
542 erit *om. H* esset *A*
543 quoniam: quantum *B*
544 CDZ: DCZ *V* / et HDZ *om. B* / equalia *H* / facialiter *D*
545 communes *F* / se *in alia manu hab. V*
546 etiam: et *H*
547 repetendo: recitando *B*
548 propositionis: demonstrationis *F* / *ante* secunde *scr. et del. F* secundo

be as *CM* to *HM*, and that is impossible.[104] Therefore that from which it follows [is also impossible], namely, that reflection occurs at point *O*. However, these demonstrations hold [only] when the two points, namely, the visible object and the center of the eye, are outside the sphere and beyond the tangent drawn at the end of the line dividing the angle of the diameters [*GDB*] into equal parts.[105]

[*Proposition*] *46. It is possible for one object to have two images in a concave mirror.*[106]

It should be understood that there are two requirements for an object to have two images. The first requirement is for reflection to the eye to occur from several parts of the mirror. The second is that the image be located at different places for different reflections; I say "different places" [meaning places separated] by a sensible distance. Therefore, depending on its position relative to the mirror, an object can have two, three, or four images, but no more. For instance, let *BDQ* and *ADG* [Fig. 34] be two diameters of the mirror intersect-

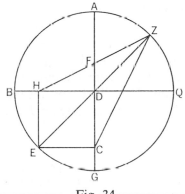

Fig. 34

ing perpendicularly. Also draw a third diameter *EDZ* dividing angle *BDG* into equal parts, and from point *E*, the end of this intermediate diameter, draw two perpendiculars *EC* and *EH* to the first two diameters; triangles *ECD* and *EHD* will then be equal. Now if the eye should be placed at *H* and the object of vision at *C*, the form of *C* would be reflected from point *E* to *H*, and the image would be located at *E* because *EH* and *CD* are parallel.[107] *C* can also be reflected from point *Z* because triangles *CDZ* and *HDZ* are equal, as can easily be proved because *DZ* is common and vertical angles are equal; furthermore angle *QDA* is divided into equal parts [by diameter *EDZ*]. However, [when the object and the eye are] in this position, reflection cannot occur from any other parts of the mirror, as is evident by a repetition of the demonstration of the preceding proposition. At any rate, the second image is located at *F*.

[*Propositio*] *47ª. Possibile est idem in speculo concavo tres habere yma-*
550   *gines.*

Quod est si accipiantur duo puncta in diversis dyametris, quorum unus
intra circulum, alius in ipsa circumferentia circuli vel extra. Sique describatur circulus hec duo puncta cum centro speculi concludens, si circulus
iste secet circulum speculi in uno loco, erit reflexio ab uno arcu tantum;
555   si in duobus secet, poterit esse reflexio ab uno puncto arcus interiacentis
dyametros aut a duobus aut a tribus et aliquando a quatuor.

[*Propositio*] *48ª. Possibile est in speculo concavo uni rei quatuor ymagi-*
nes apparere.

Verbi gratia sit speculum ut supra *ABGQ* [Fig. 35], sitque centrum *D*,
560   sumanturque due dyametri *AG QB*, sitque tertia *EZ* dividens angulum illis
contentum per equalia, sumaturque punctus *C* in dyametro *QB* propius
circumferentiam quam punctus *C* in illa de duabus ymaginibus sumebatur,
et in *AG* sumatur *AH* equalis *QC*. Dico ergo quod *C* reflectitur a puncto *E*
et a puncto *Z* sicut patet ex prehabitis. Amplius preter hoc reflectitur ab
565   aliis duobus punctis. Verbi gratia a puncto *C* extrahatur perpendicularis,
que concurret necessario cum *ZE* extra speram in puncto *O* quoniam
angulus *DCE* est acutus, qui cadit in ultimo spere; ergo oportet lineam
perpendicularem extra speram incidere. Igitur describatur circulus *DCH*
qui necessario cadet in *O*, et cum hic circulus minor secet maiorem in
570   duobus punctis, que sunt *M L*, ducantur linee *HM*, *DM*, *CM* et *CL*, *DL*,
HL. Ergo angulus *CLD* equalis est angulo *DLH* quoniam isti anguli ca-

---

551 est si *tr. V* si *D*
552 intra: infra *BF* / ipsa *om. A* / sique (*in*
   alia manu alt. V ad sicque): sicque *BAF*
552–53 describat *F* scribatur *B*
553 hoc *AH* / *post* concludens *add. B* sic / si:
   s *H*
554 iste: ille *D* / secet: ?sciret *H* / uno[1]: suo
   D / uno arcu *tr. A*
554–55 uno[2]...ab *om. F*
555 secet: sectet *H*
556 et: aut *AF*
557 uni *VBHD* unius *AWF* / *ante* quatuor
   add. F duas aut
558 *post* apparere *add. A* ergo
559 verbi gratia *om. B* / ABGQ: ABG *A* /
   sitque: sit *F*
560 sumaturque *D* / duo *A* / QB: AB *HD* /
   ante illis *add. F* ab / illum *D*
561 C: T *D* / *post* C *add. B* M / in: de *B* /

priprius (*sic*) *AD*
562 circumferentia *V* circumferentie *B* /
   quem *B* / sumebatur: sumetur *B*
563 sumatur *om. A* / AH: A *B* / QC: QT *D*
   / quod C: QC *H* / C: T *D*
564–65 ab aliis *in alia manu mg. hab. V*
565 *ante* duobus *add. V* a / C *om. D et obs. A*
566 concurrit *BA*
567 DCE (*in alia manu corr. A ex* DC *et in*
   alia manu mg. hab. W) AW DE *VBFHD*
   / ergo oportet *tr. B*
568 circulus *om. D* / DCH: ?DTH *D*
569 cadit *AF* / *ante* hic *add.* HD est / secet:
   sectet *H* sic secabit *F*
570 qui *AF* / M *om. F* / DM *obs. A* / CL *om.*
   D QL *F* / *ante* DL *add. A* et / DL *om. F*
571 *ante* HL *add. AF* et / HL *om. H*
571–72 cadent *A*

[Proposition] 47. It is possible for one object to have three images in a concave mirror.[108]

Assuming this is so, take two points[109] on different diameters, one inside the circle[110] and the other on the circumference of the circle or outside. And if a [second] circle is drawn including these two points along with the center of the mirror, then if the [second] circle intersects the circle of the mirror in one place,[111] reflection will take place from one arc only; if intersection occurs in two places, reflection can take place from one point of the arc interposed between the diameters or from two or from three or sometimes from four.[112]

[Proposition] 48. It is possible for one object to have four images in a concave mirror.

For example, let *ABGQ* [Fig. 35] be a mirror as above, and let *D* be the center; assume two diameters, *AG* and *QB*, and let *EZ* be a third diameter

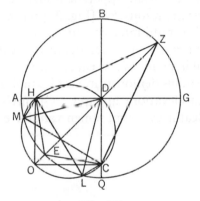

Fig. 35

dividing the angle contained by the first two into equal parts. Assume point *C* on diameter *QB* closer to the circumference than point *C* was assumed to be in that [proposition] concerning two images, and assume *AH* on *AG* equal to *QC*. I say then that *C* is reflected from points *E* and *Z*, as is evident from the above.[113] Furthermore, it is reflected also by two other points. For instance, draw a perpendicular from point *C*, which necessarily intersects *ZE* outside the sphere at point *O* because angle *DCE*, which reaches the most remote part of the sphere, is acute; therefore the perpendicular line must be incident [on *ZE*] outside the sphere. Thus draw circle *DCH*, which necessarily passes through *O*; since this smaller circle cuts the larger at two points, *M* and *L*, draw lines *HM*, *DM*, *CM*, *CL*, *DL*, and *HL*. Now angles *CLD* and *DLH* are equal because

dunt in equales arcus, in quartas scilicet, circuli minoris; igitur *C* poterit reflecti ab *L*. Item eadem ratione angulus *DMH* equalis est angulo *DMC*; ergo *C* poterit reflecti a puncto *M*. Et ita 4 habebit ymagines punctus *C*.

575   [*Propositio*] *49ᵃ*. *In solis speculis concavis res confuse et dubie apparere*.
Cuius ratio est quoniam in solis hiis speculis res apparet in oculo vel retro oculum. Visus autem non est natus acquirere formas nisi rerum facialiter obiectarum, et ideo res que aliter apparent dubie et confuse necesse est apparere.

580   [*Propositio*] *50ᵃ*. *In speculis concavis res nunc conversas nunc eversas apparere*.
Hoc ex libro *De speculis* faciliter demonstratur quoniam radii in aliquo situ concurrunt et in aliquo non. Cum autem concurrunt illa que sunt intra confluentiam radiorum apparent eversa, cum vero extra apparent
585   sicut sunt. Verbi gratia radius *BA* [Fig. 36] reflectitur ad *E*, radius autem *BG* ad *D*. Cum igitur radii intersecentur in puncto *Z* oportet res que sunt citra intersectionem aliter apparere quam que extra, quoniam que intra sunt apparent sicut in planis everse eadem ratione, que vero extra apparent sicut sunt. Et tunc huius demonstratio est iuxta illud principium sub eleva-
590   tioribus radiis visa elevatiora apparere. Quamvis enim in concursu *EO* et *DQ* ydolum videatur eversum, tamen validior est in immutando visum

572 quartis *A* quartus *H* / minores *H* / *C om.* *HD*
573 ab: ad *A* / *ante* eadem *add.* *B* in / *DMC*: *DMT D*
574 *C*[1,2]: T *D*
576 solis hiis *tr.* *F*
579 necessario *F*
580 nunc[1] *om.* *H*
582 hec *F* / *ante* ex *scr. et del.* *F* est / faciliter *BAWF* facialiter *VHD* / in *BWF*; *om.* *VAHD*
584 *ante* intra *scr. et del.* *D* extra
585 radius[1] *om.* *V* / radius[2] *incipit secunda manus in D* (The second hand continues to the end of the MS; see section on the revised version in the introduction.)
586 intersecentur (*in alia manu mg. corr. A ex ?*referentur): intrinsecentur *D* / *Z om. A*
587 citra *obs.* *F* / quam: quoniam *A* / *post* que[1] *add.* *A* est / quoniam que intra *om.* *H* / intra: infra *D*
588 everse: ense *D*
588–89 in...sicut *om.* *A*
589 huius *in alia manu alt.* *V* ad huiusmodi
590 *ante* concursu *add.* *F* conf
591 et: quod *A* / tamen: cum *D* / immutando: mutando *BFHD*

they intercept equal arcs of the smaller circle, namely, fourths;[114] therefore C can be reflected from L [to the eye at H]. For the same reason angles DMH and DMC are equal; consequently C can be reflected from point M [to the eye at H]. And so point C will have four images.

[*Proposition*] *49. Things are of confused and doubtful appearance only in concave mirrors.*

The reason for this is that only in these mirrors does a thing appear in or behind the eye. But the eye is not designed to receive the forms of things unless they are opposite the face. Therefore things that appear otherwise must be of confused and doubtful appearance.[115]

[*Proposition*] *50. In concave [spherical] mirrors things sometimes appear reversed and sometimes inverted.*[116]

This is easily demonstrated from the book *De speculis*,[117] since rays converge in one place and not in another. When they intersect, however, those objects that are before the place of intersection of the rays appear inverted; those that are beyond appear as they are [in reality].[118] For example, ray BA [Fig. 36] is reflected to E and ray BG to D.[119] Since the rays intersect at point Z,

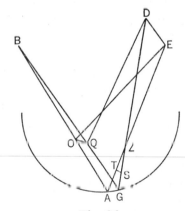

Fig. 36
V and *D* omit this figure. *F* and *W* greatly confuse it. I have reproduced the figure found in *B*, *A*, and *H*. Cf. Figure 53.

objects located before that intersection must appear different from those that are beyond, for those that are before appear inverted as in plane mirrors and for the same reason, while those that are beyond appear as they are [in reality]. This is demonstrated [in *De speculis*] according to the principle that things seen under higher rays appear higher. For although the image at the intersection of EO and DQ appears inverted,[120] nevertheless the disposition of the rays that excite the eye is more effective in altering sight than is the disposition of the

ipsa dispositio radiorum oculum moventium quam cathetorum, que linee
sunt ymaginabiles. Quod si non hoc auctor libri *De speculis* tunc intellexit,
credo quod erravit. Si quem vero prolixior delectet demonstratio sextum
595   consulat *Perspective*. Sed *ST* que est inter confluentiam eius pars inferior
videtur sub elevatiori radio et econverso plane videtur eversa, cuius eversio
patet faciliter ducendo cathetos alias ultra speculum.

[*Propositio*] *51ᵃ*. *In speculis concavis res aliquando pares, aliquando
maiores, aliquando vero apparere minores.*

600   Hoc laboriose et prolixe demonstratur in 6 *Perspective*. Sed breviter
colligitur ex premissa quoniam que intra confluentiam radiorum sunt
maiora apparent quam sunt, que vero extra sunt secundum diversitatem
situs apparere possunt maiora vel minora vel equalia iuxta quod remotiora vel propinquiora sunt ab intersectione. Et ex hoc etiam apparet quod
605   quanto a speculo remotiora sunt tanto maiora apparent.

[*Propositio*] *52ᵃ*. *In speculis concavis ex diversitate situum quedam apparere recta, quedam curva, quedam convexa.*

Hoc latuit auctorem libri *De speculis*, qui in omni situ apparentibus
curvitatem attribuit. Huius autem conclusionis diversitas diffuse demon-
610   stratur libro sexto capitulo 7. Huius autem veritas patet per oppositum
ad ea que dicuntur circa 32 et 33 propositionem huius partis.

[*Propositio*] *53ᵃ*. *In speculis columpnaribus intra politis eosdem errores
accidere quos in spericis concavis.*

Hoc diffuse demonstratur libro 6 capitulo 8, quod quia satis est pro-
615   babile non oportet in eius demonstratione laborare. Et intellige errores in

592 *ante* cathetorum *add. BH* radiorum
593 sunt ymaginabiles *tr. VA* / quod si: quia
   A / non hoc *tr. A* / tunc *om. BF*
594 si quem: siquidem *BA* / vero *om. A* /
   delectet demonstratio *tr. A* delectat demonstratio *V* delectet demonstratione *H*
595 consulatur *B* consulit *H* / sed: licet *D* /
   ST: C *B* SI *F* / qua *F* / *ante* eius *scr. et
   del. A* q / pars: potestas (*in alia manu*) *V*
   pari *H* / inferiorum *A*
596 videtur¹ *om. A* videret *B* / radios *A*
597 faciliter ducendo *AWD* facialiter ducendo *VBH* ducendo facialiter *F* / *post* ultra
   add. F vel supra
599 vero: *scr. et del. A* ?non / apparent *F*
600 demonstrantur *B*

602 maiora: minora *F* / sunt² *mg. H et om. F*
602–3 apparent…maiora *om. D*
603 equalia *om. A*
604 vel…sunt: sunt vel propinquiora *F*
604–5 vel….remotiora *om. A*
605 maiora: minora *AD*
606–7 apparere…quedam¹ *om. H*
607 recta *in alia manu hab. A*
608 *ante* auctorem *hab. H* a / qui: quod *B* /
   omnibus *B*
609 *ante* diffuse *add. A* diverse
610 sexto: 6 *BAF*
610–11 7….partis *om. A* (This is replaced
   by the text of Proposition 53 beginning
   with "8 quod…," which is denoted
   below as *A'*.)

perpendiculars, since the latter are imaginary lines.[121] But if the author of the book *De speculis* has not comprehended this, I believe he has erred. However, if a more lengthy demonstration would please anyone, he should consult the sixth book of the *Perspectiva*.[122] But if the lower part of *ST*, which is between the place of intersection [and the mirror], is seen by means of a higher ray, and vice versa, it obviously appears inverted, and the inversion is easily evident by extension of the perpendiculars somewhere beyond the mirror.[123]

[*Proposition*] *51. In concave [spherical] mirrors, objects sometimes appear equal [to their true size], sometimes larger, and sometimes smaller.*

This is demonstrated laboriously and at length in Book 6 of the *Perspectiva*.[124] However, it may be gathered briefly from previous considerations, for those things that are before the intersection of the rays appear larger than they actually are, while those that are beyond, according to different positions, can appear larger, smaller, or equal, depending on whether they are farther from or closer to the intersection. From this it is apparent also that [images] are larger as they are more remote from the mirror.[125]

[*Proposition*] *52. In concave mirrors objects sometimes appear straight, sometimes concave,[126] and sometimes convex according to different positions.*

This was unknown to the author of the book *De speculis*, who attributed a curved appearance to images in all positions.[127] However, the opposite conclusion is amply demonstrated in Book 6, Chapter 7 [of the *Perspectiva* of Alhazen].[128] Moreover, the truth of this proposition is evident by the converse of that which was said in Propositions 32 and 33 of this part.[129]

[*Proposition*] *53. The same errors occur in concave cylindrical mirrors as in concave spherical mirrors.*

This is amply demonstrated in Book 6, Chapter 8 [of the *Perspectiva* of Alhazen],[130] but since [its truth] is highly probable, it is unnecessary to labor [here] in its demonstration. This is true of all the aforesaid errors—

---

611 et *om.* BA vel *F* / propositionem *om. F*
612 *post* politis *add.* D concavis
613 spericis: speculis *F* / concavis *om.* D
614 hec *F* / 6: 6° *D* / 8 *om.* D / quod quia VBFDA'; *tr. A* quod et *H*
614–15 8...laborare (This material appears twice in *A*. It erroneously replaces part of the text of Proposition 52, and it appears again in the lower margin. I pro-

vide variant readings for both appearances, denoting the former as *A'* and the latter as *A*.) / *ante* probabile *add.* HD enim / probabile: demonstrabile *A*
615 ?intelligere *B*
615–17 et...apparitionum *om. A* (This material is found in Erfurt Q.387 only under Proposition 52, i.e., *A'*.)
615–16 in...predictis *om. B*

omnibus predictis, et de numero ymaginum, et situ, et rectitudine et curvitate apparitionum.

[*Propositio*] *54ᵃ. In pyramidalibus concavis omnes errores accidere qui accidunt in columpnaribus concavis.*

620 Et illud libro sexto capitulo 9 et satis liquet ex predictis.

[*Propositio*] *55ᵃ. In speculis concavis ad solem positis ignem generari.*

Quod speculum si sit portio spere generatur ignis in centro eius quando convertitur directe ad solem, in concursu radiorum reflexorum cum radio incidente. Secus est autem in speculis concavis sed figure irregularis, factis
625 per artem traditam in libro *De speculis comburentibus*, in illis enim reflectuntur radii omnes extra locum incidentie, prope vel longe iuxta hoc quod speculum est magis vel minus concavum. Omnes autem radii a tali speculo reflexi concurrunt in punctum unum ad aerem disgregandum et inflammandum. In speculo autem concavo sperice figure non fit reflexio omnium
630 radiorum in punctum unum sed ab aliquo circulo, unde debiliter exurit.

[*Propositio*] *56ᵃ. Stellas quasdam ex reflexione radiorum solarium ad ipsas apparenter scintillare.*

Cum enim stelle sint corpora solida equalis superficiei necesse est ut habeant superficies speculares; reflectunt ergo radios solares. Sed quia continue
635 moventur corpora celestia variatur continue angulus incidentie, et per consequens reflexionis sensibilis variatio facit quandam vibrationis apparentiam. Hoc autem auctor *Perspective* non dicit; mihi tamen videtur non totam causam scintillationis esse oculorum defectui ascribendam. Nec conatus quisquam vel radiorum involutio hoc omnino efficere videtur,
640 cum videamus superficies deauratas soli oppositas scintillare, et multa clara forti luce superfusa scintillare videntur que summa facilitate oculo presentantur. Amplius visus tantum deficit in comprehensione quorundam

---

616 situum *F*
618 que *F*
618–19 qui accidunt *om. A*
619 concavis *om. F*
620 illud: istud *A* / sexto: 6 *AF* / 9: 9° *B* / *ante* et² *add. F* probatur / satis: similiter *A* / lique *H*
621–30 in....exurit (This proposition appears in *D* as a continuation of Proposition 54. In *V* and *W*, Propositions 55 and 56 are mutually transposed, but Proposition III.16 identifies this as the next to last proposition of Part II. *H*

omits Proposition 55 altogether.)
622 quod: quia *F* / si: sit *A* / portio *in alia manu alt. V ad* proportio
623 in *om. D* / reflexiorum *A*
624 incidente *VAWF* incidentie *B* incidentis *D* / est autem *VBF*; *tr. AWD* / sed *om. F* / irregulares *B*
625 traditis *B* / comburentibus: concurentibus *D* / enim *om. B*
627 omnes: essent *D* / autem *om. F*
628 punctum unum *tr. BF* / aerem: aliquem *D*
628–29 et inflammandum *mg. hab. B* / in-

of the number of images, of position, and of the straightness and curvature of images.

[*Proposition*] *54. All errors that occur in concave cylindrical mirrors occur [also] in concave pyramidal mirrors.*

This [follows] from Book 6, Chapter 9 [of the *Perspectiva*][131] and is clearly evident from the foregoing.

[*Proposition*] *55. Fire is kindled in concave mirrors facing the sun.*[132]

If the mirror is a portion of a sphere and faces the sun directly, fire is kindled in its center at the intersection of the reflected rays and the incident rays. This is not so, however, in mirrors that are concave but of irregular shape, fabricated by the method taught in the book *De speculis comburentibus*;[133] for in such mirrors all rays are reflected outside the place of incidence [on the reflecting surface], near or far according as the mirror is more or less concave. All the rays reflected from such a mirror converge at one point so as to rarefy and ignite the air. In concave mirrors of spherical shape, on the other hand, reflection of all rays to one point occurs only from a single circle, and therefore concave spherical mirrors kindle fire weakly.[134]

[*Proposition*] *56. Certain stars appear to twinkle because they reflect solar rays.*[135]

For since stars are solid bodies of uniform surface, their surfaces must be reflective, and consequently they reflect solar rays. But since celestial bodies are continually moved, the angle of incidence is continually varied, and the resulting sensible variation in reflection produces a certain appearance of vibration. The author of the *Perspectiva*, however, does not mention this; nevertheless it does not seem to me that the whole cause of twinkling should be attributed to a defect of the eyes; nor, apparently, can any effort or straining of the rays[136] effect this by itself, since we see a gilded surface opposite the sun glitter, and since things that the eye perceives with the greatest ease seem to sparkle when bathed in an intense and very clear light. Moreover, sight is as defective in the

---

flammantur *F*

628–30 ad....unum *om. A*

629 *post* autem *in alia manu mg. hab. V* continuo

629–30 omnium radiorum *tr. B*

630 exurit: urit *B*

632 apparent *AD* apparere *F* / scintillas *F*

633 sint *om. A*

634 speculares: politas *F* / reflectant *A* / *post*

radios *add. B* suos

636 *ante* sensibilis *add. F* unde / facit quandam *tr. D*

637 auctor *om. A*

638 esse *om. F* / oculorum *om. H*

639 vel *om. V* / omne *D* non *A*

640 videmus *A*

642 presententur *B* presentatur *H* / tantum: tamen *D*

planetarum sicut aliarum stellarum. Amplius canicula et alie quedam inter
stellas fixas clariores videntur quam alie, ubi nec visus plus conatur nec
645   reverberatur magis quam in aliis. Ergo defectus visus quamvis ad hoc conferre possit non tamen sufficit.

Sed forte dices si specula sunt stelle ergo videndo stellas debemus videre
solem. Item eadem ratione planete scintillare deberent. Ad primum respondeo quod si totum celum esset speculum, oculus tamen in centro existens
650   videret se tantum, sicut patet ex 41 huius partis. Quia ergo equales sunt
anguli incidentie et reflexionis radius a sole cadens in stellam reflectitur
vel in se si perpendicularis est, vel in aliam partem celi si non est perpendicularis; ergo non in terram. Ad secundum respondeo quod planete
non scintillant quia prope sunt, radius enim solis cadens super corpus
655   stelle fixe propter remotionem stelle facit angulum magnum incidentie
stella et per consequens angulum magnum reflexionis, ita quod propter
elongationem radii a stella potest visus advertere aliquo modo diversitatem
luminis stellaris et solaris reflexi a stella. Econtra autem in corporibus
planetarum quia prope sunt angulus minor est quem constituit radius in-
660   cidentie et reflexionis cum superficie stelle, et propter hoc aspectus noster
non distinguit inter lumen ipsius stelle et lumen solare reflexum a stella.

Explicit Secunda Pars

644 fixas *om. B*
645 in *om. D*
647 sed: si *A* / debemus videre *tr. V* videmus
   F
648 deberent *om. B*
649 tamen: tantum *F*
650 patet...partis *corr. ex* patet ex 40 huius
   partis (*post* ex *scr. et del. A* ?2) *VBAHD*
   patet ex 41ª huius partis *W* ex 40 huius
   partis patet *F*
651 *ante* reflectitur *scr. et del. A* reflexionis
652 perpendicularis est: sit perpendicularis
   B / est² *om. D*

652–53 est¹...perpendicularis *om. A*
654 supra *F*
655 propter...stelle² *om. F*
655–56 incidentie...magnum *in alia manu*
   mg. hab. V
656 *ante* stella *add. F* in / stella *om. B*
658 stellaris et solaris: solaris et stellaris *D*
660 propter hoc: propterea *B* / non *om. A*
661 solarem *A*
662 explicit...pars *om. HD et mg. A* explicit
   secundus *B* et sic est finis secunde partis
   perspective *F* / *post* pars *add. V* de speculis

perception of some of the planets as in the perception of other stars, [and yet the planets do not twinkle]. Furthermore, Canis Minor and certain other fixed stars are seen more clearly than the others even though there is no greater exertion by sight nor greater reflection [of solar rays] than with the others. Therefore, although a defect in sight could contribute to this [twinkling], it does not suffice.

But perhaps you will argue that, if stars are mirrors, then in seeing stars we should see the sun. For the same reason, [you say,] planets ought to twinkle. To the first remark I reply that, even if the whole sky were a mirror, an eye located at the center would see only itself, as is evident from Proposition 41 of this part. Therefore since the angles of incidence and reflection are equal, a solar ray falling on a star is reflected either back on itself, if it is perpendicular, or to the other side, if it is not perpendicular, and consequently not to the earth. To the second assertion I reply that planets do not twinkle, because they are nearby, for a solar ray falling on the body of a fixed star has a large angle of incidence, because of the remoteness of the star, and consequently a large angle of reflection.[137] Therefore because of the elongation of the ray from the star, sight is somehow capable of perceiving the difference between stellar light and solar light reflected from a star. Conversely, the angle formed by the incident and reflected rays at the surfaces of planetary bodies is smaller because they are nearby; consequently our sight does not distinguish between light of the [planetary] star itself and solar light reflected from that star.

Here Ends Part II

Incipit Tertia Pars

[*Propositio*] *1ᵃ. Solus perpendicularis porrigitur recte alterius dyaphoneitatis medio occurente.*

Ista propositio, prima huius tertie partis, patet ex declaratione 14 et
5   15 prime partis et 16.

[*Propositio*] *2ᵃ. Fractio radii in ipsa contingit tantum superficie medii
secundi.*

Cuius ratio est quoniam lux in omni dyaphono recte movetur quantum
in se est. Ergo incurvatio vel declinatio a rectitudine esse non potest nisi
10   in continguatione duorum dyaphonorum. Quod si in eodem corpore continuo sit diversificatio secundam rarum et densum sensibiliter diversum,
an in tali dyaphono lux habeat declivem incessum, satis est perplexa
questio. Credo tamen magis quod sit quam quod non, quamvis Auctor
iste contrarium sentire videatur.

15   [*Propositio*] *3ᵃ. Anguli fractionis diversificantur secundum diversitatem
declinationis et differentiam dyaphoneitatis medii secundi.*

Huius causa patet ex premissis, quoniam due sunt cause fractionis,
una a parte radii, debilitas scilicet eius ex declinatione, alia a parte medii,
diversitas scilicet dyaphoneitatis. Quia ergo quanto maior est declinatio
20   tanto maior est debilitatio, sequitur etiam ut iuxta hoc maior sit fractio.
Amplius ex parte medii quia quanto densius est tanto magis resistit, se-

1 incipit *om. VAFHD* / tertia pars *mg. hab.
VD et in alia manu mg. hab. A et in alia
manu hab. F et om. H* liber tertius perspective *B*
2–3 dyaphoneitas *D*
4 prima *om. F*
5 prime…16: et 16 prime partis *F*
6 fractio: ratio *H* / tantum *om. A*
8 in: cum *A*
9 ergo *om. A* / incurvatio *om. A* curvatio
F / declinatio *corr. H ex* declinatione

10 contiguatione: continuatione *B* / quod:
quia *A*
10–11 continue *A*
12 declivum *A* / incessum: morsum *D* / perplexa: prolixa *FH*
13 credo *om. A* / quod¹ *in alia manu hab. V* /
sit *in alia manu hab. V* fit *AD* / quod²
scr. et del. V et om. BA / *post* non *in alia
manu add. V* sit / auctor *in alia manu
mg. hab. V*
14 iste: ille *D* / sentire videatur *tr. B*

Here Begins Part III

[*Proposition*] *1. Only a perpendicular ray continues in a straight line upon encountering a medium of different transparency.*[1]

This first proposition of Part III is evident from Propositions 14 through 16 of Part I.

[*Proposition*] *2. Rays are refracted only at the surface of the second medium.*[2]

The reason for this is that, in and of itself, light is moved directly in all transparent media. Therefore curvature or deviation from directness can occur only where one transparent medium is adjacent to another. But whether a single continuous [transparent] body varies sensibly in rarity and density and whether light would have a sloping path in such a transparent body are very perplexing questions. I incline more toward the affirmative than the negative opinion, although the Author would seem to think the contrary.

[*Proposition*] *3. The angle of refraction varies with the inclination [of the incident ray] and the difference of transparency of the second medium [in comparison to the first].*[3]

The reason for this is evident from the foregoing, for there are two causes of refraction, one on the part of the ray—namely, its weakness because of inclination—and the other on the part of the medium—namely, the variation in transparency. Since greater inclination [of the incident ray] corresponds to greater weakness, it follows also that greater refraction would result from this [greater inclination]. Furthermore, with reference to the medium, since greater ability to resist [the propagation of rays] corresponds to greater density, it

---

16 *ante* declinationis *scr. et del. A* fra
17 causa patet *tr. B* / premissis: predictis *F*
18 a[1]: ex *AF* / eius ex *tr. F* eius et ex *A* / alia *in alia manu corr. V ex* alii / a[2]: ex *F*
19 diversita *H* / maior: minor *B* / est *om. A*
20 etiam *om. FH*
21 *post* quia *add. F* igitur / quanto: tanto *A*
21–22 tanto...densiori *om. A*

quitur ut proportionalis non fiat transitus in medio densiori nisi maiori fractione quam in medio rariori. Et ideo quo densiora sunt media secunda res necesse est apparere maiores vel minores, sicut infra docebitur.

25   [*Propositio*] *4ᵃ. Locus ymaginis est in concursu perpendicularium, a re visa ymaginabilium duci in superficiem dyaphoni ipsam continentis, cum pyramide sub qua res videtur.*

Sicut enim supra patuit omnia que videntur recte apparent, et propter comprehensionem radii per quem res oculo presentatur estimatur res esse
30   in fine ipsius radii in continuum producti. Sicut ergo pro fundamento in speculis supponitur rem apparere in concursu radii cum catheto, sic in proposito fit in hac materia quod res apparet in concursu radii cum perpendiculari erigibili a re visa. Verbi gratia sit visus *A* [Fig. 37], visibile *B*, radius fractus qui rem visui ostendit *BC*, qui in *C* frangitur, et inde proce-
35   dit *CA*, sitque perpendicularis *BLD*. Dico quod punctus *B* apparet in *L*.

[*Propositio*] *5ᵃ. Rem visam per radios fractos extra locum suum necesse est apparere.*

Istud ex predictis apparet, si enim in concursu apparet perpendicularium et radiorum visualium et hic concursus est extra locum rei vise,
40   necesse est ergo rem alibi quam sit apparere. In planis autem dyaphonis semper ymago apparebit propinquior quam sit res secundum veritatem, in spericis autem aliter esse potest ut patebit infra. In planis igitur universaliter sic est. Verbi gratia *GQ* [Fig. 38] apparet in *KL*.

22 nisi: ubi *A* / maiore *A*
23 quo: quanto *B*
24 maiores vel minores: minores vel maiores *A*
25 concursum *B* / perpendicularis *F*
26 ymaginabilis *F* / dyaphoni *om. A* / *post*
   ipsam *add. F* rem
28 *ante* propter *add. F* hoc
31 supponitur: ponitur *F*
32–33 perpendiculum *D*
34 frangit *A*

35 *ante* CA *add. B* in / BLD: DLB *A* BD *B*
   / B: D *B*
38 concursu: occursu *B*
39 et¹: vel *A* / *post* locum *add. D* suum
40 alibi: aliter *B* / *post* quam *scr. et del. H*
   ?a / autem *om. A*
41 apparet *F*
42 in² *om. D*
43 sic: sicut *F* / GQ: KA *A* GQA *B* / apparet *WFHD* apparent *VBA* / KL: BL
   F

follows that traversal [of one medium by a ray] is not commensurate [with traversal of a second medium by that ray] unless refraction is greater in a denser than in a rarer [second] medium.[4] Therefore, when the second medium is denser [than the first], objects [located in that medium] must appear larger or smaller [than their true sizes], as will be shown below.[5]

[*Proposition*] 4. *The image is located at the intersection of the pyramid under which the object is seen and the perpendiculars that one can imagine dropped from the visible object to the surface of the adjacent transparent medium.*[6]

As was shown above,[7] everything that is viewed appears [as though] in a straight line; and by the apprehension of the ray through which the eye perceives the object, the object is judged to be at the end of the straight-line extension of the ray. Therefore, just as the appearance of the object at the intersection of the perpendicular and [the rectilinear extension of] the ray is considered basic to mirrors, so in the case at hand it [i.e., the image] is at the intersection of the ray and the perpendicular dropped from the visible object. For example, let *A* [Fig. 37] be the eye, *B* the visible object, *BC* the bent ray (refracted at *C*, from which [point] proceeds [ray] *CA*) that presents the object to the eye, and *BLD* the perpendicular. I say that point *B* appears at *L*.

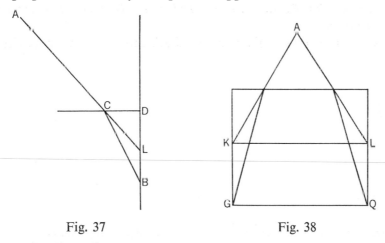

Fig. 37   Fig. 38

[*Proposition*] 5. *An object seen by refracted rays must appear outside its true place.*[8]

This is evident from the foregoing, since, if the object appears at the intersection of the perpendicular and the visual ray and if this intersection is outside the [true] place of the visible object, the object must appear outside its true place. In flat transparent media the image always appears nearer than the object actually is, although this can be otherwise in spherical media, as will be shown below.[9] In flat transparent media, then, it is universally so. For example, *GQ* [Fig. 38] appears at *KL*.

[*Propositio*] *6ᵃ. Res partim existens in aqua partim in aere fracta apparet.*

45   Sequitur enim si pars existens in aqua propinquior apparet quam sit secundum veritatem, res autem extra aquam apparet in loco suo, ergo iste partes directe continuate apparere non possunt. Apparent ergo continuate indirecte.

[*Propositio*] *7ᵃ. Possibile est aliquid videri per radios fractos, quod per*
50   *directos ad oculum non pertingit.*

Hoc experimento patet quia si ponatur aliquid in profundo vasis mediocris altitudinis latebit forte visum. Quod si aqua superfundatur statim oculo manifestabitur, cuius demonstratio hec est quoniam radii recte ad oculum pertingere non possunt propter interpositionem opaci, fracti ta-
55   men possunt. Verbi gratia sit res visibilis *BG* [Fig. 39], oculus *A*, et sit *BG* in aqua. Planum est quod non videtur sub radiis *GA* et *BA*, sed sub *BC* et *GH* fractis ad *A*. Ergo quamvis impediantur radii *GA* et *BA* ne pertingant ad oculum, non tamen impediuntur fracti. In aere autem fieret visio sub *GA* et *BA*; illis ergo impeditis in aere videri non posset. Adveniente
60   autem fractione ex diversitate medii poterit videri.

[*Propositio*] *8ᵃ. Rei vise sub radiis fractis impossibile est certificari quantitatem.*

Cuius ratio est quoniam ad quantitatis certificationem requiritur cogni-

44 *post* fracta *scr. et del. F* videtur
45 pars: res *A* / existens *om. A* / in aqua *om. B* / sit: est *A*
46 secundum: ?verum *H* / appareat *H* / loco suo *tr. V* loco *A*
50 oculos *B* / pertingit: contingit *B*
51 hoc experimento *tr. F* / quia: quod *BAH* / si ponatur *corr. H ex* supponatur
52 *post* forte *add. D* ?item
53 hec est *tr. F* / radii *om. V*
54 interpositionem: oppositionem *A*
55 BG¹: O *F* / *ante* A *add. B* etiam

55–57 BG¹....et¹ *om. H*
56 GA et BA: BA et GA *F*
56–57 sed....BA *om. A*
57 GH: HO *B* GB *D* / fractus *HD*
58 autem fieret: enim fiet *F*
59 GA: CA *F* / et *om. A* / BA *om. A* HA *F* / illis: vel *A* / ergo *om. H* autem *F* / impeditis *om. A* / aere: acte *H*
60 autem *om. D* / poterit videri *tr. F* poterit videre *D*
61 impossibile *in alia manu mg. hab. A*
63 requirit *H*

[*Proposition*] *6. An object located partly in water and partly in air appears bent.*

For it follows, if the part in water appears nearer than it actually is and the part not in water appears in its true place, that those parts cannot appear to be joined together in a straight line. Therefore they appear to be joined obliquely.

[*Proposition*] *7. It is possible for an object that is not seen by direct rays to be seen by refracted rays.*[10]

This is evident from an experiment, for if an object is placed in the bottom of a vessel of moderate height, it may be concealed from the eye; but if water is [then] added, the object is immediately manifest to the eye. The explanation of this is that direct rays cannot reach the eye because of the interposition of an opaque substance, but refracted rays can. For example, let *BG* [Fig. 39] be

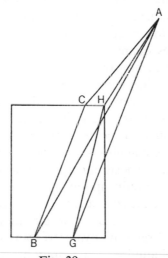

Fig. 39
I have found this figure only in *A* and *N*.

the visible object and *A* the eye, and let *BG* be in water. It is obvious that the object is seen not under rays *GA* and *BA*, but under *BC* and *GH*, refracted to *A*. Therefore, although rays *GA* and *BA* are prevented from reaching the eye, refracted rays are not. In air, then, sight would occur under *GA* and *BA*, and consequently the object could not be seen in air, since those rays would be obstructed. However, the object can be seen by the occurrence of refraction, which results from [the addition of] a different medium.

[*Proposition*] *8. It is impossible to certify the size of an object seen under refracted rays.*[11]

The reason for this is that, for certification of size, knowledge of the distance

tio distantie et comprehensio anguli pyramidis sub quo res videtur, quo-
65   rum utrumque deficit, cum radii oculum moventes franguntur, et per consequens angulus diversificetur. Ex quo sequitur ut quantitas stellarum
veraciter omnino non cognoscatur quia celum est corpus subtilius quam
aer vel ignis.

[*Propositio*] *9ª. Res visa existens in dyaphono densiori superficiei emisphe-*
70   *rialis potest apparere maior quam sit et minor et etiam equalis, convexitate*
ad oculum versa.
Hoc ex duobus patet, quoniam perpendiculares super speram non
equidistant sicut cadentes super planum; immo concurrunt in centro.
Planum est autem quod pyramis a cono suo semper procedit in dilatando
75   se. Cum hoc etiam supponendum est quod in quarta huius partis propositione demonstratur. Concursus autem radiorum cum hac pyramide potest
esse citra rem visam, id est in maiori distantia a centro spere quam sit res ipsa,
et tunc res apparet maior quam sit. Et hec est ratio quare res in aqua
apparent maiores quam sint, aqua enim superficiem habet spericam ubi-
80   cunque sit, sicut demonstratur in libro *De celo et mundo* et in hac phylosophia supponitur. Concursus ergo est necessario propinquior oculo quam
res ipsa, et est locus ymaginis in maiori dyametro pyramidis quam sit res
ipsa. Maior ergo apparet res universaliter in aqua quoniam ubicunque sit
superficies eius superior portionem spere constituit, quamvis plana appa-
85   reat propter spere magnitudinem, eadem enim est natura partis et totius.
Vel in alterius dispositionis spera potest concursus esse dictarum perpendicularium cum radiis in loco ipsius rei visibilis, et tunc apparet res in
veritate situs et quantitatis sue, vel potest tertio concursus iste esse remotior a visu quam sit res ipsa et propinquior centro spere, quod est conus
90   dicte pyramidis. Ergo quia dyametri transversales dicte pyramidis quanto
sunt cono propinquiores tanto sunt breviores necesse est ibi apparere

64 quo: qua *F*

65 frangantur *F*

66 diversificatur *BA* / ut: quod *F*

67 est *rep. A*

70 quam: quod *H* / minor et *om. F*

71 versa *corr. A ex* conversa

72 patet: apparet *A* / super speram *om. F*
/ *ante* speram *add. B* planum

73 sicut...planum *om. B*

74 autem *om. B*

75 cum: et *H* / etiam: autem *B* et *H* / quarta: 4 *A*

75–76 huius...propositione: propositione

huius partis *F*

77 citra: circa *A* nota *D* / id est: et *B* etiam
F

78 res apparet *tr. A* / sit *om. D* / res *om. B*

80 sit *om. BA* / in[1] *om. A* / de *om. F* / celo
om. D celi *F* / mundi *FD*

80–81 phylosophia *om. A*

81 supponitur *corr. A ex* proponitur / est
necessario propinquior *HLD* necessario
est propinquior *V* necessario propinquior *BA* necessario propinquior est *WF*

82 sit *om. A* / *ante* res *scr. et del. H* ?i

83 maior: minor *A* / apparet res universa-

and the angle of the pyramid under which the object is seen is required. [But] both of these [data] are lacking because the rays acting on the eye are refracted, thus altering the angle. It follows that the sizes of stars are not known with complete veracity, since the sky is a more subtle body than air or fire.

[*Proposition*] 9. *A visible object located in a denser transparent medium of hemispherical surface with its convexity toward the eye can appear larger than, smaller than, or equal to its true size.*[12]

This is evident from two considerations. [First,] lines perpendicular to a sphere are not parallel, as [they are] when they fall on a plane, but, on the contrary, intersect at the center. Moreover, it is clear that the pyramid [formed by the perpendiculars, with vertex at the center of the sphere,][13] always expands as it proceeds from its vertex. To this [first consideration] one should add that which is demonstrated in Proposition 4 of this part. Now the intersection of [the rectilinear extension of] the rays with this pyramid can be on the near side of the visible object, i.e., at a greater distance from the center of the sphere than is the visible object itself; the object then appears larger than it is. This is why objects appear larger in water than they really are, for water has a spherical surface everywhere, as is demonstrated in the book *De celo et mundo* and assumed in this philosophy.[14] Therefore the intersection is necessarily closer to the eye than is the object itself, and the image is located on a larger diameter of the pyramid than the object is. Consequently an object always appears larger in water, since, wherever the water is located, its upper surface constitutes a portion of a sphere, even though it appears flat because of the magnitude of the sphere; for the part and the whole have the same nature.[15]

In spheres differently disposed, either the intersection of the aforementioned perpendiculars and the rays can be in the place of the visible object itself—and then the object appears in its true place and of its true size—or, the third possibility, it can be farther from the eye and nearer the center of the sphere (i.e., the vertex of the aforesaid pyramid) than is the object. Therefore, since the transverse diameters of the pyramid are shorter as they approach the vertex,

---

liter *BWHD* apparet universaliter *V* apparet universaliter res ipsa *A* universaliter apparet res *F* / quoniam *V* quam *BAFHDLW* / ubicunque sit *tr. F* / post sit *add. F* enim sit

84 *post* quamvis *scr. et del. H* ?l

85 enim est (est *in alia manu hab. V*) *VWL*; *om. B* est enim *F* enim *AHD* / partis et totius: totius et partis *F*

86 dictare *D*

87 radiis *corr. ex* re visibili *VBAFHD* / res *om. B* / post in[2] *add. F* rei

88 situs *corr. H ex* sitas / tertio *om. F* / concursus iste *tr. A* concursus ille *D*

89 res ipsa *tr. A* / quod: quam *B*

90 quia *om. F* / *ante* pyramidis[2] *scr. et del. H* ?pin

91 sunt[1] *om. F* / *ante* necesse *add. F* et / ibi apparere *tr. A*

minorem. Verbi gratia sit perspicuum emisperiale *ABC* [Fig. 40], visibile
DE, centrum spere *F*. Quia ergo potest esse dictus concursus vel inter *F*
et *DE* vel ultra vel in ipsa linea *DE* sequitur quod predictum est.

95   [*Propositio*] *10ª. Rem visam existentem in dyaphono densiori quam sit
oculus et superficiem habente planam necesse est apparere maiorem quam sit.*
        Hoc patet quoniam res ipsa apparet propinquior quam sit, presentatur
etiam oculo semper sub maiori angulo quam videri possit secundum radios
directos. Ergo maior apparet quam sit secundum veritatem, maior enim
100   angulus ad equalem vel minorem distantiam relatus rem iudicat esse
maiorem, sicut patet ex prima parte. Verbi gratia sit res visa existens in
aqua *GB* [Fig. 41], oculus vero *A*. Planum est quod *GB* videretur in aere
sub angulo *GAB*, videretur etiam in loco suo; sed propter aquam franguntur radii *BC* et *GH* in ingressu aeris, et videtur res sub angulo *HAC*, qui
105   est maior illo quem includit *GAB*. Item res non apparet in loco suo sed
in linea *KL*, ut supra patet. Hoc etiam confirmatur quia concursus radiorum cum corpore dictarum perpendicularium in huius dyaphono semper
est inter visibile et visum.

        [*Propositio*] *11ª. Concavitate dyaphoni densioris ad oculum versa accidit
110   econverso illi quod contingit conversa ad oculum convexitate.*
        Res enim apparet magna vel parva secundum quantitatem dyametri
pyramidis dictarum perpendicularium, in qua fit concursus; et quia potest

92 *ante* ABC *scr. et del. F* visibile
93 F¹: P *F* / F² *corr. H ex* fi
96 habentem *VBAFH*
97 apparet *om. A*
98 etiam: et *A* autem *D* / semper sub maiori: sub maiori semper *B* / *ante* possit
   scr. et del. F potest / posset *A* / secundum: per *F*
99 directos *in alia manu corr. A ex* rectos /
   post enim *add. A* est
100 equalem vel minorem: maiorem vel
   equalem *F* / distantiam relatus *tr. A* /
   esse *om. F*

101 *ante* maiorem *scr. et del. A* minorem
102 videtur *AFH*
103 videntur *A* / suo *om. D* / *post* aquam
   scr. et del. H ?l
104 HAC: hac *D*
105 maior: minor *B* / *post* illo *add. B* angulo
   / GAB: GHB *B*
106 KL: LK *B* / supra: scilicet *A* / confirmatur: ?confluatur *H*
107 dictarum *om. B* / huiusmodi *F* / dyapha-
   na *A*
110 illi: illud *A* / quod: qui *H*
112 fit: sit *A* / *post* concursus *add. B* oculo

the object must appear smaller [than its true size] there. For example, let *ABC* [Fig. 40] be a transparent hemisphere, *DE* a visible object, and *F* the center of the sphere. Since the aforementioned intersection can be between *F* and *DE*, on the other side [of *DE*], or on line *DE* itself, what was asserted above follows.

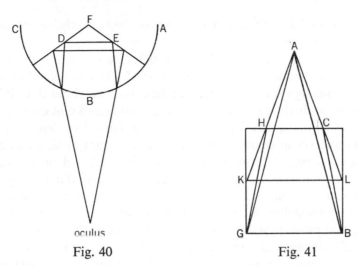

Fig. 40   Fig. 41

[*Proposition*] *10. A visible object situated in a transparent medium of flat surface and denser than* [*that in which*] *the eye* [*is situated*] *must appear larger than it is.*[16]

This is evident because the object appears nearer than it is[17] and is always perceived by the eye under a larger angle than that under which it could be seen by direct rays. Therefore it appears larger than it really is, for a larger angle combined with an equal or smaller distance causes the object to be judged larger, as is evident from Part I.[18] For example, let *GB* [Fig. 41] be the visible object situated in water and *A* the eye. It is clear that in air *GB* would be seen under angle *GAB* and in its true place; but because of the water, rays *BC* and *GH* are refracted upon entering the air, and the object is seen under angle *HAC*, which is larger than the angle enclosed by *GAB*. Moreover, the object appears not in its true place but on line *KL*, as shown above.[19] And this is confirmed by the fact that the intersection of rays with the aforesaid perpendiculars[20] in such a transparent medium is between the visible object and the eye.

[*Proposition*] *11. That which occurs when the concavity of the denser transparent medium is toward the eye is the opposite of that which occurs when the convexity is toward the eye.*[21]

For an object appears large or small according to the size of the diameter of the pyramid (formed by the aforementioned perpendiculars)[22] [at the place] where intersection [with the rays] occurs; and since intersection can occur in

triplici modo hic concursus variari, sequitur ut res possit in triplici quantitate oculo presentari, id est maior cum concursus est oculo propinquior
115   quam res, vel equalis cum concursus est in re ipsa, vel minor cum est
remotior ab oculo quam res ipsa.

[*Propositio*] *12ᵃ. Stellas ex fractione necesse est minores apparere quam
sint et quam si directe in tanta distantia apparerent.*

Universaliter enim res existens in perspicuo plano, oculo existenti in
120   perspicuo densiori, apparet minor quam sit. Tamen quando est dyaphonum alterius figure potest aliter accidere, econtra ei quod accidit quando
oculus est in dyaphono puriori. In proposito tamen non est ita, quia stelle
minores videntur quam si directe viderentur. Quando autem sunt in circulo
meridionali vel in cenith minores apparent quam alibi, cuius causa una
125   habita est supra in prima parte propositione 82. Ad propositum autem
proceditur sic, quia locus ymaginis est in concursu dictarum perpendicularium et radiorum visualium. Hic autem concursus est propinquior visui
quam corpora stellarum; ergo erit in loco dicte pyramidis minori quam sit
stella. Hoc patet quoniam si accipiantur arcus stelle que videtur, et sit *AB*
130   [Fig. 42], ducanturque inde perpendiculares in centrum mundi que sint
AC et *BC*, sitque visus *D* ad quem ducantur linee *AD* et *BD*, certum est

113–15 variari…concursus *om. A*

114 id est: idem *H* / maior: minor *W*

115 *ante* vel¹ *scr. et del. H* ut / vel¹ *om. F* /
cum²: et *B*

117 minores apparere *tr. B*

118 apparent *D*

119 perspicuo: spericuo (*in alia manu alt. ex*
sperico) *D* / oculo *om. A*

120 perspicuo: spericuo *D* / *ante* densiori
scr. et del. H ?domus

121 ei *om. B*

122 oculus *corr. H ex* oculo

123 circulo: oculo *B*

124 in *om. B* / alibi: alicubi *B* alii *A* / una

om. B

125 propositione *in alia manu alt. V ad* propositionis / 82 *corr. ex* 81 *VBAF* 81ᵃ
H 8ᵃ *D* 18ᵃ vel 4ᵃ vel 28ᵃ et 82ᵃ *W*

126 sic *om. H* / est *om. V* / dictare *D* / *post*
dictarum *scr. et del. A* ymaginum

127 visualium: visibilium *B*

128 quam: quo ad *A* / corpus *B* / minor *F*
minoris *B* minori *alt. V ad* minor

129 quoniam: quam *A* / accipiatur *BFH* /
arcus: aptus *D*

130 ducantur *AF* / sint: sunt *B*

131 BC: AB *A* / D: E *B* / quem: quam *B*

any of three modes, it follows that the size of the object, as perceived by the eye, can vary in three ways: it is larger [than the true size of the object] when the point of intersection is nearer than the object to the eye, equal when intersection is at the object itself, and smaller when intersection is farther from the eye than is the object.[23]

[*Proposition*] *12. Because of refraction, stars must appear smaller than they are* [*in reality*] *and smaller than if they were seen directly from the same distance.*[24]

An object located in a transparent medium of plane surface, the eye being in a denser medium, always appears smaller than its true size. However, when the transparent medium has another shape, it can happen otherwise, [namely,] the opposite of that which occurs [for that shape] when the eye is in the medium of purer transparency. But this is not so in the present proposition, since stars appear smaller than [they would] if they were seen directly. Moreover, when they are on the meridian circle or at the zenith, they appear smaller than elsewhere, the explanation of which is dealt with above in Proposition 82 of Part I. However, in the present proposition, the explanation proceeds as follows. The image is located at the intersection of the aforementioned perpendiculars [to the surface of the transparent medium] and the visual rays, and this intersection is nearer the eye than are the stellar bodies;[25] consequently the image is located at the place of [intersection of the rays and] the aforementioned pyramid,[26] which is smaller than the star. This is evident, since, if we take *AB* [Fig. 42] as the arc of a visible star, draw perpendiculars *AC* and *BC* from there to the

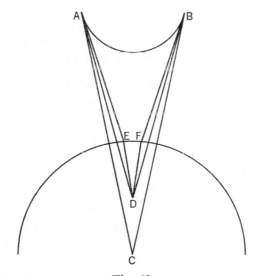

Fig. 42
None of the manuscripts place *C* at the center of curvature of the refracting surface, *EF*, but the text allows no other arrangement.

quod per istas non est visio, nulli enim non fracti radii possunt ad visum
pertingere. Radii ergo sub quibus fit visio non cadunt ambo extra *AD* et
BD, franguntur enim ad perpendicularem et non concurrent in *D* si extra
135   caderent. Cadent ergo ambo intra vel saltem unus extra et alter intra; sint
ergo *AE* et *BF* qui franguntur in punctis *E* et *F* et cadunt in *D*. Quero
ergo ubi radii *DE* et *DF* concurrent cum pyramide *ACB*, et planum est
quod citra corpus stelle propter improportionalem distantiam stellarum.
Ergo minores apparent quam si directe viderentur.

140   [*Propositio*] *13ᵃ. Stellas in orizonte propinquiores aquiloni apparere quam
meridionali circulo propinquantes.*
Hoc probo sic. Ducatur linea inter ortum cuiuscunque stelle ad meridiem
declinantis et occasum eius, ducatur et alia ei equidistans per oculos in-
spectoris utrimque ad latera orizontis. Dico quod accessus stelle ad meri-
145   diem vel elongatio ab aquilone est secundum comprehensionem distantie
harum duarum linearum. Certum est autem quod capabilior est harum
linearum distantia in medio, quod est aspectui propinquius et etiam ex
latitudine terre, que in meridie extenditur quam in extremis que magis
elongantur a visu. Et linea terminalis distantie harum duarum linearum
150   utrobique longe sub acutiori angulo videtur quam linea distantie medialis.
Verbi gratia sit prima linea *AB* [Fig. 43], secunda *CD*, sitque visus *E*, sit
linea medie distantie *FG*, sit linea distantie extreme *HK*. Planum est quod
longe maior est angulus *FEG* quam *HEK*.

132 non²: in *D*
133 AD: AB *A* / et *obs. F*
134 BD: DB *F* / *post* concurrent *scr. et del.*
        V ambo intra ergo *et add. A* ABC ca-
        dant intra ergo *et scr. et del. H* ambo /
        si: sed *B*
135 caderent: cadunt *B* caderetur *D* cadent
        H / cadent *om. A* cadunt *B* / intra²: in-
        fra *F* / sint: sunt *B* est ?dicendum *A*
136 BF: DF *F* / et² *om. F*
137 ergo *om. A* / ACB: AEB *B* ABC *F*
138 citra: extra *F* / improportionalem
        ...stellarum: proportionalem stantiam
        stellare *D*
140 orizonte: oriente *BH* / *post* apparere
        add. B minores
141 circulo: oculo *D*
142 probatur *F* / cuiuslibet *F*
143 *ante* ducatur *scr. et del. A* et / ducatur et:
        ducaturque *F* / ei equidistans *tr. F*
144 utraque *AF* / orizontis: orientis *B*

145 comprehensionem: apprehensionem *AF*
146 capabilior: temperabilior *B*
146–47 est²...linearum: harum linearum est
        B
147 aspectum *A* aspectui *mg. corr. H ex* ap-
        pectui
148 meridie *WFHD* meridiem *VBA* / exten-
        ditur *in alia manu alt. V ad* protenditur /
        extremis: exterius *H* / magis *om. A*
149 duarum linearum *tr. A*
150 *ante* sub *scr. et del. H* ab / videntur *A* /
        ante medialis *add. B* GF / medialis:
        meridionalis *F*
150–51 distantie....linea *om. A*
151 secundum *B* / E *om. D*
152 FG: F *F* / distantie extreme *tr. F* / HK:
        H *A*
152–53 planum...HEK *in alia manu mg.*
        hab. V
153 FEG: EFG *B* / HEK: EHK *B*

center of the world, and locate the eye at *D*, to which we draw lines *AD* and *BD*, it is certain that sight does not occur through the latter because no un-refracted rays can reach the eye. Therefore the rays through which sight occurs do not both lie outside *AD* and *BD*, since they are refracted toward the perpendicular and would not intersect at *D* if they should fall outside. Accordingly both of them fall inside, or at least one inside and the other outside. Let those rays be *AE* and *BF*, which are refracted at points *E* and *F* and fall to *D*. I ask, then, where [the rectilinear extensions of] rays *DE* and *DF* intersect pyramid *ACB*; clearly they do so on this side of the body of the star because of the disproportionate[27] distance of the stars. Therefore they appear smaller than [they would] if they were viewed directly.[28]

[*Proposition*] *13. Stars on the horizon appear farther north than do those near the meridian circle.*[29]

I prove this as follows. Draw a line between the places of rising and setting for any star having a declination toward the south, and draw a line parallel to it through the eyes of the observer[30] [extended] to the horizon on both sides. I say that the approach of the star to the south or its elongation from the north varies with the perception of the distance between those two lines. It is certain, however, that the distance between the two lines is greater [in appearance] at the middle because that is closer to the eye and because the breadth of the earth appears greater at the meridian than at the extremes, which are farther removed from the eye. And the line of distance between the ends of those two lines (at either horizon) is seen under a far more acute angle than is the line of distance at the middle. For example, let *AB* [Fig. 43] be the first line, *CD* the second, and *E* the eye; let line *FG* be the distance at the middle and line *HK* the distance at the end. It is clear that angle *FEG* is much larger than angle *HEK*.[31]

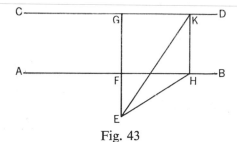

Fig. 43

Auctor autem *Perspective* hanc diversitatem attribuit fractioni, quia
155 cum stella est in cenith sub perpendicularibus radiis videtur et non fractis,
cum autem est in orizonte videtur sub radiis fractis; et reflexio vel fractio
causa est ut magis videantur aquiloni propinquare. Hec tamen ratio bona
est pro quibusdam stellis, sed non videtur pro omnibus sufficere, quia non
solum stelle que transeunt per cenith sed etiam alie que multum a cenith
160 elongantur, sicut sol et alie ultra vel citra tropicum hyemalem, sic se
habent quod remotiores a polo apparent cum sunt in sublimi. Et tamen
certum est quod sub radiis fractis videntur. Item stelle per cenith transeuntes unus solus radius perpendicularis et non fractus intrat in oculum
aspicientis.
165 Fractionem autem esse causam ut appareant aquiloni magis appro-
pinquare patet sic. Sit circulus magnus signans orizontem, in quo sit stella
AB [Fig. 44], sit circulus minor signans speram ignis, sitque oculus *D*,
ducanturque linee *AD* et *BD*. Planum est quod sub hiis non est visio.
Radius igitur sub quo videtur *A* punctus aut cadet extra istas lineas, id
170 est propinquius aquiloni, aut intra. Si extra ut in *C*, frangatur ibi versus
perpendicularem et cadat in *D*; si ponatur cadere intra, id est remotius
ab aquilone, impossibile est quod cadat in punctum *D*, quia frangitur ad
perpendicularem. Eadem ratione necesse est ut punctus *B* videatur, et ita
locus ymaginis totius stelle ad aquilonem verget respectu loci stelle. Sed

154 hanc diversitatem: diversitatem istam
    B / fractione *A* fractionem *D*
155 cum: causa *H* / sub: cum *A* / radiis vide-
    tur *tr. B*
156 cum...fractis *om. D* / est *om. B* / ori-
    zonte: oriente *B* / vel: sub *A* / fractione
    A
157 videatur *F* / propinquare: appropin-
    quare *AFD* / tamen *VBAW* autem *F* cum
    HD
159 etiam alie *tr. B* alie *F* / multam *H*
159–60 per...elongantur *om. A*
160 hyemale *HD*
161 a polo *om. B*
162 *post* radiis *scr. et del. F* perpendiculari-
    bus
162–63 transeuntis *AH*
163 et: etiam *A* / fractis *AH* / oculum: cir-
    culum *A*
165–76 fractionem....fractio *om. VADL*
    (This passage appears in only 8 of 29
    manuscripts examined. In addition to
    B, *W*, *F*, and *H*, I have collated Digby
    28 (*O*) and Prague 1272 (*P*). The passage

appears, also, in Prague 1284 and Vienna 3105.)
165 *post* ut *add. W* stelle
166 sit[1] *om. P* / circulus: oculus *O* / signans
    BOP significans *WFH* / orizontem:
    orientem *O*
167 sit *BFHO* sitque *WP* / minor: magnus
    P / signans *BWOP* significans *FH* / ocu-
    lus: circulus *F* / D *WOP*; *om. H* DC *BF*
168 ducantur *F* / *ante* linee *add. WP* due /
    AD *WHOP* AB *BF* / et: *scr. et del. B*
    D / quod *om. W*
169 aut: autem *B* / cadet *BFHO* cadit *WP* /
    istas lineas *BFHP*; *tr. W* has lineas *O*
169–70 id est *BWFO*; *om. H* et *P*
170 *ante* aut *scr. et del. F* et infra / intra *W*
    infra *BFHOP* / frangatur *BP* frangitur
    W frangantur *FH* / ibi versus: igitur ad
    P
171 perpendicularis *B* / cadat *HP* cadet *BF*
    cadit *WO* / intra *W* infra *BFHOP* / id
    est: et *P*
172 *ante* impossibile *add. B* et / frangantur *P*
173 ut: prout *F*

The author of the *Perspectiva*, however, attributes this difference to refraction,[32] since, when a star is at the zenith, it is seen under perpendicular and unrefracted rays, whereas at the horizon it is seen under refracted rays; and [thus] reflection or refraction causes them to appear farther north.[33] This explanation, however, is applicable to some stars, but is seen not to suffice for all; for not only the stars that pass through the zenith, but also others that are greatly elongated from the zenith (such as the sun and other stars beyond or on this side of the Tropic of Capricorn), behave in such a way that they appear farther from the pole when they are elevated; and yet it is certain that these [others] are [always] seen under refracted rays. Moreover, only one perpendicular, unrefracted ray from a star passing through the zenith enters the eye of the observer.

Nevertheless,[34] that refraction is a cause of the appearance of stars farther north is evident as follows. Let there be a large circle representing the horizon, on which is located star *AB* [Fig. 44], and let there be a smaller circle represent-

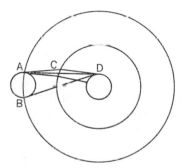

Fig. 44

I have added the innermost circle to represent the earth and placed the eye on its surface. This is required to capture the sense of the proposition, though omitted by both *F* and *W*, the two manuscripts containing this figure.

ing the sphere of fire. Let *D* be the eye, and draw lines *AD* and *BD*; it is clear that sight does not occur through these rays. Therefore the ray through which point *A* is seen falls either outside those lines (i.e., farther north) or within. If outside, as onto *C*, the ray would be refracted there toward the perpendicular and would fall to *D*; if it is assumed to fall within (i.e., farther south), it could not fall to point *D* because it would be refracted toward the perpendicular. Point *B* must be seen in a similar manner, and so the image of the whole star is located to the north of the true place of the star. However, this explanation

174 ad *om. H* / verget *FHO* vergeret *B* ver-   *BFHO* totius *WP*
    git *W* et est idem ?exemplum *P* / loci

175 ista ratio posset applicari stellis meridionali circulo appropinquantibus et
a cenith capitum elongatis, nisi forte ibi maior sit fractio. Non sufficit
ergo una ratio sine alia sicut credo.

[*Propositio*] *14ᵃ. Omne quod videtur directe videtur et refracte, una
tamen eius existente ymagine.*

180 Certum est enim ex prima parte 28 et 40 quod quilibet punctus rei vise
sigillat punctum sibi oppositum in glaciali per radios super corneam perpendiculariter orientes. Sed quia quilibet punctus in omnem partem spargit
lucem suam, necesse est quod quilibet punctus rei visibilis totam occupet
pupillam et quilibet punctus in puncto quolibet radiet glacialis. Sed quia
185 ab uno puncto super oculum non potest egredi nisi unus radius perpendicularis, franguntur omnes preter unum in ingressu cornee. Ipse autem
punctus apparet in loco suo ubi concurrit radius fractus cum perpendiculari; et quamvis in quolibet puncto perpendicularis obumbret fractum,
radii tamen fracti ad hoc valent ut res clarius videatur ex concursu utrius-
190 que luminis.

[*Propositio*] *15ᵃ. Multa per fractionem videri extra pyramidem radiosam.*
Pyramis radiosa est agregata ex radiis perpendiculariter cadentibus
super corneam et intrantibus foramen uvee, quod parvum est. Multa ergo
ex latere videntur imperfecte, que intra dictam pyramidem non continen-
195 tur, sicut ad sensum patet. Et que sic videntur debiliter videntur, quia per
radios tantum fractos, omnes enim in ingressu cornee franguntur.

[*Propositio*] *16ᵃ. Ex concursu radiorum fractorum possibile est ignem
generari.*
Ex reflexis patet supra propositione 17 secunde partis in speculis et
200 eiusdem partis penultima propositione. Contingit etiam idem in corporibus dyaphonis rotundis solaribus radiis expositis; sed inter specula et
dyaphona hec est differentia quoniam in speculis generatur ignis inter
speculum et solem, in dyaphonis autem econtra ipsum dyaphonum inter-

175 ista: illa *W* | *ante* posset *add. B* non *et*
    add. W etiam / stellas *H* | et *BHOP; om.*
    WF
176 a *BFHP* A *W* ad *O* / capitum *FH; om.*
    BAP capitis *O* / elongatis...fractio *om.*
    B | elongatis *FHP* elongantis *WO* /
    maior sit *F; tr. W* minor sit *HO* maior *P*
176–77 sufficit ergo *tr. A*
178 refracte: rei fracte *F*
179 tamen: tantum *F* / eius *om. AF* /
    existente ymagine *tr. A*
180 prima *om. B* / parte *in alia manu mg. hab.*

    V et om. F ?pro ?T *D* / *post* parte *add. A*
    et / 28 *corr. ex* 8 *VBFHD* 68 *A* / *post* 40
    scr. et del. V parte / vise: in se *AD*
181 punctum sibi *tr. A* / super: supra *F*
181–82 perpendiculariter orientes *tr. F*
182 omnem partem: omni parte *F*
183 occupat *F*
184 *post* quolibet *add. A* S
185 non *om. D*
186 preter....autem *om. A* / in *om. H*
188 perpendicularis: perpendiculari *A*
189 tamen: cum *H* / *post* concursu *scr. et*

could [also] be applied to stars near the meridian circle but elongated from the zenith unless refraction should perchance be greater there.[35] Therefore, as I believe, one explanation does not suffice without the other.

[*Proposition*] *14. Every visible object is seen* [*both*] *directly and by refraction; nevertheless there is a single image.*[36]

It is certain from Propositions 28 and 40 of Part I that each point of the visible object impresses an image on the opposite point on [the surface of] the glacial humor through rays perpendicularly incident on the cornea. But since each point spreads its light in every direction, each point of the visible object must fill the whole pupil and irradiate every point of the glacial humor; however, since only one ray from a given point can be incident on the eye perpendicularly, all except that one are refracted upon entering the cornea. Nevertheless the point appears in its own place, where the refracted ray intersects the perpendicular;[37] and although at any point the perpendicular ray prevails over the refracted ray, the refracted rays are useful in causing the object to appear more clearly, through the combination of the two lights.

[*Proposition*] *15. Many things outside the radiant pyramid are seen by refraction.*[38]

A radiant pyramid is the aggregate of rays incident on the cornea perpendicularly and entering the opening in the uvea. Since the opening is small, many things at the side, not contained within the aforesaid pyramid, are seen imperfectly, as is evident to sense. And things seen in this manner appear weakly, since they appear by refracted rays alone, for all [of their rays] are refracted upon entering the cornea.

[*Proposition*] *16. Fire can be kindled by the convergence of refracted rays.*[39]

It is evident from Proposition 17 of Part II and the next to last proposition of the same part that [fire can be kindled] by reflected rays in mirrors. The same thing happens when round transparent bodies are exposed to solar rays; but mirrors and transparent bodies are different in that fire is kindled between a mirror and the sun, whereas with transparent bodies, on the contrary, it is the

---

192 perpendicularibus *B*
193 *ante* foramen *add. F* super / est *om. D*
194 ex...videntur: videntur ex latere *A* / inter *AF*
195–96 per...tantum: tantum per radios *A*
196 in: est *H*
197 est *om. D*

199 supra *om. B* / 17ª *VD* / et *om. AD*
200 penultima: pene ultima *D* / contingit: convenit *A* / etiam: autem *B* et *H*
201 expositis *om. A*
202 hec est *tr. F*
203 autem: aut *H* / econtra: *scr. et del. F* econverso
203–4 interponitur: interpretatio *H*

ponitur. Verbi gratia sit cristallus rotundus cuius dyameter sit *YAZ* [Fig.
205   45], cadantque a sole radii super ipsum *XC, XS, XR, XQ, XP*. Certum
est quod solus *XR* cadit in centrum *A* proceditque non fractus usque in *H*.
Alii ergo franguntur ad perpendicularem et cadunt a *C* in *B* et ab *S* in *G*
et a *Q* in *N* et a *P* in *O*. Veniens ergo radius *CB* ad superficiem aeris concavam non procedit directe in *E* sed frangetur a perpendiculari *BK* usque
210   in *H*, et sic de aliis, quibus congregatis, rarefacto aere, ultra terminos sue
speciei ignis generatur.

[*Propositio*] *17ᵃ. Omnis radius directus, reflexus, vel fractus tanto debilior est adurendo quanto minus figitur in obiecto.*
Et hoc potest esse vel ex motu obiecti vel ex motu luminosi. Obiecti
215   quidem sicut propter velocem motum fluminum non fiunt in eis exala-
tiones tante sicut in aquis marinis, propter quod et salsedine carent. Propter motum velociorem luminosi accidit quod temperatior est habitatio sub
equinoctiali circulo quam sub alio paralello vie solaris, quoniam solus
equator speram dividit in duo equalia, et est maior aliis sibi paralellis. Sol
220   ergo cum in equali tempore describat equatorem motu suo quo minimum
paralellum quemvis alium, necesse est ut in illo maiori tanto velocius rapia-
tur, et per consequens virtus eius minus figatur in subiecta sibi loca quam
in alio paralello. Item circulus dividens terram in duo equalia sub equinoctiali maior est quocunque alio sibi equidistante. Ergo quando sol est
225   in aliquo paralello alio radius eius perpendiculariter cadens in locum sibi
subiectum minorem tantum in eo figitur quantum in eodem tempore radius
solis declinans in arcu terre maiori. Sub equinoctiali ergo minus urit.

204 rotundus *AW* rotunda *VBFHD*
205 XR *in alia manu mg. hab. V* XY *F*
206 XR: XC *A* XY *F* / cadat *A* / A *om. A* /
      usque *om. A*
207 ergo: autem *A* / et[1] *om. A* / B: K *A* / ab:
      AB *F* / S *om. F*
208 a Q: A *F*
209 procedit *corr. H ex* procedat / E: se *B* /
      frangentur *B* / a *om. H* / BK: BH *H*
210 congregans *A* / rarefacto: raro fracto *A*
      rarefit *F* restitutio *D* / *ante* terminos *add.*
      H et
211 ignisque *F*
212 directis *A* / reflexis *H*
214 potest: patet *A* / *ante* motu[1] *scr. et del.*
      A obiecto
215 sicut: sunt *A* / motum *om. B* / fiunt: sunt
      A
216 *post* sicut *add. F* fit / et *om. F*

217 velocem *V*
218 solus *corr. A ex* solis
219 equatior *D* / speram dividit *tr. F* / *post*
      maior *in alia manu mg. add. V* igitur /
      aliis sibi *tr. A* aliis *F* / sibi *scr. et del. V*
220 in equali: inequalitate *H* / equatores *A*
      equatiorem *D* / *ante* motu *add. A* in /
      quo *om. B*
221 quemvis *VW* quamvis *BAFHD*
222 minus: nimis *D* / fingatur *H*
223 *post* item *scr. et del. A* in alio loco /
      dividans *A*
224 quocunque: quoque *A* quicunque *D* /
      alio sibi *tr. A*
225 alio *om. F*
226 minorem: minor est *B* / figitur: ?consi-
      tur *B* / eodem: eo *B* / tempore: ipse *A*
227 declinat *B* / *ante* sub *add. A* vel

transparent body that is between. For example, let there be a round crystal of diameter *YAZ* [Fig. 45], and let rays *XC*, *XS*, *XR*, *XQ*, and *XP* fall on it from the sun. It is certain that only *XR* falls to the center *A* and proceeds unrefracted to *H*. Therefore the others are refracted toward the perpendicular and fall from *C* to *B*, from *S* to *G*, from *Q* to *N*, and from *P* to *O*. Accordingly, ray *CB* arriving at the concave surface of the air does not proceed directly to *E* but is refracted away from perpendicular *BK* to *H*, and similarly for the other rays. When these rays have been assembled and the air rarefied, fire is kindled [just] beyond the terminus of their species.

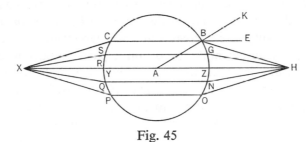

Fig. 45

[*Proposition*] *17. The less fixed a direct, reflected, or refracted ray is in an object, the less capable it is of setting the object on fire.*

This can result from the motion of either the object or the luminous body. It can result from the motion of the object just as rivers, because of their swift motion, produce fewer exhalations than do seas; and it is for this reason that rivers are not salty. Because of the swifter motion of the luminous body [i.e., the sun], the climate is more temperate under the equator than under any other parallel to the path of the sun, for only the equator divides the [celestial] sphere into two equal parts, and it is larger than other [circles] parallel to it. Therefore, since the sun by its motion circles the equator in a time equal to that in which it circles any other much smaller parallel, it must be carried along in the larger one with a proportionately greater swiftness; consequently its force is less fixed in the places lying beneath it than [would be the case] for any other parallel. Likewise, the circle dividing the earth into two equal parts under the equator is greater than any other circle parallel to it. Therefore, when the sun is on some other parallel, its ray perpendicularly incident on the smaller place lying beneath it is fixed there just as much as is a ray of the sun obliquely incident in the same period of time on a larger terrestrial circle.[40] Therefore under the equator the rays burn less.[41]

[*Propositio*] *18ª. In generatione yridis trium predictorum generum verticationes concurrere radiosas.*

230   De radiis rectis patet quia yris generatur ex opposito solis. De reflexis certum est quoniam stille sperule quedam sunt speculares et superficiei lenis, radios in modum aque reflectentes. De fractis insuper patet quoniam lumen solare intrat in profundum aque, quamvis˷reflectatur.

[*Propositio*] *19ª. Causam rotunditatis yridis principaliter consistere in*
235 *nube.*

    Quando enim nubes regulariter suspensa est terre equidistans, certum est quod roratio regulariter descendit, et hoc ad orbicularitatem sufficit; alie villose suspense et irregulariter non habent in se impressionem regularem. Quidam autem ponunt causam a parte radiorum, dicentes quod
240 lumen radiosum intrat in nubem rotundam et inde ultra nubem concurrit in puncto uno, sicut declaratur in 16 propositione huius partis. Post concursum autem iterum lumen ipsum dilatatur in pyramidem, cuius medietas cadit in nubem et facit per consequens impressionem semicircularem, alia autem medietas cadit super terram. Sed contra cadat radius
245 solaris per foramen rotundum; certum est quod erit rotundus. Opponatur ei lapis exagonus generans colores yridis; certum est quod generat yridem, non in figura radii que est orbicularis, sed in figura lapidis que est columpnaris. Si ergo consimilis passio consimilem habet causam, oportet ut causa figure arcus querenda sit in nube et non in radio. Item hec positio
250 videtur contra sensum, quoniam yris generatur a sole sine aliquo interposito in nubem roridam radiante, quod lumen cadens in nubem vocat Phylosophus radium medie rotunditatis, lumen enim figuram capit a medio in quo est.

    Alii ponunt rotunditatem in radio ex se ipso, dicunt enim quod radii
255 pyramidaliter digrediuntur a sole, et medietas pyramidis cadit in nubem et facit dictam figuram. Sed hoc nichil est, quoniam si de toto lumine solari agitur, quilibet punctus solis implet totum emisperium lumine suo;

228–29 verticationem *A* verstationes *D*
230 quia: quamvis *A* / yris *om. A* / de reflexis: deflexis *HD*
231 quoniam: quod *F* / stille: stelle *BH* / sperule: superule *H*
232 lenit *H* levis *A* / reflectentes *corr. H ex* reflectentis
233 intrat *om. B* / in *om. F*
234 causas *B*
236 quando: quoniam *H* / equidistans *in alia manu mg. hab. V*
236–37 suspensa…regulariter *om. D*

237 rotatio *H*
238 irregulariter: regulariter *A* / non *om. A*
239 radiorum *in alia manu corr. A ex* radios
240 inde: aliquando *F*
241 declaratur: declaratum est *F* / in² *om. A* / 16ª *A* / partis *om. F*
242 iterum lumen *tr. F* iterum huius lumen *D* / ipsum *om. F*
245 opponatus *B*
246 generans colores: generalis coloris *A*
247 que¹: qui *F* / lapis *D* / que²: qui *F*
248 si ergo *tr. B*

[*Proposition*] *18. The three methods of propagating rays mentioned previously concur in the generation of the rainbow.*[42]

This is evident with regard to direct rays, since the rainbow is generated opposite the sun. It is certain with regard to reflection, because certain small spherical drops are specular and of smooth surface, reflecting rays after the manner of water.[43] Moreover, it is evident with regard to refraction because solar light, although it is reflected, [also] enters into the depth of water.[44]

[*Proposition*] *19. The cause of the circularity of the rainbow resides principally in the cloud.*

When a cloud is suspended regularly, [all parts] equidistant from the earth, it is certain that moisture descends [from it] regularly, and this suffices to produce the circularity [of the rainbow]; other clouds suspended roughly and irregularly do not contain regular impressions. Some people, however, assign the cause [of the rainbow's circularity] to the rays, maintaining that light rays enter a spherical cloud and then converge to a point on the other side, as explained in Proposition 16 of this part; then, after intersection, the light spreads out a second time into a pyramid, half of which falls into the cloud and consequently produces a semicircular impression, while the other half falls on the earth.[45] But in opposition to this, let a solar ray fall through a circular aperture; it is certain that it will be circular. In front of the ray, place a hexagonal stone that generates the colors of the rainbow; it is certain that the rainbow is generated not in the shape of the ray, which is circular, but in the shape of the stone, which is columnar. Therefore, if a similar event has a similar cause, the cause of the shape of the arc must be sought in the cloud and not in the ray. Furthermore, this position [that the cause of the circularity of the rainbow is in the ray] is evidently contrary to sense, since the rainbow is generated by radiation of the sun into a moist cloud without anything interposed; such light falling into a cloud is called by the Philosopher "the ray of medial roundness," for light assumes the shape of the medium in which it is.[46]

Other people assign roundness to the ray in virtue of itself, for they say that rays diverge from the sun pyramidally, and half the pyramid falls into a cloud and produces the aforesaid figure. But this is to no avail because, if [one should say that] the figure is caused by the entire solar light, [I would reply that] every point of the sun fills a whole hemisphere with its light; if [on the

---

249 hoc *A* / positio *om. B* ponere *A*
251 in: inter *D* / *post* roridam *in alia manu mg. hab. V* rotundam / radiante *om. A* radiantem *FH*
252 phylosophus: physicus *A*

254 radio: medio *B*
255 medietatis *B*
256 hoc *in alia manu hab. V* / nichil: non *F* / toto: tuto *H*

si de particulari aliqua pyramide agitur, non sunt pyramides a se distincte et divise, sed unum est corpus continuum lucis continens in se potentialiter pyramides infinitas, quarum quedam habent conum in luminoso, quedam in obiecto vel medio.

[*Propositio*] *20ª. Diversitatem colorum yridis tam ex nubis quam luminis variatione provenire.*

Nubis variatio ex hoc accidit, quod roratio descendit ad centrum et ad angulum. Ergo per consequens est inferius strictior et superius latior, cuius tamen contrarium quidam dicunt nimis ruraliter cum certum sit omnia gravia descendere ad angulum, et ita non potest esse ut pyramis rorida habeat conum sursum et latitudinem deorsum. Superius igitur lata et paulatim in descendendo densior, tum propter pyramidis coangustationem ex descensu ad angulum pervenientem tum propter hoc quod grossiores partes citius descendunt. Aptior est superius ad colores nobiliores et luciformiores, et inferius minus.

Potest etiam esse diversitas a parte luminis directe cadentis in nubem, et magis magisque fracti in singulis partibus nubis, sed et reflexi a stillis super alias stillas, que omnia in lumine magnam solent diversitatem efficere, ut supra visum est. Quod autem dicunt quidam in eisdem nubis partibus diversos generari colores, nec in omnibus locis apparere sed in illis tantum ad quos radii eos constituentes reflectuntur, non capio quoniam impressiones quecunque non videntur per radios earum generativos, sed per speciem propriam extra locum reflexionis, sicut patet in radio transeunte per vitream coloratam usque in corpus oppositum, sicut patet in generatione colorum in lapidibus exagonis, qui videntur ex omni parte. Que autem falso dicuntur de yride multum possunt refelli per hoc quod in huiusmodi lapidibus contemplamur.

258 aliqua: alia *A* / se: sole *A*
259 est *in alia manu mg. corr. V ex* illud / *post* potentialiter *add. F* id est formaliter
260 quarum: quare *HD* / in: cum *A*
264 rotatio *A*
265 inferior *A* / superior *A* superius *corr. H ex* superior / latior *F* artior *VBHD* altior *A* amplior *W*
268 *post* rorida *add. B* vel rotunda / lata: latus est *F*
269 tum: tamen *FD*
270 tum: tamen *F*
271 aptior *in alia manu corr. A ex* aptius
273 directe cadentis *tr. F*
274 *post* magis *add. F* active / magisque:

quam *FD* / sed *om. B* vel *F* / et: etiam *FD* / reflexi: flexi *B* / stillis: stellis *VBAHD*
275 super...stillas *om. H* / stillas: stellas *VBAD*
277 locis *om. B* / in² *om. F* / illis: aliis *D*
279 eorum *A*
280 radio *corr. H ex* radios
281 *post* vitream *add. F* fenestram / in¹: ad *B*
282 qui: que *A*
283 false *A* / de yride: deinde *A* / refelli *in alia manu mg. hab. V*
284 huiusmodi *VWFH* huius *BAD* / contemplantur *B*

other hand one should maintain that] it is caused by some particular pyramid, [I would reply that] there are no distinct and separated pyramids, but one continuous body of light containing potentially an infinite number of pyramids, some of which have their vertex in the luminous body and some in the facing object or medium.[47]

[*Proposition*] 20. *The diversity of rainbow colors is produced by variation of both the cloud and the light.*

Clouds vary because moisture descends toward the center [of the world] to an angle. Consequently the lower part is more compressed and the higher more diffuse.[48] Nevertheless some people assert the contrary—and very provincially since it is certain that all heavy bodies descend to an angle; and so a pyramid of moisture cannot have its vertex upward and its base downward. Therefore [the cloud] is diffuse in the upper parts and becomes gradually denser as it descends, both because of the narrowing of the pyramid as it descends toward the angle and because the grosser parts descend more swiftly.[49] The higher part is more suited to the nobler colors and those having more of the form of light, and the lower part less so.

There can also be diversity on the part of the light, [which is variously] incident on the cloud directly, refracted more and more in individual parts of the cloud, or reflected from droplets to other droplets, all of which [mechanisms] customarily produce great diversity in light, as was seen above. However, I fail to grasp that which is maintained by some people, [namely,] that the different colors are produced in the same parts of the cloud but do not appear everywhere, being visible only in those places to which the rays constituting the colors are reflected;[50] for no impressions whatever are seen by means of the rays that generated them, but rather through their own species outside the place of reflection.[51] This is evident in a ray traversing colored glass [and continuing] as far as a facing body [and] in the generation of colors in hexagonal stones, for the colors are seen from every direction. However, those things that are erroneously maintained concerning the rainbow can frequently be disproved by observation of such stones.

285   *[Propositio] 21ª. Generationem yridis cathaclismum excludere.*

Excludit quidem per modum signi dati convenientis, sed non sufficientis causande serenitati; non enim omnis sed subtilis resolutio nubium parit yridem, colores enim nobiles in yride concurrentes, quales pictor facere non potest, densarum nubium obscuritas et grossa resolutio non admittit.
290 Significat ergo per hanc viam yris resolutionis humide paucitatem et per consequens oppositum cathaclismi. Amplius ad hoc causaliter agit concursus radiorum reflexorum a nubibus cum radiis directis, non enim generatur yris in nubibus in omni parte densatis, oportet siquidem ut radii solares libere transeant in nubes ex opposita parte celi sitas, ex quibus
295 reflexi radii concurrunt cum radiis directe porrectis, ex quo concursu fit attenuatio vaporis ut pluvie materia consumatur. Hec autem intelligenda sunt cum yris generatur secundum quantitatem arcus emisperii, quando enim fit yris secundum modicam quantitatem serenitatem aeris non pertendit.

300   *[Propositio] 22ª. Lucem solarem et syderealem in perspicuo puro efficere galaxiam.*

Quidam in hoc Philosopho contradicere non verentur, qui dicit galaxiam generari in ignis purissima regione, quasi impressio fieri non posset in corpore transparenti; cum econtra videamus solarem radium in domo
305 subobscura per aerem transeuntem, quamvis in aere non sit densitas sensi-

---

285 generationem...excludere *om. B* | generationes *F*
286–99 excludit....pertendit *om. VBWHL* (This portion of Proposition 21 appears in only 9 of 29 manuscripts examined. Moreover, the correlation between those manuscripts containing the long closing passage of Proposition III. 13 and those containing this passage is not particularly high. In addition to *A*, *F*, and *D*, I have collated Paris BN 7368 (*N*), Digby 28 (*O*), and Prague 1272 (*P*). Other manuscripts containing the passage are Digby 98, Prague 2815, and Vienna 3105.)
286 quedam *P* | dati convenientis *FO*; *tr. P* convenienter dati *N* convenientis *AD*
287 causande *NA* causandi *FP* causando *OD* | serenitati *NODP* serenitatis *A* serenitatem *F* | *post* subtilis *add. F* tantum | *post* parit *add. NAP* id est facit
288 nobiles *AFO* nobiliores *NP* nobilior *D*

289 resolutio *om. N* | admittunt *F*
290 significat *NFOD* sicut *AP* | yris: yridis *A*
291 *ante* oppositum *add. NAP* permittit | amplius...causaliter *NF* amplius ad huc causaliter *A* amplius causaliter ad hoc *OD* ad huc autem amplius causaliter *P* | *ante* agit *scr. et del. F* concurrit
291–92 concursus...reflexorum *FOD* radiorum reflexorum concursus *N* reflexio radiorum concursus *A* reflexorum radiorum concursus *P*
292 a *FOD* in *NAP* | non: ?vis *P*
293 in¹ *NAFP*; *om. OD* | *post* parte *add. F* celi | densatis *FOPD* densitatis *NA*
294–95 in...radii *FOD*; *om. NAP*
295 *ante* concurrunt *add. NAP* et | concurrunt *NFOD* concurrant *AP* | porrectis *FOD* incidentibus *NAP* | quo: quorum *F*
296 ut: et (*supra* et *hab.* ut) *O* | pluvie *FOD* pluviam *NAP* | materia *FO*; *om. A* inde *NP* minus *D* | consumatur *FOD* consumant *NAP* | intelligenda *FO* intelligen-

[*Proposition*] *21. The generation of the rainbow precludes a flood.*

Indeed it precludes [a flood] in the manner of an appropriate sign that has been given,[52] but it is insufficient for producing fair weather; for not every condensation of clouds brings forth the rainbow, but only a fine condensation, since the noble colors occurring in the rainbow—such as no painter can reproduce[53]—are not permitted by gross condensation or by the darkness of dense clouds. Thus the rainbow signifies the paucity of the moist condensation and consequently the contrary of a flood. In addition to this, the combination of direct rays and rays reflected from clouds acts causally; for the rainbow is not generated in clouds that are condensed throughout, since solar rays must pass freely into clouds situated in the opposite part of the sky, after which the reflected rays are united with the rays extended in straight lines.[54] From this union there is an attenuation of the vapor so that the matter of the rain is consumed. However, these things are true only when the rainbow is generated as an arc of a hemisphere, for when it is of small extent, it does not produce clearness of the air.

[*Proposition*] *22. Solar and sidereal light produce the Milky Way in the perfectly transparent.*

In this matter some people do not fear to contradict the Philosopher, who says that the Milky Way is generated in the purest region of fire;[55] [this they maintain] by reason of the fact that no impression can be made in a transparent body. On the contrary, however, we see a solar ray passing through the air in a rather dark house even though the air has no sensible density. Notwithstand-

dum *D*

296–99 hec...pertendit *FOD*; *om. NAP*
297 *ante* yris *add. F* fit / arcus *F*; *om. OD*
298 enim *FD* autem *O* / *ante* quantitatem *add. OD* ipsius
300–308 lucem....apparere *om. B*
302–8 qui....apparere *om. VBWHL* (Most manuscripts that omit the demonstration of Proposition 21 also omit this portion of Proposition 22. In addition to *A*, *F*, and *D*, I have collated Paris BN 7368 (*N*), Digby 28 (*O*), and Prague 1272

(*P*). In *A*, this portion of Proposition 22 appears in a new hand, beginning at the top of the verso side of the last folio.)
302 *post* verentur *add. H* et cetera / dicit *FD* dixit *O* dicunt *NAP*
303 quasi: ac si *F* / posset *NFP* potest *A* possit *OD*
304 transparenti *FOD* transparente *NAP*
305 subobscura *NOD* obscura *AFP* / transeuntem: transparentem *O* / *post* quamvis *add. F* eam *et add. OD* enim

bilis. Abscondere tamen se non potest lucis vehementia radiantis. Multiplicatio igitur radiorum stellarum concurrentium in suprema parte ignis potest ibi eadem ratione sensibilis apparere.

Explicit Perspectiva Fratris Johannis de Pecham

306 *ante* se (*in alia manu O*) *add. FO* in / se *FOPD*; *om. NA* / lucis...radiantis *D* lucis vehementiam radiantis *FO* vehementissima radiatio lucis *NAP*
306–7 multiplicatio: in ?vibratio *P*
307 radiorum stellarum *tr. O*
308 potest...apparere *OD* eadem ratione ibidem (*om. NF*) sensibilis (*om. N*) potest (*om. AF*) apparere *NAFP*
309 explicit...pecham *om. VAH* explicit perspectiva fratris Johannis picham quondam Kantuariensis archiepiscopi *B* explicit perspectiva Johannis pysani deo gratias *F*

ing [this lack of density], the intensity of the radiating light cannot be concealed. Therefore the multiplication of stellar rays in the highest part [of the region] of fire can be sensible there for the same reason.

Here Ends the Perspective of Brother John Pecham

Reference Matter

Critical Notes

Part I

1 Presumably those of the Franciscan schools or the Papal University; see the introduction, pp. 17–20, above.

2 On the after-image, see Aristotle, *De somniis* 3. 459ᵃ24–ᵇ23.

3 Pecham uses the expression *Perspectiva* only in reference to the *Perspectiva* of Alhazen; see Alhazen, *Opt. thes.*, bk. 1, sec. 1, p. 1.

4 Proposition I.47{50}.

5 Cf. Alhazen, *Opt. thes.*, bk. 1, sec. 14, p. 7.

6 Cf. *ibid.*

7 Proposition II.13; cf. Propositions I.6{8} and II.14.

8 Cf. Alhazen, *Opt. thes.*, bk. 4, chap. 3, p. 111; Grosseteste, *De lineis*, in *Phil. Werke*, p. 64. In works translated from Arabic, the term "*pyramis*" is used even when the figure has a round base and hence could aptly be designated by the term "*conus*"; and thirteenth-century scholars like Pecham conformed to the same pattern. See Marshall Clagett, "The *De curvis superficiebus Archimenidis*: A Medieval Commentary of Johannes de Tinemue on Book I of the *De sphaera et cylindro* of Archimedes," *Osiris*, vol. 11 (1954), p. 298. The term "*conus*" was employed by Pecham to designate the apex of a pyramid.

9 Cf. Alhazen, *Opt. thes.*, bk. 4, chap. 3, p. 111.

10 Cf. Proposition I.18{16}; Grosseteste, *De lineis*, in *Phil. Werke*, pp. 64–65; Bacon, *Opus maius*, pt. IV, dist. 3, chap. 2 (ed. Bridges, vol. 1, pp. 123–24); Bacon, *De mult. spec.*, bk. 5, chap. 3, pp. 539–43.

11 Cf. Bacon, *De mult. spec.*, bk. 5, chap. 2, pp. 534–35; Bacon, *Opus maius*, pt. IV, dist. 3, chap. 3 (ed. Bridges, vol. 1, pp. 126–27); Grosseteste, *De lineis*, in *Phil. Werke*, pp. 60–61. See also *Perspectiva communis*, Proposition I.15{30}, and the introduction, pp. 37–38 and 49, above.

12 Cf. Bacon, *Opus maius*, pt. IV, dist. 4, chap. 5 (ed. Bridges, vol. 1, p. 138); Bacon, *Opus tertium*, ed. Little, p. 5.

13 Moses Maimonides, *Guide for the Perplexed*, bk. 2, chap. 10. Cf. Bacon, *Opus maius*, pt. IV (ed. Bridges, vol. 1, pp. 250–51).

14 The expression "second, third, or fourth degree" must be a reference to variation in position. See Thorndike, *Sacrobosco*, p. 114, for a similar usage of the expression "*gradus*."

15 The revised version of this same proposition follows directly below. Pecham

dealt with the same problem in his *Tractatus de perspectiva* and *De sphera*, the relevant section of which has been reproduced by Duhem, *Le Système du monde*, vol. 3, pp. 524–29. Lynn Thorndike has identified the author of this section of *De sphera* (unknown to Duhem) as John Pecham in his note: "Duhem's 'Disciple of Bacon' identified with John Peckham," *Isis*, vol. 34 (1942), p. 28. For an analysis of the history of pinhole images, see my "The Theory of Pinhole Images"; Pecham's views are there analyzed at length; see the introduction, pp. 41–45, above.

Although Pecham indicates several times in this proposition that he is presenting the ideas of others, I have been able to locate only a few of his sources. Perhaps he was more original than he admits. See Alhazen, *Opt. thes.*, bk. 4, sec. 14, p. 111; Bacon, *Opus maius*, pt. IV, dist. 2, chap. 3 (ed. Bridges, vol. 1, pp. 117–19); Bacon, *De mult. spec.*, bk. 2, chap. 8, pp. 492–93; Pseudo-Euclid, *De speculis*, Proposition 9, in Björnbo and Vogl, p. 102; Witelo, *Optica*, bk. 2, secs. 36–41, pp. 74–76.

16 Bk. 1, Proposition 4, *The Thirteen Books of Euclid's Elements*, trans. Thomas L. Heath (New York, 1956), vol. 1, pp. 247–50.

17 The beam of light has the shape of the aperture immediately after its passage through the aperture, but gradually assumes the shape of the luminous body as the distance from the aperture increases.

18 Note that *KLM* (Fig. 1) is not the sun, but a circle drawn somewhere within it.

19 The argument is that even if the sun were square, a circle such as *KLM* (Fig. 1) could be drawn within it, and so a round image should be produced by the square sun. By introducing this hypothetical square sun, one can supposedly refute the argument of the previous paragraph, according to which the image of the sun is round because of the nature of the pyramids radiating from circle *KLM*. It is strange that portions of the sun (whether the latter is round or square) that lie outside circle *KLM* are here ignored. Surely it should have been evident that rays from the outermost portions of the sun determine the shape of the image projected through the aperture; thus pyramids emanating from circles drawn within the sun are irrelevant to the problem. But then one cannot attribute these absurdities to Pecham, since he claims to be presenting (and refuting) a demonstration formulated by somebody else.

20 For Grosseteste on the natural sphericity of light, see his *On Light*, trans. Riedl, p. 10; and *De lineis*, in *Phil. Werke*, p. 64. Cf. Crombie, *Grosseteste*, pp. 106–08.

21 Pecham seems not to know that the sun and its image projected through a pinhole are indeed eclipsed on opposite sides; he is here following Pseudo-Euclid's *De speculis*.

22 Up to this point Propositions I.5 and I.{7} are identical.

23 Grosseteste calls *lux* the first corporeal form; see Grosseteste, *On Light*, trans. Riedl, p. 10.

24 I.e., straight lines.

25 Proposition I.3{3}.

26 Bacon cites Euclid I.17 and I.19 in support of a similar idea; see *Opus maius*, pt. IV. dist. 3, chap. 1 (ed. Bridges, vol. 1, p. 120).

27 I.e., with base on the sun and vertex in the adjacent air.

28 I.e., if the beam is oblong, with the major axis much greater than the minor axis, the beam will have to travel a great distance before it can achieve roundness; but if the beam travels a great distance, its rays, which are continually diverging, may become so far separated as to be invisible. Note that Pecham is here treating radiation as a collection of discrete rays rather than a continuum; see also the introduction, p. 40, above.

29 Cf. Bacon, *De mult. spec.*, bk. 2, chap. 2, pp. 463–64; *Perspectiva communis*, Proposition I.40{43}. See the introduction, p. 38, above.

30 The three kinds of rays must be the two kinds of primary radiation discussed above (p. 75) as well as secondary or indirect radiation. If I correctly interpret Pecham's theory of pinhole images, by "the latter kind" he means secondary radiation.

31 Cf. Bacon, *Opus maius*, pt. IV, dist. 2, chap. 3 (ed. Bridges, vol. 1, p. 118). Bacon and Pecham introduce the pyramid of fire in similar contexts.

32 Cf. Alkindi, *De aspectibus*, in Björnbo and Vogl, pp. 23–25; Bacon, *De mult. spec.*, bk. 2, chap. 10, pp. 499–500. The revised version of this proposition follows directly as Proposition {8}.

33 See the introduction, p. 42, n. 46, above.

34 Here, as on a number of other occasions, Pecham writes "*spericus*" when he means spherically convex; cf. Propositions I.83{88}, II.32, and II.33.

35 Cf. Alhazen, *Opt. thes.*, bk. 1, sec. 29, p. 17; Bacon, *De mult. spec.*, bk. 3, chap. 3, pp. 511–16. The revised version of this proposition follows directly as Proposition {9}.

36 See the introduction, p. 40, above.

37 Cf. Alhazen, *Opt. thes.*, bk. 1, sec. 2, pp. 1–2.

38 On the possibility and history of stellar observations during the daytime from a pit, see A. Sayili, "The 'Observation Well,'" *Actes du VIIe Congrès international d'histoire des sciences* (Jerusalem, 1953), pp. 542–50; cf. Aristotle, *De generatione animalium* 5. 1. 780^b20; Bacon, *De mult. spec.*, bk. 2, chap. 2, p. 464; Galen, *De usu partium*, bk. 10, chap. 3 (trans. Daremberg, vol. 1, p. 618).

39 Cf. Alhazen, *Opt. thes.*, bk. 1, sec. 2, pp. 1–2.

40 Cf. *ibid.*

41 Cf. *ibid.*, sec. 3, pp. 2–3; Bacon, *Opus maius*, pt. V.iii, dist. 1, chap. 5 (ed. Bridges, vol. 2, pp. 141–42).

42 The revised version substitutes this longer passage for the final sentence of the unrevised version; otherwise both versions of the propositions are identical.

43 Cf. Alhazen, *Opt. thes.*, bk. 1, sec. 17, p. 9. On secondary or accidental light, see the introduction, p. 41, above; cf. Grosseteste, *De lineis*, in *Phil. Werke*, p. 63; Bacon, *Opus maius*, pt. IV, dist. 2, chap. 2 (ed. Bridges, vol. 1, p. 117).

44 Alhazen, *Opt. thes.*, bk. 7, sec. 4, p. 235; cf. Grosseteste, *De lineis*, in *Phil. Werke*, p. 63, and Bacon, *De mult. spec.*, bk. 2, chap. 3, pp. 468–70. Part III of the *Perspectiva communis* is also devoted to refraction. For Pecham's views on the nature and cause of refraction, see the introduction, pp. 48–50, above; see my "The Cause of Refraction" for a fuller discussion.

45 The text of this sentence is obscure, and I have translated it freely; nevertheless,

I believe I have captured Pecham's intended meaning. Cf. the parallel explanations in Propositions I.16{31} and III.3.

46 See the introduction, pp. 49–50, above.

47 Pecham uses the expression "*proportionalis*" to mean commensurate in a non-numerical sense, i.e., comparable or approaching equality. On occasion, "*proportionalis*" may also mean suitable or appropriate.

48 Here Pecham reproaches Bacon, whose terminology in *De mult. spec.*, bk. 2, chap. 3, p. 470, suggests that the ray *elects* the path closer to the perpendicular: "virtus naturalis generans ipsam speciem appetit faciliorem transitum et eligit illum."

49 Cf. Alhazen, *Opt. thes.*, bk. 7, sec. 7, pp. 238–40.

50 Propositions III.9–III.11.

51 Propositions are cited in my collated text and translation by their unrevised numbers.

52 Proposition 16, trans. Heath, vol. 2, pp. 37–39.

53 In the revised version this sentence reads as follows: "Therefore, light falls to point *G* from the entire arc *EABO*, but to no higher point." For the revised text, see the variant readings.

54 Cf. Grosseteste, *De lineis*, in *Phil. Werke*, p. 65; Bacon, *Opus maius*, pt. IV, dist. 3, chap. 2 (ed. Bridges, vol. 1, pp. 123–24); Bacon, *De mult. spec.*, bk. 5, chap. 3, pp. 539–40; *Perspectiva communis*, Proposition I.{6}.

55 Cf. Grosseteste, *De lineis*, in *Phil. Werke*, pp. 64–65; Bacon, *De mult. spec.*, bk. 5, chap. 3, pp. 540–41.

56 Proposition 21, trans. Heath, vol. 1, pp. 289–92.

57 At the vertex, light is completely (and therefore equally) united in long and short pyramids.

58 Cf. Grosseteste, *De natura locorum*, in *Phil. Werke*, p. 66; Richard C. Dales, "Robert Grosseteste's Scientific Works," *Isis*, vol. 52 (1961), pp. 386–87. See also Bacon, *Opus maius*, pt. IV (ed. Bridges, vol. 1, pp. 134–35, 214–15).

59 See the introduction, pp. 49–50, above.

60 Cf. Alkindi, *De aspectibus*, in Björnbo and Vogl, pp. 5–6; Bacon, *De mult. spec.*, bk. 2, chap. 10, pp. 500–01.

61 This is a citation to Book 3, Proposition 18, of Heath's English translation, but Book 3, Proposition 17, of Adelard of Bath's Latin version; cf. *Preclarissimus liber elementorum Euclidis perspicacissimi: in artem Geometrie incipit quam foelicissime*, trans. Adelard of Bath, ed. John Campanus (Venice, 1482).

62 Cf. Alkindi, *De aspectibus*, in Björnbo and Vogl, pp. 4–6.

63 See n. 61, above.

64 This is the fourth postulate in the Campanus edition (see n. 61), but the fifth postulate in Heath's translation, vol. 1, p. 155.

65 I.e., basket-shaped, the basket having a narrow base and expanding toward the top; cf. καλαθοειδος. The only earlier optical work in which I have found this expression in a similar context is *De philosophia mundi libri quatuor* of William of Conches (first half of the twelfth century), in J.-P. Migne, ed., *Patrologia Latina*, vol. 172 (Paris, 1895), col. 74 (there attributed to Honorius of Autun). However, the expression abounds in later optical literature, as, for example, Henry of

Langenstein, *Questiones super perspectivam* (Valencia, 1503), Quest. 7, fol. 56v; Gregorius Reisch, *Margarita philosophica* (Basel, 1583), p. 1392; Friedrich Risner, *Opticae libri quatuor* (Kassel, 1606), p. 81; and *Francisci Aguilonii e Societate Iesu Opticorum libri sex* (Antwerp, 1613), p. 432.

66 Pecham seems to mean that the two bodies are aligned vertically.

67 Cf. Propositions I.14{29} and I.51{54}; Grosseteste, *De natura locorum*, in *Phil. Werke*, pp. 71–72.

68 Cf. Pseudo-Aristotle, *Problemata* 15. 7. 911^{b}35; Thorndike, *Sacrobosco*, pp. 141–42; Grosseteste, *De sphera*, in *Phil. Werke*, pp. 29–30; Bacon, *Opus maius*, pt. V.ii, dist. 3, chap. 4 (ed. Bridges, vol. 2, pp. 108–14). A closer translation of the enunciation of this proposition would be, "When the moon is apparently less than half-illuminated...," but Pecham appears to mean that its lower or visible side is less than half-illuminated.

69 "appears...knife." I cannot make sense of the Latin text at this point. The source of the difficulty may be a scribal error, but since the passage occurs in only a single manuscript, there is no way of being certain. Consequently, my translation must be regarded as a rough attempt to understand Pecham's intention. Where I read "*cava*," the manuscript would equally well allow (and perhaps even prefer) "*catia*," but that reading only obscures the passage further.

70 Proposition I.26{24}.

71 There were many Gregorys in the Middle Ages, but I am unable to identify this one.

72 This is a reference to the dragon-shaped lune bounded by the inclined deferent of the moon and the projection of that deferent onto the plane of the ecliptic. Cf. Thorndike, *Sacrobosco*, pp. 114, 141; Sacrobosco refers to the projection of the deferent onto the plane of the ecliptic as the "equant."

73 Proposition I.83{88}.

74 Or approximately so, as pointed out earlier in the proposition.

75 Cf. Proposition I.{27} and the introduction, p. 40, above.

76 On the multiplication of species, see the introduction, pp. 35–36 and 39–40, above, and my "Alhazen's Theory of Vision," pp. 335–41.

77 Cf. Alhazen, *Opt. thes.*, bk. 1, sec. 18, p. 9; and the introduction, pp. 37–38, above.

78 Cf. Alhazen, *Opt. thes.*, bk. 1, sec. 35, pp. 21–22; Bacon, *Opus maius*, pt. V.i, dist. 3, chap. 1 (ed. Bridges, vol. 2, p. 18); *ibid.*, dist. 4, chap. 4 (ed. Bridges, vol. 2, pp. 29–30). Propositions 29–31 of the revised version appear as Propositions 14–16 of the unrevised version.

79 This is not what Pecham teaches below; see Propositions I.35{38} and I.40{43}. Alhazen adopts a similar approach, first insisting on convergence to a vertex, then denying it; see *Opt. thes.*, bk. 1, sec. 20, p. 13; *ibid.*, bk. 2, sec. 2, p. 25.

80 "si est falsum." Pecham does not mean merely "if this is false," but rather "if this is false, which it is" or "since this is false."

81 The text of the revised version continues beyond this point as in the unrevised version (Proposition 29).

82 Cf. Bacon, *Opus maius*, pt. V.i, dist. 3, chap. 2 (ed. Bridges, vol. 2, pp. 20–21).

83 Every member of the long medieval ophthalmological tradition provided a

description of the eye, and few of these departed very radically from Galen. For the medieval sources most likely to have been read by Pecham, see Alhazen, *Opt. thes.*, bk. 1, secs. 4–13, pp. 3–7; *ibid.*, sec. 33, pp. 20–21 (this latter passage has been translated into English in Stephen Polyak, *The Retina* [Chicago, 1941], pp. 109–11); Avicenna, *Liber canonis* (Venice, 1555), bk. 3, fen. 3, chap. 1, fols. 203v–204r; Bacon, *Opus maius*, pt. V.i, dists. 2–4 (ed. Bridges, vol. 2, pp. 12–30); Witelo, *Optica*, bk. 3, sec. 4, pp. 85–87. See also the works of Ḥunain ibn Isḥāq (Johannitius), Canamusali, Jesu Haly, Alcoatin, and others in Pansier, *Collectio ophtalmologica*; P. de Koning, *Trois traités d'anatomie Arabes par Muḥammed ibn Zakariyyā al-Rāzī, Alī ibn al-Abbās et Alī ibn Sīnā* (Leiden, 1903), pp. 51–53, 301–09, 660–67; William of Conches, *Philosophicarum et astronomicarum institutionum...libri tres* (Basel, 1531), pp. 75–76; Mondino dei Luzzi, *Anatomy*, in *The "Fasciculo di medicina," Venice 1493*, ed. and trans. Charles Singer (Florence, 1925), pt. 1, pp. 94–95; *Die Chirurgie des Heinrich von Mondeville*, ed. J. L. Pagel (Berlin, 1892), pp. 32–34; *La grand chirurgie de M. Guy de Chauliac*, trans. Laurens Joubert (Tournon, 1598), pp. 50–52.

Pecham does not refer to a drawing of the eye in the text of the *Perspectiva communis*, but the frequency with which such drawings appear in early manuscripts of the *Perspectiva communis* suggests that if Pecham himself did not include a drawing of the eye, one was added to the text at a very early date. In either case, there is no reason to believe that the drawing would have been original; for just as Pecham's description of the eye was extracted from earlier treatises, so his drawing of the eye was copied from earlier drawings. Indeed, it is clear that the source of Pecham's drawing (or, at any rate, the drawings appearing in several early manuscripts of the *Perspectiva communis*) was Alhazen's *Perspectiva*, for manuscripts *V*, *B*, and *H* of the *Perspectiva communis* (dating from the late 13th and early 14th centuries) bear a marked resemblance to the drawings contained in three early English manuscripts of Alhazen's *Perspectiva* (Cambridge, Trinity College MS 0.5.30, fol. 2v [13th century]; Edinburgh, Royal Observatory, Crawford Library, MS 9–11–3(20), fol. 4v [1269 A.D.]—reproduced in Stephen Polyak, *The Vertebrate Visual System* [Chicago, 1957], p. 25; and British Museum, Royal MS 12.G.VII, fol. 1r [14th century]). A similar drawing appears in manuscript *A* of the *Perspectiva communis* (late 14th century), where the reader is explicitly informed that it represents Alhazen's conception of the structure of the eye (see Plate 3a). It must be recognized, however, that the drawings appearing in Latin manuscripts of Alhazen's *Perspectiva* do not resemble the few that have been preserved from the Arabic optical tradition (see Polyak, *Retina*, pp. 114–19 and Figs. 7–20); it is thus probable that they are western in origin. Finally, it must be noted that the drawings of the eye appearing in the printed editions of the works of Pecham, Witelo, and Alhazen do not represent the medieval manuscript tradition, but rather reflect Renaissance conceptions of the structure of the eye.

In Figure 14 I have copied the drawing of the eye appearing in *V*, fol. 16r; in addition, a photographic reproduction of the original has been included as Plate 1. Drawings closely resembling this (taken from other manuscript copies of the *Perspectiva communis*) are reproduced in Plates 2a, 2b, 3a, and 4b, while

Plates 3b and 4a contain reproductions of drawings that vary considerably from that in *V*. In Plate 3a (from Erfurt MS Q.387) the drawing is identified as "the composition of the eye according to Alhazen," while the drawing in Plate 3b (also from Erfurt MS Q.387) is intended to represent Pecham's conception of the eye. It is impossible to determine which, if any, of these drawings actually represents Pecham's views. Not only is it impossible to reconstruct a drawing from his verbal description alone, but all existing drawings violate his description in one way or another. Consequently, for Figure 14, I have selected the drawing in *V* as representative of the early manuscript tradition, while also reproducing several other drawings in the Plates.

Other medieval drawings of the eye (including several taken from manuscripts of the *Perspectiva communis*) are reproduced in Karl Sudhoff, "Augenanatomiebilder im 15. und 16. Jahrhundert," in *Studien zur Geschichte der Medizin*, vol. 1 (Leipzig, 1907), pp. 19–26; M. Meyerhof and C. Prüfer, "Die Augenanatomie des Hunain b. Ishaq," *Sudhoffs Archiv für Geschichte der Medizin und der Naturwissenschaften*, vol. 4 (1910), pp. 172–79; J. L. Choulant, *History and Bibliography of Anatomic Illustration*, trans. Mortimer Frank (Chicago, 1920), pp. 75–80; Adam Bednarski, "Das anatomische Augenbild von Johann Peckham, Erzbischof zu Canterbury im XIII. Jahrhundert," *Sudhoffs Archiv für Geschichte der Medizin und der Naturwissenschaften*, vol. 22 (1929), pp. 352–56; and Adam Bednarski, "Die anatomische Augenbilder in den Handschriften des Roger Bacon, Johann Peckham und Witelo," *Sudhoffs Archiv für Geschichte der Medizin und der Naturwissenschaften*, vol. 24 (1931), pp. 60–78.

84 I.e., the sclera.

85 The pupil.

86 The aqueous humor.

87 "Glacial humor" sometimes denotes the combined crystalline lens and vitreous humor, sometimes the former alone. Here it is used in the broader sense.

88 Cf. Bacon, *De mult. spec.*, bk. 6, chap. 4, pp. 550–51.

89 I.e., the crystalline lens, sometimes referred to simply as the "glacial humor."

90 The retina.

91 I.e., Alhazen, *Opt. thes.*, bk. 1, sec. 4, p. 3.

92 Medieval treatises entitled *De elementis* are almost without number. I can state only the negative conclusion that Pecham's citation is not to the *De elementis* of either Galen (*Claudii Galeni De elementis libri duo* [Lyons, 1558]) or Isaac Israeli (described by Jacob Guttmann, *Die philosophischen Lehren des Isaak ben Salomon Israeli* [*BGPM*, vol. 10, pt. 4 (Münster, 1911)], pp. 56–68), two of the more important early oculists.

93 There was a good deal of medieval debate on the number of tunics, although much of this debate focused not on the actual constitution of the eye, but on what qualified as a tunic. As Pecham points out, Alhazen identified four tunics. Avicenna, in the *Canon of Medicine*, states that there are three tunics, but the first two having two parts each brings the total to five (de Koning, *Trois traités d'anatomie*, pp. 660–67). Al-Rāzī and al-'Abbās both identify seven tunics (de Koning, pp. 51–53, 301–09), as do William of Conches (*Philosophicarum et astronomicarum institutionum*, pp. 75–76), Mondino (*Anatomy*, trans. Singer, pp. 94–95), and Guy

de Chauliac (*La grande chirurgie*, trans. Joubert, pp. 51–52). Roger Bacon follows Avicenna in identifying three tunics, two of which consists of two parts each, but Bacon's tunics are identical with Avicenna's only in number.

94 I.e., the choroid; see J. Hirschberg, *Geschichte der Augenheilkunde*, in *Graefe-Saemisch Handbuch der gesamten Augenheilkunde*, ed. Theodore Saemisch, vol. 13 (Leipzig, 1908), p. 155.

95 Cf. Bacon, *Opus maius*, pt. V.i., dist. 2, chap. 1 (ed. Bridges, vol. 2, pp. 13–14). See Figure 15.

96 Cf. Galen, *De usu partium*, trans. Daremberg, vol. 1, p. 643; Lucretius, *De rerum natura*, IV, lines 434–65.

97 Cf. Alhazen, *Opt. thes.*, bk. 1, secs. 6–12, pp. 4–6; Bacon, *Opus maius*, pt. V.i, dist. 3, chap. 3–dist. 4, chap. 3 (ed. Bridges, vol. 2, pp. 21–29).

98 This is not the perpendicular to the surface of the vitreous humor or interior glacial humor, but the initial line of incidence of the species, perpendicular to the outer surface of the eye. In this same sentence Pecham appears to distinguish between the interior glacial humor and the vitreous humor; in Proposition I.40{43}, however, he identifies these two humors as one and the same. See also Proposition I.31{34}.

99 Cf. Alhazen, *Opt. thes.*, bk. 1, secs. 7–11, pp. 4–5. On Pecham's doctrine of certification, see Proposition I.38{41} and the introduction, p. 39, above.

100 This proposition extends an idea that appears in Alhazen, *Opt. thes.*, bk. 1, sec. 16, p. 8; cf. Bacon, *Opus maius*, pt. V.i, dist. 4, chap. 2 (ed. Bridges, vol. 2, p. 27). Pecham's argument is entirely valid in form, but it starts from the false premise that sight is destroyed irrevocably by damage to the lens, and therefore Pecham reaches the false conclusion that the power of sight resides in the lens. Even in the Middle Ages couching operations for removal of cataracts were performed without ensuing complete loss of sight. However, in antiquity and the Middle Ages, cataracts were not understood as corruptions of the glacial humor, and consequently their removal could not serve as counterevidence to the assertion that damage to the glacial humor is irrevocable. This is evident from Ḥunain ibn Isḥāq's argument regarding the sensitive organ of the eye: "And further proof that the vision is in this [glacial] humor…lies in the circumstance that the vision ceases when cataract intervenes between it (the lens) and the perceptible object, and that the vision returns when the cataract is removed from it by couching (operation)" (*Ten Treatises on the Eye*, trans. Meyerhof, p. 4). The same misconception of cataract is evident in the *Anatomy* of Mondino dei Luzzi (d. 1326): "Now there is cataract when vapour is generated which falleth from the brain or riseth from the stomach and passeth through the pupil to the humor between the *crystallinus* and the *pupilla*" (trans. Singer, p. 95). See also Aryeh Feigenbaum, "Cataract Operation—Its Origin in Antiquity and Its Spread from East to West," *Actes du VIIe Congrès international d'histoire des sciences* (Jerusalem, 1953), pp. 298–301.

101 Cf. Alhazen, *Opt. thes.*, bk. 1, secs. 16–18, pp. 8–10; *ibid.*, sec. 24, p. 15; Bacon, *Opus maius*, pt. V.i, dist. 6, chap. 1 (ed. Bridges, vol. 2, pp. 35–37). I cannot prove that Pecham means "on [the surface of] the glacial humor" rather than "in the glacial humor." However, the former view is expressed clearly by both Alhazen

and Bacon, and Pecham's theory makes more sense if so interpreted; cf. Proposition I.41{44}.

102 Cf. Alhazen, *Opt. thes.*, bk. 2, chap. 1, p. 29; *ibid.*, bk. 2, sec. 65, pp. 67–69; Bacon, *Opus maius*, pt. V.i, dist. 7, chap. 4 (ed. Bridges, vol. 2, p. 53); Witelo, *Optica*, bk. 3, sec. 52, p. 109. On certification see also the introduction, p. 39, above.

103 Euclid, *Optica*, Proposition 1, trans. Ver Eecke, p. 2.

104 *Elements*, III.16, trans. Heath, vol. 2, pp. 37–43.

105 This is illustrated in Figure 46, in which the circle represents the sphere of the uvea, *C* its center, and *AB* the opening in the uvea as seen from the side. If *AB*

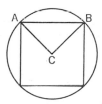

Fig. 46

is the side of the square that can be inscribed within the sphere of the uvea, then angle *ACB* is obviously a right angle. Pecham does not seem to recognize the variability in the diameter of the pupil. Alhazen is similarly silent, though the phenomenon had been noted long before; cf. Ḥunain Ibn Isḥāq, *Ten Treatises on the Eye*, trans. Meyerhof, p. 25.

106 Cf. Bacon, *Opus maius*, pt. V.i, dist. 8, chap. 3 (ed. Bridges, vol. 2, p. 61). Bacon and Pecham agree that the field of vision is slightly less than 90 degrees.

107 Propositions I.42{45} and III.15.

108 Proposition I.33{36}. The perpendicular Pecham has in mind is the initial line of incidence of the rays, perpendicular to the outer surface of the eye.

109 This claim is in direct conflict with Proposition I.29{32}; cf. Alhazen, *Opt. thes.*, bk. 1, chap. 5, pp. 15 ff.; *ibid.*, bk. 2, chap. 1, pp. 24 ff. By the expression "inclined toward an angle," Pecham means "inclined toward a vertex" in the center of the eye.

110 Cf. Proposition I.33{36}, and the Critical Notes, n. 98, just above.

111 Cf. Bacon, *De mult. spec.*, bk. 2, chap. 2, pp. 463–64.

112 Cf. Alhazen, *Opt. thes.*, bk. 2, sec. 36, pp. 50–51.

113 Proposition I.74{77}.

114 Cf. Bacon, *Opus maius*, pt. V.i, dist. 6, chap. 2 (ed. Bridges, vol. 2, pp. 37–39); *ibid.*, pt. V.iii, dist. 2, chap. 1 (ed. Bridges, vol. 2, pp. 146–48). In the former of these passages, Bacon claims that the refracted rays coming from a point on the object eventually reach the same point in the eye or optic nerve as does the perpendicular ray—an idea Pecham never expresses. See *Perspectiva communis*, Proposition III.14.

115 The meaning of this passage would be more obvious if it were emended to read "wider than that of [the largest] objects...." However, the manuscripts are nearly unanimous on the reading I have adopted, and it is not impossible to make sense of the passage as it is. Pecham's meaning seems to be that objects larger than the

largest ones visible at a single glance will be of such size that, if one portion of them is seen by rays outside the pyramid of radiation, other portions will extend over into the pyramid of radiation, and still other portions may not be seen at all. Therefore if an object is to be seen in its entirety outside the pyramid of radiation, it must be smaller than the largest objects visible at a single glance. See Bacon, *Opus maius*, pt. V.i, dist. 6, chap. 2 (ed. Bridges, vol. 2, p. 39), for a discussion that sheds light on Pecham's meaning.

116 Proposition III.14.

117 The meaning of this statement in the present context is obscure. Cf. the similar remarks in Grosseteste's *De lineis*, in *Phil. Werke*, p. 60, and Bacon's *De mult. spec.*, bk. 1, chap. 1, p. 417.

118 Alhazen, *Opt. thes.*, bk. 1, sec. 26, pp. 15–16. At the close of the proposition, Pecham disagrees with Alhazen's conclusion that *every* action of light is painful.

119 *Ibid.*, sec. 23, pp. 14–15.

120 Alkindi, *De aspectibus*, in Björnbo and Vogl, pp. 9, 12.

121 On Plato's theory of vision, see *Timaeus*, 45b–46a. Cf. Adelard of Bath, *Questiones naturales*, chap. 23 (edition of Louvain, 1480); Adelard not only describes Plato's theory but also affirms its truth.

122 Cf. Alhazen, *Opt. thes.*, bk. 1, sec. 23, pp. 14–15; Avicenna, *On Physics*, German trans. Eilhard Wiedemann, in "Ibn Sînâ's Anschauung vom Sehvorgang," *Archiv für die Geschichte der Naturwissenschaften und der Technik*, vol. 4 (1913), p. 239. On the argument of this proposition, see my "Alhazen's Theory of Vision," pp. 324–25.

123 Cf. Proposition I.48{51}; Alhazen, *Opt. thes.*, bk. 1, secs. 23–24, pp. 14–15; Bacon, *Opus maius*, pt. V.i, dist. 7, chaps. 3–4 (ed. Bridges, vol. 2, pp. 50–53); and the introduction, p. 35, above. On Alhazen's attitude toward the theory of visual rays, see my "Alhazen's Theory of Vision," pp. 324–27.

124 *De generatione animalium* 5. 1. 780^{a}5–15, 781^{a}1–10.

125 On the idea of a proportion between light and the visual power, see Wallace, *Theodoric of Freiberg*, pp. 155–56.

126 *De generatione animalium* 5. 1. 780^{a}5–15.

127 It is evident that "the Author" is Alhazen from Proposition II.20, where a similar expression is used and the identification as Alhazen is indisputable.

128 Cf. Alhazen, *Opt. thes.*, bk. 1, sec. 14, p. 7; *ibid.*, sec. 39, pp. 22–23.

129 Cf. *ibid.*, sec. 37, p. 22.

130 Cf. Aristotle, *De generatione animalium* 5. 1. 780^{b}34–781^{a}14. Robert Grosseteste quotes this same passage in his *De iride*, in *Phil. Werke*, p. 73.

131 Cf. Alhazen, *Opt. thes.*, bk. 1, sec. 38, p. 22.

132 Propositions I.28{28} and I.38{41}.

133 Part II.

134 Cf. Alhazen, *Opt. thes.*, bk. 1, sec. 40, p. 23.

135 Proposition I.38{41}.

136 Cf. Alhazen, *Opt. thes.*, bk. 1, sec. 41, p. 23.

137 Cf. Bacon, *Opus maius*, pt. IV, dist. 2, chap. 2 (ed. Bridges, vol. 1, p. 114); *Speculator consiliorum enigmaticus...*, trans. Lawn, in *Salernitan Questions*, p. 163.

138 Cf. Alhazen, *Opt. thes.*, bk. 1, sec. 42, p. 23; *Perspectiva communis*, Proposition I.47{50}.

139 Cf. Alhazen, *Opt. thes.*, bk. 2, sec. 21, pp. 37–38.

140 I do not find this demonstration. In the expression "*illa phylosophia*," the proper translation of "*illa*" is in doubt; I have assumed that Pecham means well-known or commonly accepted philosophy.

141 See Alhazen, *Opt. thes.*, bk. 2, sec. 15, p. 34, from which Pecham has borrowed the entire list of twenty-two visible intentions; Bacon, *Opus maius*, pt. V.i, dist. 1, chap. 3 (ed. Bridges, vol. 2, pp. 5–6). An *intention* is that which acts upon and can be grasped by the interior senses (as opposed to the five exterior senses); for the specific views of Bacon and Avicenna, see Vescovini, *Studi*, pp. 64–69, 80–85. Consult the entry for this word in *The Oxford English Dictionary*.

142 Cf. Alhazen, *Opt. thes.*, bk. 2, sec. 16, pp. 34–35; *ibid.*, sec. 61, p. 66. Also see Hans Bauer, *Die Psychologie Alhazens* (*BGPM*, vol. 10, pt. 5 [Münster, 1911]), pp. 48–53. On the *virtus distinctiva* and *memoria*, see Wolfson, "Internal Senses," pp. 114–29.

143 Cf. Alhazen, *Opt. thes.*, bk. 2, sec. 16, pp. 34–35. On the *ultimum sentiens*, see Bauer, *Die Psychologie Alhazens*, pp. 48–53.

144 Cf. Alhazen, *Opt. thes.*, bk. 2, sec. 16, p. 35.

145 Cf. *ibid.*, sec. 17, p. 35.

146 Cf. *ibid.*, sec. 18, p. 35.

147 Cf. Aristotle, *De anima* 2. 7. 418^{a}27–419^{b}2.

148 There seems to be no way to relieve the awkwardness of this sentence and yet translate it with fidelity. It could be rendered even more literally as "The color in color is perceived before its essence," but that makes little sense in English. What Pecham means is that an observer, presented with a colored object, perceives that it is colored before he is aware of the particular hue; cf. Alhazen, *Opt. thes.*, bk. 2, sec. 19. p. 36.

149 Cf. *ibid.*, secs. 24 25, pp. 39–42; *Perspectiva communis*, Proposition I.67{70}.

150 "this philosophy." Perhaps Pecham means the "philosophy" he has outlined in Propositions I.55{58} through I.62{65}, or perhaps commonly accepted contemporary philosophy. On the other hand, the parallel with Proposition III.9 suggests that this might be a reference to the philosophy of Alhazen.

151 A more literal translation would be "resident in the soul."

152 Cf. Alhazen, *Opt. thes.*, bk. 2, sec. 25, pp. 39–42.

153 Cf. *ibid.*, secs. 22–25, pp. 38–40. This proposition appears to maintain that sight has direct knowledge of the length of rays, contrary to the argument of Proposition I.63{66}.

154 I.e., the likeness of the object of which it is the species. Cf. Bacon, *De mult. spec.*, bk. 1, chap. 2, p. 431; *Perspectiva communis*, Proposition II.5.

155 As Pecham points out, the eye might have knowledge of the length of its own rays (on the visual ray theory), but it is not evident that it could be aware of the length of rays incident upon it from luminous bodies. Nevertheless, Pecham does not here commit himself to the visual ray theory.

156 Cf. Proposition I.56{59}; Alhazen, *Opt. thes.*, bk. 2, sec. 27, pp. 42–44.

157 Cf. Alhazen, *Opt. thes.*, bk. 2, sec. 28, pp. 44–45.

158 Cf. *ibid.*, sec. 30, pp. 46–47.

159 Cf. *ibid.*, sec. 30, p. 47; *ibid.*, secs. 33–34, p. 49.

160 Cf. *ibid.*, sec. 30, p. 47.

161 Cf. *ibid.*, sec. 36, pp. 50–51; Bacon, *Opus maius*, pt. V.ii, dist. 3, chap. 5 (ed. Bridges, vol. 2, pp. 114–16).

162 Cf. Alhazen, *Opt. thes.*, bk. 2, sec. 38, pp. 51–53.

163 Perhaps Proposition I.74{77}.

164 Cf. Euclid, *Optica*, Propositions 23–27, trans. Ver Eecke, pp. 17–20.

165 Propositions I.17{15}, I.22{20}, I.23{21}, and I.24{22}.

166 Cf. Alhazen, *Opt. thes.*, bk. 2, sec. 46, p. 59.

167 See Proposition I.55{58} on the visible intentions.

168 Cf. Alhazen, *Opt. thes.*, bk. 2, sec. 49, p. 60.

169 Cf. *ibid.*, bk. 3, secs. 2–3, p. 76; Bacon, *Opus maius*, pt. V.ii, dist. 2, chap. 1 (ed. Bridges, vol. 2, pp. 93–94).

170 Proposition I.38{41}.

171 Cf. Alhazen, *Opt. thes.*, bk. 3, secs. 4–5, pp. 77–78; Bacon, *Opus maius*, pt. V.ii, dist. 2, chap. 2 (ed. Bridges, vol. 2, pp. 94–95).

172 Proposition I.32{35}.

173 Cf. Alhazen, *Opt. thes.*, bk. 3, sec. 19, p. 89.

174 Propositions I.60{63}–I.62{65}.

175 Pecham and Alhazen follow Ptolemy in attributing this phenomenon to optical illusion; cf. Ptolemy, *Optica*, III.59 (ed. Lejeune, pp. 115–16); Alhazen, *Opt. thes.*, bk. 7, secs. 51–54, pp. 278–80; Bacon, *Opus maius*, V.ii, dist. 3, chap. 6 (ed. Bridges, vol. 2, pp. 116–17); Witelo, *Optica*, bk. 10, sec. 54, pp. 448–49. The details of the question are still being debated, but it appears that the approach of Ptolemy and his successors was correct; see Howard E. Gruber, William L. King, and Stephen Link, "Moon Illusion: An Event in Imaginary Space," *Science*, vol. 139 (1963), pp. 750–51.

176 The conclusion does not follow from the premises. If the true distance at the horizon were greater than that at the zenith, the angle would in fact be smaller; but the natural tendency to judge distances toward the horizon as greater than distances toward the zenith could conceivably compensate sufficiently for the smaller angle so that the object would still appear of equal or larger size rather than smaller.

177 Proposition III.13. In the *Almagest*, Ptolemy attributed the enlargement of celestial bodies near the horizon to atmospheric refraction; see Morris R. Cohen and I. E. Drabkin, *A Source Book in Greek Science* (Cambridge, Mass., 1958), p. 283. Bacon adopts this explanation in the *Opus maius*, pt. V.iii, dist. 2, chap. 4 (ed. Bridges, vol. 2, pp. 155–57), although (following Ptolemy) he had previously explained the phenomenon in terms of optical illusion; see n. 175, just above.

178 The same problem is discussed in different terms in Proposition III.13. Cf. Euclid, *Optica*, Proposition 6, trans. Ver Eecke, pp. 4–5.

179 Pecham appears to mean that the eye is located within or almost within the *surface* formed by the two lines.

180 On the translation of "*spericus*" or "*spericitas*," see the Critical Notes, n. 34 to this part, above.

181 Cf. Propositions I.71{74} and I.72{75}.

Part II

1 On reflection, see Pseudo-Euclid, *De speculis*, in Björnbo and Vogl, pp. 97–101, 104–05; Alkindi, *De aspectibus*, *ibid.*, pp. 28–36; Alhazen, *Opt. thes.*, bks. 4–6, pp. 102–230; Grosseteste, *De lineis*, in *Phil. Werke*, pp. 61–63; Bacon, *Opus maius*, pt. V.iii, dist. 1 (ed. Bridges, vol. 2, pp. 130–46); Bacon, *De mult. spec.*, bk. 2, pp. 463–64, 478–91; Witelo, *Optica*, bks. 5–9, pp. 189–403.

2 Cf. Proposition I.19{17} and the Critical Notes, Part I, n. 58, above.

3 For an analysis of Pecham's views on the cause of reflection, see the introduction, pp. 45–46, above.

4 Cf. Grosseteste, *De lineis*, in *Phil. Werke*, pp. 62–63; Bacon, *Opus maius*, pt. V.iii, dist. 1, chap. 1 (ed. Bridges, vol. 2, pp. 130–31).

5 I.e., altered in position.

6 Cf. Alhazen, *Opt. thes.*, bk. 4, sec. 4, p. 103; Grosseteste, *De lineis*, in *Phil. Werke*, pp. 62–63.

7 Cf. Alhazen, *Opt. thes.*, bk. 4, sec. 3, p. 103.

8 Cf. Proposition I.67{70}; Bacon, *De mult. spec.*, bk. 1, chap. 2, p. 431.

9 Proposition II.20.

10 Cf. Hero, *Catoptrica*, in *Opera*, vol. 2, fasc. 1, pp. 324–30; Pseudo-Euclid, *De speculis*, in Björnbo and Vogl, p. 100; Alkindi, *De aspectibus*, *ibid.*, pp. 29–31; Ptolemy, *Optica*, bk. 3 (ed. Lejeune, p. 88); Alhazen, *Opt. thes.*, bk. 4, secs. 10–13, pp. 108–09; Grosseteste, *De lineis*, in *Phil. Werke*, p. 62; Bacon, *Opus maius*, pt. V.iii, dist. 1, chap. 1 (ed. Bridges, vol. 2, pp. 131–32); Bacon, *De mult. spec.*, bk. 2, chap. 6, pp. 481–86; Witelo, *Optica*, bk. 5, secs. 10–17, pp. 195–98.

11 Euclid, *Elements*, I.15, trans. Heath, vol. 1, pp. 277–79.

12 It appears that the mechanical analogy presented here is meant to explain the equality of angles in the reflection of light, not the causes of reflection or the nature of the reflected entity; see the introduction, pp. 45–46, above.

13 Cf. Bacon, *Opus maius*, pt. V.iii, dist. 1, chap. 2 (ed. Bridges, vol. 2, pp. 134–35).

14 Cf. Alhazen, *Opt. thes.*, bk. 4, sec. 6, p. 104.

15 Cf. *ibid.*, bk. 6, sec. 1, p. 188.

16 Cf. *James* 1:23–24.

17 Cf. Alhazen, *Opt. thes.*, bk. 4, sec. 14, p. 111.

18 Cf. *ibid.*

19 Cf. *ibid.*

20 Propositions II.12–II.14.

21 The number of individual points from which reflection can occur is finite, since sight takes place through "natural lines" having breadth (Proposition II.18) and thereby requiring a point of finite area for reflection. However, when Pecham claims that "the parts from which reflection can occur...are infinite by various combinations with other parts," he appears to mean that, although a finite number of points (or small areas) exhausts the surface area of the mirror, those small areas can be defined in an infinite number of ways. Such reasoning is consistent with the argument later in the proposition that all the pyramids through which reflection occurs constitute a single body of light.

22 Cf. Alhazen, *Opt. thes.*, bk. 4, sec. 11, p. 108.

23 Cf. Pseudo-Euclid, *De speculis*, in Björnbo and Vogl, pp. 104–05; Grosseteste, *De lineis*, in *Phil. Werke*, p. 63; Bacon, *Opus maius*, pt. IV, dist. 2, chap. 2 (ed. Bridges, vol. 1, pp. 115–17); Bacon, *De mult. spec.*, bk. 2, chap. 7, pp. 486–91; Witelo, *Optica*, bk. 9, pp. 392–403; *Perspectiva communis*, Proposition II.55.

24 "*plus infinita*." I have rendered this expression freely.

25 I.e., all rays incident on a given circle of the mirror converge to a point, and the collection of all such points constitutes a line. The inability of a spherical concave mirror to focus all the incident solar rays on a single point was understood also by Bacon and Witelo (see references in n. 23, just above). Alhazen does not make this point in his *Perspectiva*, but Pecham may have learned it from his *De speculis comburentibus*; see H. J. J. Winter and W. ʿArafat, "Ibn al-Haitham on the Paraboloidal Focussing Mirror," *Journal Royal Asiatic Society of Bengal*, Ser. 3, vol. 15, nos. 1–2 (Calcutta, 1949), pp. 25–40. Cf. Pseudo-Euclid, *De speculis*, in Björnbo and Vogl, pp. 104–05.

26 Cf. Alhazen, *Opt. thes.*, bk. 4, sec. 16, p. 112; Bacon, *De mult. spec.*, bk. 2, chap. 1, pp. 459–60; Witelo, *Optica*, bk. 2, sec. 3, pp. 63–64.

27 Cf. Alhazen, *Opt. thes.*, bk. 4, sec. 20, pp. 113–14; Bacon, *Opus maius*, pt. V.iii, dist. 1, chap. 2 (ed. Bridges, vol. 2, pp. 132–33). See the introduction, pp. 47–48, above.

28 This and the preceding sentence are somewhat obscure. The question at issue seems to be: What acts on sight, the object or the image? The view described in the first sentence is that the object acts on sight through the mediation of the image; in the second sentence, that the image alone acts on sight.

29 Propositions I.32{35} and I.80{84}.

30 Propositions II.20–II.22, II.24, and II.46–II.48.

31 Cf. Alhazen, *Opt. thes.*, bk. 5, chap. 2, pp. 125–31. Bacon, *Opus maius*, pt. V.iii, dist. 1, chap. 3 (ed. Bridges, vol. 2, pp. 134–36), admits the truth of the principle only for plane mirrors. On this principle, see Turbayne, "Ancient Optical Principle." Although the principle was demonstrated to be inexact as early as the seventeenth century, it continues to be taught in modern texts on *geometrical* optics; its fault is that it ignores the psychological factors in sight.

32 Alhazen, *Opt. thes.*, pp. 125–88.

33 Cf. *ibid.*, bk. 5, sec. 11, pp. 131–32.

34 Proposition I.67{70}.

35 Proposition II.30, II.36, and II.39.

36 "*Facies*" could be translated "faces" as well as "figures"; cf. Proposition II.9.

37 By Euclid, *Elements*, I.16, trans. Heath, vol. 1, pp. 279–81.

38 See the Critical Notes to Part I, n. 64, above.

39 By this Pecham means a shift of point *C* (in Fig. 22) through a distance perpendicular to the plane of the paper on which the figure is printed.

40 I.e., for monocular vision. Roughly half the manuscripts read "*circuli*" for "*oculi*," but with that reading the statement becomes unintelligible.

41 Cf. Bacon, *Opus maius*, pt. V.iii, dist. 1, chap. 4 (ed. Bridges, vol. 2, pp. 144–46).

42 Propositions II.46–II.48.

43 Cf. Alhazen, *Opt. thes.*, bk. 5, sec. 15, pp. 133–34.

44 There is a plane of reflection for each eye, formed by the incident ray, reflected ray, and perpendicular.

45 Cf. Alhazen, *Opt. thes.*, bk. 4, sec. 23, p. 115. The "plane of reflection" is defined in n. 44, just above.

46 The axis is defined in Proposition I.35{38}. The syntax at this point implies that the axis is perpendicular to the mirror, but Pecham means that the axis is perpendicular to the tunics and humors of the eye.

47 Cf. Alhazen, *Opt. thes.*, bk. 5, sec. 12, p. 132.

48 Proposition II.21.

49 Proposition I.80{84}.

50 It is evident that Pecham is comparing the absolute size of the object and image, rather than the angles subtended at the observer's eye. This concern with absolute sizes characterizes his treatment of reflection and distinguishes it from his treatment of refraction. Pecham follows Alhazen in this peculiarity; see Alhazen, *Opt. thes.*, bk. 6, sec. 2, p. 189. But see the Critical Notes to Part II, n. 125, below.

51 Proposition II.21.

52 I.e., the image, though as large as the object in a plane mirror, is more remote from the observer than is the object and therefore subtends a smaller angle.

53 A more literal translation would be "spherical mirrors polished on the outside," but elsewhere (e.g., Proposition II.9) Pecham refers to such mirrors as *convex*, and the circumlocution seems to have no point. Cf. Alhazen, *Opt. thes.*, bk. 6, chap. 4, pp. 189–205.

54 Propositions II.3, II.11, II.20, and II.22.

55 Propositions II.46–II.52.

56 Cf. Alhazen, *Opt. thes.*, bk. 5, sec. 16, p. 134; Bacon, *Opus maius*, pt. V.iii, dist. 1, chap. 3 (ed. Bridges, vol. 2, pp. 135–36); Euclid, *Catoptrica*, trans. Ver Eecke, p. 99, definitions 2 and 5. On this principle, see the Critical Notes, n. 31 to this part, just above.

57 Proposition II.20.

58 Although it is impossible for the image to be located anywhere except *behind* a convex mirror, it is true as Pecham asserts that the image may be inside, outside,

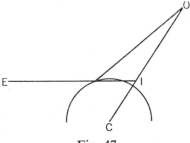

Fig. 47

or on the surface. As Figure 47 illustrates, when the image is outside or on the surface of the mirror, it is nevertheless *behind* that surface of the mirror closest to the observer (i.e., over the "horizon"). In the figure, *E* is the eye, *O* the object, *I* the image, and *C* the center of the mirror.

59 Moving the object closer to a spherical mirror will not necesarily move the image outside the sphere as Pecham implies, since the position of the image is a function not solely of the distance between the object and the mirror but also of the angular separation between the object and observer (as measured from the center of the sphere). However, moving the object closer to the mirror reduces the angular separation between the object and observer required to produce an image outside the mirror.

60 Cf. Alhazen, *Opt. thes.*, bk. 5, sec. 31, p. 142.

61 *Ibid.*, sec. 39, pp. 150–51.

62 Proposition II.21. Pecham's conclusion is correct.

63 Cf. Alhazen, *Opt. thes.*, bk. 6, secs. 4–5, pp. 189–90.

64 In spherical mirrors (according to Pecham) the image of any point is located on the perpendicular dropped from the point to the center of the sphere (Proposition II.30). Since the perpendiculars maintain a fixed order, points on the image are ordered exactly as the corresponding points on the object.

65 Since the same lines serve as perpendiculars (see n. 64) for both AB and OB, the argument establishing a similar order for points of the object and image of AB applies also to OB.

66 Cf. Alhazen, *Opt. thes.*, bk. 6, secs. 11–23, pp. 199–205; Bacon, *Opus maius*, pt. V.iii, dist. 1, chap. 3 (ed. Bridges, vol. 2, pp. 136–37). On the translation of "*spericis*," see the Critical Notes to Part I, n. 34.

67 The two alternatives, bending in toward the center of the mirror and turning away from the mirror, the former of which is denied while the latter is affirmed, seem to describe identical states of affairs, since the image in convex mirrors is always between the reflecting surface and its center of curvature. It is probable that Pecham has misstated an idea that he correctly states later in the proposition: "it is necessary...that curvature of the object should appear not as a bending back toward the mirror but as a turning away from it." On the other hand, it is possible that Pecham is here simply stating that the *cause* of curvature is associated not with the center but with the surface of the mirror.

68 Cf. Alhazen, *Opt. thes.*, bk. 6, sec. 12, pp. 199–200.

69 The manuscripts read "straight things sometimes appear *bent*," but emendation is clearly required. Cf. Alhazen, *Opt. thes.*, bk. 6, sec. 18, p. 202.

70 Pecham has in mind the absolute sizes of object and image, in which case the image is *always* smaller than the object; see the Critical Notes to Part II, n. 50, just above. See also Alhazen, *Opt. thes.*, bk. 6, secs. 5–6, pp. 190–97. On the translation of "*spericis*," see the Critical Notes to Part I, n. 34, above.

71 Proposition II.30.

72 The closest approach to this idea that I can locate is in the Pseudo-Euclidean *Catoptrica*, Proposition 4, trans. Ver Eecke, pp. 102–03.

73 Alhazen, *Opt. thes.*, bk. 6, secs. 5–6, pp. 190–97.

74 Pecham errs in thinking that the image (considered absolutely) can be equal to or larger than the object in a convex spherical mirror. The simplest case, in which the object directly faces the mirror, is illustrated in Figure 48. This is the case for which Pecham correctly asserts that the image is smaller than the object. However, Pecham believes that, if the object should be oriented obliquely with respect to

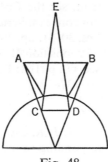

Fig. 48

the mirror, the image might be of equal or greater size. Figure 49, in which the image is of greater length than the object, illustrates what he had in mind. However, *CD* is larger than *AB* in Figure 49 only because the figure is carelessly drawn; if care is taken to make the angles of incidence and reflection equal, the obliquely situated object will always have an image smaller than itself, as illustrated in

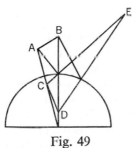

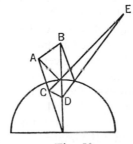

Fig. 49   Fig. 50

Figure 50. Had Pecham been referring to the sizes of the object and image as seen by an observer, i.e., the ratio of angles subtended at the eye, his statement would be entirely correct, but it is evident from the form of the proposition that this is not what he had in mind. In each of Figures 48–50, *E* is the eye, *AB* the object, and *CD* the image.

75 On the errors of convex columnar mirrors, see Alhazen, *Opt. thes.*, bk. 6, chap. 5, pp. 205–09.

76 Here, as in the discussion of spherical mirrors, the convexity of the mirrors is not explicitly stated, but understood; see the Critical Notes to Part I, n. 34, above.

77 I.e., an elliptical section.

78 Proposition II.32; see also Proposition II.18.

79 "in...reflection." I have emended the text, which otherwise reads, "at the center of the circle of reflection." Pecham could not have intended the latter, since it is clearly contradicted by the rest of the sentence and by Proposition II.30. My emendation not only makes Pecham's statement true and consistent with what follows, but recalls his own argument of Proposition II.26.

80 Propositions II.30 and II.32.

81 For a discussion of this statement, see the Critical Notes to Part II, n. 58, just above; the argument is identical for convex spherical and convex columnar mirrors.

82 Cf. Alhazen, *Opt. thes.*, bk. 6, secs. 30–31, pp. 209–11.

83 I.e., in the manner described in Proposition II.36.

84 Cf. Alhazen, *Opt. thes.*, bk. 5, sec. 60, p. 162; Bacon, *Opus maius*, pt. V.iii, dist. 1, chap. 4 (ed. Bridges, vol. 2, pp. 137–39).

85 Because AE and YF are parallel. It is evident from the context that the perpendicular Pecham has in mind is YF, which is the perpendicular to the surface of the mirror passing through points M, T, K, and Q.

86 I.e., the reflected ray, AE, corresponding to incident ray TE, does not intersect perpendicular YF.

87 A ray from point K is also reflected between E and G. Pecham has followed Alhazen in the awkward step of considering the reflection at C, which produces a reflected ray incident on the back of the head (since the eye is facing in the general direction of E) and hence not perceived. This neglect of even the most fundamental physiological factors illustrates how purely geometrical was their approach to problems of reflection.

88 Note that the perpendicular to the surface of the mirror from point Z is line ZDA rather than line FDY.

89 But the image of K is invisible for the reasons presented in n. 87, just above. If the head were turned around, the image would be perceived at S.

90 Judged by his own concept of image formation, which is also the basis for most modern discussions of *geometrical* optics, Pecham has reached the correct conclusion. However, the presence of an observer greatly complicates the situation, introducing physiological and psychological factors, which neither Pecham nor modern geometrical optics takes into account. In fact, no observer ever has the impression that the image he is perceiving is located behind his head; rather, the image of Q would be perceived outside the mirror in the general direction of L, its precise position being determined by a number of psychological factors. On this problem, see Vasco Ronchi, *Optics: The Science of Vision*, trans. Edward Rosen (New York, 1957), pp. 135–38.

91 As is true for Q, psychological factors interfere with the principles of geometrical optics and produce an image of Z appearing somewhere beyond the mirror. See n. 90.

92 I.e., it has magnitude, as any *visible* point must. Cf. Proposition II.18.

93 The "higher part" of the point is the part closer to M, the "lower part" closer to Q. Pecham recognizes that T constitutes a transition between images formed as is the image of M and those formed as is the image of Q, and consequently he considers each half of T as producing its image differently; expressed in modern terms, T is at the focal point of the mirror. Continuing to exhibit remarkable insight, Pecham argues that, since T is a unity, its two halves cannot be perceived as two distinct entities. Thus far, Pecham's conclusions are fully correct. But when he concludes that, since the two halves of T cannot be separately perceived, T must be perceived as a whole at an intermediate position, he errs. The theory of modern *geometrical* optics predicts that an observer will perceive an infinitely large image of T located in the direction of L at an infinite distance. In fact, how-

ever, psychological and physiological factors determine that the image will be perceived at only a short distance beyond the mirror, in the direction of *L*. See Ronchi, *Optics: the Science of Vision*, pp. 131–34; for a more popular presentation of the argument, see Vasco Ronchi, "Twenty Embarrassing Questions," trans. Edward Rosen, *Atti della Fondazione Giorgio Ronchi*, vol. 13 (1958), pp. 86–87.

94 Here Pecham recognizes the awkwardness, from a geometrical and physiological standpoint, of an image located in or behind the eye, though he was unaware of the compensating psychological factors mentioned above in notes 90 and 93. However, his conclusion appears to run counter to his own theory of vision, since rays from an object at *Z* should assume the same order on the surface of the glacial humor as the points on the object from which they originated, just as do rays from an object at *M*. Yet, Pecham asserts, the object at *M* is clearly perceived while the object at *Z* is not. See the introduction, p. 51, above.

95 Cf. Alhazen, *Opt. thes.*, bk. 5, sec. 62, p. 163.

96 Except *itself*, of course. Cf. *ibid.*, sec. 63, p. 163.

97 Cf. *ibid.*, sec. 68, pp. 165–66.

98 See the Critical Notes to Part II, n. 90, above.

99 Cf. Alhazen, *Opt. thes.*, bk. 5, secs. 65, 69, pp. 164, 166–67.

100 I.e., the great circle passing through *B* and *G* (Fig. 32) and perpendicular to diameter *AZ*. Pecham correctly affirms the truth of Alhazen's claim that reflection from the visible point to the eye may occur from any point of the great circle, but Alhazen and Pecham are wrong in supposing that the observer perceives an image as though situated within his eye; see the Critical Notes to Part II, n. 90, above.

101 Cf. Alhazen, *Opt. thes.*, bk. 5, sec. 70, pp. 167–68.

102 "Proposition 26." I have emended the text, the manuscripts reading "Proposition 18." Yet Pecham's statement, which does not follow at all from Proposition II.18, does not follow directly from Proposition II.26. In general terms, however, Proposition II.26 asserts that the plane of reflection, containing the eye, the object, and the point of reflection, is perpendicular to the reflecting surface, a condition fulfilled by circle *EBAG* referred to in Proposition II.45. Thus circle *EBAG* must coincide with the plane of reflection and consequently must contain the point of reflection.

103 Line *ODM* (Fig. 33) obviously fails to divide angle *HOC* into equal parts, but, as Pecham realized (following Alhazen), the line bisecting angle *HOC* must pass through the center of the sphere, for otherwise it would not be perpendicular to the reflecting surface at the point of reflection. The demonstration proceeding from this construction is valid.

104 Since *ODM* (Fig. 33) passes through the center of the sphere, if *O* is to the left of *Z*, *M* must be to the right of *L*. Consequently it is impossible that $CO/HO = CM/HM$, since *CO* is greater than *HO* while *CM* is smaller than *HM*.

105 Pecham insists that the object and the eye be outside the sphere, since, if they were not, reflection could occur at two points (as demonstrated in Proposition II.46), contrary to the proposition being demonstrated. However, there is no reason why the object and eye must be outside the tangent line.

106 Cf. Alhazen, *Opt. thes.*, bk. 5, sec. 71, p. 168.

107 The image would be located at *E* (Fig. 34) by the reasoning of Proposition II.39.

108 Cf. Alhazen, *Opt. thes.*, bk. 5, sec. 86, pp. 179–81; Witelo, *Optica*, bk. 8, sec. 40, pp. 342–44.

109 The point seen and the center of the eye.

110 I.e., the mirror.

111 Pecham does not mean that there is only one point of intersection between the two circles considered in their entirety, for that would be true only if they were tangent. He means that there is but one point of intersection along the arc intercepted by the two diameters; see n. 112, just below.

112 This proposition seems to be a somewhat garbled version of Alhazen's demonstration in the passage cited in n. 108. Briefly summarized, Alhazen argues that when one of the two points (*A*) is inside mirror *BDNL* (Fig. 51) and the other point (*B*) is on the circumference, the circle (*BGA*) passing through these two points and the center of the mirror intersects arc *BL* at a single point *T*. With this arrangement, there will be either three or four reflections and the same number of

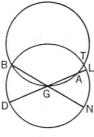   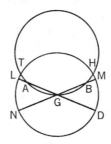

Fig. 51   Fig. 52

images: one or two from arc *TB*, one from arc *LT*, and one from arc *ND*. However, when both points *A* and *B* are within the circle of the mirror (as in Fig. 52), the circle passing through them and the center of the mirror intersects arc *ML* at two points, *T* and *H*. Under these circumstances there will also be three or four reflections: two or three from arc *LM* and one from arc *ND*. See Witelo (reference in n. 108) for a more elaborate demonstration of the same thing.

113 Proposition II.46. *H* is the eye.

114 By Euclid, *Elements*, III. 21, trans. Heath, vol. 2, pp. 49–51.

115 See the Critical Notes to Part II, nn. 90 and 93, above.

116 It is evident from the context that Pecham has spherical mirrors in mind, though the demonstration would hold as well for cylindrical mirrors.

117 Pseudo-Euclid, *Catoptrica*, Proposition 12, trans. Ver Eecke, pp. 107–08; cf. Witelo, *Optica*, bk. 8, sec. 53, p. 355; Bacon, *Opus maius*, pt. V.iii, dist. 1, chap. 4 (ed. Bridges, vol. 2, pp. 139–41).

118 The "intersection of the rays" is point *Z* (Fig. 36). "Before the place of intersection" means before *Z* from the standpoint of the observer, as object *TS*. Pecham could not mean before intersection *Z* from the standpoint of the object, since it is the object he is trying to locate. "Beyond the intersection" means beyond *Z* from the standpoint of the observer, as object *DE*.

119 Since *B* is the eye, this is the language of the visual ray theory. The theory of

visual rays also underlies Pecham's decription of the location of objects before or beyond the intersection of the rays, as discussed in n. 118. That Pecham's source for this demonstration was the medieval version of the Pseudo-Euclidean *Catoptrica* is clearly indicated both by this use of the visual ray theory and by the great similarity between Pecham's demonstration and that of the Greek text of Pseudo-Euclid. It is surprising that Pecham did not translate this proposition into the language of luminous rays, as did Witelo; Bacon, in his demonstration of this same proposition, speaks in terms of both luminous rays and visual rays.

120 The intersection of *EO* and *DQ* is the center of curvature of the mirror, and no image is located there. Perhaps Pecham means the image *OQ* of line *DE*.

121 The meaning of this sentence is obscure. An examination of the particular version of *De speculis* available to Pecham might shed light on it.

122 Alhazen, *Opt. thes.*, bk. 6, secs. 41–44, pp. 216–18.

123 This proposition can be clarified by reference to the corresponding demonstration in Witelo's *Perspectiva* and its accompanying figure, reproduced here as Figure 53. Rays from the endpoints of object *DE* are reflected at points *A* and *G* to the eye at *B*. The image of *DE* is located at *LN*, where the rays incident on the eye intersect perpendiculars (to the mirror) *DM* and *EM*, dropped from the object through the center of the mirror, *M*. Since *N*, the uppermost point of the image, corresponds

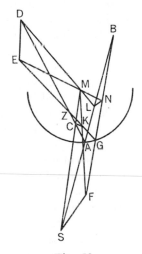

Fig. 53

to *E*, the lowest point of the object, it is evident that the image is inverted with respect to the object. Consider a second object *CK*, so drawn as to be visible by means of the same rays as object *DE*. The image of *CK* is located at *SF*, where the rays incident on the eye intersect perpendiculars *MC* and *MK* dropped from the object to the surface of the mirror. It is evident from the figure that there is no inversion or reversal of this image, since corresponding points on *CK* and *SF* are directly opposite one another.

Pecham's statement of this proposition is exceedingly obscure. In the first place, he refers several times to "the place of intersection of the rays," by which he evidently means point Z (in either Fig. 36 or Fig. 53). He correctly identifies this as the point separating objects that have an inverted image from those that do not. (In Fig. 53, *DE* has an inverted image, but *CK* does not.) This point of intersection, Z, will have a different location for different objects and different observers, but the collection of all such points constitutes a surface that corresponds in position and function to the modern focal plane of the mirror, located (for spherical mirrors) about halfway between the mirror and its center of curvature.

But a point requiring even more clarification is Pecham's conception of image inversion and image reversal. In the technical sense in which these terms are employed in modern optics, they denote only a lack of correspondence between points directly opposite each other on the object and image, i.e., the case in which the image has been flipped end for end relative to the object; inversion and reversal are geometrically indistinguishable, except that the former applies to phenomena in a vertical plane and the latter to phenomena in a horizontal plane. Thus *LN* (Fig. 53) is a reversed or inverted image of *DE*, while *SF* is an erect image of *CK*. According to this precise usage, then, there is neither reversal nor inversion in plane or convex mirrors. In concave mirrors, the image is reversed and inverted when the object is more than a focal length from the mirror, but unreversed and erect when the object is between the mirror and the focal plane.

Yet there is another sense in which we employ the terms "inversion" and "reversal." When a person observes himself in a plane mirror, we speak of the reversal of his image, since he is right-handed while his image is left-handed, even though corresponding points of the person and the image remain directly opposite each other. Again, a person standing on a plane mirror placed in a horizontal plane is said to have an inverted image, even though there is a direct correspondence between opposite points on the person and his image.

It is in this latter, less technical sense that Pecham employs the terms "inversion" and "reversal." This is evident from Propositions II.21 and II.22, where he refers to inversion in plane mirrors; for according to the more technical usage described above, images are inverted only in concave mirrors. In Proposition II.50, Pecham claims that objects located before the intersection of the rays, i.e., between Z and the mirror, "appear inverted as in plane mirrors and for the same reason." This statement is entirely correct according to Pecham's nontechnical usage of the term "inversion," though false if inversion is taken in our more technical sense. For unexplained reasons Pecham did not draw the image of such objects in his diagram, but in the final line of the proposition he refers to the advantages of so doing; such an image is included, however, in the corresponding figures of Witelo and Bacon. (Bacon refers to the incorrect figure contained in *De speculis*, and it is possible that Pecham's incomplete figure is to be explained thus; see Bacon, *Opus maius*, pt. V.iii, dist. 1, chap. 4 [ed. Bridges, vol. 2, pp. 139–41]. Note, however, that the figure appearing in Bridges's edition of Bacon's *Opus maius* is also incorrect, the error, it would seem, being due to Bridges rather than Bacon.) On the other hand, objects located beyond the intersection of the rays, Pecham says, do not appear inverted. This statement is false, for image *LN* of object *DE* (Fig. 53) and image *OQ* of object *DE* (Fig. 36) are inverted according to either the technical or nontechnical sense of inversion, as the figures reveal. Pecham's entire discussion may be obscure, but this seems to be its only outright error.

124 Alhazen, *Opt. thes.*, bk. 6, secs. 38–44, pp. 214–18.

125 Actually, for an object between the center of the mirror and the point of reflection, the absolute size of the image is greater than the absolute size of the object; for an object beyond the center, the image is smaller than the object. Apparently Pecham is here concerned with the ratio between the angles subtended at the eye of the observer by the object and the image (an exception to my earlier generalization regarding his approach to image formation by reflection—see the Critical Notes to Part II, n. 50); thus the observer's position and the obliquity of the object and image relative to the line of sight must be introduced, greatly complicating the problem and discouraging generalization.

126 The text reads "curved," but "concave" appears to be a more appropriate translation in this context.

127 Cf. Pseudo-Euclid, *Catoptrica*, Proposition 23, trans. Ver Eecke, pp. 115–16.

128 *Opt. thes.*, bk. 6, secs. 45–50, pp. 218–25.

129 Proposition 33 is not directly relevant to the topic under discussion.

130 *Opt. thes.*, bk. 6, chap. 8, pp. 225–29.

131 *Ibid.*, chap. 9, pp. 229–30.

132 Cf. Pseudo-Euclid, *De speculis*, in Björnbo and Vogl, pp. 104–05; Bacon, *Opus maius*, pt. IV, dist. 2, chap. 2 (ed. Bridges, vol. 1, pp. 115–17); Bacon, *De mult. spec.*, bk. 1, chap. 7, pp. 486–91; Witelo, *Optica*, bk. 10, secs. 36–44, pp. 392–403.

133 Pecham is apparently referring to parabolic mirrors, undoubtedly as described in the *De speculis comburentibus* of Alhazen. See J. L. Heiberg and Eilhard Wiedemann, "Ibn al Haitams Schrift über parabolische Hohlspiegel," *Bibliotheca Mathematica*, Ser. 3, vol. 10 (1910), pp. 201–37; Winter and Aralat, "Ibn al-Haitham on the Paraboloidal Focussing Mirror." On the translation of this work into Latin, see Eilhard Wiedemann, "Zur Geschichte der Brennspiegel," *Annalen der Physik und Chemie*, N.S., vol. 39 (1890), pp. 126–27.

134 Cf. Proposition II.17.

135 Cf. Bacon, *Opus maius*, pt. V.ii, dist. 3, chap. 7 (ed. Bridges, vol. 2, pp. 120–26); Witelo, *Optica*, bk. 10, sec. 55, p. 449. Pecham's conclusion agrees with neither Bacon's nor Witelo's.

136 Cf. Bacon, *Opus maius*, pt. V.ii, dist. 3, chap. 7 (ed. Bridges, vol. 2, pp. 122–24). Bacon seems to use the term "*involutio*" in the sense of "straining," and I have interpreted Pecham similarly.

137 Pecham is measuring the angles with respect to the reflecting surface rather than the perpendicular to the reflecting surface; cf. Proposition II.6.

Part III

1 Cf. Alhazen, *Opt. thes.*, bk. 7, secs. 3–6, pp. 233–38. On refraction, see also *Perspectiva communis*, Propositions I.14{29}–I.16{31}.

2 Cf. Alhazen, *Opt. thes.*, bk. 7, sec. 4, p. 235; Bacon, *De mult. spec.*, bk. 4, chap. 1,

pp. 520–21; *Opus maius*, pt. IV, dist. 4, chap. 2 (ed. Bridges, vol. 1, p. 132). In the final two sentences, Pecham backs away from the view expressed in the enunciation. Alhazen and Bacon, on the other hand, never compromise the claim that refraction occurs only at the interface separating two media.

3 Pecham appears to be using "angle of refraction" to denote the angle of deviation, i.e., the angle between the incident ray and the refracted ray, rather than the angle between the refracted ray and a perpendicular to the refracting surface, although the enunciation and its demonstration would hold true for either case. Similar terminology is employed by Alhazen and Witelo.

On the quantitative approach to refraction in Pecham's sources, see the introduction, pp. 48–49, above, and the references given there in the footnote. On the cause of refraction, see the introduction, pp. 49–50; cf. Alhazen, *Opt. thes.*, bk. 7, sec. 8, pp. 240–42; Bacon, *De mult. spec.*, bk. 2, chap. 3, pp. 468–70. See also my "The Cause of Refraction," and Sabra, "Explanation of Optical Reflection and Refraction," pp. 552–53.

4 Having discussed, in the first part of the proposition, the relationship between refraction and the inclination of the incident ray, Pecham is here discussing the relationship between refraction and the density of the second (or denser) medium. Thus the "denser" and "rarer" media to which he refers are not the two media through which a given refracted ray has passed, but rather more and less dense "second media." Pecham is pointing out, therefore, that light passing obliquely from a rare into a dense medium, if presented with several alternative "dense media," will be more refracted in the more dense of these than in the less dense.

5 Proposition III.9. The object may also appear equal to its true size, as Proposition III.9 demonstrates.

6 Cf. Alhazen, *Opt. thes.*, bk. 7, sec. 18, pp. 253–55. On the validity of this principle, see the Critical Notes to Part II, n. 31, above.

7 Proposition II.20.

8 Cf. Alhazen, *Opt. thes.*, bk. 7, sec. 17, p. 253; *ibid.*, sec. 19, pp. 271–72.

9 Proposition III.9.

10 Cf. Pseudo-Euclid, *Catoptrica*, def. 6, trans. Ver Eecke, p. 99; Ptolemy, *Optica*, ed. Lejeune, bk. 5, pp. 225–26; Grosseteste, *De iride*, in *Phil. Werke*, p. 74.

11 Cf. Alhazen, *Opt. thes.*, bk. 7, secs. 52–55, pp. 278–82.

12 Both the enunciation of the proposition and its demonstration are incorrect. Under the conditions stated, the object will always appear larger than its true size. (Alhazen, Bacon, and Witelo all avoid Pecham's error.) Pecham seems to have been misled by the fact that the image may be farther from the eye than is the object, but, when that is so, the enlargement of the image more than compensates for its greater distance. This is illustrated in Figure 54, taken from Bacon's *Opus maius*, ed. Bridges, vol. 2, p. 152. The other case, in which the image is nearer the eye than is the object, is illustrated by Pecham's own figure (Fig. 40). It should be noted that, in treating image formation by refraction, Pecham is concerned with the ratio of angles intercepted at the observer's eye by the object and image; this subjective treatment contrasts with his general approach to image formation by reflection.

Cf. Alhazen, *Opt. thes.*, bk. 7, secs. 44–47, pp. 274–76; Bacon, *Opus maius*, pt.

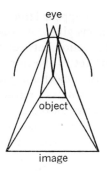

Fig. 54

V.iii, dist. 2, chap. 3 (ed. Bridges, vol. 2, pp. 152–53); Witelo, *Optica*, bk. 10, secs. 36–41, pp. 436–40.

13 This is pyramid *FDE* in Figure 40.

14 Aristotle, *De caelo* 297ª9–298ª20. Since Alhazen presents the same explanation (*Opt. thes.*, bk. 7, sec. 48, p. 276), the expression "this philosophy" may be a reference to his work; cf. Proposition I.63{66} and the Critical Notes to Part I, n. 150, above.

15 There was no need for Pecham to attribute the apparent enlargement of an object submerged in water to the curvature of the surface, for in Proposition III.10 he proves that the same enlargement occurs when the interface between the two media is flat. Cf. Alhazen, *Opt. thes.*, bk. 7, sec. 48, pp. 276–77.

16 Cf. Alhazen, *Opt. thes.*, bk. 7, secs. 39–43, pp. 271–74.

17 By Proposition III.5.

18 Proposition I.74{77}.

19 Proposition III.5.

20 "the aforesaid perpendiculars." More literally, Pecham says "the body of the aforesaid perpendiculars," but I see no reason for the circumlocution.

21 Cf. Bacon, *Opus maius*, pt. V.iii, dist. 2, chap. 3 (ed. Bridges, vol. 2, p. 151). Alhazen and Witelo fail to treat this case explicitly.

22 See Proposition III.9 and n. 13, just above.

23 Pecham's conclusion is incorrect. It is true that an object located within a denser

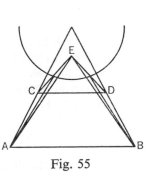

Fig. 55

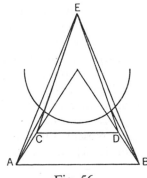

Fig. 56

medium of concave surface can appear larger than, smaller than, or equal to its true size, but not for the reasons given. As Bacon stated very clearly (see n. 21, just above), the points of intersection between the refracted rays and the perpendiculars dropped from the object to the refracting surface—and hence also the images—are always between the object and the eye. Now when the eye is inside the center of curvature of the concave refracting surface, the object will thus appear larger than its true size; when the eye is at the center of curvature, equal to its true size; and when the eye is beyond the center, smaller than its true size. The first and third of these conditions are illustrated in Figures 55 and 56, respectively; AB is the object, CD the image, and E the eye. In Figure 55 it is evident that $\angle CED > \angle AEB$; hence the image appears larger than the object. In Figure 56 $\angle AEB > \angle CED$; hence the image appears smaller than the object.

24 Cf. Ptolemy, *Optica*, ed. Lejeune, bk. 5, pp. 237–40; Alhazen, *Opt. thes.*, bk. 7, secs. 51–54, pp. 278–80; Witelo, *Optica*, bk. 10, secs, 51–53, pp. 445–48.

25 Pecham's conclusion regarding the location of the intersection is false. As Figure 42 reveals, the extensions of rays DE and DF (not drawn) would intersect the star AB before they could possibly intersect perpendiculars AC and BC, regardless of the immense distance Pecham assumes between the earth and the stars (see next to last sentence of the proposition); indeed, there is no necessity that they ever intersect these perpendiculars.

   Pecham's reference to visual rays in this same sentence suggests that his source for the demonstration may have been an advocate of the visual ray theory. This suggestion in turn points toward Ptolemy, whose discussion of atmospheric refraction in the *Optica* provides all the elements Pecham needed for this demonstration. See Ptolemy, *Optica*, ed. Lejeune, bk. 5, pp. 237–40; Cohen and Drabkin, *Source Book*, pp. 281–82.

26 I.e., pyramid ABC (Fig. 42).

27 I.e., immense.

28 Judged by the principles of medieval optics, Pecham has reached the correct conclusion: the stars would indeed appear smaller, but only because of the refraction of the rays, as illustrated in Figure 42. While Pecham makes this point clearly in the enunciation of the proposition, he then obscures the issue with his discussion of the location of the intersections of the visual rays and the perpendiculars. In reality, however, Pecham's conclusion is false, for diffraction (which was never noted before the seventeenth century) introduces a larger image than that predicted by ray geometry, with the result that the stars would appear to have the same size, with or without refraction.

29 Cf. Euclid, *Optica*, Proposition 6, trans. Ver Eecke, pp. 4–5; Ptolemy, *Optica*, ed. Lejeune, bk. 5, pp. 237–40; Alhazen, *Opt. thes.*, bk. 7, sec. 15, pp. 251–52; *ibid.*, sec. 52, pp. 278–79; Bacon, *De mult. spec.*, bk. 2, chap. 4, pp. 472–78. See also the alternative account of this same phenomenon in Proposition I.{87}. Since the revised version preserved in D does not extend to Part III (by my construction, as presented in the introduction, pp. 21–24, above), it is possible that Proposition I.{87} was meant to replace rather than complement Proposition III.13.

30 It is clear from the context and Figure 43 that Pecham intends the line to pass not

through the eyes of the observer but through a point directly overhead. Cf. Proposition I.{87}.

31 *EF* and *EG* are distinct lines and consequently form an angle at *E*, although the particular perspective assumed in the figure makes it invisible.

32 *Opt. thes.*, bk. 7, sec. 15, pp. 251–52.

33 There can be no purpose in introducing reflection at this point; perhaps we have here an instance of an early scribal error (from "deflexio"?).

34 This entire paragraph, with the exception of the final sentence, appears in a minority of the manuscripts; see the variant readings.

35 The manuscripts also permit the following reading: "unless refraction should perchance be *smaller* there." Either way, it is not clear what consequences are foreseen by variation in refraction.

36 Cf. Alhazen, *Opt. thes.*, bk. 7, secs. 19–20, pp. 255–56; *Perspectiva communis*, Proposition I.42{45}.

37 Cf. Proposition III.4. The refracted ray does not intersect the perpendicular in the point's "own place"; intersection occurs either behind the center of curvature of the eye or beyond the object (from the standpoint of the observer). See Alhazen's discussion, cited in n. 36, just above.

38 Cf. Proposition I.42{45}.

39 Cf. Pseudo-Euclid, *De speculis*, in Björnbo and Vogl, pp. 105–06; Grosseteste, *De natura locorum*, in *Phil. Werke*, p. 71 (Crombie translates this passage in *Grosseteste*, pp. 122–23); Bacon, *Opus maius*, pt. IV, dist. 2, chap. 2 (ed. Bridges, vol. 1, pp. 113–14); Bacon, *De mult. spec.*, bk. 2, chap. 3, pp. 470–72; Witelo, *Optica*, bk. 10, sec. 48, pp. 443–44; Theodoric of Freiberg, *De iride et radialibus impressionibus*, ed. Joseph Würschmidt (*BGPM*, vol. 12, pts. 5–6 [Münster, 1914]), pp. 121–23. Alhazen did not deal explicitly with the burning glass in his *Perspectiva*, but for an account of his views as expressed by a Muslim commentator, see Eilhard Wiedemann, "Ueber das Sehen durch ein Kugel bei den Arabern," *Annalen der Physik und Chemie*, N.S., vol. 39 (1890), pp. 565–76.

40 By "ray" Pecham means a pencil of light, presumably of the same width as the sun.

41 The authorities available to Pecham were divided on the question of the climate at the equator. Sacrobosco, in his *Tractatus de sphera*, argues, "That zone which lies between the tropics is said to be uninhabitable because of the fervor of the sun, which ever courses above it" (Thorndike, *Sacrobosco*, p. 129). William of Conches agrees with Sacrobosco on the uninhabitable climate at the equator; see *De philosophia mundi* in Migne, *Patrologia Latina*, vol. 172, col. 85. Grosseteste and Bacon agree with Pecham on the effect, but explain it somewhat differently; see Grosseteste, *De natura locorum*, in *Phil. Werke*, pp. 66–67; Dales, "Grosseteste's Scientific Works," pp. 394–95; Bacon, *Opus maius*, pt. IV, dist. 4, chap. 4 (ed. Bridges, vol. 1, pp. 135–37). Robertus Anglicus presents a number of arguments in support of a temperate climate at the equator in his *Commentary* on Sacrobosco's *Tractatus de sphera*; see Thorndike, *Sacrobosco*, pp. 237–39. Ptolemy reports the view of some persons who think the regions under the equator are habitable, but he confesses that he has no firsthand testimony on the matter; see *Almagest*, bk. 2, chap. 6.

42 See Proposition III.17. I am uncertain about the precise meaning of the term *verticatio*, but it is evident from the context that Pecham is here employing it to denote the modes of propagation of light. By attributing the rainbow to both reflected and refracted rays, Pecham stands in contrast to Grosseteste, who subordinated the rainbow to refraction, and Bacon, who argued that reflection was its sole cause. On the rainbow theories of Grosseteste and Bacon, see my "Roger Bacon's Theory of the Rainbow"; Bruce S. Eastwood, "Robert Grosseteste's Theory of the Rainbow," *Archives internationales d'histoire des sciences*, vol. 19 (1966), pp. 313–32; Grosseteste, *De iride*, in *Phil. Werke*, pp. 75–78; Bacon, *Opus maius*, pt. VI, chaps. 2–12 (ed. Bridges, vol. 2, pp. 172–98); Carl B. Boyer, *The Rainbow: From Myth to Mathematics* (New York, 1959), chap. 4; Crombie, *Grosseteste*, pp. 124–27, 155–61. Cf. Witelo, *Optica*, bk. 10, secs. 65–84, pp. 457–74. Alhazen's treatise on the rainbow was never available in Latin; see Eilhard Wiedemann, "Theorie des Regenbogens von Ibn al Haitam," *Sitzungsberichte der physikalisch-medizinischen Societät in Erlangen*, vol. 46 (1914), pp. 39–56. On medieval theories of the rainbow in general, see the excellent accounts in Boyer and Crombie.

43 The theories of both Bacon and Witelo made use of reflection from individual drops.

44 Cf. Proposition II.1.

45 This is an account of Grosseteste's theory; see Grosseteste, *De iride*, in *Phil. Werke*, p. 76; Crombie, *Grosseteste*, p. 126.

46 "The Philosopher" normally denoted Aristotle in the Middle Ages, but I have been unable to locate the passage cited.

47 Cf. Propositions I.4{4}, I.{5}, and II.15.

48 Instead of "more diffuse," the manuscripts favor a reading of "narrower," but the context seems to demand the reading that I have selected.

49 Cf. the passage from Pecham's *De sphera*, reproduced in Duhem, *Le Système du monde*, vol. 3, pp. 525–26.

50 This seems to be a denial of Bacon's claim that "color appears only in the drops from which there is reflection to the eye [of the observer]" (*Opus maius*, pt. VI, chap. 11 [ed. Bridges, vol. 2, p. 196]). See the introduction, p. 14, n. 13, above.

51 Bacon had argued that rainbow colors were seen by means of the very rays that generated them, reflected from individual droplets of moisture to the observer's eye. It is this view that Pecham attacks with the claim that "no impressions whatever are seen by means of the rays that generated them," but by emission of their own species "outside the place of reflection," i.e., in every direction. Bacon, however, would have denied that the rainbow was an "impression." Grosseteste, on the other hand, considered the rainbow an impression in the cloud, which emanated its own species in all directions. See Bacon, *Opus maius*, pt. VI, chap. 8 (ed. Bridges, vol. 2, pp. 191–92); Grosseteste, *De iride*, in *Phil. Werke*, p. 76; Lindberg, "Roger Bacon's Theory of the Rainbow," p. 239.

52 Cf. *Genesis* 9:12–17.

53 Cf. Aristotle, *Meteorology* 3.2.372ª5; Grosseteste, *De iride*, in *Phil. Werke*, p. 77.

54 Here Pecham attributes the rainbow chiefly to reflected rays, whereas in Proposition III.20, he attributes it to both reflected and refracted rays. His ambivalence

suggests that he was unable to choose between the refraction theory of Grosseteste and the reflection theories of Aristotle, Bacon, and others.

55 Aristotle, *Meteorology* 1. 8. 345^{a}11–346^{b}15. Cf. Bacon, *Opus maius*, pt. V.ii, dist. 3, chap. 1 (ed. Bridges, vol. 2, pp. 100–01).

Bibliography

This bibliography is meant to serve two purposes. In the first place, it includes works bearing on the life of John Pecham and the contents and influence of the *Perspectiva communis*. In addition, it is intended as a selective list of works on the history of optics from antiquity through the Renaissance. I have endeavored to be particularly exhaustive with regard to recent publications, which do not appear in older bibliographies; to that end, I have added a number of works that appeared too late to exert a significant influence on my conclusions. Islamic authors are cited in this bibliography by their Western names.

Adam Marsh. *Adae de Marisco epistolae*, in *Monumenta Franciscana*, vol. 1, ed. J. S. Brewer. London, 1858.

Aguilonius, Franciscus. *Opticorum libri sex*. Antwerp, 1613.

Alessio, Franco. "Per uno studio sull'Ottica del Trecento," *Studi medievali*, Ser. 3, vol. 2 (1961), pp. 444–504.

———. "Questioni inedite di ottica di Biagio Pelacani da Parma," *Rivista critica di storia della filosofia*, vol. 16 (1961), pp. 79–110, 188–221.

Alhazen. *Opticae thesaurus Alhazeni Arabis libri septem, nunc primum editi a Federico Risnero*. Basel, 1572.

———. *See* Baarmann, J.; *see* Heiberg, J. L., and Eilhard Wiedemann; *see* Rashed, Roshdi; *see* Wiedemann, Eilhard; *see* Winter, H. J. J., and W. 'Arafat.

Alkindi. *See* Björnbo, Axel Anthon, and Sebastian Vogl.

Anthemius. *See* Ver Eecke, Paul.

'Arafat, W. *See* Winter, H. J. J., and W. 'Arafat.

Avicenna. *De anima*. Venice, 1508; reprinted Louvain, 1961.

———. *De natura animalium*. Venice, 1508; reprinted Louvain, 1961.

———. *Liber canonis...a Gerardo Carmonensi...in latinum conversa*. Venice, 1555.

———. *See* Koning, P. de; *see* Rahman, F.

Baarmann, J. "Abhandlung über das Licht von Ibn al-Haitam," *Zeitschrift der deutschen morgenländischen Gesellschaft*, vol. 36 (1882), pp. 195–237.

Bacon, Roger. *Opera hactenus inedita Fr. Rogeri Baconis*, ed. Robert Steele and F. Delorme. 12 fascs. Oxford, 1905–1940.

———. *Opera quaedam hactenus inedita*, vol. 1, ed. J. S. Brewer. London, 1859.

———. *The "Opus Majus" of Roger Bacon*, ed. J. H. Bridges. 3 vols. London, 1900. (Vol. 2 includes *De multiplicatione specierum*.)

———. *The "Opus Majus" of Roger Bacon*, trans. R. B. Burke. 2 vols. Philadelphia,

1928. (An English translation of the preceding bibliographic entry, excluding the introduction, notes, and *De multiplicatione specierum*.)

———. *Part of the "Opus tertium" of Roger Bacon, Including a Fragment now Printed for the First Time*, ed. A. G. Little. (British Society of Franciscan Studies, vol. 4.) Aberdeen, 1912.

———. *Perspectiva*, ed. Iohannis Combach. Frankfurt, 1614.

———. *Specula mathematica*, ed. Iohannis Combach. Frankfurt, 1614.

———. *Un Fragment inédit de "L'Opus tertium" de Roger Bacon précédé d'une étude sur ce fragment*, ed. Pierre Duhem. Quaracchi, 1909.

Baeumker, Clemens. *Witelo, ein Philosoph und Naturforscher des XIII. Jahrhunderts.* (*BGPM*, vol. 3, pt. 2.) Münster, 1908.

Bailey, Cyril. *The Greek Atomists and Epicurus*. Oxford, 1928.

Bartholomew the Englishman. *De proprietatibus rerum*, trans. John of Trevisa. Westminister, 1495.

Bartoli, Cosimo. *Del modo di misurare le distantie....* Venice, 1614.

Bauer, Hans. *Die Psychologie Alhazens.* (*BGPM*, vol. 10, pt. 5.) Münster, 1911.

Baur, Ludwig. *Die Philosophie des Robert Grosseteste, Bischofs von Lincoln.* (*BGPM*, vol. 18, pts. 4–6.) Münster, 1917.

———. *See* Grosseteste, Robert.

Beare, J. I. *Greek Theories of Elementary Cognition from Alcmaeon to Aristotle*. Oxford, 1906.

Beaujouan, Guy. "Motives and Opportunities for Science in the Medieval Universities," in *Scientific Change*, ed. A. C. Crombie (New York, 1963), pp. 219–36.

Bednarski, Adam. "Das anatomische Augenbild von Johann Peckham, Erzbischof zu Canterbury im XIII. Jahrhundert," *Sudhoffs Archiv für Geschichte der Medizin und der Naturwissenschaften*, vol. 22 (1929), pp. 352–56.

———. "Die anatomischen Augenbilder in den Handschriften des Roger Bacon, Johann Peckham und Witelo," *Sudhoffs Archiv für Geschichte der Medizin und der Naturwissenschaften*, vol. 24 (1931), pp. 60–78.

———. "O krakowskich rękopisach perspektywy arcybiskupa Jana Peckhama [On the Cracow Manuscripts of the Perspective of Archbishop John Peckham]," *Archiwum historji i filozofji medycyny oraz historji nauk przyrodniczych*, vol. 12 (1932), pp. 1–14.

Benevenutus Grassus of Jerusalem. *De oculis eorumque egritudinibus et curis*, trans. Casey A. Wood. Stanford, 1929.

Birkenmajer Aleksander. "Études sur Witelo, I–IV, *"Bulletin international de l'Académie polonaise des sciences et des lettres*. Cracow, 1918, pp. 4–6; 1920, pp. 354–60; 1922, pp. 6–9.

———. "Robert Grosseteste and Richard Fournival," *Medievalia et Humanistica*, vol. 5 (1948), pp. 36–41.

———. "Studja nad Witelonem, I: Dwa nieznane pisemka Witelona [Studies on Witelo, I: Two Unknown Works of Witelo]," *Archiwum komisji do badania historji filozofji w polsce*, vol. 2, pt. 1 (1921), pp. 1–149.

———. "Witelo e lo studio di Padova," in *Omaggio dell'Accademia Polacca di Scienze e Lettere all'Università di Padova nel settimo centenario della sua fondazione* (Cracow, 1922), pp. 145–68.

Björnbo, Axel Anthon, and Sebastian Vogl. "Alkindi, Tideus und Pseudo-Euklid. Drei optische Werke," *Abhandlung zur Geschichte der mathematischen Wissenschaften*, vol. 26, pt. 3 (1912), pp. 1–176.

Blasius of Parma. *See* Alessio, Franco; *see* Vescovini, Graziella Federici.

Boyer, Carl B. "Descartes and the Radius of the Rainbow," *Isis*, vol. 43 (1952), pp. 95–98.

———. *The Rainbow: From Myth to Mathematics.* New York, 1959.

———. "Robert Grosseteste on the Rainbow," *Osiris*, vol. 11 (1954), pp. 247–58.

———. "The Tertiary Rainbow: An Historical Account," *Isis*, vol. 49 (1958), pp. 141–54.

———. "The Theory of the Rainbow: Medieval Triumph and Failure," *Isis*, vol. 49 (1958), pp. 378–90.

Bradbury, S., and G. L'E. Turner. *See* Crombie, A. C.

Brewer, J. S. *See* Adam Marsh; *see* Bacon, Roger.

Bridges, John Henry. *The Life and Work of Roger Bacon: An Introduction to the Opus Majus.* London, 1914.

———. *See* Bacon, Roger.

Burke, Robert B. *See* Bacon, Roger.

Burton, H. E. *See* Euclid.

Callebaut, André, O.F.M. "Jean Pecham, O.F.M. et l'Augustinisme. Aperçus historiques (1263–1285)," *Archivum Franciscanum Historicum*, vol. 18 (1925), pp. 441–72.

Cantore, Enrico. "Genetical Understanding of Science: Some Considerations about Optics," *Archives internationales d'histoire des sciences*, vol. 19 (1966), pp. 333–63.

Carton, Raoul. *L'expérience mystique de l'illumination intérieure chez Roger Bacon.* (*Études de philosophie médiévale*, vol. 3.) Paris, 1924.

Caussin, M. "Mémoire sur l'Optique de Ptolémée," *Mémoires de l'Institut Royale de France, Académie des inscriptions et belles-lettres*, vol. 6 (1822), pp. 1–39.

Chauliac, Guy de. *Cyrurgia parva Guidonis.* Venice, 1500.

———. *La Grand Chirurgie de M. Guy de Chauliac...composée l'an de grace 1363*, trans. Laurens Joubert. Tours, 1598.

Choulant, Johann Ludwig. *History and Bibliography of Anatomic Illustration*, trans. Mortimer Frank. Chicago, 1920.

Cirvelo, Pedro. *Breve compendium Perspective communis domini Ioannis archiepiscopi Cantuariensis*, in *Cursus quatuor mathematicarum artium liberalium*. Alcalá, 1526.

Clagett, Marshall. "Some General Aspects of Physics in the Middle Ages," *Isis*, vol. 39 (1948), pp. 29–44.

Clivaxo, Dominicus de. *See* Vescovini, Graziella Federici.

Corner, George W. (trans.). *Anatomical Texts of the Earlier Middle Ages.* Washington, D.C., 1927.

Crew, Henry. *See* Maurolyco, Francesco.

Crombie, A. C. *Augustine to Galileo*, 2nd ed. 2 vols. Cambridge, Mass., 1961.

———. "Early Concepts of the Senses and the Mind," *Scientific American*, vol. 210, no. 5 (1964), pp. 108–16.

——. "Kepler: De modo visionis," in *Mélanges Alexandre Koyré*, I: *L' Aventure de la science* (Paris, 1964), pp. 135–72.

——. "The Mechanistic Hypothesis and the Scientific Study of Vision: Some Optical Ideas as a Background to the Invention of the Microscope," in *Historical Aspects of Microscopy*, ed. S. Bradbury and G. L'E. Turner (Cambridge, 1967), pp. 3–112.

——. "Quantification in Medieval Physics," *Isis*, vol. 52 (1961), pp. 143–60.

——. *Robert Grosseteste and the Origins of Experimental Science, 1100–1700*. Oxford, 1953.

Crowley, Theodore, O.F.M. "John Peckham, O.F.M., Archbishop of Canterbury, Versus the New Aristotelianism," *Bulletin of the John Rylands Library*, vol. 33 (1950–51), pp. 242–55.

——. *Roger Bacon: The Problem of the Soul in his Philosophical Commentaries*. Louvain and Dublin, 1950.

Curtze, Maximilian. "Die Dunkelkammer. Eine Untersuchung über die Vorgeschichte derselben," *Himmel und Erde*, vol. 13 (1901), pp. 225–36.

Dales, Richard C. "Robert Grosseteste's Scientific Works," *Isis*, vol. 52 (1961), pp. 381–402.

Daremberg, Charles. *See* Galen; *see* Rufus of Ephesus.

Delambre, Jean B. J. "Sur l'Optique de Ptolémée comparée à celle qui porte le nom d'Euclide et à celles d'Alhazen et de Vitellion," in *Histoire de l'astronomie ancienne*, vol. 2 (Paris, 1817), pp. 411–32.

Delorme, Ferdinand M. "Le prologue de Roger Bacon à son traité *De influentiis agentium*," *Antonianum*, vol. 18 (1943), pp. 81–90.

Dijksterhuis, E. J. *The Mechanization of the World Picture*. Oxford, 1961.

Diocles (Tideus). *See* Björnbo, Axel Anthon, and Sebastian Vogl.

Diogenes Laertius. *Lives of Eminent Philosophers*, trans. R. D. Hicks. 2 vols. London, 1931.

Disney, Alfred N. *Origin and Development of the Microscope,...preceded by an Historical Survey on the Early Progress of Optical Science*. London, 1928.

Doesschate, Gezienus Ten. *De Derde Commentaar van Lorenzo Ghiberti in Verband met de Middeleeuwsche Optiek*. Utrecht, n.d. (1940?).

——. "Oxford and the Revival of Optics in the Thirteenth Century," *Vision Research*, vol. 1 (1961–62), pp. 313–42.

——. "Robert Grosseteste, Bishop of Lincoln, on Optics," *Ophthalmologica*, vol. 98 (1939), pp. 333–49.

Dominis, Marc Antonio de. *De radiis visus et lucis in vitris perspectivis et iride tractatus*. Venice, 1611.

Doucet, Victorinus. "Notulae bibliographicae de quibusdam operibus Fr. Ioannis Pecham O.F.M.," *Antonianum*, vol. 8 (1933), pp. 307–28, 425–59.

Douie, Decima L. *Archbishop Pecham*. Oxford, 1952.

——. *The Conflict Between the Seculars and the Mendicants at the University of Paris in the Thirteenth Century*. (The Aquinas Society of London, Aquinas Paper No. 23.) London, 1954.

Duckworth, W. L. H. *See* Galen.

Duhem, Pierre. *Le Système du monde*. 10 vols. Paris, 1913–59.

————. *See* Bacon, Roger.

Duns Scotus, John. *Joannis Duns Scoti doctoris subtilis ordinis minorum opera omnia editio nova.* 24 vols. Paris, 1891–95.

————. *Philosophical Writings*, ed. Allan Wolter, O.F.M. New York, 1962.

Easton, Stewart. *Roger Bacon and His Search for a Universal Science.* Oxford, 1952.

Eastwood, Bruce S. "Averroes' View of the Retina—a Reappraisal," *Journal of the History of Medicine*, vol. 24 (1969), pp. 77–82.

————. "The Geometrical Optics of Robert Grosseteste." Unpublished Ph.D. dissertation, University of Wisconsin, 1964.

————. "Grosseteste's 'Quantitative' Law of Refraction: A Chapter in the History of Non-Experimental Science," *Journal of the History of Ideas*, vol. 28 (1967), pp. 403–14.

————. "Medieval Empiricism: The Case of Grosseteste's Optics," *Speculum*, vol. 43 (1968), pp. 306–21.

————. "Robert Grosseteste's Theory of the Rainbow," *Archives internationales d'histoire des sciences*, vol. 19 (1966), pp. 313–32.

Ehrle, Franz, S. J. "John Peckham über den Kampf des Augustinismus und Aristotelismus in der zweiten Hälfte des 13. Jahrhunderts," *Zeitschrift für katholische Theologie*, vol. 13 (1889), pp. 172–93.

Elsässer, W. "Die Funktion des Auges bei Leonardo da Vinci," *Zeitschrift für Mathematik und Physik, historisch-literarische Abteilung*, vol. 45 (1900), pp. 1–6.

Emden, A. B. *A Biographical Register of the University of Oxford to A.D. 1500.* 3 vols. Oxford, 1957–59.

Euclid. *Opera omnia*, ed. J. L. Heiberg and H. Menge, vol. 7: *Optica, Opticorum recensio Theonis, Catoptrica cum scholiis antiquis.* Leipzig, 1895.

————. "The Optics of Euclid," trans. H. E. Burton, *Journal of the Optical Society of America*, vol. 35 (1945), pp. 357–72.

————. *L'Optique et la Catoptrique*, trans. Paul Ver Eecke. Paris, 1959.

————. *The Thirteen Books of Euclid's Elements*, trans. Thomas L. Heath. 3 vols. New York, 1956.

Euclid, Pseudo-. *See* Björnbo, Axel Anthon, and Sebastian Vogl.

Fabricius of Aquapendente, Hieronymus. *Tractatus anatomicus triplex quorum primus de oculo, visus organo....* Venice, 1614.

Fleischer, Johannes. *De iridibus doctrina Aristotelis et Vitellionis....* Wittenberg, 1571.

Galen. *Oeuvres anatomiques, physiologiques et médicales de Galien*, trans. Charles Daremberg. 2 vols. Paris, 1854–56.

————. *On Anatomical Procedures: The Later Books*, trans. W. L. H. Duckworth. Cambridge, 1962.

Ghalioungui, Paul. *See* Nazif, M., and Paul Ghalioungui.

Gliozzi, Mario. "L'invenzione della camera oscura," *Archeion*, vol. 14 (1932), pp. 221–29.

Glorieux, Palémon. *Répertoire des maîtres en théologie de Paris au XIIIe siècle.* (*Études de philosophie médiévale*, vols. 17–18.) Paris, 1933.

Goclenius, Rudolf. *Isagoge optica....* Frankfurt, 1593.

Grosseteste, Robert. *On Light*, trans. Clare Riedl. Milwaukee, 1942.

————. *Die philosophischen Werke des Robert Grosseteste*, ed. Ludwig Baur. (*BGPM*, vol. 9.) Münster, 1912.

Haas, Arthur Erich. "Antike Lichttheorien," *Archiv für Geschichte der Philosophie*, vol. 20 (1907), pp. 345–86.

Halbertsma, K. T. A. *A History of the Theory of Colour*. Amsterdam, 1949.

Haly Abbas. *See* Koning, P. de.

Haskins, Charles Homer. *Studies in the History of Mediaeval Science*. New York, 1960.

Heath, Thomas L. "The Fragment of Anthemius on Burning Mirrors and the 'Fragmentum mathematicum Bobiense,'" *Bibliotheca Mathematica*, Ser. 3, vol. 7 (1907), pp. 225–33.

————. *See* Euclid.

Heiberg, J. L. *See* Euclid.

Heiberg, J. L., and Eilhard Wiedemann. "Ibn al Haitams Schrift über parabolische Hohlspiegel," *Bibliotheca Mathematica*, Ser. 3, vol. 10 (1910), pp. 201–37.

Heliodorus of Larissa. *Heliodori Larissaei capita opticorum*. Cambridge, 1670.

Helssig, Rudolf. *Die wissenschaftlichen Vorbedingungen für Baccalaureat in artibus und Magisterium im ersten Jahrhundert der Universität*, in *Beiträge zur Geschichte der Universität Leipzig im fünfzehnten Jahrhundert*. Leipzig, 1909.

Henry of Langenstein. *Questiones super perspectivam*, in *Preclarissimum mathematicarum opus in quo continentur...Thome Brauardini arismetica et...geometria necnon et...Pisani carturiensis perspectiva...cum...Ioannis d'assia super eadem perspectiva questionibus....* Valencia, 1503.

Hero of Alexandria. *Opera quae supersunt omnia*, vol. 1, fasc. 1: *Mechanica et Catoptrica*, ed. L. Nix and W. Schmidt. Leipzig, 1900.

Hirschberg, J. *Geschichte der Augenheilkunde*, in *Graefe-Saemisch Handbuch der gesamten Augenheilkunde*, ed. Theodor Saemisch, vols. 12–13. Leipzig, 1899–1908.

————. "Die Optik der alten Griechen," *Zeitschrift für Psychologie und Physiologie der Sinnesorgane*, vol. 16 (1898), pp. 321–51.

Hook, Walter Farquhar. *Lives of the Archbishops of Canterbury*. 12 vols. London, 1860–76.

Hoppe, Edmund. *Geschichte der Optik*. Leipzig, 1926.

Hudeczek, Methodius, O.P. "De lumine et coloribus [according to Albertus Magnus]," *Angelicum*, vol. 21 (1944), pp. 112–38.

Hunain ibn Ishāq. *See* Meyerhof, Max; *see* Sbath, P., and M. Meyerhof.

Ibn al-Haitham. *See* Alhazen.

Itard, Jean. "Les Lois de la réfraction de la lumière chez Kepler," *Revue d'histoire des sciences et de leurs applications*, vol. 10 (1957), pp. 59–68.

Jesu Haly. *Memorandum Book of a Tenth-Century Oculist for the Use of Modern Ophthalmologists*, trans. Casey A. Wood. Chicago, 1936.

Job of Edessa. *Book of Treasures*, trans. A. Mingana. Cambridge, 1935.

Joubert, Laurens. *See* Chauliac, Guy de.

Kästner, Abraham. *Geschichte der Mathematik*. 4 vols. Göttingen, 1796–1800.

Kepler, Johannes. *Ad Vitellionem paralipomena, quibus astronomiae pars optica traditur.* (*Gesammelte Werke*, vol. 2.) Munich, 1939.

————. *Dioptrice seu Demonstratio eorum quae visui et visibilibus propter Conspicilla non ita pridem inventa accidunt.* Augsburg, 1611; reprinted Cambridge, 1962.

Kingsford, Charles L. "John Peckham," in *Dictionary of National Biography* (Oxford, 1949–50), vol. 15, pp. 635–42.

———. *See* Pecham, John.

Knowles, David. *The Evolution of Medieval Thought*. New York, 1964.

———. "Some Aspects of the Career of Archbishop Pecham," *English Historical Review*, vol. 57 (1942), pp. 1–18, 178–201.

Koning, P. de (trans.). *Trois traités d'anatomie Arabes par Muḥammed ibn Zakariyyā al-Rāzī, ʾAli ibn al-ʾAbbās et ʾAli ibn Sīnā*. Leiden, 1903.

Lampen, P. W. "Jean Pecham, O.F.M. et son office de la S. Trinité," *La France franciscaine*, vol. 11 (1928), pp. 211–29.

Lawn, Brian. *The Salernitan Questions*. Oxford, 1963.

Lejeune, Albert. "Archimède et la loi de la réflexion," *Isis*, vol. 38 (1947), pp. 51–53.

———. *Euclide et Ptolémée, deux stades de l'optique géométrique grecque*. Louvain, 1948.

———. "La Dioptre d'Archimède," *Annales de la Société scientifique de Bruxelles*, Ser. 1, vol. 61 (1947), pp. 27–47.

———. "Les Lois de la réflexion dans l'Optique de Ptolémée," *L'antiquité classique*, vol. 15 (1946), pp. 245–56.

———. "Les 'postulats' de la Catoptrique dite d'Euclide," *Archives internationales d'histoire des sciences*, vol. 2 (1949), pp. 598–613.

———. "Les Tables de réfraction de Ptolémée," *Annales de la Société scientifique de Bruxelles*, Ser. 1, vol. 60 (1946), pp. 93–101.

———. *Recherches sur la catoptrique grecque*. Brussels, 1957.

———. *See* Ptolemy, Claude.

Lindberg, David C. "Alhazen's Theory of Vision and Its Reception in the West," *Isis*, vol. 58 (1967), pp. 321–41.

———. "The Cause of Refraction in Medieval Optics," *British Journal for the History of Science*, vol. 4 (1968–69), pp. 23–38.

———. "Introduction," in *Opticae thesaurus Alhazeni et Vitellonis* (Risner edition), facsimile reprint forthcoming.

———. "Lines of Influence in Thirteenth-Century Optics: Bacon, Witelo, and Pecham," *Speculum*, forthcoming.

———. "The *Perspectiva communis* of John Pecham: Its Influence, Sources, and Content," *Archives internationales d'histoire des sciences*, vol. 18 (1965), pp. 37–53.

———. "A Reconsideration of Roger Bacon's Theory of Pinhole Images," *Archive for History of Exact Sciences*, in press.

———. "Roger Bacon's Theory of the Rainbow: Progress or Regress?" *Isis*, vol. 57 (1966), pp. 235–48.

———. "The Theory of Pinhole Images from Antiquity to the Thirteenth Century," *Archive for History of Exact Sciences*, vol. 5, pt. 2 (1968), pp. 154–76.

Little, A. G. "The Franciscan School at Oxford in the Thirteenth Century," *Archivum Franciscanum Historicum*, vol. 19 (1926), pp. 803–74.

———. *The Grey Friars in Oxford*. Oxford, 1892.

——— (ed.). *Roger Bacon Essays*. London, 1914.

———. *See* Bacon, Roger; *see* Pecham, John.

Lohne, Johannes. "Der Eigenartige Einfluss Witelos auf die Entwicklung der Dioptrik," *Archive for History of Exact Sciences*, vol. 4, pt. 5 (1968), pp. 414–26.

———. "Regenbogen und Brechzahl," *Sudhoffs Archiv für Geschichte der Medizin und der Naturwissenschaften*, vol. 49 (1965), pp. 401–15.

———. "Thomas Harriott (1560–1621): The Tycho Brahe of Optics," *Centaurus*, vol. 6 (1959), pp. 113–21.

———. "Zur Geschichte des Brechungsgesetzes," *Sudhoffs Archiv für Geschichte der Medizin und der Naturwissenschaften*, vol. 47 (1963), pp. 152–72.

Lucretius Carus, Titus. *De natura rerum.*

Lynch, Lawrence E. "The Doctrine of Divine Ideas and Illumination in Robert Grosseteste, Bishop of Lincoln," *Mediaeval Studies*, vol. 3 (1941), pp. 161–73.

Mach, Ernst. *The Principles of Physical Optics.* London, 1926.

McKeon, Charles K. *A Study of the "Summa philosophiae" of the Pseudo-Grosseteste.* New York, 1948.

Mac Lean, J. "De Kleurentheorie der Arabieren," *Scientiarum Historia*, vol. 7 (1965), pp. 143–55.

———. "De Kleurentheorie in West-Europa (1200–1500)," *Scientiarum Historia*, vol. 8 (1966), pp. 30–50.

———. "De Kleurentheorie in West-Europa van ca 600–1200," *Scientiarum Historia*, vol. 7 (1965), pp. 213–18.

———. "De Kleurentheorie van Aristoteles," *Scientiarum Historia*, vol. 7 (1965), pp. 109–16.

———. "Geschiedenis van de Kleurentheorie in de zestiende Eeuw.," *Scientiarum Historia*, vol. 9 (1967), pp. 23–39.

Madre, Alois. *Nikolaus von Dinkelsbühl, Leben und Schriften.* (*BGPM*, vol. 40, pt. 4.) Münster, 1965.

Marsh, Adam. *See* Adam Marsh.

Martin, Charles T. *See* Pecham, John.

Martin, Th. Henri. "Ptolémée, auteur de l'*Optique* traduite en Latin par *Ammiratus Eugenius Siculus* sur une traduction arabe incomplète, est-il le même que Claude Ptolémée, auteur de l'*Almageste*?" *Bullettino di bibliografia e di storia delle scienze matematiche e fisiche*, vol. 4 (1871), pp. 466–69.

Maurolyco, Francesco. *The Photismi de lumine of Maurolycus: A Chapter in Late Medieval Optics*, trans. Henry Crew. New York, 1940.

Melani, P. Gaudentius. *See* Pecham, John.

Meyerhof, Max (trans.). *The Book of the Ten Treatises of the Eye, ascribed to Hunain ibn Ishâq (809–877 A.D.).* Cairo, 1928.

———. "Die Optik der Araber," *Zeitschrift für ophthalmologische Optik*, vol. 8 (1920), pp. 16–29, 42–54, 86–90.

———. *See* Sbath, P., and Max Meyerhof.

Meyerhof, Max, and C. Prüfer. "Die Augenanatomie des Hunain b. Ishaq," *Sudhoffs Archiv für Geschichte der Medizin und der Naturwissenschaften*, vol. 4 (1910), pp. 163–90.

———, and ———. "Die Lehre vom Sehen bei Hunain b. Ishaq," *Sudhoffs Archiv für Geschichte der Medizin und der Naturwissenschaften*, vol. 6 (1912), pp. 21–33.

Mondeville, Henry. *Die Chirurgie des Heinrich von Mondeville (Hermondaville) nach*

Berliner, Erfurter und Pariser Codices, ed. Julius Leopold Pagel. Berlin, 1892.

Mondino dei Luzzi. *Anatomy*, in *The "Fasciculo di medicina," Venice 1493*, ed. and trans. Charles Singer. 2 pts. Florence, 1925.

Monumenta Franciscana. See Adam Marsh.

Mugler, Charles. *Dictionnaire historique de la terminologie optique des Grecs: Douze siècles de dialogues avec la lumière.* Paris, 1964.

Müntz, Eugène. "Léonard de Vinci et l'invention de la chambre noire," *Revue scientifique*, Ser. 4, vol. 10 (1898), pp. 545–47.

Naldoni, Maria Amalia. *See* Porta, Giovanni Battista della.

Narducci, Enrico. "Intorno ad una traduzione italiana, fatta nel secolo decimoquarto, del trattato d'ottica d'Alhazen, matematico del secolo undecimo, e ad altri lavori di questo scienziato," *Bullettino di bibliografia e di storia delle scienze matematiche e fisiche*, vol. 4 (1871), pp. 1–48.

Nazif, M., and Paul Ghalioungui. "Ibn al Haitham, an 11th Century Physicist," *Actes du dixième congrès international d'histoire des sciences* (Ithaca, 1962), vol. 1, pp. 569–71.

Nebbia, Giorgio. "Ibn al-Haytham nel millesimo anniversario della nascita," *Physis*, vol. 9 (1967), pp. 165–214.

Oltramare, Paul. *See* Seneca, Lucius Annaeus.

Pagel, J. L. *See* Mondeville, Henry.

Panofsky, Erwin. "Die Perspective als 'symbolische Form,'" *Vorträge der Bibliothek Warburg, 1924–25* (Berlin, 1927), pp. 258–330.

Pansier, Pierre. *Collectio ophtalmologica veterum auctorum*, 7 fascs. Paris, 1903–33.

——. "La Pratique de l'ophtalmologie dans le moyen-âge latin," *Janus*, vol. 9 (1904), pp. 3–26.

Pecham, John. *Quaestiones tractantes de anima, quas nunc primum in lucem edidit notisque illustravit*, ed. P. Hieronymus Spettman. (*BGPM*, vol. 19, pts. 5–6.) Münster, 1918. (This work includes Pecham's *Questiones de anima, Questiones de beatitudine corporis et anime*, and selected questions from his commentary on Book I of the *Sentences*.)

——. *Registrum epistolarum fratris Johannis Peckham archiepiscopi Cantuariensis*, ed. Charles T. Martin. 3 vols. London, 1882–85.

——. *Tractatus de anima Ioannis Pecham*, ed. P. Gaudentius Melani, O.F.M. (*Biblioteca di studi francescani*, vol. 1.) Florence, 1948.

——. *Tractatus tres de paupertate, cum bibliographia*, ed. C. L. Kingsford, A. G. Little, and F. Tocco. (British Society of Franciscan Studies, vol. 2.) Aberdeen, 1910.

Peckham, John Laimbeer. *Archbishop Peckham as a Religious Educator.* Scottdale, Pa., 1934.

——. "Recent Recognition of Peckham," *Church History*, vol. 3 (1934), pp. 126–45.

Pedersen, Olaf. "The Theorica-planetarum Literature of the Middle Ages," *Actes du dixième congrès international d'histoire des sciences* (Ithaca, 1962), vol. 1, pp. 615–18.

Polyak, Stephen. *The Retina.* Chicago, 1941.

——. *The Vertebrate Visual System.* Chicago, 1957. (Polyak's orientation is historical, and he includes a very extensive bibliography of early works in optics.)

Porta, Giovanni Battista della. *Natural Magick*. London, 1658; reprinted New York, 1957.

———. *De refractione optices parte libri novem*. Naples, 1593.

———. *De telescopio*, ed. Vasco Ronchi and Maria Amalia Naldoni. Florence, 1962.

Poudra, Noël G. *Histoire de la perspective ancienne et moderne*. Paris, 1864.

Priestley, Joseph. *The History and Present State of Discoveries Relating to Vision, Light, and Colours*. London, 1772.

Prüfer, C. *See* Meyerhof, Max, and C. Prüfer.

Ptolemy, Claude. *L'Optique de Claude Ptolémée, dans la version latine d'après l'arabe de l'émir Eugène de Sicile*, ed. Albert Lejeune. Louvain, 1956.

Rahman, F. *Avicenna's Psychology*. Oxford, 1952.

Rashdall, Hastings. *The Universities of Europe in the Middle Ages*, ed. F. M. Powicke and A. B. Emden. 3 vols. Oxford, 1936.

Rashed, Roshdi. "Le 'Discours de la Lumière' d'Ibn al-Haytham (Alhazen)," *Revue d'histoire des sciences et de leurs applications*, vol. 21 (1968), pp. 197–224.

Registrum epistolarum. *See* Pecham, John.

Rhazes. *See* Koning, P. de.

Rhodius, Ambrosius. *Optica*. Wittenberg, 1611.

Riedl, Clare. *See* Grosseteste, Robert.

Risner, Friedrich. *Risneri Optica cum annotationibus Willebrordi Snellii*, ed. J. A. Vollgraff. Gandavi, 1918.

———. *Opticae libri quatuor*. Kassel, 1606.

———. *See* Alhazen; *see* Witelo.

Rohmer, Jean. "La Théorie de l'abstraction dans l'école franciscaine de Alexandre de Hales à Jean Peckham," *Archives d'histoire doctrinale et littéraire du Moyen Âge*, vol. 3 (1928), pp. 105–84.

Rome, A. "Note sur les passages des catoptriques d'Archimède conservés par Théon d'Alexandrie," *Annales de la Société scientifique de Bruxelles*, Ser. A, vol. 52 (1932), pp. 30–41.

Ronchi, Vasco. "A proposito di recenti 'Studi sulla prospettiva medievale,'" *Atti della Fondazione Giorgio Ronchi*, vol. 21 (1966), pp. 575–90. (A review of Vescovini's book.)

———. "The Evolution of the Meaning of 'Light' in Natural Philosophy," *Actes du dixième congrès international d'histoire des sciences* (Ithaca, 1962), vol. 2, pp. 725–27.

———. "The General Influence of the Development of Optics in the Seventeenth Century on Science and Technology," in *Vistas in Astronomy*, ed. Arthur Beer, vol. 9 (New York, 1968), pp. 123–33.

———. *Histoire de la lumière*, trans. Juliette Taton. Paris, 1956. (A translation of the *Storia della luce*.)

———. *Optics, the Science of Vision*, trans. Edward Rosen. New York, 1957.

———. "L'Optique au XVIe siècle," in *La Science au seizième siècle* (Paris, 1960), pp. 47–65.

———. "L'Optique de Léonard de Vinci," in *Léonard de Vinci et l'expérience scientifique au XVIe siècle* (Paris, 1953), pp. 115–20.

———. "Rilievi a proposito dell'ottica di Tito Lucrezio Caro," *Archives internationales d'histoire des sciences*, vol. 18 (1965), pp. 161–74.

———. *Storia della luce*. Bologna, 1952.

———. "Sul Contributo di Ibn-Al-Haitham alle teorie della Visione e della Luce," *Actes du VIIe congrès international d'histoire des sciences* (Jerusalem, 1953), pp. 516–21.

———. "Twenty Embarrassing Questions," trans. Edward Rosen, *Atti della Fondazione Giorgio Ronchi*, vol. 13 (1958), pp. 173–90.

———. "Un Aspect peu connu de l'activité de Léonard De Vinci dans le domain de l'optique," *Atti della Fondazione Giorgio Ronchi*, vol. 20 (1965), pp. 394–405.

———. *See* Porta, Giovanni Battista della.

Rosen, Edward. "Did Roger Bacon Invent Eyeglasses?" *Archives internationales d'histoire des sciences*, vol. 7 (1954), pp. 3–15.

———. "The Invention of Eyeglasses," *Journal of the History of Medicine and Allied Sciences*, vol. 11 (1956), pp. 13–46, 183–218.

———. "The Title of Maurolico's *Photismi*," *American Journal of Physics*, vol. 25 (1957), pp. 226–28.

Ruelle, Ch. Émile. *See* Rufus of Ephesus.

Rufus of Ephesus. *Oeuvres de Rufus d'Éphèse*, ed. and trans. Charles Daremberg and Ch. Émile Ruelle. Paris, 1879.

Sabra, A. I. "The Authorship of the *Liber de crepusculis*, an Eleventh-Century Work on Atmospheric Refraction," *Isis*, vol. 58 (1967), pp. 77–85.

———. "Explanation of Optical Reflection and Refraction: Ibn-al-Haytham, Descartes, Newton," *Actes du dixième congrès international d'histoire des sciences* (Ithaca, 1962), vol. 1, pp. 551–54.

———. "Ibn Al-Haytham's Criticisms of Ptolemy's *Optics*," *Journal of the History of Philosophy*, vol. 4 (1966), pp. 145–49.

———. *Theories of Light from Descartes to Newton*. London, 1967.

Sa'di, Lutfi M. "Ibn-al-Haitham (Alhazen), Medical Scientist," *University of Michigan Medical Bulletin*, vol. 22 (1956), pp. 249–73.

Sambursky, S. "Philoponus' Interpretation of Aristotle's Theory of Light," *Osiris*, vol. 13 (1958), pp. 114–26.

———. *The Physical World of Late Antiquity*. London, 1962.

———. *Physics of the Stoics*. London, 1959.

Sarton, George. *Introduction to the History of Science*. 3 vols. Baltimore, 1927–48.

———. Review of Muṣṭafā Naẓif, *Al-Ḥasan ibn al-Haitham: His Optical Studies and Discoveries* [in Arabic], in *Isis*, vol. 34 (1942–43), pp. 217–18.

———. "The Tradition of the Optics of Ibn al-Haitham," *Isis*, vol. 29 (1938), pp. 403–6.

Sayili, Aydin M. "Al Qarāfī and His Explanation of the Rainbow," *Isis*, vol. 32 (1940), pp. 16–26.

———. "The Aristotelian Explanation of the Rainbow," *Isis*, vol. 30 (1939), pp. 65–83.

Sbath, P., and M. Meyerhof. *Le Livre des questions sur l'œil de Honaïn ibn Isḥaq*. (Mémoires présentés à l'Institut d'Égypte, vol. 36.) Cairo, 1938.

Schmidt, W. *See* Hero of Alexandria.

Schnaase, Leopold. *Die Optik Alhazens*. Stargard, 1889.

Schramm, Matthias. *Ibn al-Haythams Weg zur Physik*. Wiesbaden, 1963.

———. "Steps Toward the Idea of Function: A Comparison between Eastern and

Western Science of the Middle Ages," *History of Science*, vol. 4 (1965), pp. 70–103.

——. "Zur Entwicklung der physiologischen Optik in der arabischen Literatur," *Sudhoffs Archiv für Geschichte der Medizin und der Naturwissenschaften*, vol. 43 (1959), pp. 289–316.

Schweig, Bruno. "Mirrors," *Antiquity*, vol. 15 (1941), pp. 257–68.

Scotus, John Duns. *See* Duns Scotus, John.

Seeman, H. J. "Eilhard Wiedemann," *Isis*, vol. 14 (1930), pp. 166–86. (A bibliography of Wiedemann's publications.)

Seneca, Lucius Annaeus. *Questions naturelles*, trans. Paul Oltramare. 2 vols. Paris, 1929.

Sharp, D. E. *Franciscan Philosophy at Oxford in the Thirteenth Century*. Oxford, 1930.

Shirley, John. "An Early Experimental Determination of Snell's Law," *American Journal of Physics*, vol. 19 (1951), pp. 507–08.

Shuja, F. M. *Cause of Refraction as Explained by the Moslem Scientists*. Delhi, 1936. (Privately printed.)

Singer, Charles. "Steps Leading to the Invention of the First Optical Apparatus," in *Studies in the History and Method of Science*, ed. Charles Singer, vol. 2 (Oxford, 1921), pp. 385–413.

——. *See* Mondino dei Luzzi.

Spettman, P. Hieronymus, O.F.M. "Das Schriften 'De oculo morali' und sein Verfasser," *Archivum Franciscanum Historicum*, vol. 16 (1923), pp. 309–22.

——. *Die Psychologie des Johannes Pecham*. (*BGPM*, vol. 20, pt. 6.) Münster, 1919.

——. "Quellenkritisches zur Biographie des Johannes Pecham," *Franziskanische Studien*, vol. 2 (1915), pp. 170–207, 266–85.

——. *See* Pecham, John.

Squadrani, Irenaeus, O.F.M. "Tractatus de luce Fr. Bartholomaei de Bononia," *Antonianum*, vol. 7 (1932), pp. 201–38, 465–94.

Sudhoff, Karl. "Augenanatomiebilder im 15. und 16. Jahrhundert," in *Studien zur Geschichte der Medizin*, vol. 1 (Leipzig, 1907), pp. 19–26.

Tea, Eva. "Witelo, prospettico del secolo XIII," *L'Arte*, vol. 30 (1927), pp. 3–30.

Teetaert, A. "Jean Pecham," in *Dictionnaire de théologie catholique*, vol. 12, pt. 1 (Paris, 1933), cols. 100–140.

Themon Judaeus. *Questiones super quattuor libros metheororum*. Venice, 1507.

Theodoric of Freiberg. *De iride et radialibus impressionibus*, ed. Joseph Würschmidt. (*BGPM*, vol. 12, pts. 5–6.) Münster, 1914.

Thorndike, Lynn. "Duhem's 'Disciple of Bacon' Identified with John Peckham," *Isis*, vol. 34 (1942), p. 28.

——. *A History of Magic and Experimental Science*. 8 vols. New York, 1923–56.

——. "A John Peckham Manuscript," *Archivum Franciscanum Historicum*, vol. 45 (1952), pp. 451–61.

—— (ed.). *The Sphere of Sacrobosco and Its Commentators*. Chicago, 1949.

Tideus (Diocles). *See* Björnbo, Axel Anthon, and Sebastian Vogl.

Tocco, F. *See* Pecham, John.

Turbayne, Colin M. "Berkeley and Ronchi on Optics," in *Proceedings of the XIIth International Congress of Philosophy*, vol. 12 (Florence, 1961), pp. 453–60.

——. "Grosseteste and an Ancient Optical Principle," *Isis*, vol. 50 (1959), pp. 467–72.

————. *The Myth of Metaphor*. New Haven, 1962.

Turrière, Émile. "Introduction à l'histoire de l'optique: Le développement de l'industrie verrière d'art depuis l'époque vénitienne jusqu'à la fondation des verreries d'optique," *Isis*, vol. 7 (1925), pp. 77–104.

Van Steenberghen, Fernand. *The Philosophical Movement in the Thirteenth Century*. London, 1955.

Vavilov, S. I. "Galileo in the History of Optics," *Soviet Physics Uspekhi*, vol. 7 (1965), pp. 596–616.

Venturi, G. B. *Commentari sopra la storia e la teoria dell'ottica*. Bologna, 1814.

Ver Eecke, Paul (trans.). *Les Opuscules mathématiques de Didyme, Diophane et Anthemius suivis du fragment mathématique de Bobbio*. Paris and Bruges, 1940.

————. *See* Euclid.

Vescovini, Graziella Federici. "Contributo per la storia della fortuna di Alhazen in Italia: Il volgarizzamento del MS. Vat. 4595 e il 'Commentario Terzo' del Ghiberti," *Rinascimento*, Ser. 2, vol. 5 (1965), pp. 17–49.

————. "La 'perspectiva' nell'enciclopedia del sapere medievale," *Vivarium*, vol. 6 (1968), pp. 35–45.

————. "Le questioni di 'Perspectiva' di Biagio Pelacani da Parma," *Rinascimento*, Ser. 2, vol. 1 (1961), pp. 163–243.

————. "Les Questions de 'perspective' de Dominicus de Clivaxo," *Centaurus*, vol. 10 (1964), pp. 232–46.

————. *Studi sulla prospettiva medievale*. Turin, 1965.

Vogl, Sebastian. *Die Physik Roger Bacos*. Erlangen, 1906.

————. "Roger Bacons Lehre von der sinnlichen Spezies und vom Sehvorgange," in *Roger Bacon Essays*, ed. A. G. Little (Oxford, 1914), pp. 205–27.

————. "Über die (Pseudo-) Euklidische Schrift 'De Speculis,'" *Archiv für die Geschichte der Naturwissenschaften und der Technik*, vol. 1 (1909), pp. 419–35.

————. *See* Björnbo, Axel Anthon, and Sebastian Vogl.

Vollgraff, J. A. "Pierre de la Ramée (1515–1572), et Willebrord Snel van Royen (1580–1626)," *Janus*, vol. 18 (1913), pp. 595–625.

————. *See* Risner, Friedrich.

von Fritz, Kurt. "Democritus' Theory of Vision," in *Science Medicine and History, Essays on the Evolution of Scientific Thought and Medical Practice, Written in Honour of Charles Singer*, ed. E. A. Underwood, vol. 1 (London, 1953), pp. 83–99.

Wallace, William A., O.P. *The Scientific Methodology of Theodoric of Freiberg*. Fribourg, 1959.

Waterhouse, James. "Camera Obscura: History," in *Encyclopædia Britannica*, 11th ed. (New York, 1910–11), vol. 5, pp. 105–07.

Weisheipl, James A., O.P. "Classification of the Sciences in Medieval Thought," *Mediaeval Studies*, vol. 27 (1965), pp. 54–90.

Werner, Otto. *Zur Physik Leonardo da Vincis*. Erlangen, 1910.

White, John. "Developments in Renaissance Perspective—I," *Journal of the Warburg and Courtauld Institutes*, vol. 12 (1949), pp. 58–79.

Wiedemann, Eilhard. "Aus al Kindîs Optik," *Sitzungsberichte der physikalisch-medizinischen Societät in Erlangen*, vol. 39 (1907), pp. 245–48.

――――. "Beiträge zur Geschichte der Naturwissenschaften bei den Arabern," *Annalen der Physik und Chemie*, vol. 159 (1876), pp. 656–58.

――――. "Ibn al Haitam, ein arabischer Gelehrter," in *Festschrift, J. Rosenthal* (Leipzig, 1906), pp. 147–78.

――――. "Ibn al Haitams Schrift über die sphärischen Hohlspiegel," *Bibliotheca Mathematica*, Ser. 3, vol. 10 (1910), pp. 293–307.

――――. "Ibn Sînâ's Anschauung vom Sehvorgang," *Archiv für die Geschichte der Naturwissenschaften und der Technik*, vol. 4 (1913), pp. 239–41.

――――. "Roger Bacon und seine Verdienste um die Optik," in *Roger Bacon Essays*, ed. A. G. Little (Oxford, 1914), pp. 185–203.

――――. "Sull'ottica degli Arabi," trans. Alfonso Sparagna, *Bullettino di bibliografia e di storia delle scienze matematiche e fisiche*, vol. 14 (1881), pp. 219–25.

――――. "Theorie des Regenbogens von Ibn al Haitam," *Sitzungsberichte der physikalisch-medizinischen Societät in Erlangen*, vol. 46 (1914), pp. 39–56.

――――. "Ueber das Sehen durch ein Kugel bei den Arabern," *Annalen der Physik und Chemie*, N.S., vol. 39 (1890), pp. 565–76.

――――. "Ueber den Apparat zur Untersuchung und Brechung des Lichtes von Ibn al Haitam," *Annalen der Physik und Chemie*, N.S., vol. 21 (1884), pp. 541–44.

――――. "Über die Camera obscura bei Ibn al Haitam," *Sitzungsberichte der physikalisch-medizinischen Societät in Erlangen*, vol. 46 (1914), pp. 155–69.

――――. "Über die Erfindung der Camera obscura," *Verhandlung der deutschen physikalischen Gesellschaft*, vol. 12 (1910), pp. 177–82.

――――. "Ueber die erste Erwähnung der Dunkelkammer durch Ibn al Haitam," *Jahrbuch für Photographie und Reproduktionstechnik*, vol. 24 (1910), pp. 12–13.

――――. "Zu Ibn al-Haitams Optik," *Archiv für die Geschichte der Naturwissenschaften und der Technik*, vol. 3 (1910–11), pp. 1–53.

――――. "Zur Geschichte der Brennspiegel," *Annalen der Physik und Chemie*, N.S., vol. 39 (1890), pp. 110–30.

――――. "Zur Geschichte der Lehre vom Sehen," *Annalen der Physik und Chemie*, N.S., vol. 39 (1890), pp. 470–74.

――――. *See* Heiberg, J. L., and Eilhard Wiedemann; *see* Seeman, H. J.

Wilde, Emil. *Geschichte der Optik*. 2 vols. Berlin, 1838–43.

William of Conches. *De philosophia mundi libri quatuor*, in J.-P. Migne, ed., *Patrologia Latina*, vol. 172 (Paris, 1895), cols. 39–102 (there attributed to Honorius of Autun).

――――. *Philosophicarum et astronomicarum institutionum, Guilielmi Hirsaugiensis olim abbatis, libri tres*. Basel, 1531.

Winter, H. J. J. "The Arabic Achievement in Physics," *Endeavour*, vol. 9 (1950), pp. 76–79.

――――. "The Arabic Optical MSS. in the British Isles (Mathematical and Physical Optics)," *Centaurus*, vol. 5 (1956), pp. 73–88.

――――. "The Optical Researches of Ibn al-Haitham," *Centaurus*, vol. 3 (1954), pp. 190–210.

Winter, H. J. J., and W. 'Arafat. "A Discourse on the Concave Spherical Mirror of Ibn al-Haitham," *Journal of the Royal Asiatic Society of Bengal*, Ser. 3, vol. 16, nos. 1–2 (1950), pp. 1–16.

――――, and ――――. "Ibn al-Haitham on the Paraboloidal Focussing Mirror,"

Journal of the Royal Asiatic Society of Bengal," Ser. 3, vol. 15, nos. 1–2 (1949), pp. 25–40.

——, and ——. "A Statement on Optical Reflection and 'Refraction' Attributed to Naṣīr ud-Dīn aṭ-Ṭūsī," *Isis,* vol. 42 (1951), pp. 138–42.

Witelo. *Vitellonis Thuringopoloni opticae libri decem,* ed. Friedrich Risner. Basel, 1572. (Bound as part of Alhazen, *Opticae thesaurus....*)

Wolfson, Harry A. "The Internal Senses in Latin, Arabic, and Hebrew Philosophic Texts," *Harvard Theological Review,* vol. 28 (1935), pp. 69–133.

Wolter, Allan. *See* Duns Scotus, John.

Wood, Casey A. *See* Jesu Haly; *see* Benevenutus Grassus of Jerusalem.

Würschmidt, J. "Die Theorie des Regenbogens und des Halo bei Ibn al Haiṭam und bei Dietrich von Freiberg," *Meteorologische Zeitschrift,* vol. 31 (1914), pp. 484–87.

——. "Roger Bacons Art des wissenschaftlichen Arbeitens, dargestellt nach seiner Schrift *De Speculis,*" in *Roger Bacon Essays,* ed. A. G. Little (Oxford, 1914), pp. 229–39.

——. "Zur Geschichte, Theorie und Praxis der Camera obscura," *Zeitschrift für mathematischen und naturwissenschaftlichen Unterricht aller Schulgattungen,* vol. 46 (1915), pp. 466–76.

——. "Zur Theorie der Camera obscura bei *Ibn al Haiṭam,*" *Sitzungsberichte der physikalisch-medizinischen Societät in Erlangen,* vol. 46 (1914), pp. 151–54.

——. *See* Theodoric of Freiberg.

Zubov, Vasilli P. *Leonardo da Vinci,* trans. David H. Kraus. Cambridge, Mass., 1968.

Index of Manuscripts Cited

General Index

For most entries pertaining to the text and translation of the *Perspectiva communis*, I have given page numbers only to the English translation; the only exception to this rule is in the case of Latin technical terms, where I have provided page numbers to both the Latin text and the English translation. I have not here indexed manuscripts, since they are listed separately in the Index of Manuscripts Cited, or the bibliography, since it is arranged alphabetically by author. Medieval figures have been indexed according to either their Christian name or their surname, depending on what has seemed to me to be the most common usage. Islamic figures are indexed according to the name by which they were known in the Latin West.

THE UNIVERSITY OF WISCONSIN PUBLICATIONS IN MEDIEVAL SCIENCE

Marshall Clagett, *General Editor*

8

Kūshyār ibn Labbān: "Principles of Hindu Reckoning"
A Translation with introduction and notes by Martin Levey and
Marvin Petruck of the *Kitāb fī uṣūl ḥisāb al-hind*
128 pages $ 6.00

9

Nicole Oresme: "De proportionibus proportionum" and "Ad pauca respicientes"
Edited with introductions, English translations, and critical notes
by Edward Grant
488 pages $10.75

10

The "Algebra" of Abū Kāmil, "Kitāb fī al-jābr wa'l-muqābala,"
in a Commentary by Mordecai Finzi
Hebrew text, translation, and commentary, with special reference
to the Arabic text, by Martin Levey
240 pages $10.00

11

Nicole Oresme: "Le Livre du ciel et du monde"
Edited by Albert D. Menut and Alexander J. Denomy, C.S.B.
Translated with an introduction by Albert D. Menut
792 pages $17.50

12

Nicole Oresme and the Medieval Geometry of Qualities and Motions:
A Treatise on the Uniformity and Difformity of Intensities
Known as "Tractatus de configurationibus qualitatum et motuum"
Edited with an introduction, English translation, and commentary
by Marshall Clagett
728 pages $15.00

13

Mechanics in Sixteenth-Century Italy:
Selections from Tartaglia, Benedetti, Guido Ubaldo, and Galileo
Edited and translated by Stillman Drake and I. E. Drabkin
440 pages $12.50

14

John Pecham and the Science of Optics: "Perspectiva communis"
Edited with an introduction, English translation, and critical notes
by David C. Lindberg
320 pages $15.00